Henry Beston

THE
HOLIDAY
READER

EDITED BY Bernard Smith AND

Philip Van Doren Stern

SIMON AND SCHUSTER · NEW YORK

Acknowledgments

"Big Two-Hearted River" from *In Our Time* by Ernest Hemingway, copyright, 1928, 1930, by Charles Scribner's Sons.

"Red" from *The Trembling of a Leaf* by W. Somerset Maugham, copyright, 1921. Reprinted in the U. S. by permission of Doubleday and Company, Inc., and in Canada by permission of Messrs. William Heinemann, Ltd.

"The Romance of Rosy Ridge," copyright 1937, by MacKinlay Kantor. Reprinted by permission of Coward-McCann, Inc., Publishers.

"Dusk Before Fireworks" from *The Portable Dorothy Parker*, copyright, 1933, 1944, by Dorothy Parker. Reprinted by permission of The Viking Press, Inc.

"Search Through the Streets of the City" from *Welcome to the City*, copyright, 1942, by Irwin Shaw. Reprinted by permission of Random House, Inc.

"Desire" from *Etched in Moonlight* by James Stephens, copyright, 1928, by The Macmillan Company.

"Country Full of Swedes" from *Jackpot*, copyright, 1940, by Erskine Caldwell. Reprinted by permission of Duell, Sloan & Pearce, Inc.

iv

"The Biscuit Eater" by James Street, copyright, 1939, by the Curtis Publishing Company. Reprinted by permission of Dial Press.

"By the Waters of Babylon," copyright, 1937, by Stephen Vincent Benét. From *The Selected Works of Stephen Vincent Benét*, published by Farrar & Rinehart, Inc.

"The Lesson," copyright, 1936, 1941, by Pearl S. Buck. From *Today and Forever Stories of China* by Pearl S. Buck, published by The John Day Company.

"The Bear," from *Go Down, Moses*, copyright, 1942, by William Faulkner. Reprinted by permission of Random House, Inc.

"The Knife," copyright, 1925, by John Russell.

"Crime Without Passion" from *The Collected Stories of Ben Hecht*, copyright, 1945, by Ben Hecht. By permission of Crown Publishers.

"A. V. Laider" from *Seven Men*, copyright, 1920, by Max Beerbohm. Reprinted by permission of Alfred A. Knopf, Inc.

"Mother and Pug Dogs and Rubber Trees" from *Life with Mother* by Clarence Day, copyright, 1935, by Estate of Clarence Day. Reprinted by permission of Alfred A. Knopf, Inc.

"Women" from *The Love Nest and Other Stories* by Ring Lardner, copyright, 1926, by Charles Scribner's Sons.

"You Should Live So, Walden Pond!" from *Crazy Like a Fox*, copyright, 1944, by S. J. Perelman. Reprinted by permission of Random House, Inc.

"The Schartz-Metterklume Method" from *The Short Stories of Saki (H. H. Munro)*, copyright, 1930, by The Viking Press, Inc. Reprinted in Canada by permission of John Lane the Bodley Head Ltd., London.

"Farewell, My Lovely" by Lee Strout White, copyright, 1936, by F-R Publishing Corporation. Reprinted by permission of the author and *The New Yorker*.

"Camp Nomopo" from *I Love You, I Love You, I Love You*, copyright, 1942, by Ludwig Bemelmans. Reprinted by permission of The Viking Press, Inc.

"Le Scandale International" from *My Sister Eileen*, copyright, 1938, by Ruth McKenney. By permission of Harcourt, Brace and Company, Inc.

"Bottoms Up!" from *How to Do Practically Anything*, copyright, 1942, by Jack Goodman and Alan Green. Reprinted by permission of Simon and Schuster, Inc.

"Johnny One-Eye" from *Runyon à la Carte*, copyright, 1933, 1944, by Damon Runyon. Published by J. B. Lippincott Company.

"One Kind Word for Hollywood" from *Life in a Putty Knife Factory* by H. Allen Smith, copyright, 1943. Reprinted by permission of Doubleday and Company, Inc.

"Grab Bag" from *Try and Stop Me*, copyright, 1944, by Bennett Cerf. Reprinted by permission of Simon and Schuster, Inc.

"The Last Day" from *Inside Benchley* by Robert Benchley, copyright, 1925, by Harper & Brothers.

"The Lure of the Limerick" by Louis Untermeyer, copyright, 1946, by *Good Housekeeping*. Reprinted by permission of the author.

"The Demon Host" from *I Take It Back* by Margaret Fishback, copyright, 1935, by E. P. Dutton & Co., Inc.

"Lines to Long Island and Westchester" from *Time for a Quick One*, copyright, 1940, by Margaret Fishback. By permission of Harcourt, Brace and Company, Inc.

"Song of the Open Road" from *The Face Is Familiar* by Ogden Nash. Reprinted by permission of Little, Brown & Company. Copyright, 1938, by Random House.

"Song to Be Sung by the Fathers of Six-Month-Old Female Children" from *The Face Is Familiar* by Ogden Nash. Reprinted by permission of Little, Brown & Company. Copyright, 1931, by F-R Publishing Corporation.

"I Want New York" from *Hard Lines* by Ogden Nash, reprinted by permission of Little, Brown & Company. Copyright, 1931, by F-R Publishing Corporation.

"A Father Does His Best" from *The Fox of Peapack* by E. B. White, published by Harper & Brothers. Copyright, 1938, by E. B. White.

"Love Song," "One Perfect Rose," and "The Searched Soul" from *The Portable Dorothy Parker*, copyright, 1926, 1944, by Dorothy Parker. Reprinted by permission of The Viking Press, Inc.

"Lovely Lady" from *Poems in Praise of Practically Nothing* by Samuel Hoffenstein, published by Liveright Publishing Corp.

"On the Vanity of Earthly Greatness" from *Gaily the Troubadour* by Arthur Guiterman, copyright, 1936, by E. P. Dutton & Co., Inc.

"Mad Dogs and Englishmen" from *Collected Sketches and Lyrics* by Noel Coward, copyright, 1931, 1932. Reprinted by permission of Doubleday and Company, Inc.

"Elegy from a Country Dooryard" and "Ode to the End of Summer" from *A Pocketful of Rye*, copyright, 1940, by Phyllis McGinley. Reprinted by permission of Duell, Sloan & Pearce, Inc.

"From a Train Window" from *Of Time and the River* by Thomas Wolfe, copyright, 1935, by Charles Scribner's Sons.

"Reflections on a Scientific Fishing Trip" from *Sea of Cortez*, copyright, 1941, by John Steinbeck and Edward F. Ricketts. Reprinted by permission of The Viking Press, Inc.

"Summit of the World" from *High Conquest*, copyright, 1941, by James Ramsey Ullman.

"The Headlong Wave" from *The Outermost House* by Henry Beston, copyright, 1928, by Doubleday and Company, Inc.

"Odyssey of the Eel" from *Under the Sea-Wind*, copyright, 1941, by Rachel L. Carson. Reprinted by permission of Simon and Schuster, Inc.

"The Deer Mouse" from *One Day on Beetle Rock*, copyright, 1944, by Sally Carrighar. Reprinted by permission of Alfred A. Knopf, Inc.

"The Dance of the Sprouting Corn" from *Mornings in Mexico* by D. H. Lawrence, copyright, 1927, by Alfred A. Knopf, Inc.

"Beduin Hospitality" from *The Seven Pillars of Wisdom* by T. E. Lawrence, copyright, 1926, by Doubleday and Company, Inc. Reprinted by permission of the Trustees of the late Col. T. E. Lawrence, and Raymond Savage, Literary Agent, London.

"On Being the Right Size" from *Possible Worlds* by J. B. S. Haldane, copyright, 1927, 1928, by Harper & Brothers.

"The Machine Stops" from *The Eternal Moment* by E. M. Forster, copyright, 1928, by Harcourt, Brace and Company, Inc.

"Our Feathered Friends" by Philip MacDonald, copyright by the author and reprinted with his permission.

"By the Rude Bridge" from *While Rome Burns*, copyright, 1934, by Alexander Woollcott. Reprinted by permission of The Viking Press, Inc.

"Oh, Whistle, and I'll Come to You, My Lad" from *The Collected Ghost Stories of M. R. James*, by permission of Edward Arnold & Co.

"A Psychical Invasion" from *The Tales of Algernon Blackwood*, published by E. P. Dutton & Co. Reprinted in Canada by permission of The Richards Press Ltd., London.

"Back for Christmas," copyright, 1939, by John Collier.

"Couching at the Door" by D. K. Broster, reprinted by permission of the author.

"The Disappearance of Doctor Parkman" from *Murder at Smutty Nose* by Edmund Pearson, copyright, 1927, by Doubleday and Company, Inc.

"I'll Be Waiting" by Raymond Chandler, copyright, 1939, by the Curtis Publishing Company. Reprinted by permission of the author.

"As I Walked Out One Evening" from *Another Time*, copyright, 1945, by W. H. Auden. Reprinted by permission of Random House, Inc., and Faber and Faber Ltd., London.

"The Ballad of William Sycamore" from *Ballads and Poems: 1915–1930*, copyright, 1930, by Stephen Vincent Benét. Reprinted by permission of Rinehart & Company, Inc.

"Heaven" from *The Collected Poems of Rupert Brooke*, copyright, 1915, by Dodd, Mead and Company, Inc. Reprinted in Canada by permission of McClelland and Stewart Ltd., Toronto.

"The Road Not Taken" from *Collected Poems* by Robert Frost, copyright, 1930, 1939, by Henry Holt and Company, Inc., copyright, 1936, by Robert Frost.

Six Poems from *A Shropshire Lad* reprinted by permission of Henry Holt and Company and The Society of Authors, London.

"The Long Trail" from *Barrack Room Ballads* by Rudyard Kipling, copyright, 1892, 1927. Reprinted by permission of Mrs. G. Bambridge and Doubleday & Company, Inc., and The Macmillan Company of Canada Ltd.

"The Flower-Fed Buffaloes" from *Going to the Stars* by Vachel Lindsay, copyright, 1926, by D. Appleton & Company. Reprinted by permission of D. Appleton-Century Company.

"Sea Fever" from *Poems* by John Masefield, copyright, 1935, by John Masefield. Reprinted by permission of The Macmillan Company.

"You, Andrew Marvell" from MacLeish's *Poems, 1924–1933,* reprinted by permission of Houghton Mifflin Company.

"The Penitent" from *A Few Figs from Thistles,* published by Harper & Brothers. Copyright, 1918, 1946, by Edna St. Vincent Millay.

"The Express" from *Poems* by Stephen Spender, copyright, 1934, by Modern Library, Inc. Reprinted by permission of Random House, Inc., and Faber and Faber Ltd., London.

"Earth" from *Dust and Light* by John Hall Wheelock, copyright, 1919, by Charles Scribner's Sons.

"Wild Peaches" from *Collected Poems of Elinor Wylie,* copyright, 1921, by Alfred A. Knopf, Inc.

"The Lake Isle of Innisfree" from *Collected Poems of W. B. Yeats,* copyright, 1933, by The Macmillan Company. Reprinted in Canada by permission of Mrs. Yeats and The Macmillan Company of Canada, Ltd.

"A Mess of Clams" from *McSorley's Wonderful Saloon,* copyright, 1939, by Joseph Mitchell. Reprinted by permission of Duell, Sloan & Pearce, Inc.

"The Days of the Giants" from *Newspaper Days* by H. L. Mencken, copyright, 1940, 1941, by Alfred A. Knopf, Inc.

"Madame Is Pleased" from *The Gastronomical Me,* copyright, 1943, by M. F. K. Fisher. Reprinted by permission of Duell, Sloan & Pearce, Inc.

"*Vouvray, Terrines,* and the Slopes of Gold" from *Bouquet* by G. B. Stern. Reprinted by permission of Harold Matson.

"A Simple Christmas" from *The Country Kitchen* by Della T. Lutes. Reprinted by permission of Little, Brown & Company and Atlantic Monthly Press.

"Of Cheese in General" from *A Little Book of Cheese* by Osbert Burdett. Reprinted by permission of John Lane the Bodley Head Ltd., London, and A. D. Peters, Literary Agent, London.

"Food and Drink" from *Food and Drink* by Louis Untermeyer, copyright, 1932, by Harcourt, Brace and Company, Inc.

"Bacon and Eggs" from *Laughing Ann and Other Poems* by A. P. Herbert, copyright, 1926, by Doubleday & Company, Inc. Reprinted by permission of Sir Alan Herbert and the proprietors of *Punch,* and in Canada by permission of Ernest Benn Ltd., London.

Introduction

THE IDEA *for this book originated in the country a few years ago when we were sitting in front of an open fire talking about the stories, articles, and poems that had made sufficient impression upon us to cause them to be remembered. We agreed that the best test for any piece of writing is its "memorability."*

It seemed to us that the writing we remembered—the harvest of many years of reading—must have had some very special quality to keep it fresh in our minds. Countless thousands of stories, articles, and poems are printed each year, and most of them are lost in oblivion before the year is out. It occurred to us that the pieces we remembered most fondly would be likely to appeal to others. And then, probably because we ourselves were on a holiday, we decided to concentrate on material that would be especially appropriate for holiday reading.

There has, of course, been much talk about the kind of reading one should do on a holiday. Actually it is a matter of taste, for what might seem brain-taxing to one person will seem easy-going to another. A man who habitually reads Kant and Hegel might very well find Gibbon sheer entertainment. Our discussion, however, was on a more popular level. What sort of reading matter would the average, fairly well-educated person like to have on hand during a vacation? Certainly it would have to be varied, to suit various tastes; and even one person's taste differs according to mood and circumstance. There would have to be reading for fair as well as stormy weather, for night-time as well as daytime reading. Some people would be en route to strange places; others would be seeking relaxation by returning to familiar scenes. And holidays are taken in all seasons and temperatures.

We had to define what we meant by "holiday." Obviously, it could be a long trip, a whole summer's stay at a resort, the conventional two weeks' vacation that is so long anticipated and then so quickly spent, or even just a week end. But we felt that it might also be a period of convalescence, a rainy Sunday at home, or indeed any time at all that is a break in the routine of everyday living when the mind is relaxed and pleasure rather than work is the order of the day.

So then, appropriately enough, we spent a joint holiday in a big, old book-filled house where we went around excitedly recalling this piece and that until we had a running start on the project. After that there were long hours spent in libraries and book stores to round out the table of contents and give it the balance that is as necessary in an anthology as it is in a well-planned meal.

We chose stories of romance and adventure, accounts of strange experiences, nature sketches, and travel tales. And then we wanted stories of murder, mystery, and ghosts, for reading after sundown— but not when you are alone in some isolated place! And we included humor to leaven the tales of blood lust and direful revenants.

When it came to poetry, we felt that the best poems for a holiday mood should be the old favorites that everyone promises himself to re-read but seldom finds the time to do so. Hence we selected some of the deathless sonnets of Shakespeare, great poems by Donne, Keats, Shelley, Wordsworth, and Walt Whitman. Many of them reflect the spirit of the countryside, but the selection is not a narrow one—it includes a wide range of subjects and moods. There is light verse, too, and both prose and poetry on food and drink.

All these, together with a few quizzes, make up our book. We hope you enjoy reading it as much as we enjoyed putting it together. And we shall like to think of it going as a companion on many happy holidays, to all sorts of strange places and in all sorts of company.

THE EDITORS

Contents

1. STORIES

xi

2. HUMOR

3. TRAVEL, EXPLORATION, AND NATURE

6. EATING AND DRINKING

1
STORIES

Big Two-Hearted River: Part 1

BY

ERNEST HEMINGWAY

THE TRAIN went on up the track out of sight, around one of the hills of burnt timber. Nick sat down on the bundle of canvas and bedding the baggage man had pitched out of the door of the baggage car. There was no town, nothing but the rails and the burned-over country. The thirteen saloons that had lined the one street of Seney had not left a trace. The foundations of the Mansion House hotel stuck up above the ground. The stone was chipped and split by the fire. It was all that was left of the town of Seney. Even the surface had been burned off the ground.

Nick looked at the burned-over stretch of hillside, where he had expected to find the scattered houses of the town and then walked down the railroad track to the bridge over the river. The river was there. It swirled against the log spiles of the bridge. Nick looked down into the clear, brown water, colored from the pebbly bottom, and watched the trout keeping themselves steady in the current with wavering fins. As he watched them they changed their positions by quick angles, only to hold steady in the fast water again. Nick watched them a long time.

He watched them holding themselves with their noses into the current, many trout in deep, fast moving water, slightly distorted as he watched far down through the glassy convex surface of the pool, its surface pushing and swelling smooth against the resistance of the log-driven piles of the bridge. At the bottom of the pool were the big trout. Nick did not see them at first. Then he saw them at the bottom of the pool, big trout looking to hold themselves on the gravel bottom in a varying mist of gravel and sand, raised in spurts by the current.

Nick looked down into the pool from the bridge. It was a hot day. A kingfisher flew up the stream. It was a long time since Nick had looked into a stream and seen trout. They were very satisfactory. As the shadow of the kingfisher moved up the stream, a big trout shot upstream in a long angle, only his shadow marking the angle, then lost his shadow as he came through the surface of the water, caught the sun, and then, as he went back into the stream under the surface, his shadow seemed to float down the stream with the current, unresisting, to his post under the bridge where he tightened facing up into the current.

Nick's heart tightened as the trout moved. He felt all the old feeling.

He turned and looked down the stream. It stretched away, pebbly-bottomed with shallows and big boulders and a deep pool as it curved away around the foot of a bluff.

Nick walked back up the ties to where his pack lay in the cinders beside the railway track. He was happy. He adjusted the pack harness around the bundle, pulling straps tight, slung the pack on his back, got his arms through the shoulder straps and took some of the pull off his shoulders by leaning his forehead against the wide band of the tump-line. Still, it was too heavy. It was much too heavy. He had his leather rod-case in his hand and leaning forward to keep the weight of the pack high on his shoulders he walked along the road that paralleled the railway track, leaving the burned town behind in the heat, and then turned off around a hill with a high, fire-scarred hill on either side onto a road that went back into the country. He walked along the road feeling the ache from the pull of the heavy pack. The road climbed steadily. It was hard work walking up-hill. His muscles ached and the day was hot, but Nick felt happy. He felt he had left everything behind, the need for thinking, the need to write, other needs. It was all back of him.

From the time he had gotten down off the train and the baggage man had thrown his pack out of the open car door things had been different. Seney was burned, the country was burned over and changed, but it did not matter. It could not all be burned. He knew that. He hiked along the road, sweating in the sun, climbing to cross the range of hills that separated the railway from the pine plains.

The road ran on, dipping occasionally, but always climbing. Nick went on up. Finally the road after going parallel to the burnt hillside reached the top. Nick leaned back against a stump and slipped out of the pack harness. Ahead of him, as far as he could see, was the pine plain. The burned country stopped off at the left with the range of hills. On ahead islands of dark pine trees rose out of the plain. Far off to the left was the line of the river. Nick followed it with his eye and caught glints of the water in the sun.

There was nothing but the pine plain ahead of him, until the far blue hills that marked the Lake Superior height of land. He could hardly see them, faint and far away in the heat-light over the plain. If he looked too steadily they were gone. But if he only half-looked they were there, the far-off hills of the height of land.

Nick sat down against the charred stump and smoked a cigarette. His pack balanced on the top of the stump, harness holding ready, a hollow molded in it from his back. Nick sat smoking, looking out over the country. He did not need to get his map out. He knew where he was from the position of the river.

As he smoked, his legs stretched out in front of him, he noticed a grasshopper walk along the ground and up onto his woolen sock. The grasshopper was black. As he had walked along the road, climbing, he had started many grasshoppers from the dust. They were all black. They were not the big grasshoppers with yellow and black or red and black wings whirring out from their black wing sheathing as they fly up. These were just ordinary hoppers, but all a sooty black in color. Nick had wondered about them as he walked, without really thinking about them. Now, as he watched the black hopper that was nibbling at the wool of his sock with its fourway lip, he realized that they had all turned black from living in the burned-over land. He realized that the fire must have come the year before, but the grasshoppers were all black now. He wondered how long they would stay that way.

Carefully he reached his hand down and took hold of the hopper by the wings. He turned him up, all his legs walking in the air, and looked at his jointed belly. Yes, it was black too, iridescent where the back and head were dusty.

"Go on, hopper," Nick said, speaking out loud for the first time. "Fly away somewhere."

He tossed the grasshopper up into the air and watched him sail away to a charcoal stump across the road.

Nick stood up. He leaned his back against the weight of his pack where it rested upright on the stump and got his arms through the shoulder straps. He stood with the pack on his back on the brow of the hill looking out across the country, toward the distant river and then struck down the hillside away from the road. Underfoot the ground was good walking. Two hundred yards down the hillside the fire line stopped. Then it was sweet fern, growing ankle high, to walk through, and clumps of jack pines; a long undulating country with frequent rises and descents, sandy underfoot and the country alive again.

Nick kept his direction by the sun. He knew where he wanted to strike the river and he kept on through the pine plain, mounting small rises to see other rises ahead of him and sometimes from the top of a rise a great solid island of pines off to his right or his left. He broke off some sprigs of the heathery sweet fern, and put them under his pack straps. The chafing crushed it and he smelled it as he walked.

He was tired and very hot, walking across the uneven, shadeless pine plain. At any time he knew he could strike the river by turning off to his left. It could not be more than a mile away. But he kept on toward the north to hit the river as far upstream as he could go in one day's walking.

For some time as he walked Nick had been in sight of one of the big islands of pine standing out above the rolling high ground he was crossing. He dipped down and then as he came slowly up to the crest of the bridge he turned and made toward the pine trees.

There was no underbrush in the island of pine trees. The trunks of the trees went straight up or slanted toward each other. The trunks were straight and brown without branches. The branches were high above. Some interlocked to make a solid shadow on the brown forest floor. Around the grove of trees was a bare space. It was brown and soft underfoot as Nick walked on it. This was the over-lapping of the pine needle floor, extending out beyond the width of the high branches. The trees had grown tall and the branches moved high, leaving in the sun this bare space they had once covered with shadow. Sharp at the edge of this extension of the forest floor commenced the sweet fern.

Nick slipped off his pack and lay down in the shade. He lay on his back and looked up into the pine trees. His neck and back and the small of his back rested as he stretched. The earth felt good against his back. He looked up at the sky, through the branches, and then shut his eyes. He opened them and looked up again. There was a wind high up in the branches. He shut his eyes again and went to sleep.

Nick woke stiff and cramped. The sun was nearly down. His pack was heavy and the straps painful as he lifted it on. He leaned over with the pack on and picked up the leather rod-case and started out from the pine trees across the sweet fern swale, toward the river. He knew it could not be more than a mile.

He came down a hillside covered with stumps into a meadow. At the edge of the meadow flowed the river. Nick was glad to get to the river. He walked upstream through the meadow. His trousers were soaked with the dew as he walked. After the hot day, the dew had come quickly and heavily. The river made no sound. It was too fast and smooth. At the edge of the meadow, before he mounted to a piece of high ground to make camp, Nick looked down the river at the trout rising. They were rising to insects come from the swamp on the other side of the stream when the sun went down. The trout jumped out of water to take them. While Nick walked through the little stretch of meadow alongside the stream, trout had jumped high out of water. Now as he looked down the river, the insects must be settling on the surface, for the trout were feeding steadily all down the stream. As far down the long stretch as he could see, the trout were rising, making circles all down the surface of the water, as though it were starting to rain.

The ground rose, wooded and sandy, to overlook the meadow, the stretch of river and the swamp. Nick dropped his pack and rod-case and looked for a level piece of ground. He was very hungry and he wanted to make his camp before he cooked. Between two jack pines, the ground was quite level. He took the ax out of the pack and chopped out two projecting roots. That leveled a piece of ground large enough to sleep on. He smoothed out the sandy soil with his hand and pulled all the sweet fern bushes by their roots. His hands smelled good from the sweet fern. He smoothed the uprooted earth. He did not want anything making lumps under the blankets. When he had the ground smooth, he spread his three blankets. One he folded double, next to the ground. The other two he spread on top.

With the ax he slit off a bright slab of pine from one of the stumps and split it into pegs for the tent. He wanted them long and solid to hold in the ground. With the tent unpacked and spread on the ground, the pack, leaning against a jackpine, looked much smaller. Nick tied the rope that served the tent for a ridge-pole to the trunk of one of the pine trees and pulled the tent up off the ground with the other end of the rope and tied it to the other pine. The tent hung on the rope like a canvas blanket on a clothesline. Nick poked a pole he had cut up under the back peak of the canvas and then made it a tent by pegging out the sides. He pegged the sides out taut and drove the pegs deep, hitting them down into the ground with the flat of the ax until the rope loops were buried and the canvas was drum tight.

Across the open mouth of the tent Nick fixed cheesecloth to keep out mosquitoes. He crawled inside under the mosquito bar with various things from the pack to put at the head of the bed under the slant of the canvas. Inside the tent the light came through the brown canvas. It smelled pleasantly of canvas. Already there was something mysterious and homelike. Nick was happy as he crawled inside the tent. He had not been unhappy all day. This was different though. Now things were done. There had been this to do. Now it was done. It had been a hard trip. He was very tired. That was done. He had made his camp. He was settled. Nothing could touch him. It was a good place to camp. He was there, in the good place. He was in his home where he had made it. Now he was hungry.

He came out, crawling under the cheesecloth. It was quite dark outside. It was lighter in the tent.

Nick went over to the pack and found, with his fingers, a long nail in a paper sack of nails, in the bottom of the pack. He drove it into the pine tree, holding it close and hitting it gently with the flat of the ax. He hung the pack up on the nail. All his supplies were in the pack. They were off the ground and sheltered now.

Nick was hungry. He did not believe he had ever been hungrier. He opened and emptied a can of pork and beans and a can of spaghetti into the frying pan.

"I've got a right to eat this kind of stuff, if I'm willing to carry it," Nick said. His voice sounded strange in the darkening woods. He did not speak again.

He started a fire with some chunks of pine he got with the ax from a stump. Over the fire he stuck a wire grill, pushing the four legs down into the ground with his boot. Nick put the frying pan

on the grill over the flames. He was hungrier. The beans and
spaghetti warmed. Nick stirred them and mixed them together.
They began to bubble, making little bubbles that rose with difficulty to the surface. There was a good smell. Nick got out a bottle
of tomato catchup and cut four slices of bread. The little bubbles
were coming faster now. Nick sat down beside the fire and lifted
the frying pan off. He poured about half the contents out into the
tin plate. It spread slowly on the plate. Nick knew it was too hot.
He poured on some tomato catchup. He knew the beans and spaghetti were still too hot. He looked at the fire, then at the tent, he
was not going to spoil it all by burning his tongue. For years he had
never enjoyed fried bananas because he had never been able to
wait for them to cool. His tongue was very sensitive. He was very
hungry. Across the river in the swamp, in the almost dark, he saw
a mist rising. He looked at the tent once more. All right. He took a
full spoonful from the plate.

"Chrise," Nick said, "Geezus Chrise," he said happily.

He ate the whole plateful before he remembered the bread. Nick
finished the second plateful with the bread, mopping the plate
shiny. He had not eaten since a cup of coffee and a ham sandwich
in the station restaurant at St. Ignace. It had been a very fine experience. He had been that hungry before, but had not been able to
satisfy it. He could have made camp hours before if he had wanted
to. There were plenty of good places to camp on the river. But this
was good.

Nick tucked two big chips of pine under the grill. The fire flared
up. He had forgotten to get water for the coffee. Out of the pack
he got a folding canvas bucket and walked down the hill, across the
edge of the meadow, to the stream. The other bank was in the
white mist. The grass was wet and cold as he knelt on the bank and
dipped the canvas bucket into the stream. It bellied and pulled
hard in the current. The water was ice cold. Nick rinsed the bucket
and carried it full up to the camp. Up away from the stream it was
not so cold.

Nick drove another big nail and hung up the bucket full of water.
He dipped the coffee pot half full, put some more chips under the
grill onto the fire and put the pot on. He could not remember
which way he made coffee. He could remember an argument about
it with Hopkins, but not which side he had taken. He decided to

bring it to a boil. He remembered now that was Hopkins's way. He had once argued about everything with Hopkins. While he waited for the coffee to boil, he opened a small can of apricots. He liked to open cans. He emptied the can of apricots out into a tin cup. While he watched the coffee on the fire, he drank the juice syrup of the apricots, carefully at first to keep from spilling, then meditatively, sucking the apricots down. They were better than fresh apricots.

The coffee boiled as he watched. The lid came up and coffee and grounds ran down the side of the pot. Nick took it off the grill. It was a triumph for Hopkins. He put sugar in the empty apricot cup and poured some of the coffee out to cool. It was too hot to pour and he used his hat to hold the handle of the coffee pot. He would not let it steep in the pot at all. Not the first cup. It should be straight Hopkins all the way. Hop deserved that. He was a very serious coffee drinker. He was the most serious man Nick had ever known. Not heavy, serious. That was a long time ago. Hopkins spoke without moving his lips. He had played polo. He made millions of dollars in Texas. He had borrowed carfare to go to Chicago, when the wire came that his first big well had come in. He could have wired for money. That would have been too slow. They called Hop's girl the Blonde Venus. Hop did not mind because she was not his real girl. Hopkins said very confidently that none of them would make fun of his real girl. He was right. Hopkins went away when the telegram came. That was on the Black River. It took eight days for the telegram to reach him. Hopkins gave away his .22 caliber Colt automatic pistol to Nick. He gave his camera to Bill. It was to remember him always by. They were all going fishing again next summer. The Hop Head was rich. He would get a yacht and they would all cruise along the north shore of Lake Superior. He was excited but serious. They said good-bye and all felt bad. It broke up the trip. They never saw Hopkins again. That was a long time ago on the Black River.

Nick drank the coffee, the coffee according to Hopkins. The coffee was bitter. Nick laughed. It made a good ending to the story. His mind was starting to work. He knew he could choke it because he was tired enough. He spilled the coffee out of the pot and shook the grounds loose into the fire. He lit a cigarette and went inside the tent. He took off his shoes and trousers, sitting on the blankets,

rolled the shoes up inside the trousers for a pillow and got in between the blankets.

Out through the front of the tent he watched the glow of the fire,
when the night wind blew on it. It was a quiet night. The swamp
was perfectly quiet. Nick stretched under the blanket comfortably.
A mosquito hummed close to his ear. Nick sat up and lit a match.
The mosquito was on the canvas, over his head. Nick moved the
match quickly up to it. The mosquito made a satisfactory hiss in the
flame. The match went out. Nick lay down again under the blanket.
He turned on his side and shut his eyes. He was sleepy. He felt sleep
coming. He curled up under the blanket and went to sleep.

Big Two-Hearted River: Part II

IN THE morning the sun was up and the tent was starting to get
hot. Nick crawled out under the mosquito netting stretched
across the mouth of the tent, to look at the morning. The grass was
wet on his hands as he came out. He held his trousers and his shoes
in his hands. The sun was just up over the hill. There was the
meadow, the river and the swamp. There were birch trees in the
green of the swamp on the other side of the river.

The river was clear and smoothly fast in the early morning. Down
about two hundred yards were three logs all the way across the
stream. They made the water smooth and deep above them. As Nick
watched, a mink crossed the river on the logs and went into the
swamp. Nick was excited. He was excited by the early morning and
the river. He was really too hurried to eat breakfast, but he knew
he must. He built a little fire and put on the coffee pot.

While the water was heating in the pot he took an empty bottle
and went down over the edge of the high ground to the meadow.
The meadow was wet with dew and Nick wanted to catch grasshoppers for bait before the sun dried the grass. He found plenty

of good grasshoppers. They were at the base of the grass stems. Sometimes they clung to a grass stem. They were cold and wet with the
dew, and could not jump until the sun warmed them. Nick picked
them up, taking only the medium-sized brown ones, and put them
into the bottle. He turned over a log and just under the shelter of
the edge were several hundred hoppers. It was a grasshopper lodg-
ing house. Nick put about fifty of the medium browns into the
bottle. While he was picking up the hoppers the others warmed in
the sun and commenced to hop away. They flew when they hopped.
At first they made one flight and stayed stiff when they landed, as
though they were dead.

Nick knew that by the time he was through with breakfast they
would be as lively as ever. Without dew in the grass it would take
him all day to catch a bottle full of good grasshoppers and he would
have to crush many of them, slamming at them with his hat. He
washed his hands at the stream. He was excited to be near it. Then
he walked up to the tent. The hoppers were already jumping stiffly
in the grass. In the bottle, warmed by the sun, they were jumping
in a mass. Nick put in a pine stick as a cork. It plugged the mouth
of the bottle enough, so the hoppers could not get out and left
plenty of air passage.

He had rolled the log back and knew he could get grasshoppers
there every morning.

Nick laid the bottle full of jumping grasshoppers against a pine
trunk. Rapidly he mixed some buckwheat flour with water and
stirred it smooth, one cup of flour, one cup of water. He put a handful of coffee in the pot and dipped a lump of grease out of a can
and slid it sputtering across the hot skillet. On the smoking skillet
he poured smoothly the buckwheat batter. It spread like lava, the
grease spitting sharply. Around the edges the buckwheat cake began to firm, then brown, then crisp. The surface was bubbling
slowly to porousness. Nick pushed under the browned under surface
with a fresh pine chip. He shook the skillet sideways and the cake
was loose on the surface. I won't try and flop it, he thought. He
slid the chip of clean wood all the way under the cake, and flopped
it over onto its face. It sputtered in the pan.

When it was cooked Nick regreased the skillet. He used all the
batter. It made another big flapjack and one smaller one.

Nick ate a big flapjack and a smaller one, covered with apple butter. He put apple butter on the third cake, folded it over twice, wrapped it in oiled paper and put it in his shirt pocket. He put the apple butter jar back in the pack and cut bread for two sandwiches.

In the pack he found a big onion. He sliced it in two and peeled the silky outer skin. Then he cut one half into slices and made onion sandwiches. He wrapped them in oiled paper and buttoned them in the other pocket of his khaki shirt. He turned the skillet upside down on the grill, drank the coffee, sweetened and yellow brown with the condensed milk in it, and tidied up the camp. It was a good camp.

Nick took his fly rod out of the leather rod-case, jointed it, and shoved the rod-case back into the tent. He put on the reel and threaded the line through the guides. He had to hold it from hand to hand, as he threaded it, or it would slip back through its own weight. It was a heavy, double tapered fly line. Nick had paid eight dollars for it a long time ago. It was made heavy to lift back in the air and come forward flat and heavy and straight to make it possible to cast a fly which has no weight. Nick opened the aluminum leader box. The leaders were coiled between the damp flannel pads. Nick had wet the pads at the water cooler on the train up to St. Ignace. In the damp pads the gut leaders had softened and Nick unrolled one and tied it by a loop at the end to the heavy fly line. He fastened a hook on the end of the leader. It was a small hook; very thin and springy.

Nick took it from his hook book, sitting with the rod across his lap. He tested the knot and the spring of the rod by pulling the line taut. It was a good feeling. He was careful not to let the hook bite into his finger.

He started down to the stream, holding his rod, the bottle of grasshoppers hung from his neck by a thong tied in half hitches around the neck of the bottle. His landing net hung by a hook from his belt. Over his shoulder was a long flour sack tied at each corner into an ear. The cord went over his shoulder. The sack flapped against his legs.

Nick felt awkward and professionally happy with all his equipment hanging from him. The grasshopper bottle swung against his chest. In his shirt the breast pockets bulged against him with the lunch and his fly book.

He stepped into the stream. It was a shock. His trousers clung tight to his legs. His shoes felt the gravel. The water was a rising cold shock.

Rushing, the current sucked against his legs. Where he stepped in, the water was over his knees. He waded with the current. The gravel slid under his shoes. He looked down at the swirl of water below each leg and tipped up the bottle to get a grasshopper.

The first grasshopper gave a jump in the neck of the bottle and went out into the water. He was sucked under in the whirl by Nick's right leg and came to the surface a little way down stream. He floated rapidly, kicking. In a quick circle, breaking the smooth surface of the water, he disappeared. A trout had taken him.

Another hopper poked his face out of the bottle. His antennæ wavered. He was getting his front legs out of the bottle to jump. Nick took him by the head and held him while he threaded the slim hook under his chin, down through his thorax and into the last segments of his abdomen. The grasshopper took hold of the hook with his front feet, spitting tobacco juice on it. Nick dropped him into the water.

Holding the rod in his right hand he let out line against the pull of the grasshopper in the current. He stripped off line from the reel with his left hand and let it run free. He could see the hopper in the little waves of the current. It went out of sight.

There was a tug on the line. Nick pulled against the taut line. It was his first strike. Holding the now living rod across the current, he brought in the line with his left hand. The rod bent in jerks, the trout pumping against the current. Nick knew it was a small one. He lifted the rod straight up in the air. It bowed with the pull.

He saw the trout in the water jerking with his head and body against the shifting tangent of the line in the stream.

Nick took the line in his left hand and pulled the trout, thumping tiredly against the current, to the surface. His back was mottled the clear, water-over-gravel color, his side flashing in the sun. The rod under his right arm, Nick stooped, dipping his right hand into the current. He held the trout, never still, with his moist right hand, while he unhooked the barb from his mouth, then dropped him back into the stream.

He hung unsteadily in the current, then settled to the bottom beside a stone. Nick reached down his hand to touch him, his arm to the elbow under water. The trout was steady in the moving stream, resting on the gravel, beside a stone. As Nick's fingers touched him, touched his smooth, cool, underwater feeling he was gone, gone in a shadow across the bottom of the stream.

He's all right, Nick thought. He was only tired.

He had wet his hand before he touched the trout, so he would not disturb the delicate mucus that covered him. If a trout was touched with a dry hand, a white fungus attacked the unprotected spot. Years before when he had fished crowded streams, with fly fishermen ahead of him and behind him, Nick had again and again come on dead trout, furry with white fungus, drifted against a rock, or floating belly up in some pool. Nick did not like to fish with other men on the river. Unless they were of your party, they spoiled it.

He wallowed down the stream, above his knees in the current, through the fifty yards of shallow water above the pile of logs that crossed the stream. He did not rebait his hook and held it in his hand as he waded. He was certain he could catch small trout in the shallows, but he did not want them. There would be no big trout in the shallows this time of day.

Now the water deepened up his thighs sharply and coldly. Ahead was the smooth dammed-back flood of water above the logs. The water was smooth and dark; on the left, the lower edge of the meadow; on the right the swamp.

Nick leaned back against the current and took a hopper from the bottle. He threaded the hopper on the hook and spat on him for good luck. Then he pulled several yards of line from the reel and tossed the hopper out ahead onto the fast, dark water. It floated down towards the logs, then the weight of the line pulled the bait under the surface. Nick held the rod in his right hand, letting the line run out through his fingers.

There was a long tug. Nick struck and the rod came alive and dangerous, bent double, the line tightening, coming out of water, tightening, all in a heavy, dangerous, steady pull. Nick felt the moment when the leader would break if the strain increased and let the line go.

The reel ratcheted into a mechanical shriek as the line went out in a rush. Too fast. Nick could not check it, the line rushing out, the reel note rising as the line ran out.

With the core of the reel showing, his heart feeling stopped with the excitement, leaning back against the current that mounted icily his thighs, Nick thumbed the reel hard with his left hand. It was awkward getting his thumb inside the fly reel frame.

As he put on pressure the line tightened into sudden hardness and beyond the logs a huge trout went high out of water. As he jumped, Nick lowered the tip of the rod. But he felt, as he dropped the tip to ease the strain, the moment when the strain was too great; the hardness too tight. Of course, the leader had broken. There was no mistaking the feeling when all spring left the line and it became dry and hard. Then it went slack.

His mouth dry, his heart down, Nick reeled in. He had never seen so big a trout. There was a heaviness, a power not to be held, and then the bulk of him, as he jumped. He looked as broad as a salmon.

Nick's hand was shaky. He reeled in slowly. The thrill had been too much. He felt, vaguely, a little sick, as though it would be better to sit down.

The leader had broken where the hook was tied to it. Nick took it in his hand. He thought of the trout somewhere on the bottom, holding himself steady over the gravel, far down below the light, under the logs, with the hook in his jaw. Nick knew the trout's teeth would cut through the snell of the hook. The hook would imbed itself in his jaw. He'd bet the trout was angry. Anything that size would be angry. That was a trout. He had been solidly hooked. Solid as a rock. He felt like a rock, too, before he started off. By God, he was a big one. By God, he was the biggest one I ever heard of.

Nick climbed out onto the meadow and stood, water running down his trousers and out of his shoes, his shoes squlchy. He went over and sat on the logs. He did not want to rush his sensations any.

He wriggled his toes in the water, in his shoes, and got out a cigarette from his breast pocket. He lit it and tossed the match into the fast water below the logs. A tiny trout rose at the match, as it swung around in the fast current. Nick laughed. He would finish the cigarette.

He sat on the logs, smoking, drying in the sun, the sun warm on his back, the river shallow ahead entering the woods, curving into the woods, shallows, light glittering, big water-smooth rocks, cedars along the bank and white birches, the logs warm in the sun, smooth to sit on, without bark, gray to the touch; slowly the feeling of disappointment left him. It went away slowly, the feeling of disappointment that came sharply after the thrill that made his shoulders ache. It was all right now. His rod lying out on the logs, Nick tied a new hook on the leader, pulling the gut tight until it grimped into itself in a hard knot.

He baited up, then picked up the rod and walked to the far end of the logs to get into the water, where it was not too deep. Under and beyond the logs was a deep pool. Nick walked around the shallow shelf near the swamp shore until he came out on the shallow bed of the stream.

On the left, where the meadow ended and the woods began, a great elm tree was uprooted. Gone over in a storm, it lay back into the woods, its roots clotted with dirt, grass growing in them, rising a solid bank beside the stream. The river cut to the edge of the uprooted tree. From where Nick stood he could see deep channels, like ruts, cut in the shallow bed of the stream by the flow of the current. Pebbly where he stood and pebbly and full of boulders beyond; where it curved near the tree roots, the bed of the stream was marly and between the ruts of deep water green wed fronds swung in the current.

Nick swung the rod back over his shoulder and forward, and the line, curving forward, laid the grasshopper down on one of the deep channels in the weeds. A trout struck and Nick hooked him.

Holding the rod far out toward the uprooted tree and sloshing backward in the current, Nick worked the trout, plunging, the rod bending alive, out of the danger of the weeds into the open river. Holding the rod, pumping alive against the current, Nick brought the trout in. He rushed, but always came, the spring of the rod yielding to the rushes, sometimes jerking under water, but always bringing him in. Nick eased downstream with the rushes. The rod above his head he led the trout over the net, then lifted.

The trout hung heavy in the net, mottled trout back and silver sides in the meshes. Nick unhooked him; heavy sides, good to hold, big undershot jaw, and slipped him, heaving and big sliding, into the long sack that hung from his shoulders in the water.

Nick spread the mouth of the sack against the current and it filled, heavy with water. He held it up, the bottom in the stream, and the water poured out through the sides. Inside at the bottom was the big trout, alive in the water.

Nick moved downstream. The sack out ahead of him sunk heavy in the water, pulling from his shoulders.

It was getting hot, the sun hot on the back of his neck.

Nick had one good trout. He did not care about getting many trout. Now the stream was shallow and wide. There were trees along both banks. The trees of the left bank made short shadows on the current in the forenoon sun. Nick knew there were trout in each shadow. In the afternoon, after the sun had crossed toward the hills, the trout would be in the cool shadows on the other side of the stream.

The very biggest ones would lie up close to the bank. You could always pick them up there on the Black. When the sun was down they all moved out into the current. Just when the sun made the water blinding in the glare before it went down, you were liable to strike a big trout anywhere in the current. It was almost impossible to fish then, the surface of the water was blinding as a mirror in the sun. Of course, you could fish upstream, but in a stream like the Black, or this, you had to wallow against the current and in a deep place, the water piled up on you. It was no fun to fish upstream with this much current.

Nick moved along through the shallow stretch watching the banks for deep holes. A beech tree grew close beside the river, so that the branches hung down into the water. The stream went back in under the leaves. There were always trout in a place like that.

Nick did not care about fishing that hole. He was sure he would get hooked in the branches.

It looked deep though. He dropped the grasshopper so the current took it under water, back in under the overhanging branch. The line pulled hard and Nick struck. The trout threshed heavily, half out of water in the leaves and branches. The line was caught. Nick pulled hard and the trout was off. He reeled in and holding the hook in his hand, walked down the stream.

Ahead, close to the left bank, was a big log. Nick saw it was hollow; pointing up river the current entered it smoothly, only a little ripple spread each side of the log. The water was deepening. The top of the hollow log was gray and dry. It was partly in the shadow.

Nick took the cork out of the grasshopper bottle and a hopper clung to it. He picked him off, hooked him and tossed him out. He held the rod far out so that the hopper on the water moved into the current flowing into the hollow log. Nick lowered the rod and the hopper floated in. There was a heavy strike. Nick swung the rod against the pull. It felt as though he were hooked into the log itself, except for the live feeling.

He tried to force the fish out into the current. It came, heavily.

The line went slack and Nick thought the trout was gone. Then he saw him, very near, in the current, shaking his head, trying to get the hook out. His mouth was clamped shut. He was fighting the hook in the clear flowing current.

Looping in the line with his left hand, Nick swung the rod to make the line taut and tried to lead the trout toward the net, but he was gone, out of sight, the line pumping. Nick fought him against the current, letting him thump in the water against the spring of the rod. He shifted the rod to his left hand, worked the trout upstream, holding his weight, fighting on the rod, and then let him down into the net. He lifted him clear of the water, a heavy half circle in the net, the net dripping, unhooked him and slid him into the sack.

He spread the mouth of the sack and looked down in at the two big trout alive in the water.

Through the deepening water, Nick waded over to the hollow log. He took the sack off, over his head, the trout flopping as it came out of water, and hung it so the trout were deep in the water. Then he pulled himself up on the log and sat, the water from his trousers and boots running down into the stream. He laid his rod down, moved along to the shady end of the log and took the sandwiches out of his pocket. He dipped the sandwiches in the cold water. The current carried away the crumbs. He ate the sandwiches and dipped his hat full of water to drink, the water running out through his hat just ahead of his drinking.

It was cool in the shade, sitting on the log. He took a cigarette out and struck a match to light it. The match sunk into the gray wood, making a tiny furrow. Nick leaned over the side of the log, found a hard place and lit the match. He sat smoking and watching the river.

Ahead the river narrowed and went into a swamp. The river became smooth and deep and the swamp looked solid with cedar trees, their trunks close together, their branches solid. It would not be possible to walk through a swamp like that. The branches grew so low. You would have to keep almost level with the ground to move at all. You could not crash through the branches. That must be why the animals that lived in swamps were built the way they were, Nick thought.

He wished he had brought something to read. He felt like reading. He did not feel like going on into the swamp. He looked down the river. A big cedar slanted all the way across the stream. Beyond that the river went into the swamp.

Nick did not want to go in there now. He felt a reaction against deep wading with the water deepening up under his armpits, to hook big trout in places impossible to land them. In the swamp the banks were bare, the big cedars came together overhead, the sun did not come through, except in patches; in the fast deep water, in the half light, the fishing would be tragic. In the swamp fishing was a tragic adventure. Nick did not want it. He did not want to go down the stream any further today.

He took out his knife, opened it and stuck it in the log. Then he pulled up the sack, reached into it and brought out one of the trout. Holding him near the tail, hard to hold, alive, in his hand, he whacked him against the log. The trout quivered, rigid. Nick laid him on the log in the shade and broke the neck of the other fish the same way. He laid them side by side on the log. They were fine trout.

Nick cleaned them, slitting them from the vent to the tip of the jaw. All the insides and the gills and tongue came out in one piece. They were both males; long gray-white strips of milt, smooth and clean. All the insides clean and compact, coming out all together. Nick tossed the offal ashore for the minks to find.

He washed the trout in the stream. When he held them back up in the water they looked like live fish. Their color was not gone yet. He washed his hands and dried them on the log. Then he laid the trout on the sack spread out on the log, rolled them up in it, tied the bundle and put it in the landing net. His knife was still standing, blade stuck in the log. He cleaned it on the wood and put it in his pocket.

Nick stood up on the log, holding his rod, the landing net hanging heavy, then stepped into the water and splashed ashore. He climbed the bank and cut up into the woods, toward the high ground. He was going back to camp. He looked back. The river just showed through the trees. There were plenty of days coming when he could fish the swamp.

Red

BY

W. SOMERSET MAUGHAM

THE SKIPPER thrust his hand into one of his trouser pockets and with difficulty, for they were not at the sides but in front and he was a portly man, pulled out a large silver watch. He looked at it and then looked again at the declining sun. The Kanaka at the wheel gave him a gance, but did not speak. The skipper's eyes rested on the island they were approaching. A white line of foam marked the reef. He knew there was an opening large enough to get his ship through, and when they came a little nearer he counted on seeing it. They had nearly an hour of daylight still before them. In the lagoon the water was deep and they could anchor comfortably. The chief of the village which he could already see among the coconut trees was a friend of the mate's, and it would be pleasant to go ashore for the night. The mate came forward at that minute and the skipper turned to him.

"We'll take a bottle of booze along with us and get some girls in to dance," he said.

"I don't see the opening," said the mate.

He was a Kanaka, a handsome, swarthy fellow, with somewhat the look of a later Roman emperor, inclined to stoutness; but his face was fine and clean-cut.

"I'm dead sure there's one right here," said the captain, looking through his glasses. "I can't understand why I can't pick it up. Send one of the boys up the mast to have a look."

The mate called one of the crew and gave him the order. The captain watched the Kanaka climb and waited for him to speak. But the Kanaka shouted down that he could see nothing but the unbroken line of foam. The captain spoke Samoan like a native, and he cursed him freely.

22

"Shall he stay up there?" asked the mate.

"What the hell good does that do?" answered the captain. "The blame fool can't see worth a cent. You bet your sweet life I'd find the opening if I was up there."

He looked at the slender mast with anger. It was all very well for a native who had been used to climbing up coconut trees all his life. He was fat and heavy.

"Come down," he shouted. "You're no more use than a dead dog. We'll just have to go along the reef till we find the opening."

It was a seventy-ton schooner with paraffin auxiliary, and it ran, when there was no head wind, between four and five knots an hour. It was a bedraggled object; it had been painted white a very long time ago, but it was now dirty, dingy, and mottled. It smelt strongly of paraffin and of the copra which was its usual cargo. They were within a hundred feet of the reef now and the captain told the steersman to run along it till they came to the opening. But when they had gone a couple of miles he realized that they had missed it. He went about and slowly worked back again. The white foam of the reef continued without interruption and now the sun was setting. With a curse at the stupidity of the crew the skipper resigned himself to waiting till next morning.

"Put her about," he said. "I can't anchor here."

They went out to sea a little and presently it was quite dark. They anchored. When the sail was furled the ship began to roll a good deal. They said in Apia that one day she would roll right over; and the owner, a German-American who managed one of the largest stores, said that no money was big enough to induce him to go out in her. The cook, a Chinese in white trousers, very dirty and ragged, and a thin white tunic, came to say that supper was ready, and when the skipper went into the cabin he found the engineer already seated at table. The engineer was a long, lean man with a scraggy neck. He was dressed in blue overalls and a sleeveless jersey which showed his thin arms tattooed from elbow to wrist.

"Hell, having to spend the night outside," said the skipper.

The engineer did not answer, and they ate their supper in silence. The cabin was lit by a dim oil lamp. When they had eaten the canned apricots with which the meal finished the Chink brought them a cup of tea. The skipper lit a cigar and went on the upper deck. The island now was only a darker mass against the night.

The stars were very bright. The only sound was the ceaseless breaking of the surf. The skipper sank into a deck-chair and smoked
idly. Presently three or four members of the crew came up and sat
down. One of them had a banjo and another a concertina. They
began to play, and one of them sang. The native song sounded
strange on these instruments. Then to the singing a couple began
to dance. It was a barbaric dance, savage and primeval, rapid, with
quick movements of the hands and feet and contortions of the
body; it was sensual, sexual even, but sexual without passion. It was
very animal, direct, weird without mystery, natural in short, and
one might almost say childlike. At last they grew tired. They
stretched themselves on the deck and slept, and all was silent. The
skipper lifted himself heavily out of his chair and clambered down
the companion. He went into his cabin and got out of his clothes.
He climbed into his bunk and lay there. He panted a little in the
heat of the night.

But next morning, when the dawn crept over the tranquil sea,
the opening in the reef which had eluded them the night before
was seen a little to the east of where they lay. The schooner entered the lagoon. There was not a ripple on the surface of the water.
Deep down among the coral rocks you saw little coloured fish swim.
When he had anchored his ship the skipper ate his breakfast and
went on deck. The sun shone from an unclouded sky, but in the
early morning the air was grateful and cool. It was Sunday, and
there was a feeling of quietness, a silence as though nature were
at rest, which gave him a peculiar sense of comfort. He sat, looking
at the wooded coast, and felt lazy and well at ease. Presently a slow
smile moved his lips and he threw the stump of his cigar into the
water.

"I guess I'll go ashore," he said. "Get the boat out."

He climbed stiffly down the ladder and was rowed to a little cove.
The coconut trees came down to the water's edge, not in rows, but
spaced out with an ordered formality. They were like a ballet of
spinsters, elderly but flippant, standing in affected attitudes with
the simpering graces of a bygone age. He sauntered idly through
them, along a path that could be just seen winding its tortuous
way, and it led him presently to a broad creek. There was a bridge
across it, but a bridge constructed of single trunks of coconut trees,
a dozen of them, placed end to end and supported where they met

by a forked branch driven into the bed of the creek. You walked on a smooth, round surface, narrow and slippery, and there was no support for the hand. To cross such a bridge required sure feet and a stout heart. The skipper hesitated. But he saw on the other side, nestling among the trees, a white man's house; he made up his mind and, rather gingerly, began to walk. He watched his feet carefully, and where one trunk joined on to the next and there was a difference of level, he tottered a little. It was with a gasp of relief that he reached the last tree and finally set his feet on the firm ground of the other side. He had been so intent on the difficult crossing that he never noticed anyone was watching him, and it was with surprise that he heard himself spoken to.

"It takes a bit of nerve to cross these bridges when you're not used to them."

He looked up and saw a man standing in front of him. He had evidently come out of the house which he had seen.

"I saw you hesitate," the man continued, with a smile on his lips, "and I was watching to see you fall in."

"Not on your life," said the captain, who had now recovered his confidence.

"I've fallen in myself before now. I remember, one evening I came back from shooting, and I fell in, gun and all. Now I get a boy to carry my gun for me."

He was a man no longer young, with a small beard, now somewhat grey, and a thin face. He was dressed in a singlet, without arms, and a pair of duck trousers. He wore neither shoes nor socks. He spoke English with a slight accent.

"Are you Neilson?" asked the skipper.

"I am."

"I've heard about you. I thought you lived somewheres round here."

The skipper followed his host into the little bungalow and sat down heavily in the chair which the other motioned him to take. While Neilson went out to fetch whisky and glasses he took a look round the room. It filled him with amazement. He had never seen so many books. The shelves reached from floor to ceiling on all four walls, and they were closely packed. There was a grand piano littered with music, and a large table on which books and magazines lay in disorder. The room made him feel embarrassed. He remembered that Neilson was a queer fellow. No one knew very much about him, although he had been in the islands for so many years, but those who knew him agreed that he was queer. He was a Swede.

"You've got one big heap of books here," he said, when Neilson returned.

"They do no harm," answered Neilson with a smile.

"Have you read them all?" asked the skipper.

"Most of them."

"I'm a bit of a reader myself. I have the *Saturday Evening Post* sent me regler."

Neilson poured his visitor a good stiff glass of whisky and gave him a cigar. The skipper volunteered a little information.

"I got in last night, but I couldn't find the opening, so I had to anchor outside. I never been this run before, but my people had some stuff they wanted to bring over here. Gray, d'you know him?"

"Yes, he's got a store a little way along."

"Well, there was a lot of canned stuff that he wanted over, an' he's got some copra. They thought I might just as well come over as lie idle at Apia. I run between Apia and Pago-Pago mostly, but they've got smallpox there just now, and there's nothing stirring."

He took a drink of his whisky and lit a cigar. He was a taciturn man, but there was something in Neilson that made him nervous, and his nervousness made him talk. The Swede was looking at him with large dark eyes in which there was an expression of faint amusement.

"This is a tidy little place you've got here."

"I've done my best with it."

"You must do pretty well with your trees. They look fine. With copra at the price it is now. I had a bit of a plantation myself once, in Upolu it was, but I had to sell it."

He looked round the room again, where all those books gave him a feeling of something incomprehensible and hostile.

"I guess you must find it a bit lonesome here though," he said.

"I've got used to it. I've been here for twenty-five years."

Now the captain could think of nothing more to say, and he smoked in silence. Nielson had apparently no wish to break it. He looked at his guest with a meditative eye. He was a tall man, more than six feet high, and very stout. His face was red and blotchy, with a network of little purple veins on the cheeks, and his features were sunk into its fatness. His eyes were bloodshot. His neck was buried in rolls of fat. But for a fringe of long curly hair, nearly white, at the back of his head, he was quite bald; and that immense, shiny surface of forehead, which might have given him a false look of intelligence, on the contrary gave him one of peculiar imbecility. He wore a blue flannel shirt, open at the neck and showing his fat chest covered with a mat of reddish hair, and a very old pair of blue serge trousers. He sat in his chair in a heavy ungainly attitude, his great belly thrust forward and his fat legs uncrossed. All elasticity had gone from his limbs. Neilson wondered idly what sort of man he had been in his youth. It was almost impossible to imagine that this creature of vast bulk had ever been a boy who ran about. The skipper finished his whisky, and Neilson pushed the bottle towards him.

"Help yourself."

The skipper leaned forward and with his great hand seized it.

"And how come you in these parts anyway?" he said.

"Oh, I came out to the islands for my health. My lungs were bad and they said I hadn't a year to live. You see they were wrong."

"I meant, how come you to settle down right here?"

"I am a sentimentalist."

"Oh!"

Neilson knew that the skipper had not an idea what he meant, and he looked at him with an ironical twinkle in his dark eyes. Perhaps just because the skipper was so gross and dull a man the whim seized him to talk further.

"You were too busy keeping your balance to notice, when you crossed the bridge, but this spot is generally considered rather pretty."

"It's a cute little house you've got here."

"Ah, that wasn't here when I first came. There was a native hut, with its beehive roof and its pillars, over-shadowed by a great tree with red flowers; and the croton bushes, their leaves yellow and red and golden, made a pied fence around it. And then all about were the coconut trees, as fanciful as women, and as vain. They stood at the water's edge and spent all day looking at their

reflections. I was a young man then—Good Heavens, it's a quarter of
a century ago—and I wanted to enjoy all the loveliness of the
world in the short time allotted to me before I passed into the
darkness. I thought it was the most beautiful spot I had ever
seen. The first time I saw it I had a catch at my heart, and I was
afraid I was going to cry. I wasn't more than twenty-five, and
though I put the best face I could on it, I didn't want to die.
And somehow it seemed to me that the very beauty of this place
made it easier for me to accept my fate. I felt when I came here
that all my past life had fallen away, Stockholm and its University,
and then Bonn: it all seemed the life of somebody else, as though
now at last I had achieved the reality which our doctors of philosophy—I am one myself, you know—had discussed so much. 'A year,'
I cried to myself. 'I have a year. I will spend it here and then I
am content to die.'

"We are foolish and sentimental and melodramatic at twenty-
five, but if we weren't perhaps we should be less wise at fifty.

"Now drink, my friend. Don't let the nonsense I talk interfere
with you."

He waved his thin hand towards the bottle, and the skipper
finished what remained in his glass.

"You ain't drinking nothin'," he said, reaching for the whisky.

"I am of a sober habit," smiled the Swede. "I intoxicate myself
in ways which I fancy are more subtle. But perhaps that is only
vanity. Anyhow, the effects are more lasting and the results less
deleterious."

"They say there's a deal of cocaine taken in the States now," said
the captain.

Neilson chuckled.

"But I do not see a white man often," he continued, "and for
once I don't think a drop of whisky can do me any harm."

He poured himself out a little, added some soda, and took a sip.

"And presently I found out why the spot had such an unearthly
loveliness. Here love had tarried for a moment like a migrant bird
that happens on a ship in mid-ocean and for a little while folds
its tired wings. The fragrance of a beautiful passion hovered over
it like the fragrance of hawthorn in May in the meadows of my
home. It seems to me that the places where men have loved or
suffered keep about them always some faint aroma of something

that has not wholly died. It is as though they had acquired a
spiritual significance which mysteriously affects those who pass. I
wish I could make myself clear." He smiled a little. "Though I cannot imagine that if I did you would understand."

He paused.

"I think this place was beautiful because here I had been loved
beautifully." And now he shrugged his shoulders. "But perhaps it
is only that my æsthetic sense is gratified by the happy conjunction of
young love and a suitable setting."

Even a man less thick-witted than the skipper might have been
forgiven if he were bewildered by Neilson's words. For he seemed
faintly to laugh at what he said. It was as though he spoke from
emotion which his intellect found ridiculous. He had said himself
that he was a sentimentalist, and when sentimentality is joined with
scepticism there is often the devil to pay.

He was silent for an instant and looked at the captain with eyes
in which there was a sudden perplexity.

"You know, I can't help thinking that I've seen you before
somewhere or other," he said.

"I couldn't say as I remember you," returned the skipper.

"I have a curious feeling as though your face were familiar to
me. It's been puzzling me for some time. But I can't situate my recollection in any place or at any time."

The skipper massively shrugged his heavy shoulders.

"It's thirty years since I first come to the islands. A man can't
figure on remembering all the folk he meets in a while like that."

The Swede shook his head.

"You know how one sometimes has the feeling that a place one
has never been to before is strangely familiar. That's how I seem to
see you." He gave a whimsical smile. "Perhaps I knew you in some
past existence. Perhaps, perhaps you were the master of a galley in
ancient Rome and I was a slave at the oar. Thirty years have you
been here?"

"Every bit of thirty years."

"I wonder if you knew a man called Red?"

"Red?"

"That is the only name I've ever known him by. I never knew
him personally. I never even set eyes on him. And yet I seem to
see him more clearly than many men, my brothers, for instance,

with whom I passed my daily life for many years. He lives in my
imagination with the distinctness of a Paolo Malatesta or a Romeo.
But I daresay you have never read Dante or Shakespeare?"

"I can't say as I have," said the captain.

Neilson, smoking a cigar, leaned back in his chair and looked
vacantly at the ring of smoke which floated in the still air. A smile
played on his lips, but his eyes were grave. Then he looked at the
captain. There was in his gross obesity something extraordinarily
repellent. He had the plethoric self-satisfaction of the very fat. It
was an outrage. It set Neilson's nerves on edge. But the contrast
between the man before him and the man he had in mind was
pleasant.

"It appears that Red was the most comely thing you ever saw.
I've talked to quite a number of people who knew him in those
days, white men, and they all agree that the first time you saw him
his beauty just took your breath away. They called him Red on
account of his flaming hair. It had a natural wave and he wore it
long. It must have been of that wonderful colour that the pre-
Raphaelites raved over. I don't think he was vain of it, he was much
too ingenuous for that, but no one could have blamed him if he
had been. He was tall, six feet and an inch or two—in the native
house that used to stand here was the mark of his height cut with
a knife on the central trunk that supported the roof—and he was
made like a Greek god, broad in the shoulders and thin in the
flanks; he was like Apollo, with just that soft roundess which
Praxiteles gave him, and that suave, feminine grace which has in it
something troubling and mysterious. His skin was dazzling white,
milky, like satin; his skin was like a woman's."

"I had kind of a white skin myself when I was a kiddie," said
the skipper, with a twinkle in his bloodshot eyes.

But Neilson paid no attention to him. He was telling his story
now and interruption made him impatient.

"And his face was just as beautiful as his body. He had large
blue eyes, very dark, so that some say they were black, and unlike most red-haired people he had dark eyebrows and long dark
lashes. His features were perfectly regular and his mouth was like
a scarlet wound. He was twenty."

On these words the Swede stopped with a certain sense of the
dramatic. He took a sip of whisky.

"He was unique. There never was anyone more beautiful. There was no more reason for him than for a wonderful blossom to flower on a wild plant. He was a happy accident of nature.

"One day he landed at that cove into which you must have put this morning. He was an American sailor, and he had deserted from a man-of-war in Apia. He had induced some good-humoured native to give him a passage on a cutter that happened to be sailing from Apia to Safoto, and he had been put ashore here in a dug-out. I do not know why he deserted. Perhaps life on a man-of-war with its restrictions irked him, perhaps he was in trouble, and perhaps it was the South Seas and these romantic islands that got into his bones. Every now and then they take a man strangely, and he finds himself like a fly in a spider's web. It may be that there was a softness of fibre in him, and these green hills with their soft airs, this blue sea, took the northern strength from him as Delilah took the Nazarite's. Anyhow, he wanted to hide himself, and he thought he would be safe in this secluded nook till his ship had sailed from Samoa.

"There was a native hut at the cove and as he stood there, wondering where exactly he should turn his steps, a young girl came out and invited him to enter. He knew scarcely two words of the native tongue and she as little English. But he understood well enough what her smiles meant, and her pretty gestures, and he followed her. He sat down on a mat and she gave him slices of pineapple to eat. I can speak of Red only from hearsay, but I saw the girl three years after he first met her, and she was scarcely nineteen then. You cannot imagine how exquisite she was. She had the passionate grace of the hibiscus and the rich colour. She was rather tall, slim, with the delicate features of her race, and large eyes like pools of still water under the palm trees; her hair, black and curling, fell down her back, and she wore a wreath of scented flowers. Her hands were lovely. They were so small, so exquisitely formed, they gave your heart-strings a wrench. And in those days she laughed easily. Her smile was so delightful that it made your knees shake. Her skin was like a field of ripe corn on a summer day. Good Heavens, how can I describe her? She was too beautiful to be real.

"And these two young things, she was sixteen and he was twenty, fell in love with one another at first sight. That is the real love, not the love that comes from sympathy, common interests, or intellec-

tual community, but love pure and simple. That is the love that
Adam felt for Eve when he awoke and found her in the garden gazing at him with dewy eyes. That is the love that draws the beasts to
one another, and the Gods. That is the love that makes the world a
miracle. That is the love which gives life its pregnant meaning. You
have never heard of the wise, cynical French duke who said that
with two lovers there is always one who loves and one who lets himself be loved; it is a bitter truth to which most of use have to resign
ourselves; but now and then there are two who love and two who
let themselves be loved. Then one might fancy that the sun stands
still as it stood when Joshua prayed to the God of Israel.

"And even now after all these years, when I think of these two, so
young, so fair, so simple, and of their love, I feel a pang. It tears my
heart just as my heart is torn when on certain nights I watch the
full moon shining on the lagoon from an unclouded sky. There is
always pain in the contemplation of perfect beauty.

"They were children. She was good and sweet and kind. I know
nothing of him, and I like to think that then at all events he was
ingenuous and frank. I like to think that his soul was as comely as
his body. But I daresay he had no more soul than the creatures of
the woods and forests who made pipes from reeds and bathed in the
mountain streams when the world was young, and you might catch
sight of little fawns galloping through the glade on the back of a
bearded centaur. A soul is a troublesome possession and when man
developed it he lost the Garden of Eden.

"Well, when Red came to the island it had recently been visited
by one of those epidemics which the white man has brought to the
South Seas, and one third of the inhabitants had died. It seems that
the girl had lost all her near kin and she lived now in the house of
distant cousins. The household consisted of two ancient crones,
bowed and wrinkled, two younger women, and a man and a boy.
For a few days he stayed there. But perhaps he felt himself too near
the shore, with the possibility that he might fall in with white men
who would reveal his hiding-place; perhaps the lovers could not
bear that the company of others should rob them for an instant of
the delight of being together. One morning they set out, the pair of
them, with the few things that belonged to the girl, and walked
along a grassy path under the coconuts, till they came to the creek
you see. They had to cross the bridge you crossed, and the girl

laughed gleefully because he was afraid. She held his hand till they came to the end of the first tree, and then his courage failed him and he had to go back. He was obliged to take off all his clothes before he could risk it, and she carried them over for him on her head. They settled down in the empty hut that stood here. Whether she had any rights over it (land tenure is a complicated business in the islands), or whether the owner had died during the epidemic, I do not know, but anyhow no one questioned them, and they took possession. Their furniture consisted of a couple of grass-mats on which they slept, a fragment of looking-glass, and a bowl or two. In this pleasant land that is enough to start housekeeping on.

"They say that happy people have no history, and certainly a happy love has none. They did nothing all day long and yet the days seemed all too short. The girl had a native name, but Red called her Sally. He picked up the easy language very quickly, and he used to lie on the mat for hours while she chattered gaily to him. He was a silent fellow, and perhaps his mind was lethargic. He smoked incessantly the cigarettes which she made him out of the native tobacco and pandanus leaf, and he watched her while with deft fingers she made grass mats. Often natives would come in and tell long stories of the old days when the island was disturbed by tribal wars. Sometimes he would go fishing on the reef, and bring home a basket full of coloured fish. Sometimes at night he would go out with a lantern to catch lobster. There were plantains round the hut and Sally would roast them for their frugal meal. She knew how to make delicious messes from coconuts, and the breadfruit tree by the side of the creek gave them its fruit. On feast-days they killed a little pig and cooked it on hot stones. They bathed together in the creek; and in the evening they went down to the lagoon and paddled about in a dugout, with its great outrigger. The sea was deep blue, wine-coloured at sundown, like the sea of Homeric Greece; but in the lagoon the colour had an infinite variety, aquamarine and amethyst and emerald; and the setting sun turned it for a short moment to liquid gold. Then there was the colour of the coral, brown, white, pink, red, purple; and the shapes it took were marvellous. It was like a magic garden, and the hurrying fish were like butterflies. It strangely lacked reality. Among the coral were pools with a floor of white sand and here, where the water was dazzling clear, it was very good to bathe. Then, cool and happy, they wan-

dred back in the gloaming over the soft grass road to the creek,
walking hand in hand, and now the mynah birds filled the coconut
trees with their clamour. And then the night, with that great sky
shining with gold, that seemed to stretch more widely than the skies
of Europe, and the soft airs that blew gently through the open hut,
the long night again was all too short. She was sixteen and he was
barely twenty. The dawn crept in among the wooden pillars of the
hut and looked at those lovely children sleeping in one another's
arms. The sun hid behind the great tattered leaves of the plantains
so that it might not disturb them, and then, with playful malice,
shot a golden ray, like the outstretched paw of a Persian cat, on
their faces. They opened their sleepy eyes and they smiled to welcome another day. The weeks lengthened into months, and a year
passed. They seemed to love one another as—I hesitate to say passionately, for passion has in it always a shade of sadness, a touch of
bitterness or anguish, but as wholeheartedly, as simply and naturally as on that first day on which, meeting, they had recognised
that a god was in them.

"If you had asked them I have no doubt that they would have
thought it impossible to suppose their love could ever cease. Do we
not know that the essential element of love is a belief in its own
eternity? And yet perhaps in Red there was already a very little
seed, unknown to himself and unsuspected by the girl, which would
in time have grown to weariness. For one day one of the natives
from the cove told them that some way down the coast at the anchorage was a British whaling-ship.

" 'Gee,' he said, 'I wonder if I could make a trade of some nuts
and plantains for a pound or two of tobacco.'

"The pandanus cigarettes that Sally made him with untiring
hands were strong and pleasant enough to smoke, but they left him
unsatisfied; and he yearned on a sudden for real tobacco, hard, rank,
and pungent. He had not smoked a pipe for many months. His
mouth watered at the thought of it. One would have thought some
premonition of harm would have made Sally seek to dissuade him,
but love possessed her so completely that it never occurred to her
any power on earth could take him from her. They went up into
the hills together and gathered a great basket of wild oranges, green,
but sweet and juicy; and they picked plantains from around the hut,
and coconuts from their trees, and breadfruit and mangoes; and

they carried them down to the cove. They loaded the unstable canoe with them, and Red and the native boy who had brought them the news of the ship paddled along outside the reef.

"It was the last time she ever saw him.

"Next day the boy came back alone. He was all in tears. This is the story he told. When after their long paddle they reached the ship and Red hailed it, a white man looked over the side and told them to come on board. They took the fruit they had brought with them and Red piled it up on the deck. The white man and he began to talk, and they seemed to come to some agreement. One of them went below and brought up tobacco. Red took some at once and lit a pipe. The boy imitated the zest with which he blew a great cloud of smoke from his mouth. Then they said something to him and he went into the cabin. Through the open door the boy, watching curiously, saw a bottle brought out and glasses. Red drank and smoked. They seemed to ask him something, for he shook his head and laughed. The man, the first man who had spoken to them, laughed too, and he filled Red's glass once more. They went on talking and drinking, and presently, growing tired of watching a sight that meant nothing to him, the boy curled himself up on the deck and slept. He was awakened by a kick; and, jumping to his feet, he saw that the ship was slowly sailing out of the lagoon. He caught sight of Red seated at the table, with his head resting heavily on his arms, fast asleep. He made a movement towards him, intending to wake him, but a rough hand seized his arm, and a man, with a scowl and words which he did not understand, pointed to the side. He shouted to Red, but in a moment he was seized and flung overboard. Helpless, he swam round to his canoe which was drifting a little way off, and pushed it on to the reef. He climbed in and, sobbing all the way, paddled back to shore.

"What had happened was obvious enough. The whaler, by desertion or sickness, was short of hands, and the captain when Red came aboard had asked him to sign on; on his refusal he had made him drunk and kidnapped him.

"Sally was beside herself with grief. For three days she screamed and cried. The natives did what they could to comfort her, but she would not be comforted. She would not eat. And then, exhausted, she sank into a sullen apathy. She spent long days at the cove, watching the lagoon, in the vain hope that Red somehow or other would manage to escape. She sat on the white sand, hour after hour, with the tears running down her cheeks, and at night dragged herself wearily back across the creek to the little hut where she had been happy. The people with whom she had lived before Red came to the island wished her to return to them, but she would not; she was convinced that Red would come back, and she wanted him to find her where he had left her. Four months later she was delivered of a still-born child, and the old woman who had come to help her through her confinement remained with her in the hut. All joy was taken from her life. If her anguish with time became less intolerable it was replaced by a settled melancholy. You would not have thought that among these people, whose emotions, though so violent, are very transient, a woman could be found capable of so enduring a passion. She never lost the profound conviction that sooner or later Red would come back. She watched for him, and every time someone crossed this slender little bridge of coconut trees she looked. It might at last be he."

Neilson stopped talking and gave a faint sigh.

"And what happened to her in the end?" asked the skipper.

Neilson smiled bitterly.

"Oh, three years afterwards she took up with another white man."

The skipper gave a fat, cynical chuckle.

"That's generally what happens to them," he said.

The Swede shot him a look of hatred. He did not know why that gross, obese man excited in him so violent a repulsion. But his thoughts wandered and he found his mind filled with memories of the past. He went back five and twenty years. It was when he first came to the island, weary of Apia, with its heavy drinking, its gambling and coarse sensuality, a sick man, trying to resign himself to the loss of the career which had fired his imagination with ambitious thoughts. He set behind him resolutely all his hopes of making a great name for himself and strove to content himself with the few poor months of careful life which was all that he could count on. He was boarding with a half-caste trader who had a store a couple of miles along the coast at the edge of a native village; and one day, wandering aimlessly along the grassy paths of the coconut groves, he had come upon the hut in which Sally lived. The beauty of the spot had filled him with a rapture so great that it was almost painful, and then he had seen Sally. She was the loveliest

creature he had ever seen, and the sadness in those dark, magnificent
eyes of hers affected him strangely. The Kanakas were a handsome
race, and beauty was not rare among them, but it was the beauty
of shapely animals. It was empty. But those tragic eyes were dark
with mystery, and you felt in them the bitter complexity of the
groping, human soul. The trader told him the story and it moved
him.

"Do you think he'll ever come back?" asked Neilson.

"No fear. Why, it'll be a couple of years before the ship is paid
off, and by then he'll have forgotten all about her. I bet he was
pretty mad when he woke up and found he'd been shanghaied, and
I shouldn't wonder but he wanted to fight somebody. But he'd got
to grin and bear it, and I guess in a month he was thinking it the
best thing that had ever happened to him that he got away from
the island."

But Neilson could not get the story out of his head. Perhaps because he was sick and weakly, the radiant health of Red appealed
to his imagination. Himself an ugly man, insignificant of appearance, he prized very highly comeliness in others. He had never been
passionately in love, and certainly he had never been passionately
loved. The mutual attraction of those two young things gave him a
singular delight. It had the ineffable beauty of the Absolute. He
went again to the little hut by the creek. He had a gift for languages
and an energetic mind, accustomed to work, and he had already
given much time to the study of the local tongue. Old habit was
strong in him and he was gathering together material for a paper
on the Samoan speech. The old crone who shared the hut with
Sally invited him to come in and sit down. She gave him *kava* to
drink and cigarettes to smoke. She was glad to have someone to chat
with and while she talked he looked at Sally. She reminded him of
the Psyche in the museum at Naples. Her features had the same
clear purity of line, and though she had borne a child she had still
a virginal aspect.

It was not till he had seen her two or three times that he induced
her to speak. Then it was only to ask him if he had seen in Apia a
man called Red. Two years had passed since his disappearance, but
it was plain that she still thought of him incessantly.

It did not take Neilson long to discover that he was in love with
her. It was only by an effort of will now that he prevented himself

from going every day to the creek, and when he was not with Sally his thoughts were. At first, looking upon himself as a dying man, he asked only to look at her, and occasionally hear her speak, and his love gave him a wonderful happiness. He exulted in its purity. He wanted nothing from her but the opportunity to weave around her graceful person a web of beautiful fancies. But the open air, the equable temperature, the rest, the simple fare, began to have an unexpected effect on his health. His temperature did not soar at night to such alarming heights, he coughed less and began to put on weight; six months passed without his having a hæmorrhage; and on a sudden he saw the possibility that he might live. He had studied his disease carefully, and the hope dawned upon him that with great care he might arrest its course. It exhilarated him to look forward once more to the future. He made plans. It was evident that any active life was out of the question, but he could live on the islands, and the small income he had, insufficient elsewhere, would be ample to keep him. He could grow coconuts; that would give him an occupation; and he would send for his books and a piano; but his quick mind saw that in all this he was merely trying to conceal from himself the desire which obsessed him.

He wanted Sally. He loved not only her beauty, but that dim soul which he divined behind her suffering eyes. He would intoxicate her with his passion. In the end he would make her forget. And in an ecstasy of surrender he fancied himself giving her too the happiness which he had thought never to know again, but had now so miraculously achieved.

He asked her to live with him. She refused. He had expected that and did not let it depress him, for he was sure that sooner or later she would yield. His love was irresistible. He told the old woman of his wishes, and found somewhat to his surprise that she and the neighbours, long aware of them, were strongly urging Sally to accept his offer. After all, every native was glad to keep house for a white man, and Neilson according to the standards of the island was a rich one. The trader with whom he boarded went to her and told her not to be a fool; such an opportunity would not come again, and after so long she could not still believe that Red would ever return. The girl's resistance only increased Neilson's desire, and what had been a very pure love now became an agonising passion. He was determined that nothing should stand in his way. He gave Sally no peace. At last, worn out by his persistence and the persuasions, by turns pleading and angry, of everyone around her, she consented. But the day after when, exultant, he went to see her he found that in the night she had burnt down the hut in which she and Red had lived together. The old crone ran towards him full of angry abuse of Sally, but he waved her aside; it did not matter; they would build a bungalow on the place where the hut had stood. A European house would really be more convenient if he wanted to bring out a piano and a vast number of books.

And so the little wooden house was built in which he had now lived for many years, and Sally became his wife. But after the first few weeks of rapture, during which he was satisfied with what she gave him he had known little happiness. She had yielded to him, through weariness, but she had only yielded what she set no store on. The soul which he had dimly glimpsed escaped him. He knew that she cared nothing for him. She still loved Red, and all the time she was waiting for his return. At a sign from him, Neilson knew that, notwithstanding his love, his tenderness, his sympathy, his generosity, she would leave him without a moment's hesitation. She would never give a thought to his distress. Anguish seized him and he battered at that impenetrable self of hers which sullenly resisted him. His love became bitter. He tried to melt her heart with kindness, but it remained as hard as before; he feigned indifference, but she did not notice it. Sometimes he lost his temper and abused her, and then she wept silently. Sometimes he thought she was nothing but a fraud, and that soul simply an invention of his own, and that he could not get into the sanctuary of her heart because there was no sanctuary there. His love became a prison from which he longed to escape, but he had not the strength merely to open the door—that was all it needed—and walk out into the open air. It was torture and at last he became numb and hopeless. In the end the fire burnt itself out and, when he saw her eyes rest for an instant on the slender bridge, it was no longer rage that filled his heart but impatience. For many years now they had lived together bound by the ties of habit and convenience, and it was with a smile that he looked back on his old passion. She was an old woman, for the women on the islands age quickly, and if he had no love for her any more he had tolerance. She left him alone. He was contented with his piano and his books.

His thoughts led him to a desire for words.

"When I look back now and reflect on that brief passionate love of Red and Sally, I think that perhaps they should thank the ruthless fate that separated them when their love seemed still to be at its height. They suffered, but they suffered in beauty. They were spared the real tragedy of love."

"I don't know exactly as I get you," said the skipper.

"The tragedy of love is not death or separation. How long do you think it would have been before one or other of them ceased to care? Oh, it is dreadfully bitter to look at a woman whom you have loved with all your heart and soul, so that you felt you could not bear to let her out of your sight, and realise that you would not mind if you never saw her again. The tragedy of love is indifference."

But while he was speaking a very extraordinary thing happened. Though he had been addressing the skipper he had not been talking to him, he had been putting his thoughts into words for himself, and with his eyes fixed on the man in front of him he had not seen him. But now an image presented itself to them, an image not of the man he saw, but of another man. It was as though he were looking into one of those distorting mirrors that make you extraordinarily squat or outrageously elongate, but here exactly the opposite took place, and in the obese, ugly old man he caught the shadowy glimpse of a stripling. He gave him now a quick, searching scrutiny. Why had a haphazard stroll brought him just to this place? A sudden tremor of his heart made him slightly breathless. An absurd suspicion seized him. What had occurred to him was impossible, and yet it might be a fact.

"What is your name?" he asked abruptly.

The skipper's face puckered and he gave a cunning chuckle. He looked then malicious and horribly vulgar.

"It's such a damned long time since I heard it that I almost forget it myself. But for thirty years now in the islands they've always called me Red."

His huge form shook as he gave a low, almost silent laugh. It was obscene. Neilson shuddered. Red was hugely amused, and from his bloodshot eyes tears ran down his cheeks.

Neilson gave a gasp, for at that moment a woman came in. She was a native, a woman of somewhat commanding presence, stout without being corpulent, dark, for the natives grow darker with age, with very grey hair. She wore a black Mother Hubbard, and its thinness showed her heavy breasts. The moment had come.

She made an observation to Neilson about some household matter and he answered. He wondered if his voice sounded as unnatural to her as it did to himself. She gave the man who was sitting in the chair by the window an indifferent glance, and went out of the room. The moment had come and gone.

Neilson for a moment could not speak. He was strangely shaken. Then he said:

"I'd be very glad if you'd stay and have a bit of dinner with me. Pot luck."

"I don't think I will," said Red. "I must go after this fellow Gray. I'll give him his stuff and then I'll get away. I want to be back in Apia tomorrow."

"I'll send a boy along with you to show you the way."

"That'll be fine."

Red heaved himself out of his chair, while the Swede called one of the boys who worked on the plantation. He told him where the skipper wanted to go, and the boy stepped along the bridge. Red prepared to follow him.

"Don't fall in," said Neilson.

"Not on your life."

Neilson watched him make his way across and when he had disappeared among the coconuts he looked still. Then he sank heavily in his chair. Was that the man who had prevented him from being happy? Was that the man whom Sally had loved all these years and for whom she had waited so desperately? It was grotesque. A sudden fury seized him so that he had an instinct to spring up and smash everything around him. He had been cheated. They had seen each other at last and had not known it. He began to laugh, mirthlessly, and his laughter grew till it became hysterical. The Gods had played him a cruel trick. And he was old now.

At last Sally came in to tell him dinner was ready. He sat down in front of her and tried to eat. He wondered what she would say if he told her now that the fat old man sitting in the chair was the lover whom she remembered still with the passionate abandonment of her youth. Years ago, when he hated her because she made him so unhappy, he would have been glad to tell her. He wanted to hurt her then as she hurt him, because his hatred was only love. But now he did not care. He shrugged his shoulders listlessly.

"What did that man want?" she asked presently.

He did not answer at once. She was old too, a fat old native woman. He wondered why he had ever loved her so madly. He had laid at her feet all the treasures of his soul, and she had cared nothing for them. Waste, what waste! And now, when he looked at her, he felt only contempt. His patience was at last exhausted. He answered her question.

"He's the captain of a schooner. He's come from Apia."

"Yes."

"He brought me news from home. My eldest brother is very ill and I must go back."

"Will you be gone long?"

He shrugged his shoulders.

The Romance of Rosy Ridge

BY

MacKINLAY KANTOR

IT WAS GOOD corn-growing weather that July night when the stranger first came along, making his music through the hollow all the way up to Rosy Ridge. Old Gill MacBean and his wife and the younguns were sitting out on the stoop when they heard the man coming.

Sairy MacBean and her daughter, Lissy Ann, had turkey-wing fans, and they felt kind of elegant, with nothing to do but sit there in the coolness of the hilltop and wave their fans, just as if they hadn't worked their arms off at the elbows all day long. The younguns had made a smudge in front of the step, partly to drive away the mosquitoes and partly to play Indian, and old Gill was just smoking his pipe and not thinking about anything much.

At usual times you couldn't hear any creatures but whippoorwills in the dusk; it was only in the winter that you heard wolves, and panthers had been persecuted out of the country years agone. But this night the stranger sent his music on ahead of him, and it was hard for anyone to conclude just what kind of music it might be.

The younguns believed it might be a ghost, and they skedaddled up on the stoop behind the old folks—all except young Andrew; and he ran into the house for the pepper-box revolver that he kept hidden under his pillow.

Old Gill himself listened to the tune for a while; and then, without saying a word to anybody, he went and got the repeating rifle he had captured from a Yankee at Nashville. It wasn't customary for night riders to make that kind of a sound when they were coming after you, but in times like these you didn't dare take risk.

But Lissy Ann and her mother were both struck dumb by the beauty of the sounds—pretty much scared, too, but not scared

43

enough to leave their chairs—and they sat there with their ears peeled, and finally Lissy Ann dropped her turkey-wing fan and let it lie forgotten at her feet.

Because the man who came up out of the dark woods was playing Gentle Annie in some kind of strange humming fashion none of the MacBeans had ever heard before. Lissy Ann said afterward it sounded like someone had captured a lot of grasshoppers and tree peepers, and katydids that were out ahead of their time, and had trained them to play the fiddle until they all played right smack together, as if one hand were drawing the bow across the strings.

Still, it wasn't fiddling and it wasn't ballad singing, but something kind of between the two, and it got hold of your heart when you heard it. It bestirred all the sadness and prettiness that ever grew in those woods, in spring or high summer; and you thought of honeysuckle creeping wild, and morning-glories in the corn, and you thought, too, about how butternuts smelt in the fall, when the first frost browned their fuzz.

The music changed from Gentle Annie into Billy Boy, and then on into Jack o' Diamonds. Gill MacBean walked down to the fence and leaned against a rail with the repeating rifle in the hollow of his arm. He made young Andrew stay well behind him, though this didn't sound like any night rider who had ever crossed the hills.

The stranger came up the road, walking slow in the dusk, and yet kind of pert on his feet. He made you think that he had walked twenty miles through the brush, and still had enough get-up-and-go to dance all night, if anybody invited him. He couldn't have missed seeing the house or sheds, or the way the family were staring at him, because the darkness wasn't yet thick enough for that. But he never made a break in his tune. He kept right on, brave and contented, and he quit Jack o' Diamonds when he first struck the rail fence, but he flowed right on into Arkansas Traveler, and that was the tune he was making when finally he stopped square in front of old Gill and said, "Howdy."

"Stranger," said old Gill, "that's a likely kind of noise you're making."

"I make the best there is," said the stranger, and young Andrew came out from behind his father, but still holding the pepper-box revolver.

And the stranger said, "Why do you folks come to welcome me with shooting irons? I have got no intention of harming a soul I meet along the way."

Old Gill told him, "There's people that ride through this country sometimes that have got worse intentions than yourn."

"But they don't come playing tunes, do they?"

"No," said Gill MacBean, "I ain't never heard them do that. Not yet. But they're liable to try anything once."

The rest of the family came down to the fence now, coming a little slow and fearful, but mighty sure that this man hadn't brought any harm with him. They all crowded close and looked him over, silent and wondering, and trying to figure what kind of instrument he had used to contrive such music, because he didn't seem to have a horn or a fiddle to his name. He just stood there and smiled, and at the first look Sairy MacBean thought he couldn't be much older than Andrew, although he was a mighty sight bigger. He was nowhere as big as old Gill, though, nor as big as the two boys who had been killed in the war. At the next look, they saw that surely he was a man grown, although there was a kind of fancy and a peculiar secret in his face that wouldn't make him more than a child in some ways, if he grew to be a hundred and ten.

He took off the old hat he wore, and he bowed to the womenfolks —a real courteous bow, good as any gentleman could have done. They saw now that he wore spectacles with brass rims. Nobody ever wore spectacles in those parts, except the parson and a few of the old folks, and some of the old folks wore them for pride. But this stranger had real spectacles with glass fronts in them, and if you peered close in the gloom, you could see his little dark squirrel eyes, pitying and goodnatured, behind them. He sort of slid around inside his skin, and inside the woolsey coat he wore, with a manner that said he was lithe and quick-moving as a minnow.

The family looked to see what kind of pants he had, because pants meant a lot in Barbary County that year. The butternut and blue pants were pretty well divided, though I reckon the butternut had the edge. But the stranger's pants were such a funny faded color that nobody could tell what their dye was in the first place. They might have been Yankee breeches all soiled, and faded gray by the sun; or else they might have been the kind of pale gray breeches—not butternut—that the Confederates wore in the early days of the war, and that some of the officers hung on to for dress uniform, right up to the last gun.

"Stranger," old Gill MacBean said, and he set the butt of his rifle against the ground and put his hands around the barrel, "I make apology to you, because I came down here to the road thinking you might be a bushwhacker. Now I'll take my oath you ain't any such. But I surely wouldn't take my oath on where those breeches came from. Are you one of those that's inflicted with the oath, or one that's trying to inflict?"

The stranger laughed. He shook his head a little, and made a gay step into the road. He snapped his fingers at the younguns and began to recite a little poem—a sing-song one, that might have been part of a play-party game. It was something about

> *Free as a ground hog, lazy as a possum,*
> *If I've had troubles I reckon I've lost 'em.*
> *Fit at Pea Ridge, fit in Tennessee!*
> *If that ain't fit, then don't ask me!*

The younguns jumped up and down in excitement, for this was just pie for them, and the old folks kind of smiled.

"At any rate," Gill MacBean told him, "you talk like the right color."

"They say there's no right nor wrong any more," the man told him, a bit guarded in his manner.

"Right will always be right," said old Gill. "I lost a brother at Wilson's Creek, and two boys in Arkansas. I'm still one of the meanest rebs in Missouri, but you don't talk like no Yankee that ever breathed."

And then Lissy Ann pulled at his elbow and whispered something to him, and so he spoke up to the stranger and said, "We'd admire to know just how you make that music of yourn."

The stranger told them in an amused whisper, but still as if he meant it: "It comes from a heart that would like to be carefree. It comes out of the berry bushes, and the mink holes down by the river, and the cleared land where folks grow potatoes. It's a variety of potato-bug music, among other things. I just comb it out of the air."

Then up comes his thin brown hand with a comb in it, and that's what he's made all this music with—just a comb with thin paper around it, like any boy would blow when he was playing circus out behind the stable. But the stranger has got some curious trick that no one else seemed ever to learn before—a way of hardening his lips against the paper and suddenly letting them grow soft again; and he uses his tongue and his teeth, too, as if he has to bite right into the heart of the tune, no matter how soft he plays it. That's the kind of music the stranger brought up to Rosy Ridge— just tin-comb-and-paper music, but he calculated it to charm anybody's soul away, and I reckon he succeeded before he was through.

"I sing for my supper," he informed the MacBean folks, "like minstrels bold in days of old," and with that he didn't go back into the Traveler song that he was humming with his comb, but he trilled sadly and easily into something none of them had ever heard before. It was a most important melody, and Lord knows you couldn't have danced to it, nor swung your partner's heels off the floor on any of the breaks; and you couldn't have stomped, because it would have spoiled the music if you had. But they said— or at least Lissy Ann said—that it was the kind of tune you could die to; not the tune the old cat died on, nor the old dog, neither. But a song to make you make love, and perish happy in the remarkable joy of doing it.

It was long-drawn-out, and there was firing and bugling in the middle; it ended up with an anguish that was so sweet you couldn't get your breath.

"Stranger," said Gill MacBean, when at last he had got his, "I'd like mighty well to know where you ever scared up that tunefulness. It don't seem decent, somehow—not strictly so. But I think you've confounded all the whippoorwills."

The man told them, kind of hesitating, "Well, maybe it hasn't never been played before in these parts. It comes all the way from Europe, and a man named Liszt made it up." And he smiled at the two hound pups sitting there eying him and looking like their hearts would break if he walked out of their sight. "I used to have a good foxhound," he said.

Gill MacBean found himself liking this stranger better than he had liked anybody for a long time. "Them two are good. That's Paul and Agrippa, and they're by Danger out of Yeary's old Jezebel. There used to be plenty of hill-topping around here. I reckon it can be revived again, though I don't admire to set down with my Yankee neighbors."

And the stranger wanted to know why he called the pups Paul and Agrippa.

"It's easy to see you don't know your Scriptures, young man, no matter how many tunes you know," Gill told him. "These was second and third born in the litter, and Paul came before Agrippa, didn't he? Leastways, that's what it says in the Bible."

"You haven't got Jesus and Pontius Pilate, then, somewhere around?" the stranger wanted to know. "Because I seem to have read that Jesus came before Pilate too."

But the family was plumb scandalized at that, and they shushed him up proper, and old Gill tapped his shoulder and said he reckoned the fried pork wasn't stone-cold yet. So they brought him into the house and told him they couldn't offer to let him sleep in the barn because the 'whackers had burnt it a month before, but they could and would let him sleep in the loft over the shed, where there was room beside young Andrew.

But the cat kind of got the stranger's tongue, as soon as the tallow dips were burning, and Sairy MacBean had set out the tin lamp she kept for company. Sure enough, the cat might catch anybody's tongue, when he looked at Lissy Ann, because she was growing more easy to look at every week of the world.

Finally, though, he said his name was Henry Bohun. And right away—this being the fashion—they called him Henry; and when they wanted to know what he had done before the war, before he became a comb-humming wanderer, he said promptly that he had been a schoolmaster. It was hard for the younguns to believe this, because he didn't look like any schoolmaster they had ever gone to. Still, he could use powerful words when he wanted to—the big, five-legged kind—and there was that song all the way from Europe, and he knew a lot more than that.

He entertained them in wonderful style, for a solid hour after he had eaten, and his pants did look pretty nigh gray in the candle-light, and the last thing he looked at before he went to the loft to sleep with young Andrew was Lissy Ann's face. I reckon any man, even one who wasn't a comb hummer, would do that; and he would forget all about the war and the bushwhackers and the hard, troublous times. He'd just see that strawberry-yellow hair and the clear blue eyes and the little freckles that were on her smooth round cheeks, and see her soft mouth smiling and hear her soft mouth murmuring something about what a pleasurable evening it was. And then he'd go off to the loft, and lie there unclad with the Missouri wind blowing in through the cracks, out of the forests and cornfields. And still he'd think about a face like hers, and see it when he slept.

I reckon it was the Yeary boys from the next place who first called him Comb-Hummin' Henry, because they stood in old Gill's oat field the next day and marveled at the music the stranger could make. Old Gill had a habit of trading work with the Yearys, and they came over to help him cut the stand of late oats which he had on the flat pasture behind his barn, or at least behind where the barn used to be before the 'whackers burnt it.

But when old Gill and Joe Yeary squatted down in the fence corner to have a pull at the jug, old Gill reckoned aloud that he didn't have much need of the Yearys. Comb-Hummin' Henry could bind up more oats than most young fellows. He seemed to have wire in his back and wire in his arms, and the wondrous thing about it was the way he kept singing little songs all the time he worked; though, naturally, he couldn't raise his comb to his lips and work too.

It was gray breeches in the Yeary family, and they still had a couple of extra boys circulating around somewhere who hadn't come home yet. Old Joe had begun to think that the boys were plumb dead and gone, but his wife had dreamt that they'd show up in good time. Old Joe hadn't been with the rebel army, because he was too lame, but both the youngest boys had got themselves chased around Arkansas for a spell. They talked big about it, but they weren't more than sixteen years old, and it was a caution to see how their eyes would bug out and their jaws hang open when Henry Bohun made some music for them, after the noon eating. He played two combs that time—his own tin one and a nice white comb that he had loaned off of Sairy MacBean, and he had them both wrapped in the remarkable white paper that his pockets were full of. One had a high tone and one was deep and mournful, and he changed them about, in the same song, until you couldn't tell which he had at his mouth.

And he knew what to do for a sick ox, too, for Bum, the nigh ox, was down with the colic that day. Old Gill couldn't get the medicine down Bum's throat, but Comb-Hummin' Henry mixed it up with bran mash, and they do say that Bum was a better ox from that day forth.

And he could make soft soap, because in the afternoon he went to help Sairy and Lissy Ann with the batch they were cooking. He fetched it off the fire, tender and sweet as butter, and he said it was all in talking to the spirits that roosted in the soap when it was stewing. Sairy didn't like such talk about spirits, because spirits reminded her of the bushwhackers and the way they came in their hoods, looking like so many ghosts. But she did say that such soap beat the nation, and a good half of Barbary County besides.

Comb-Hummin' Henry didn't hang around there to get praised. He just lit out for the oat field, and for an hour afterward you could see him heaving the big bundles, and tying straw around them so snug and tight that no wind in the world could blow them loose. And all the time he sang a song about the Arrow Rock jail, and how a man lived in it until he was hung.

Gill MacBean had worked a man or two, in the days before the war and the hard times following. But he had never worked a man like this, and, to tell the truth, he was kind of uneasy in his heart. Henry Bohun's breeches did look a mite bluish in the sunlight, when you were working side by side with him. Old Gill sought to try him out by cussing the Yankees in general, at first, and then certain Yankees he knew that were particularly ornery; then he slandered the new United States President, and all of Congress and the Constitution, too, for good measure; and he said he would refuse to be reconstructed until his dying breath; then he rounded off with some belittling remarks about the battle of Nashville and the Yankee from whom he had captured his repeating rifle; and he said that he'd keep that rifle till his dying breath. But Comb-Hummin' Henry just listened with a dreamy smile, though his bright shiny black squirrel's eyes were jumping quick and lively behind his spectacles.

And old Gill said, "One thing I've sworn, and I'll hold to it until the last bone rots out of my back. I won't have no Yankee grandchildren. I keep my gun loaded for anybody who claims different."

That was when Henry quit smiling. "Mysterious things," he said, "do happen in this world."

"Like what?" Gill demanded.

"Like love, for one thing," said Comb-Hummin' Henry. "Your daughter is mighty pretty."

But Gill MacBean just hauled at his beard a couple of times, and he looked right over what Henry may have meant. I reckon the thought had sneaked around in his brain more than once that Henry was a Yankee, but he wasn't going to recognize it until he had to. I reckon nobody could hate Yankees as bad as old Gill said he hated them. "As soon as my brother got killed at Wilson's Creek," he said, "I up and left my wife and younguns and went to Springfield, and I became a private in Company I, Second Missouri Infantry, Little's Brigade, Price's Division, Army of the Trans-Mississippi. And I fought until Vicksburg, and then I joined the cavalry. I tell you direct and honest that I do hate a Yankee worse than poison, and we got all too many around here. Do you look what they did to my barn," and he showed Henry where the burnt parts of it were ugly and black.

Henry said, quiet and mild, "I have it in my mind that you talked about bushwhackers."

"Sure enough. Yankee bushwhackers! And they still ride these roads. It's not safe for a woman or child to go abroad without a man to bear them company," said old Gill MacBean, and he sliced a mullein leaf clean down the center.

"Why, now," said Comb-Hummin' Henry, "I have it in my mind that the Yearys told about Yankee barns that had been burnt, and Yankee people who had been robbed."

But Gill MacBean growled and said it was just a blind—a trick to throw dust in the eyes of everybody else, and make it look as if the wartime bushwhackers were still ranging around the neighborhood. He knew well enough, he said, that these 'whackers were just Yankee sympathizers who didn't have pity or sympathy in their hearts for anybody who came back from the army wearing gray pants. If a man had been a rebel, or his son or nephew had, they'd burn his barn quick as scat, and they'd even made bold to burn some houses.

These 'whackers lived somewhere close to hand, and they knew just when a man had sold his horse or his cow, and even if his children had scratched together some few dollars, trapping in the winter. They'd been that way all along, he declared; the war was over since spring, but the bushwhackers weren't over by a pretty sight. They robbed travelers on the highroad, and when they raided a farm they always made sure the man who owned it wasn't home. That was a regular Yankee trick, according to Gill MacBean, and he only hoped he'd live to give them a bellyful of hot lead from the repeater he captured at Nashville.

Well, there is no way to tell what Comb-Hummin' Henry might have said in answer, for about this time Lissy Ann came skimming out into the oat field with her skirts blowing behind her, and Henry Bohun stood up and took off his hat. He took out his comb, too, and had the paper around it before you could say "grandpappy," and he was humming a tune by the time Lissy Ann got to where the men were. It was a lively, sweet song that he gave her; the one some folks call Buffalo Gals and others call Louisiana Gals. It was a song about coming out at night and dancing by the light of the moon, and it looked like Lissy Ann was charmed to death by it.

"Pap," she said, when she could tear her eyes away from Comb-Hummin' Henry. "Pap, one of the Willhearts just rode by, and he says they're having a gathering down at Delight after supper. Mr. Callaway Baggett has got his new granary floor all laid, and it's going to be a play-party. Mam reckoned you'd better hang up your sickle and get some grease on your boots."

Nobody on Rosy Ridge, or all the way back to Lorn Widow Crossing, brought more enjoyment to a play-party than old Gill MacBean. "Why, daughter," he said, "one of my boots was sticking out from under the bed when I arose this morning, and I was certain it winked at me. But if they do Happy Is the Miller, I'm bound to go through it barefooted. . . . Henry Bohun, are you any great shakes at play-parties?"

"I never miss a fiddle bar or a smidgen of fried cake if I can help it," said Comb-Hummin' Henry. He was smiling down at Lissy Ann all the time he said it, and I know she was beautiful with the low sun golden on her face, for I've seen her that way many a time. The little bugs fiddled in the grasses while the three people walked down towards the house; and redbirds don't sing frequently in July, but I know they were singing that evening, because Lissy Ann said so.

The whole family caught their snack on the fly, while they ran around combing their hair and washing behind their ears; and Henry Bohun shaved clean with a bright little razor that he carried in his pocket. He helped young Andrew grease his hair, too, and before it was dead dark, the whole biling of them crowded aboard the wagon and headed down through the hollow towards Delight, and Comb-Hummin' Henry made Lorena go shivering up every little gully they passed. Old Gill MacBean said that was one of his favorite tunes, and it looked as if he was ready to forget the kind of bluish color he saw in Henry's breeches, until he had to face the fact out in the open, in the sight of God and the general public. And Paul and Agrippa sat on the front stoop at home and howled a mournful song of their own, because the whole family and their new friend had gone away.

The town of Delight was well named that evening, for there hadn't been a decent play-party anywhere along Agony Creek since the news traipsed north that Kirby Smith had surrendered. People came to the gathering sort of geeing and hawing, as you might say; but in most cases the womenfolks hung onto the reins, and the teams may have been fractious, but they were kept well in the road.

There were gray breeches aplenty and blue breeches, too, although as usual, the grays had a little edge. There were Lynches and Dessarks and Johnsons and Yearys on the one side, and Odoms and Mercers and Willhearts and Billinses on the other. But the green hill where Mr. Callaway Baggett's house and barns spread out was certainly neutral ground. Callaway Baggett himself was too old and fat and good-natured to go to war, no matter whose cat got singed. He had a lot of daughters, and some of them were married to National men and some of them to Claib Jackson men; and people used to whisper around that Callaway Baggett himself had letters written to him by young Francis Preston Blair.

But tonight it didn't make any difference; the Baggetts always lived in plenty and had plenty, and they were plumb willing to share it. Around the back part of the house opposite the big barn of stone and logs, there was a wide gallery built, and on that gallery there were sawbucks with boards across them. On those boards the Baggett women had laid out more piles of fried cakes and sugar cookies than anybody could eat, and more vinegar pies—rich ones, too, with hazelnuts in them—than the parson himself could eat in a month of Sundays. There was cornbread, too, and sides of cold pork, and crab-apple pickles, and down around where the playing took place, alongside the new granary floor, people had some big brown jugs with cobs stuck in the top, though the cobs were out of the jugs a good share of the time. The young bucks mostly gathered down there, but there wasn't any angriness among them, because Cal Baggett wouldn't stand for that, and his sons by marriage were big men who could throw a steer over a corn-crib without half trying.

And the music was of the best: they had Ninny Nat Tinley with his fiddle, and a banjo player, and a nigger man sitting on a bucket with bones in his hand.

Folks were kind of stiff and chilly when this unknown stranger climbed down over Gill MacBean's wagon wheel. Too many strangers had gone through those parts in the years just past, and had gone through in a mighty unkind way, to make people brim their hearts when they saw a new face close by them. But that was just pie for Comb-Hummin' Henry, because he liked to brim the hearts of those he met, and start from scratch doing it; and the Yeary boys had already talked his fame to everybody who would listen.

So the end of the first hour found Henry up on the board pile alongside Ninny Nat, and old Ninny Nat was gurgling and smacking his lips underneath his beard, because he hoped he'd die happy before he ever met another person who could tantalize a pocket comb like Henry Bohun. They went right down the list of tunes and around the corner, and there wasn't a one of them that Ninny Nat might strike up that Comb-Hummin' Henry didn't have dwelling ready in his mouth. This was potato-bug music for fair, as Henry had said, and when Lissy Ann looked at him—famous and contented and important beside the fiddler—it didn't seem possible to her that he could ever have played that heart-breaking melody which he played the night before—the one he declared came all the way from Europe.

The young folks danced and swung on the shadowy side of the barn, because play-party games aren't really dancing, and good church people can go to play-parties, where I've seen them many a time. But there wasn't allowed any dancing, as such, at Mr. Cal-

laway Baggett's. So, pretty soon, the most eager people came out
of the shadows and stepped up on the granary floor, and then the
games began. And the moon looked much amazed to see gray
breeches and blue breeches stomping the smooth planks side by side,
but there wasn't a single fist fight took place that night.

Gill MacBean was one of the leaders now, and he stood in the
center of the ring and howled out the miller song:

> *". . . . the wheel goes around,*
> *He's gaining on his pelf—*
> *One hand in the hopper*
> *And the other in the bag—*
> *Wheel goes around——"*

and when they came to "grab!" you can be mighty certain that old
Gill came grabbing down on the prettiest girl present. But Sairy
MacBean didn't object too loudly, for she reckoned to the other
womenfolks that there wasn't any bigger boy in Barbary County
than Gill MacBean, and heaven knew how he might have disported
himself when he was gone with the rebel army.

Well, the fun went on, piled higher than pumpkins, and then,
as happens all too frequently in the most pleasurable moments,
something had to whistle sour. It wasn't Comb-Hummin' Henry;
you can look in the book of records and see for yourself that it
wasn't his fault. It may have been old Ninny Nat, for he was so
innocent he scarcely knew that there had been a war, with folks
who didn't come back from it, and other folks who did and who had
raw feelings. The moon was high and white, and the whippoorwills
had gone home disgusted, when all of a sudden the music swung
into The Picnic.

If an entire company of Yankee cavalry hadn't squatted down in
Delight for three mortal months, there were a lot of folks present
who wouldn't have known the difference. And as for the men who
had come creeping home in their worn-out butternut rags, many
of them had been captured at one time or another, and they forgot, when they heard this eventful music, just how they might have
played games to it when they were younguns.

From the far end of the granary floor a voice cried out, "Stop
that damn Yankee quickstep!" and the musicians did stop, surprised
wholly out of breath.

And then, from the other end of the floor, somebody else hollered, "Why do they have to stop it?" and a girl sort of yelped in fear and astonishment, and everybody seemed to freeze silent and unhappy in the moonlight.

Mr. Callaway Baggett came a-tumbling down the hill, and he panted his way through the crowd and got up, with a mighty puff, to where the fiddle and banjo people were, and to where Comb-Hummin' Henry sat, his comb in his hand.

"Unless I miscalculate," said Cal Baggett, "there is an open division of opinion concerning the melody just offered by the band. Shall we put it to a vote?"

A lot of folks yelled, "Yes," and more said, "No," and Callaway Baggett had to spread his hands and warn them to consider the matter calm and judicial. He said he was ready to hear evidence from both sides, and right away the evidence began to pour in. The people who had been National sympathizers swore that The Picnic was one of the best play-party tunes, and just as innocent as Oars on the Boat or London Bridge. But the butternut crowd all squalled their heads off at this, and they said that it was a guard mount used by half the Yankee regiments that they had met. They said they'd just as soon listen to Yankee Doodle and The Star-Spangled Banner, and some said they'd a blame sight rather.

"We'll ballot, ladies and gentlemen!" cried Mr. Callaway Baggett. "I demand that my guests be satisfied, and unprejudiced and elective in their choice." And so he began to marshal the guests to right and left. He ended up with two groups, one crowded on the nigh end of the floor and one on the far end, and when he counted noses, they were matched number by number.

There were a few scare-cats who hauled out and said they had to get home. They were afraid to register their votes, and they piled into their wagons or onto their mules, and talked about how they had to be in the fields early in the morning. But those who were earnest and bold and firmly sot in opinion stayed there, resolved to hold to their rights; and Mr. Callaway Baggett said that he approved them for their sincerity.

He said, "The musicians must vote and settle this dispute, for we're wasting a lot of God's best moonlight, and the fried cakes aren't half gone yet."

So the nigger who rattled the bones went scooting down to join his white folks at the far end, and folks agreed that that would count for half a vote. They couldn't persuade Ninny Nat to make up his mind, because he just laughed and didn't understand any of this racket; and the fellow who had been playing the banjo stepped down and registered himself as in favor of The Picnic.

Now Comb-Hummin' Henry was left high and dry. Lissy Ann MacBean, standing beside her pap, heard the old man draw in his breath and kind of groan.

"Stranger," Cal Baggett challenged Henry, "I can't make out the color of your breeches. I guess you'd better walk to one end or t'other."

Henry looked at him awhile, and his little spectacles caught the moonlight and the house lights and the flare from the fire in the yard, and the reflection made him look dangerous and spooklike.

"The war's over," he said, finally. "But I reckon The Picnic's a good tune, no matter who plays it or who dances to it, and we used to call it The Village Quickstep when I was in the Union Army." And then he walked to the nigh end of the platform with the Yankee sympathizers, and people stared at him and saluted his honesty.

Gill MacBean stared, too, and in spite of his disappointment, he must have respected Comb-Hummin' Henry—as a good man respects anybody who speaks his mind, firm and sane. Then he turned around to his daughter and said, "Lizzy Ann, the moon's high, and it's a long way to Rosy Ridge. You and young Andrew hustle and see if you can scare up the younguns." Then he went over to the jugs and poured himself a stanch drink of corn liquor, and those near by him tell that he drank to the name of Claiborne Fox Jackson.

Well, they played The Picnic, but kind of half-hearted, and only two of the rebel folks danced to it. But when the tune had changed to Needle's Eye, Comb-Hummin' Henry put away his musical instrument and slid down from the pile of boards. He went hunting through the shadows and the white patches of moon glow, and sure enough he found Lissy Ann up on the hill by the gooseberry bushes, as if she had been waiting there for a purpose.

"Lissy Ann," he whispered to her, "I reckon I won't be riding back with you-all."

"I reckon you won't," said Lissy Ann, "and Paul and Agrippa are going to feel mighty bad about it."

He wanted to know if they were the only ones who would feel bad, but Lissy Ann, she began to fidget with her bonnet and say that she'd have to follow along towards the wagon. "Do you plan to go wandering again?" she asked Henry Bohun.

Henry said it all depended. He said that wandering was a kind of easy occupation, in spite of missing a meal every now and then, and sleeping out with the nighthawks. He told Lissy Ann that he had had to work hard all his life; that he had had to work hard on his father's farm, and that was right there in Missouri, a hundred miles away. And when he went to the academy, he had to keep humping to make both ends meet, and to study in his books; he chopped wood for the principal of the academy all winter long, and looked after cows and horses. And then he was a school-master, he told Lissy Ann; and then the war happened. He returned from the Union Army faint and sick, and schoolmastering came mighty hard. "Maybe sometime I'll tell you," he said, "just why I quit teaching the three R's, and took up comb humming instead. It's a long story."

Lissy Ann MacBean said that she reckoned it was a long story, but she couldn't wait to hear it, because her father would be hitched up by now, and it sounded as if young Andrew was yelling for her.

"If I stay in these parts for a while," Henry Bohun asked her, "if I stay close at hand and don't go wandering too far away, do you reckon you'll find time to listen? It's a peculiar tale, and must be told only to someone who listens in sympathy."

Then she began to cry, or it sounded that way; she covered her face from the moonlight, and she went running away to the wagon. The story goes that Gill MacBean didn't utter speech all the way to his house on Rosy Ridge, and the music seemed to have fallen out of Henry Bohun's tunes, as if the teeth were broke clean out of his comb.

But he stayed to hand. He didn't go wandering the next day, for Mr. Callaway Baggett took him in that night, and the next day he went to work in Mr. Callaway Baggett's mill. But the millstones ground a most doleful melody, all the while on into September, and in another month Henry Bohun began to slack up in his work. He took to roving through the brush when he should have been toting wheat sacks up and down ladders, and only when he thought

he was sole alone in the timberland did he give breath to the kind
of music he loved to make, and then it was mortal sad.

How Mr. Callaway Baggett could prosper in this world seemed
plumb miraculous to some people, for he was always quoting
that a merciful man is merciful to his beast, and he never was
a driver to any man that worked for him. Some millers would
have sent Comb-Hummin' Henry packing up the road, the first
time he didn't come willing to his toil, but Callaway Baggett never
said a word to him. I reckon he hadn't agreed to pay Henry Bohun
any great wages in hard money or paper money. Still, there was
always a plate for him when Henry wanted to eat, and he slept
comfortable in the Baggett barn. But most of the time, as the leaves
got faded and crisp, Henry was walking the timberland all over
that country.

Mean folks took joy in pestering him, and Barbary County was
a fair land, but it had its share of the mean ones. There was
Badger Dessark, for one, and the Lynch boys, and Roll Odom and
Jack Billins. They were a wild and reckless lot, who didn't work
more than the law allowed, and who used to get full of whisky and
go along the roads whooping until the windows rattled. If mischief
of any kind was brought forth, you could guess quick as scat who
had made it. And whenever they couldn't think of anything else
to do, they'd put turpentine on a dog, and perform all manner of
orneriness.

At the play-party in July, when Comb-Hummin' Henry first came
to the neighborhood, the wild boys had kind of pulled in their
horns, for they didn't want to bring the wrath of any of the
Baggett folks down on them. Badger Dessark claimed to have
fought in Forrest's cavalry, but some people believed it was just a
forest cavalry, and a mighty irregular regiment at that. And Jack
Billins was a bounty man for the Union, but just the same he and
Badge Dessark and the others were thick as fleas.

Henry Bohun was their meat, because he was gentle and mild
in his manner, and used big words sometimes, and knew the names
of all the flowers that grew in the wilderness. But he never went
hunting the way they did; he used to lie for hours beside the mill
race, trying to tame the little shiners that swam there.

It is told how Badge Dessark and the Lynch boys came abreast of Comb-Hummin' Henry when he was walking back to the mill, one afternoon in fall. They pulled in their horses and sat still and grinned at him, and anyone could see that they were trying to think of some deviltry.

"What you got there in your pocket, Henry Bohun?" Badge Dessark wanted to know, and other parties who were passing by pulled up their teams, because it looked like trouble.

"It's a bird," said Henry. "A thrush."

"Oh," Badge Dessark said, "I reckoned it was a titmouse, because a titmouse would be just your kind of fare"—and the Lynch boys laughed heartily at that.

But Henry brought the thrush out of his pocket and showed them. "It got hurt one way or another," he explained, "and I found it fluttering in the brush. I reckoned I'd take it home until I could decide what to with it."

"Sonny," said Badge Dessark, laughing deep inside his chest, "you've met just the man to decide for you," and he leaned down quick from his horse and jerked the bird out of Henry's hands, drawing out his .44 at the same time.

He heaved the thrush into the air and began to crack away at it while the bird flopped round and round, aiming hard to fly and not being able to do so. Not many people could hit a song bird on the wing, but Badge Dessark was a dead shot, and anyway the thrush was sorely crippled in its flight. So he put a chunk of lead through it that made the feathers scatter, and then he shoved his weapon back inside his shirt.

He said to Comb-Hummin' Henry, "Didn't I tell you I'd decide for you?"—and the Lynch boys nearly busted.

"Badge," said Henry Bohun, in a high, nervous voice that sounded as if he was ready to cry, "you've decided more than you know." He kicked the remainders of the dead bird into the weeds and started to walk past, but Dessark and the Lynches looked mighty solemn now, and they brought their horses together to block Henry's way, and demanded what he meant by such a speech.

Henry said, "I only meant this: I may be a kind of thrush myself, but something tells me I'll be bewitched into a catamount when the time is ripe. You're three against one, and any one of you is too big for me to whip, and you've got shooting irons, and I haven't got the price of a cartridge. Maybe I will have, one day."

Well, they rared around and called him names, and Badge Dessark demanded heaven to witness that he ought to shoot Comb-Hummin' Henry down like a dog. But he was the kind that shoots from behind a hedge, and usually when there isn't much sun or many people to see him.

So they let Henry go, and he traipsed slowly down to the mill and flung himself in the grass and lay there for a long time with his eyes shut; and he kept listening to the sound of the wheel, and the water sighing through the flume, as if he stood in need of good advice.

Long before sundown, he was on foot again, and he didn't tarry to take food with the Baggetts. He went off among the thick trees that seemed like his friends and relatives, and that he was happiest among. He followed Agony Creek for a mile or two, and then he struck off over the Spur, where he hadn't trod since the first night he walked into the lives of those neighbors who knew him.

It was close onto dark when he prowled through the hazel brush that grew around the MacBean place, and I reckon he was aware that old Gill MacBean had rode to Billingsgate that day, for Gill had to take the highway past Baggett's mill. There were just Sairy and Lissy Ann and Andrew and the younguns at home; Lissy Ann's pap was nowhere close by to chide her, when she first heard Comb-Hummin' Henry's music stealing through the blue dusk.

He was playing Gentle Annie, as he had that night when first he wandered out of the hollow, and after she had listened to him awhile, Lissy Ann walked to the stoop. The younguns wanted to follow her, because they were plumb excited at hearing Henry's tunefulness again, but their mother counseled them back; and young Andrew took a pattern after his father, and swore what he'd do with his pepper-box revolver if any Yankees came bothering around.

Sairy MacBean felt tender in her heart towards Lissy Ann, for it grieved her to see the girl pining the way she had pined since summer. It wasn't natural nor wise for a girl of her sort to look so droopy, and Sairy had cooked up the best tonic that Granny Yeary could recommend, but still it didn't seem to do any good. So, feeling generous towards Lissy Ann in her affliction, Sairy let her go out to the gate without a challenge, and the girl just stood there, waiting, while Henry Bohun hummed Gentle Annie amongst the hazel brush.

It might have been her very own tune, for it's certain fact that she was christened Annie—Melissa Ann MacBean—and her Great-Aunt Annie was the one who gave her the use of her name. And Lissy Ann's portion of this song must have been made up especially for her own sake: "Shall I never more behold thee . . . and the wild flowers are scattered o'er the plain?" I reckon she thought of the long story which Henry had desired to tell her, and maybe for the first time she saw the faith that he offered—by staying at hand instead of going away down the road, even when he wasn't allowed to court her properly. There were wild flowers all around, sure enough; though you couldn't call Rosy Ridge a plain.

Henry Bohun came closer and closer, until he was full in view, and Sairy MacBean felt something grab close and fearful around her heart. She came to the door with the younguns clustering behind, and she ordered Lissy Ann back into the house. Lissy Ann never heard her, and by that time she wouldn't have batted an eye if she had.

Henry Bohun grew bigger and more important in the shadows, and the song was still Gentle Annie, and the birds of the forest, and the coons, too, whickered about it. When he ceased his song, he was close enough to Lissy Ann to hear her speech, though all she did was to ask for a certain tune. "That one you played the first night," she said. "That tune the man made up out of his own heart, all the way off in Europe."

Well, he obliged her quickly enough, and by that time she was standing well beyond the fence. Her mother cried out, angered and bereaved at having her daughter charmed away before her eyes, though the frosty night was so deep and hazy now that Sairy could scarely make out their figures. She cried, "Lissy Ann!" in terror, and then she thought to hunt for old Gill's rifle, but he had taken it away with him in prospect of meeting 'whackers along the road. And the family tells how young Andrew tore around and got his pepper-box revolver and snapped it a dozen times, aiming at the shape of Henry Bohun, but missing fire every occasion because there wasn't any life in the spring.

Then the night had swallowed the two of them. They had gone

forth together into the brush that was so friendly to Comb-Hummin' Henry, and Sairy MacBean put her apron over her face and began to cry.

They call it Lovers' Walk nowadays, and it's a beautiful path that leads along the height of Rosy Ridge past the end of Gill Mac-Bean's land and clean above the Yeary place, and on and on, far up to the wide wilderness where Uncle Davis Tinley built his cabin in the early days. It's a beautiful place to go meandering when you can see the violets, or the horse mint and wild geraniums in their season; and Sairy MacBean used to pick ladyslippers there when she was just a mite of a girl. This night Lissy Ann walked the path speechless and entranced, at her lover's side, and I reckon Comb-Hummin' Henry must have had the eyes of a cat, for in more than one spot the bushes grew fair in front of them. But they didn't fall into any gullies, and their feet seemed to know the safest parts in which to plant themselves.

"It's nowhere near," Henry told her. "It's a forsaken place, but I walked there frequently when I was eating my heart out. There's an old chimney, too, and people have stabled horses there in recent days. But I reckon we won't be disturbed while I tell my story to you."

And when they got to that distant clearing, they sat close together in a bed of dry leaves, and he told her all the misery that had been in his soul early and late. He told her how he came back from the war to go to schoolmastering again, and how he couldn't stand the squeeze of the four walls, but needed to take his scholars out into the grass. People in the community thought he was crazy for doing it. He hankered, he said, to instruct the scholars that it was wickedness to kill unless one was sure he killed for the world's benefit; and that, he said, was the reason so many good people went to war. He grew weary oftentimes of setting up sums on the children's slates, because it was a sight more interesting and profitable if he split a daisy with his pocketknife and showed them how the Lord had put it together. And when the men in his community who set themselves up as the wisest ones banded together and drove him out for wasting the younguns' time and taking their parents' hard-earned money for it, he just put his comb in his pocket and paced away with a light heart.

But his spirit had grown forlorn and heavy, since he made his declaration at the Baggetts'. He swore there was no justice in a world where resentfulness locked him away from Lissy Ann. That misery had driven him nigh to distraction, but now he planned to make an end of it, and take Lissy Ann out along the highroads with him, if she was brave enough and willing to go.

She put her arms around his neck and laid her lips against his, and announced, by all that was holy to her, that she'd take starvation and nighthawks at Henry Bohun's side before she'd lie beneath her father's roof another night. There was no ravishment nor sin nor such love-making, but a kind of dark and secret comfort. And all night long Henry told her what creatures made the sounds they heard, and what kind of leaves were rustling loose in the groves; and he even made a little fire, and saw Lissy Ann's face shining, confident and pink, in the light of it. He hummed more tunes with his comb, too, including the European one she fancied. Thus the color of dawn came around them when they heard Paul and Agrippa giving voice down the ridge, and old Gill coming, too, driven mad with his rage and sadness, and toting his rifle along.

Paul and Agrippa were by no means bloodhounds, nor nigger dogs such as some people kept in the days before the war; but they had good noses, and they knew the smell of Lissy Ann's shoes, and maybe they were attracted by the thought of Comb-Hummin' Henry mingling his footsteps with hers. Whatever those two hounds thought, they were of assistance to Gill MacBean in finding his daughter who had run away, and the man who had lured her. They high-tailed it straight across the clearing, to leap at the two and desire to be fondled and made over. The lovers stood there scarcely feeling the noses that touched them, as they watched Gill MacBean coming past the towering chimney that showed against the sky.

"This gun is for you, Henry Bohun," were the first words old Gill said. "It's got your name on it! It's a repeating Henry rifle that I captured from a Yankee at Nashville."

Lissy Ann hung close on Henry's shoulder, her two arms hugging him hard, and she vowed that if a bullet found Henry's heart, it would have to pass through hers on the way. But Gill just laughed in his craziness, and tore her loose, and Comb-Hummin' Henry stood there like he was stuffed and let him do it.

"I don't aim to slay the daughter that I sired and raised from the cradle," said Gill MacBean. "I do aim to punish her despoiler."

Henry said, "You ask your daughter if she has been betrayed."

"No," cried Lissy Ann. "I came with him of my own free will, and I intend to share his joys and sorrows, and wander wherever he goes."

"You'd wander," said her father, "with a pack of woods colts trailing after you. You'd be deplored by all people, and your name would be an abomination to those that once loved you"—and he dragged her back beside him. He cocked his rifle, though the girl fought hard to grab it loose from his hands.

She cried to Henry Bohun, "Pap's gone mad! for pity's sake, don't stand there like Ninny Nat and let yourself be killed in cold blood!"—and the hounds tangled and yapped underfoot.

Then Henry Bohun came forward like a wildcat off a limb, and when he sprang free from Gill, he had the gun in his clutch. "Down," he whispered. "Down, the two of you!"

But old MacBean went towering after him with the spit flying through his beard. "This has been a wicked night," he whooped, "and I am to finish it with one just deed! The Yankee bush-whackers came down on old Granny Yeary and whipped her nigh to death, to make her tell where her money jar was hid. A Yankee stole my daughter from me," he bellowed, still raving and clawing for the gun, "and you'll find I'm strong enough to do punishment!"

Smack through the whirl of their wrestling and turmoil, Comb-Hummin' Henry thrashed out and fetched Gill MacBean a clip with the butt of the gun. It staggered the old man, and he dropped down on one knee.

"Stay beside him, Lissy Ann," said Henry Bohun, "and lay flat against the ground!" For all along he had seen what they did not see, with their backs against the sunrise; and what he saw was men on horseback approaching from the east.

They were the bushwhackers who had burnt Gill MacBean's barn and had done every sort of evil throughout Barbary County and into the hills that lay south of it. They stood up in their stirrups, now, and yelled as they came; and they looked like bad dreams a-riding, for they wore enormous hoods of black cloth such as they always wore, and fluttering black cloth to cover up their horses. Henry Bohun ran forward and got beside the ancient chimney of Uncle Davis Tinley's one-time cabin, and I reckon that was the first that Lissy Ann could recognize what Henry might have meant when he said there were marks of horses being stabled near by.

The riders shouted like all possessed, and the big leader who galloped ahead shouted loudest of all. "We know you, Comb-Hummin' Henry!" he called. "We haven't tasted blood yet in these parts, but we'll taste it quick enough if you don't lay down that rifle and fling up your hands for mercy!"

"I reckon you've tasted blood," said Henry, "for I hear you've whipped the back of a poor old woman, and I warn you, your deviltries will betray you! Dismount and give yourselves up, before I shoot."

He kept the chimney on his flank, and the riders spread out to circle their horses. "Knuckle under," they cried, "or we'll sacrifice you all, and the girl too!"

"Last warning," said Henry. "This is a Henry rifle, and it's in good hands."

Then they upped with their .44's, and rock splinters flew from the chimney, but Comb-Hummin' Henry fired calm, and he drilled the leader through his body. He shot him clean out of his stirrups, and the horse went bucking away. In another moment the smoke was so thick that you couldn't have told what was happening. Then it lifted a little, and now there were three 'whackers on the ground, and two who galloped for the timber as if wolves were after them. Comb-Hummin' Henry had his back against the chimney, and blood ran down from his ear, and his broken spectacles dangled loose. But he was white and proud, for all that; Gill Mac-Bean's rifle was hot in his hands.

"Go look at that first one," he told Gill, when the old man had clumb to his feet. "I warrant you'll find gray breeches." And so they did, for it was Badge Dessark, and he was as dead as a locust husk.

The next was blue breeches, or what should have been—the man was dressed in ordinary store clothes under his black cloth. He was Jack Billins, and henceforth the neighborhood could understand why Jack Billins had dwelt without toiling or spinning, apparently. The third man was dying when they lifted him up, and he was Luke Lynch, and his ghost dragged loose from its wickedness even while Lissy Ann was holding his handsome head and crying for the pity of it.

"When the other two are located," Comb-Hummin' Henry said, "I expect you'll find that blue breeches and gray breeches are mingled together."

And it turned out according to his prophecy, for the two were detected near Lorn Widow Crossing that day, and one was Roll Odom and the other was Sylvester Lynch.

Comb-Hummin' Henry demanded to know of Gill MacBean whether he hadn't been sinful in his rage, and whether the evil weren't truly evil and the good truly good, no matter how they breeched themselves. But old Gill had no word to say, such was his weakness and bewilderment; so at last the three of them set out down the ridge to carry this news abroad, and Comb-Hummin' Henry and Lissy Ann waded in clouds to meet the sun, with Paul and Agrippa whining behind, and Gill walking with bowed head and carrying the Henry rifle.

Very soon thereafter the marriage was celebrated, just when folks wanted a taste of sweetness to take the shock and gall out of their mouths. They declare that it was one of the biggest weddings ever managed in those parts, with half an acre of dinner tables set out under the trees. It was a fruitful union and a loving one; I know, for I was born of it.

Dusk Before Fireworks

BY

DOROTHY PARKER

H<small>E WAS</small> a very good-looking young man indeed, shaped to be annoyed. His voice was intimate as the rustle of sheets, and he kissed easily. There was no tallying the gifts of Charvet handkerchiefs, *art moderne* ash-trays, monogrammed dressing-gowns, gold key-chains, and cigarette-cases of thin wood, inlaid with views of Parisian comfort stations, that were sent him by ladies too quickly confident, and were paid for with the money of unwitting husbands, which is acceptable any place in the world. Every woman who visited his small, square apartment promptly flamed with the desire to assume charge of its redecoration. During his tenancy, three separate ladies had achieved this ambition. Each had left behind her, for her brief monument, much too much glazed chintz.

The glare of the latest upholstery was dulled, now, in an April dusk. There was a soft blur of mauve and gray over chairs and curtains, instead of the daytime pattern of heroic-sized double poppies and small, sad elephants. (The most recent of the volunteer decorators was a lady who added interest to her ways by collecting all varieties of elephants save those alive or stuffed; her selection of the chintz had been made less for the cause of contemporary design than in the hope of keeping ever present the wistful souvenirs of her hobby and, hence, of herself. Unhappily, the poppies, those flowers for forgetfulness, turned out to be predominant in the pattern.)

The very good-looking young man was stretched in a chair that was legless and short in back. It was a strain to see in that chair any virtue save the speeding one of modernity. Certainly it was a peril to all who dealt with it; they were far from their best within its arms, and they could never have wished to be remembered as they appeared while easing into its depths or struggling out again. All, that is, save the young man. He was a long young man, broad at the shoulders and chest and narrow everywhere else, and his muscles obeyed him at the exact instant of command. He rose and lay, he moved and was still, always in beauty. Several men disliked him, but only one woman really hated him. She was his sister. She was stump-shaped, and she had straight hair.

On the sofa opposite the difficult chair there sat a young woman, slight and softly dressed. There was no more to her frock than some dull, dark silk and a little chiffon, but the recurrent bill for it demanded, in bitter black and white, a sum well on toward the second hundred. Once the very good-looking young man had said that he liked women in quiet and conservative clothes, carefully made. The young woman was of those unfortunates who remember every word. This made living peculiarly trying for her when it was later demonstrated that the young man was also partial to ladies given to garments of slap-dash cut, and color like the sound of big brass instruments.

The young woman was temperately pretty in the eyes of most beholders; but there were a few, mainly hand-to-mouth people, artists and such, who could not look enough at her. Half a year before, she had been sweeter to see. Now there was tension about her mouth and unease along her brow, and her eyes looked wearied and troubled. The gentle dusk became her. The young man who shared it with her could not see these things.

She stretched her arms and laced her fingers high above her head. "Oh, this is nice," she said. "It's nice being here."

"It's nice and peaceful," he said. "Oh, Lord. Why can't people just be peaceful? That's little enough to ask, isn't it? Why does there have to be so much hell, all the time?"

She dropped her hands to her lap.

"There doesn't have to be at all," she said. She had a quiet voice, and she said her words with every courtesy to each of them, as if she respected langauge. "There's never any need for hell."

"There's an awful lot of it around, sweet," he said.

"There certainly is," she said. "There's just as much hell as there are hundreds of little shrill, unnecessary people. It's the second-raters that stir up hell; first-rate people wouldn't. You need never have another bit of it in your beautiful life if—if you'll pardon my pointing—you could just manage to steel yourself against that

band of spitting hell-cats that is included in your somewhat over-
crowded acquaintance, my lamb. Ah, but I mean it, Hobie, dear.
I've been wanting to tell you for so long. But it's so rotten hard to
say. If I say it, it makes me sound just like one of them—makes me
seem inexpensive and jealous. Surely, you know, after all this
time, I'm not like that. It's just that I worry so about you. You're
so fine, you're so lovely, it nearly kills me to see you just eaten
up by a lot of things like Margot Wadsworth and Mrs. Holt and
Evie Maynard and those. You're so much better than that. You
know that's why I'm saying it. You know I haven't got a stitch of
jealousy in me. Jealous! Good heavens, if I were going to be jealous,
I'd be it about someone worth while, and not about any silly,
stupid, idle, worthless, selfish, hysterical, vulgar, promiscuous, sex-
ridden——"

"Darling!" he said.

"Well, I'm sorry," she said. "I guess I'm sorry. I didn't really
mean to go into the subject of certain of your friends. Maybe the
way they behave isn't their fault, said she, lying in her teeth. After
all, you can't expect them to know what it's about. Poor things,
they'll never know how sweet it can be, how lovely it always is when
we're alone together. It is, isn't it? Ah, Hobie, isn't it?"

The young man raised his slow lids and looked at her. He smiled
with one end of his beautiful curly mouth.

"Uh-huh," he said.

He took his eyes from hers and became busy with an ash-tray
and a spent cigarette. But he still smiled.

"Ah, don't," she said. "You promised you'd forget about—about
last Wednesday. You said you'd never remember it again. Oh, whatever made me do it! Making scenes. Having tantrums. Rushing out
into the night. And then coming crawling back. Me, that wanted
to show you how different a woman could be! Oh, please, please
don't let's think about it. Only tell me I wasn't as terrible as I
know I was."

"Darling," he said, for he was often a young man of simple
statements, "you were the worst I ever saw."

"And doesn't that come straight from Sir Hubert!" she said. "Oh,
dear. Oh, dear, oh, dear. What can I say? 'Sorry' isn't nearly
enough. I'm broken. I'm in little bits. Would you mind doing something about putting me together again?"

She held out her arms to him.

The young man rose, came over to the sofa, and kissed her. He had intended a quick, good-humored kiss, a moment's stop on a projected trip out to his little pantry to mix cocktails. But her arms clasped him so close and so gladly that he dismissed the plan. He lifted her to her feet, and did not leave her.

Presently she moved her head and hid her face above his heart.

"Listen," she said, against cloth. "I want to say it all now, and then never say it any more. I want to tell you that there'll never, never be anything like last Wednesday again. What we have is so much too lovely ever to cheapen. I promise, oh, I promise you, I won't ever be like—like anybody else."

"You couldn't be, Kit," he said.

"Ah, think that always," she said, "and say it sometimes. It's so sweet to hear. Will you, Hobie?"

"For your size," he said, "you talk an awful lot." His fingers slid to her chin and he held her face for his greater convenience.

After a while she moved again.

"Guess who I'd rather be, right this minute, than anybody in the whole world," she said.

"Who?" he said.

"Me," she said.

The telephone rang.

The telephone was in the young man's bedroom, standing in frequent silence on the little table by his bed. There was no door to the bed-chamber; a plan which had disadvantages, too. Only a curtained archway sequestered its intimacies from those of the living-room. Another archway, also streaming chintz, gave from the bedroom upon a tiny passage, along which were ranged the bathroom and the pantry. It was only by entering either of these, closing the door behind, and turning the faucets on to the full that any second person in the apartment could avoid hearing what was being said over the telephone. The young man sometimes thought of removing to a flat of more sympathetic design.

"There's that damn telephone," the young man said.

"Isn't it?" the young woman said. "And wouldn't it be?"

"Let's not answer it," he said. "Let's let it ring."

"No, you mustn't," she said. "I must be big and strong. Anyway, maybe it's only somebody that just died and left you twenty mil-

lion dollars. Maybe it isn't some other woman at all. And if it
is, what difference does it make? See how sweet and reasonable I
am? Look at me being generous."

"You can afford to be, sweetheart," he said.

"I know I can," she said. "After all, whoever she is, she's way
off on an end of a wire, and I'm right here."

She smiled up at him. So it was nearly half a minute before
he went away to the telephone.

Still smiling, the young woman stretched her head back, closed
her eyes and flung her arms wide. A long sigh raised her breast.
Thus she stood, then she went and settled back on the sofa. She
essayed whistling softly, but the issuing sounds would not resemble
the intended tune and she felt, though interested, vaguely betrayed.
Then she looked about the dusk-filled room. Then she pondered
her finger nails, bringing each bent hand close to her eyes, and
could find no fault. Then she smoothed her skirt along her legs
and shook out the chiffon frills at her wrists. Then she spread her
little handkerchief on her knee and with exquisite care traced
the "Katherine" embroidered in script across one of its corners.
Then she gave it all up and did nothing but listen.

"Yes?" the young man was saying. "Hello? Hello. I *told* you this
is Mr. Ogden. Well, I *am* holding the wire. I've *been* holding the
wire. *You're* the one that went away. Hello? Ah, now listen—Hello?
Hey. Oh, what the hell *is* this? Come back, will you? Operator!
Hello, *Yes,* this is Mr. Ogden. Who? Oh, hello, Connie. How are
you, dear? What? You're what? Oh, that's too bad. What's the
matter? Why can't you? Where are you, in Greenwich? Oh, I see.
When, now? Why, Connie, the only thing is I've got to go right
out. So if you came in to town now, it really wouldn't do much—
Well, I couldn't very well do that, dear. I'm keeping these people
waiting as it is. I say I'm late now, I was just going out the door
when you called. Why, I'd better not say that, Connie, because
there's no telling when I'll be able to break away. Look, why don't
you wait and come in to town tomorrow some time? What? Can't
you tell me now? Oh— Well— Oh, Connie, there's no reason to talk
like that. Why, of course I'd do anything in the world I could, but
I tell you I can't tonight. No, no, no, no, no, it isn't that at all. No,
it's nothing like that, I tell you. These people are friends of my
sister's, and it's just one of those things you've got to do. Why don't

you be a good girl and go to bed early, and then you'll feel better tomorrow? Hm? Will you do that? What? Of course I do, Connie. I'll try to later on if I can, dear. Well, all right, if you want to, but I don't know what time I'll be home. Of course I do. Of course I do. Yes, *do*, Connie. You be a good girl, won't you? 'By, dear."

The young man returned, through the chintz. He had a rather worn look. It was, of course, becoming to him.

"God," he said, simply.

The young woman on the sofa looked at him as if through clear ice.

"And how *is* dear Mrs. Holt?" she said.

"Great," he said. "Corking. Way up at the top of her form." He dropped wearily into the low chair. "She says she has something she wants to tell me."

"It can't be her age," she said.

He smiled without joy. "She says it's too hard to say over the wire," he said.

"Then it may be her age," she said. "She's afraid it might sound like her telephone number."

"About twice a week," he said, "Connie has something she must tell you right away, that she couldn't possibly say over the telephone. Usually it turns out she's caught the butler drinking again."

"I see," she said.

"Well," he said. "Poor little Connie."

"Poor little Connie," she said. "Oh, my God. That saber-toothed tigress. Poor little Connie."

"Darling, why do we have to waste time talking about Connie Holt?" he said. "Can't we just be peaceful?"

"Not while that she-beast prowls the streets," she said. "Is she coming in to town tonight?"

"Well, she was," he said, "but then she more or less said she wouldn't."

"Oh, she will," she said. "You get right down out of that fool's paradise you're in. She'll shoot out of Greenwich like a bat out of hell, if she thinks there's a chance of seeing you. Ah, Hobie, you don't really want to see that old thing, do you? Do you? Because if you do—Well, I supose maybe you do. Naturally, if she has something she must tell you right away, you want to see her. Look, Hobie, you know you can see me any time. It isn't a bit important, seeing me tonight. Why don't you call up Mrs. Holt and tell her to take the next train in? She'd get here quicker by train than by motor, wouldn't she? Please go ahead and do it. It's quite all right about me. Really."

"You know," he said, "I knew that was coming. I could tell it by the way you were when I came back from the telephone. Oh, Kit, what makes you want to talk like that? You know damned well the last thing I want to do is to see Connie Holt. You know how I want to be with you. Why do you want to work up all this? I watched you just sit there and deliberately talk yourself into it, starting right out of nothing. Now what's the idea of that? Oh, good Lord, what's the matter with women, anyway?"

"Please don't call me 'women,' " she said.

"I'm sorry, darling," he said. "I didn't mean to use bad words." He smiled at her. She felt her heart go liquid, but she did her best to be harder won.

"Doubtless," she said, and her words fell like snow when there is no wind, "I spoke ill-advisedly. If I said, as I must have, something to distress you, I can only beg you to believe that that was my misfortune, and not my intention. It seemed to me as if I were do-ing only a courteous thing in suggesting that you need feel no ob-ligation about spending the evening with me, when you would naturally wish to be with Mrs. Holt. I simply felt that—Oh, the hell with it! I'm no good at this. Of course I didn't mean it, dearest. If you had said, 'All right,' and had gone and told her to come in, I should have died. I just said it because I wanted to hear you say it was me you wanted to be with. Oh, I need to hear you say that, Hobie. It's—it's what I live on, darling."

"Kit," he said, "you ought to know, without my saying it. You know. It's this feeling you *have* to say things—that's what spoils everything."

"I suppose so," she said. "I suppose I know so. Only—the thing is, I get so mixed up, I just—I just can't go on, I've got to be re-assured, dearest. I didn't need to be at first, when everything was gay and sure, but things aren't—well, they aren't the same now. There seem to be so many others that— So I need so terribly to have you tell me that it's me and not anybody else. Oh, I *had* to have you say that, a few minutes ago. Look, Hobie. How do you think it makes me feel to sit here and hear you lie to Connie Holt—to hear you say you have to go out with friends of your sister's? Now why couldn't you say you had a date with me? Are you ashamed of me, Hobie? Is that it?"

"Oh, Kit," he said, "for heaven's sake! I don't know why I did it. I did it before I even thought. I did it—well, sort of instinctively, I guess, because it seemed to be the easiest thing to do. I suppose I'm just weak."

"No!" she said. "You weak? Well! And is there any other news tonight?"

"I know I am," he said. "I know it's weak to do anything in the world to avoid a scene."

"Exactly what," she said, "is Mrs. Holt to you and you to her that she may make a scene if she learns that you have an engagement with another woman?"

"Oh, God!" he said. "I told you I don't give a damn about Connie Holt. She's nothing to me. Now will you for God's sake let it drop?"

"Oh, she's nothing to you," she said. "I see. Naturally, that would be why you called her 'dear' every other word."

"If I did," he said, "I never knew I was saying it. Good Lord, that doesn't mean anything. It's simply a—a form of nervousness, I suppose. I say it when I can't think what to call people. Why, I call telephone operators 'dear.' "

"I'm sure you do!" she said.

They glared. It was the young man who gave first. He went and sat close to her on the sofa, and for a while there were only murmurs. Then he said, "Will you stop? Will you stop it? Will you always be just like this—just sweet and the way you're meant to be and no fighting?"

"I will," she said. "Honest, I mean to. Let's not let anything come between us again ever. Mrs. Holt, indeed! Hell with her."

"Hell with her," he said. There was another silence, during which the young man did several things that he did extraordinarily well.

Suddenly the young woman stiffened her arms and pushed him away from her.

"And how do I know," she said, "that the way you talk to me about Connie Holt isn't just the way you talk to her about me when I'm not here? How do I know that?"

"Oh, my Lord," he said. "Oh, my dear, sweet Lord. Just when

everything was all right. Ah, stop it, will you, baby? Let's just be quiet. Like this. See?"

A little later he said, "Look, sweet, how about a cocktail? Mightn't that be an idea? I'll go make them. And would you like the lights lighted?"

"Oh, no," she said. "I like it better in the dusk, like this. It's sweet. Dusk is so personal, somehow. And this way you can't see those lampshades. Hobie, if you knew how I hate your lampshades!"

"Honestly?" he said, with less injury than bewilderment in his voice. He looked at the shades as if he saw them for the first time. They were of vellum, or some substance near it, and upon each was painted a panorama of the right bank of the Seine, with the minute windows of the buildings cut out, under the direction of a superior mind, so that light might come through. "What's the matter with them, Kit?"

"Dearest, if you don't know, I can't ever explain it to you," she said. "Among other things, they're banal, inappropriate, and un-beautiful. They're exactly what Evie Maynard *would* have chosen. She thinks, just because they show views of Paris, that they're pretty darned sophisticated. She is that not uncommon type of woman that thinks any reference to la belle France is an invitation to the waltz. 'Not uncommon.' If that isn't the mildest word-picture that ever was painted of that——"

"Don't you like the way she decorated the apartment?" he said.

"Sweetheart," she said, "I think it's poisonous. You know that."

"Would you like to do it over?" he said.

"I should say not," she said. "Look, Hobie, don't you remember me? I'm the one that doesn't want to decorate your flat. Now do you place me? But if I ever *did,* the first thing I should do would be to paint these walls putty color—no, I guess first I'd tear off all this chintz and fling it to the winds, and then I'd——"

The telephone rang.

The young man threw one stricken glance at the young woman and then sat motionless. The jangles of the bell cut the dusk like little scissors.

"I think," said the young woman, exquisitely, "that your telephone is ringing. Don't let me keep you from answering it. As a matter of fact, I really must go powder my nose."

She sprang up, dashed through the bedroom, and into the bathroom. There was the sound of a closed door, the grind of a firmly turned key, and then immediately the noise of rushing waters.

When she returned, eventually, to the living-room, the young man was pouring a pale, cold liquid into small glasses. He gave one to her, and smiled at her over it. It was his wistful smile. It was of his best.

"Hobie," she said, "is there a livery stable anywhere around here where they rent wild horses?"

"What?" he said.

"Because if there is," she said, "I wish you'd call up and ask them to send over a couple of teams. I want to show you they couldn't drag me into asking who that was on the telephone."

"Oh," he said, and tried his cocktail. "Is this dry enough, sweet? Because you like them dry, don't you? Sure it's all right? Really? Ah, wait a second, darling. Let *me* light your cigarette. There. Sure you're all right?"

"I can't stand it," she said. "I just lost all my strength of purpose—maybe the maid will find it on the floor in the morning. Hobart Ogden, who was that on the telephone?"

"Oh, that?" he said. "Well, that was a certain lady who shall be nameless."

"I'm sure she should be," she said. "She doubtless has all the other qualities of a—Well. I didn't quite say it, I'm keeping my head. Ah, dearest, was that Connie Holt again?"

"No, that was the funniest thing," he said. "That was Evie Maynard. Just when we were talking about her."

"Well, well, well," she said. "Isn't it a small world? And what's on her mind, if I may so flatter her? Is *her* butler tight, too?"

"Evie hasn't got a butler," he said. He tried smiling again, but found it better to abandon the idea and concentrate on refilling the young woman's glass. "No, she's just dizzy, the same as usual. She's got a cocktail party at her apartment, and they all want to go out on the town, that's all."

"Luckily," she said, "you had to go out with these friends of your sister's. You were just going out the door when she called."

"I never told her any such thing!" he said. "I said I had a date I'd been looking forward to all week."

"Oh, you didn't mention any names?" she said.

"There's no reason why I should, to Evie Maynard," he said.

"It's none of her affair, any more than what she's doing and who she's doing it with is any concern of mine. She's nothing in my life. You know that. I've hardly seen her since she did the apartment. I don't care if I never see her again. I'd *rather* I never saw her again."

"I should think that might be managed, if you've really set your heart on it," she said.

"Well, I do what I can," he said. "She wanted to come in now for a cocktail, she and some of those interior decorator boys she has with her, and I told her absolutely no."

"And you think that will keep her away?" she said. "Oh, no. She'll be here. She and her feathered friends. Let's see—they ought to arrive just about the time that Mrs. Holt has thought it over and come in to town. Well. It's shaping up into a lovely evening, isn't it?"

"Great," he said. "And if I may say so, you're doing everything you can to make it harder, you little sweet." He poured more cocktails. "Oh, Kit, why are you being so nasty? Don't do it, darling. It's not like you. It's so unbecoming to you."

"I know it's horrible," she said. "It's—well, I do it in defense, I suppose, Hobie. If I didn't say nasty things, I'd cry. I'm afraid to cry; it would take me so long to stop. I—oh, I'm so hurt, dear. I don't know what to think. All these women. All these awful women. If they were fine, if they were sweet and gentle and intelligent, I shouldn't mind. Or maybe I should. I don't know. I don't know much of anything, any more. My mind goes round and round. I thought what we had was so different. Well—it wasn't. Sometimes I think it would be better never to see you any more. But then I know I couldn't stand that. I'm too far gone now. I'd do anything to be with you! And so I'm just another of those women to you. And I used to come first, Hobie—oh, I did! I did!"

"You did!" he said. "And you do!"

"And I always will?" she said.

"And you always will," he said, "as long as you'll only be your own self. Please be sweet again, Kit. Like this, darling. Like this, child."

Again they were close, and again there was no sound.

The telephone rang.

They started as if the same arrow had pierced them. Then the young woman moved slowly back.

"You know," she said, musingly, "this is my fault. I did this. It was me. I was the one that said let's meet here, and not at my house. I said it would be quieter, and I had so much I wanted to talk to you about. I said we could be quiet and alone here. Yes. I said that."

"I give you my word," he said, "that damn thing hasn't rung in a week."

"It was lucky for me, wasn't it?" she said, "that I happened to be here the last time it did. I am known as Little Miss Horseshoes. Well. Oh, please do answer it, Hobie. It drives me even crazier to have it ring like this."

"I hope to God," the young man said, "that it's a wrong number." He held her to him, hard. "Darling," he said. Then he went to the telephone.

"Hello," he said into the receiver. "Yes? Oh, hello there. How are you, dear—how are you? Oh, did you? Ah, that's too bad. Why, you see I was out with these friends of my—I was out till quite late. Oh, you did? Oh, that's too bad, dear, you waited up all that time. No, I did *not* say that, Margot, I said I'd come if I possibly could. That's exactly what I said. I did so. Well, then you misunderstood me. Well, you must have. Now, there's no need to be unreasonable about it. Listen, what I said, I said I'd come if it was possible, but I didn't think there was a chance. If you think hard, you'll remember, dear. Well, I'm terribly sorry, but I don't see what you're making so much fuss about. It was just a misunderstanding, that's all. Why don't you calm down and be a good little girl? Won't you? Why, I can't tonight, dear. Because I *can't*. Well, I have a date I've had for a long time. Yes. Oh, no, it isn't anything like that! Oh, now, please, Margot! Margot, please don't! Now don't do that! I tell you I won't be here. All right, come ahead, but I won't be in. Listen, I can't talk to you when you're like this. I'll call you tomorrow, dear. I tell you I won't be *in*, dear! Please be good. Certainly I do. Look. I have to run now. I'll call you, dear. 'By."

The young man came back to the living-room, and sent his somewhat shaken voice ahead of him.

"How about another cocktail, sweet?" he said. "Don't you think we really ought—" Through the thickening dark, he saw the young woman. She stood straight and tense. Her fur scarf was knotted about her shoulders, and she was drawing on her second glove.

"What's this about?" the young man said.

"I'm so sorry," the young woman said, "but I truly must go home."

"Oh, really?" he said. "May I ask why?"

"It's sweet of you," she said, "to be interested enough to want to know. Thank you so much. Well, it just happens, I can't stand any more of this. There is somewhere, I think, some proverb about a worm's eventually turning. It is doubtless from the Arabic. They so often are. Well, good night, Hobie, and thank you so much for those delicious cocktails. They've cheered me up wonderfully."

She held out her hand. He caught it tight in both of his.

"Ah, now listen," he said. "Please don't do this, Kit. Please, don't, darling. Please. This is just the way you were last Wednesday."

"Yes," she said. "And for exactly the same reason. Please give me back my hand. Thank you. Well, good night, Hobie, and good luck, always."

"All right," he said. "If this is what you want to do."

"Want to do!" she said. "It's nothing *I* want. I simply felt it would be rather easier for you if you could be alone, to receive your telephone calls. Surely you cannot blame me for feeling a bit *de trop*."

"My Lord, do you think I want to talk to those fools?" he said. "What can I do? Take the telephone receiver off? Is that what you want me to do?"

"It's a good trick of yours," she said. "I gather that was what you did last Wednesday night, when I kept trying to call you after I'd gone home, when I was in holy agony there."

"I did not!" he said. "They must have been calling the wrong number. I tell you I was alone here all the time you were gone."

"So you said," she said.

"I don't lie to you, Kit," he said.

"That," she said, "is the most outrageous lie you have ever told me. Good night, Hobie."

Only from the young man's eyes and voice could his anger be

judged. The beautiful scroll of his mouth never straightened. He took her hand and bowed over it.

"Good night, Kit," he said.

"Good night," she said. "Well, good night. I'm sorry it must end like this. But if you want other things—well, they're what you want. You can't have both them and me. Good night, Hobie."

"Good night, Kit," he said.

"I'm sorry," she said. "It does seem too bad. Doesn't it?"

"It's what you want," he said.

"I?" she said. "It's what *you* do."

"Oh, Kit, can't you understand?" he said. "You always used to. Don't you know how I am? I just say things and do things that don't mean anything, just for the sake of peace, just for the sake of not having a feud. That's what gets me in trouble. You don't have to do it, I know. You're luckier than I am."

"Luckier?" she said. "Curious word."

"Well, stronger, then," he said. "Finer. Honester. Decenter. All those. Ah, don't do this, Kit. Please. Please take those things off, and come sit down."

"Sit down?" she said. "And wait for the ladies to gather?"

"They're not coming," he said.

"How do you know?" she said. "They've come here before, haven't they? How do you know they won't come tonight?"

"I don't know!" he said. "I don't know what the hell they'll do. I don't know what the hell you'll do, any more. And I thought you were different!"

"I was different," she said, "just so long as you thought I was different."

"Ah, Kit," he said, "Kit. Darling. Come and be the way we were. Come and be sweet and peaceful. Look. Let's have a cocktail, just to each other, and then let's go out to some quiet place for dinner, where we can talk. Will you?"

"Well—" she said. "If you think——"

"I think," he said.

The telephone rang.

"Oh, my *God!*" shrieked the young woman. "Go answer it, you damned—you damned *stallion!*"

She rushed for the door, opened it, and was gone. She was, after all, different. She neither slammed the door nor left it stark open.

The young man stood, and he shook his remarkable head slowly. Slowly, too, he turned and went into the bedroom.

He spoke into the telephone receiver drearily at first, then he seemed to enjoy both hearing and speaking. He used a woman's name in address. It was not Connie; it was not Evie; it was not Margot. Glowingly he besought the unseen one to meet him; tepidly he agreed to await her coming where he was. He besought her, then, to ring his bell first three times and then twice, for admission. No, no, no, he said, this was not for any reason that might have occurred to her; it was simply that some business friend of his had said something about dropping in, and he wanted to make sure there would be no such intruders. He spoke of his hopes, indeed his assurances, of an evening of sweetness and peace. He said "good-by," and he said "dear."

The very good-looking young man hung up the receiver, and looked long at the dial of his wrist-watch, now delicately luminous. He seemed to be calculating. So long for a young woman to reach her home, and fling herself upon her couch, so long for tears, so long for exhaustion, so long for remorse, so long for rising tenderness. Thoughtfully he lifted the receiver from its hook and set it on end upon the little table.

Then he went into the living-room, and sped the dark before the tiny beams that sifted through the little open windows in the panoramas of Paris.

Search Through the Streets of the City

BY

IRWIN SHAW

WHEN HE FINALLY SAW HER, he nearly failed to recognize her. He walked behind her for a half block, vaguely noticing that the woman in front of him had long legs and was wearing a loose, college-girl polo coat and a plain brown felt hat.

Suddenly something about the way she walked made him remember —the almost affected rigidity of her back and straightness of throat and head, with all the movement of walking, flowing up to the hips and stopping there, like Negro women in the South and Mexican and Spanish women carrying baskets on their heads.

For a moment, silently, he watched her walk down Twelfth Street, on the sunny side of the street, in front of the little tired gardens behind which lay the quiet, pleasantly run-down old houses. Then he walked up to her and touched her arm.

"Low heels," he said. "I never thought I'd live to see the day."

She looked around in surprise, then smiled widely, took his arm. "Hello, Paul," she said. "I've gone in for health."

"Whenever I think of you," he said, "I think of the highest heels in New York City."

"The old days," Harriet said. They walked slowly down the sunny street, arm in arm, toward Sixth Avenue. "I was a frivolous creature."

"You still walk the same way. As though you ought to have a basket of laundry on your head."

"I practiced walking like that for six months. You'd be surprised how much attention I get walking into a room that way."

"I wouldn't be surprised," Paul said, looking at her. She had black hair and pale clear skin and a long, full body, and her eyes

83

were deep gray and always brilliant, even after she'd been drinking for three days in a row.

Harriet closed her coat quickly and walked a little faster. "I'm going to Wanamaker's," she said. "There're a couple of things I have to buy. Where are you going?"

"Wanamaker's," Paul said. "I've been dying to go to Wanamaker's for three years."

They walked slowly, in silence, Harriet's arm in his.

"Casual," Paul said. "I bet to the naked eye we look casual as hell. How do you feel?"

Harriet took her arm away. "Casual."

"O.K. Then that's how I feel, too." Paul whistled coldly to himself. He stopped and looked critically at her and she stopped, too, and turned toward him, a slight puzzled smile on her face. "What makes you dress that way?" he asked. "You look like Monday morning in Northampton."

"I just threw on whatever was nearest," Harriet said. "I'm just going to be out about an hour."

"You used to look like a nice big box of candy in your clothes." Paul took her arm again and they started off. "Viennese bonbons. Every indentation carefully exploited in silk and satin. Even if you were just going down to the corner for a pint of gin, you'd look like something that ought to be eaten for dessert. This is no improvement."

"A girl has different periods in clothes. Like Picasso," Harriet said. "And if I'd known I was going to meet you, I'd've dressed differently."

Paul patted her arm. "That's better."

Paul eyed her obliquely as they walked: the familiar, long face, the well-known wide mouth with always a little too much lipstick on it, the little teeth that made her face, when she smiled, look suddenly like a little girl's in Sunday school.

"You're getting skinny, Paul," Harriet said.

Paul nodded. "I'm as lean as a herring. I've been leading a fevered and ascetic life. What sort of life have you been leading?"

"I got married." Harriet paused a moment. "Did you hear I got married?"

"I heard," Paul said. "The last time we crossed Sixth Avenue together the L was still up. I feel a nostalgic twinge for the Sixth Avenue L." They hurried as the light changed. "On the night of January ninth, 1940," Paul said, holding her elbow, "you were not home."

"Possible," Harriet said. "I'm a big girl now; I go out at night."

"I happened to pass your house, and I noticed that the light wasn't on." They turned down toward Ninth Street. "I remembered how hot you kept that apartment—like the dahlia greenhouse in the Botanical Gardens."

"I have thin blood," Harriet said gravely. "Long years of inbreeding in Massachusetts."

"The nicest thing about you," Paul said, "was you never went to sleep."

"Every lady to her own virtue," Harriet said. "Some women're beautiful, some're smart—me—I never went to sleep. The secret of my great popularity. . . ."

Paul grinned. "Shut up."

Harriet smiled back at him and they chuckled together. "You know what I mean," he said. "Any time I called you up, two, three in the morning, you'd come right over, lively and bright-eyed, all the rouge and mascara in the right places. . . ."

"In my youth," said Harriet, "I had great powers of resistance."

"In the morning we'd eat breakfast to Beethoven. The Masterwork Hour. WNYC. Beethoven, by special permission of His Honor, the Mayor, from nine to ten." Paul closed his eyes for a moment. "The Little Flower, Mayor For Lovers."

Paul opened his eyes and looked at the half-strange, half-familiar woman walking lightly at his side. He remembered lying close to her, dreamily watching the few lights of the towers of the nighttime city, framed by the big window of his bedroom against the black sky, and one night when she moved sleepily against him and rubbed the back of his neck where the hair was sticking up in sharp little bristles because he had had his hair cut that afternoon. Harriet had rubbed them the wrong way, smiling, dreamily, without opening her eyes. "What a delicious thing a man is . . ." she'd murmured. And she'd sighed, then chuckled a little and fallen asleep, her hand still on the shaven back of his neck.

Paul smiled, remembering.

"You still laughing at my clothes?" Harriet asked.

"I remembered something I heard some place . . ." Paul said. " 'What a delicious thing a man is . . .' "

Harriet looked at him coldly. "Who said that?"

Paul squinted suspiciously at her. "Oswald Spengler."

"Uhuh," Harriet said soberly. "It's a famous quotation."

"It's a well-turned phrase," said Paul.

"That's what I think, too." Harriet nodded agreeably and walked a little faster.

They passed the little run-down bar where'd they'd sat afternoons all winter drinking martinis and talking and talking, and laughing so loud the people at the other tables would turn and smile. Paul waited for Harriet to say something about the bar, but she didn't even seem to notice it. "There's Eddie's Bar," Paul said.

"Uhuh." Harriet nodded briskly.

"He's going to start making his martinis with sherry when all the French vermouth runs out," Paul said.

"It sounds horrible." Harriet made a face.

"Is that all you have to say?" Paul said loudly, remembering all the times he'd looked in to see if she was there.

"What do you want me to say?" Harriet looked honestly puzzled, but Paul had never known when she was lying to him or telling the truth, anyway, and he hadn't improved in the two years, he discovered.

"I don't want you to say anything. I'll take you in and buy you a drink."

"No, thanks. I've really got to get to Wanamaker's and back home in a hurry. Give me a raincheck."

"Yeah," Paul said sourly.

They turned up Ninth Street toward Fifth Avenue.

"I knew I'd meet you some place, finally," Paul said. "I was curious to see what would happen."

Harriet didn't say anything. She was looking absently at the buildings across the street.

"Don't you ever talk any more?" Paul asked.

"What *did* happen?"

"Every once in a while," he started, "I meet some girl I used to know . . ."

"I bet the country's full of them," Harriet said.

"The country's full of everybody's ex-girls."

Harriet nodded. "I never thought of it that way, but you're right."

"Most of the time I think, isn't she a nice, decent person? Isn't it wonderful I'm no longer attached to her? The first girl I ever had," Paul said, "is a policewoman now. She subdued a gangster single-handed in Coney Island last summer. Her mother won't let her go out of the house in her uniform. She's ashamed for the neighbors."

"Naturally," Harriet said.

"Another girl I used to know changed her name and dances in the Russian Ballet. I went to see her dance the other night. She has legs like a Fordham tackle. I used to think she was beautiful. I used to think you were beautiful, too."

"We were a handsome couple," Harriet said. "Except you always needed a shave. That electric razor . . ."

"I've given it up."

They were passing his old house now and he looked at the door-way and remembered all the times he and Harriet had gone in and come out, the rainy days and the early snowy mornings with the milkman's horse silent on the white street behind them. They stopped and looked at the old red house with the shabby shutters and the window on the fourth floor they had both looked out of time and time again to see what the weather was and Paul remem-bered the first time, on a winter's night, when he and Harriet had gone through that door together.

"I was so damn polite," Paul said softly.

Harriet smiled, knowing what he was talking about. "You kept dropping the key and saying, 'Lord, Lord,' under your breath while you were looking for it."

"I was nervous. I wanted to make sure you knew exactly how matters stood—no illusions. Good friends, everybody understanding everybody else, another girl coming in from Detroit in six weeks, no claims on me, no claims on you . . ." Paul looked at the window on the fourth floor and smiled. "What a fool!"

"It's a nice, quiet street," Harriet said, looking up at the window on the fourth floor, too. She shook her head, took Paul's arm again. "I've got to get to Wanamaker's."

They started off.

"What're you buying at Wanamaker's?" Paul asked.

Harriet hesitated for a moment. "Nothing much. I'm looking at some baby clothes. I'm going to have a baby." They crowded over to one side to let a little woman with four dachshunds pass them in a busy tangle. "Isn't it funny—me with a baby?" Harriet smiled. "I lie around all day and try to imagine what it's going to be like. In between, I sleep and drink beer to nourish us. I've never had such a good time in all my life."

"Well," said Paul, "at least it'll keep your husband out of the army."

"Maybe. He's a raging patriot."

"Good. When he's at Fort Dix I'll meet you in Washington Square Park when you take the baby out for an airing in its perambulator. I'll put on a policeman's uniform to make it proper. I'm not such a raging patriot."

"They'll get you anyway, won't they?"

"Sure. I'll send you my picture in a lieutenant's suit. From Bulgaria. I have a premonition I'm going to be called on to defend a strategic point in Bulgaria."

"How do you feel about it?" For the first time Harriet looked squarely and searchingly at him.

Paul shrugged. "It's going to happen. It's all damned silly, but it isn't as silly now as it was ten years ago."

Suddenly Harriet laughed.

"What's so funny?" Paul demanded.

"My asking you how you felt about something. I never used to have a chance . . . You'd let me know how you felt about everything. Roosevelt, James Joyce, Jesus Christ, Gypsy Rose Lee, Matisse, Yoga, liquor, sex, architecture . . ."

"I was full of opinions in those days." Paul smiled a little regretfully. "Lust and conversation. The firm foundations of civilized relations between the sexes."

He turned and looked back at the window on the fourth floor. "That was a nice apartment," he said softly. "Lust and conversation . . ."

"Come on, Paul," Harriet said. "Wanamaker's isn't going to stay open all night."

Paul turned up his collar because the wind was getting stronger as they neared Fifth Avenue. "You were the only girl I ever knew I could sleep in the same bed with."

"That's a hell of a thing to say to a girl." Harriet laughed. "Is that your notion of a compliment?"

Paul shrugged. "It's an irrelevant fact. Or a relevant fact. Is it polite to talk to a married lady this way?"

"No."

Paul walked along with her. "What do you think of when you look at me?" he asked.

"Nothing much," Harriet said carefully.

"What're you lying about?"

"Nothing much," Harriet said flatly.

"Don't you even think, 'What in the name of God did I ever see in him?'"

"No." Harriet put her hands deep in her pockets and walked quickly along the railings.

"Should I tell you what I think of when I look at you?"

"No."

"I've been looking for you for two years," Paul said.

"My name's been in the telephone book." Harriet hurried even more, wrapping her coat tightly around her.

"I didn't realize I was looking for you until I saw you."

"Please, Paul . . ."

"I would walk along the street and I'd pass a bar we'd been in together and I'd go in and sit there, even though I didn't want a drink, not knowing why I was sitting there. Now I know. I was waiting for you to come in. I didn't pass your house by accident."

"Look, Paul," Harriet pleaded. "It was a long time ago and it was fine and it ended. . . ."

"I was wrong," Paul said. "Do you like hearing that? I was wrong. You know, I never did get married, after all."

"I know," Harriet said. "Please shut up."

"I walk along Fifth Avenue and every time I pass St. Patrick's I half look up to see if you're passing, because I met you that day right after you'd had a tooth pulled, and it was cold; you were walking along with the tears streaming from your eyes and your eyes red and that was the only time I ever met you by accident any place . . ."

Harriet smiled. "That certainly sounds like a beautiful memory."

"Two years . . ." Paul said. "I've gone out with a lot of girls in the last two years." He shrugged. "They've bored me and I've bored them. I keep looking at every woman who passes to see if it's you. All the girls I go out with bawl the hell out of me for it. I've been walking around, following girls with dark hair to see if it'll turn out to be you, and girls with a fur jacket like that old one you had and girls that walk in that silly, beautiful way you walk. . . . I've been searching the streets of the city for you for two years and this is the first time I've admitted it even to myself. That little Spanish joint we went the first time. Every time I pass it I remember everything—how many drinks we had and what the band played and what we said and the fat Cuban who kept winking at you from the bar and the very delicate way we landed up in my apartment . . ."

They were both walking swiftly now, Harriet holding her hands stiffly down at her sides.

"There is a particular wonderful way you are joined together . . ."

"Paul, stop it." Harriet's voice was flat but loud.

"Two years. In two years the edge should be dulled off things like that. Instead . . ." How can you make a mistake as big as that? Paul thought, how can you deliberately be as wrong as that? And no remedy. So long as you live, no remedy. He looked harshly at Harriet. Her face was set, as though she weren't listening to him and only intent on getting across the street as quickly as possible. "How about you?" he asked. "Don't you remember . . . ?"

"I don't remember anything," she said. And then, suddenly, the tears sprang up in her eyes and streamed down the tight, distorted cheeks. "I don't remember a goddamn thing!" she wept. "I'm not going to Wanamaker's. I'm going home! Good-bye!" She ran over to a cab that was parked at the corner and opened the door and sprang in. The cab spurted past Paul and he had a glimpse of Harriet sitting stiffly upright, the tears bitter and unheeded in her eyes.

He watched the cab go down Fifth Avenue until it turned. Then he turned the other way and started walking, thinking, I must move away from this neighborhood. I've lived here long enough.

Desire

BY

JAMES STEPHENS

1.

H E WAS excited, and as he leaned forward in his chair and told this story to his wife he revealed to her a degree or a species of credulity of which she could not have believed him capable.

He was a level-headed man, and habitually conducted his affairs on hard-headed principles. He had conducted his courtship, his matrimonial and domestic affairs in a manner which she should not have termed reckless or romantic. When, therefore, she found him excited, and over such a story, she did not know just how to take the matter.

She compromised by agreeing with him, not because her reason was satisfied or even touched, but simply because he was excited, and a woman can welcome anything which varies the dull round and will bathe in exclamations if she gets the chance.

This was what he told her.

As he was walking to lunch a motor car came down the street at a speed much too dangerous for the narrow and congested thoroughfare. A man was walking in front of him, and, just as the car came behind, this man stepped off the path with a view to crossing the road. He did not even look behind as he stepped off. Her husband stretched a ready arm that swept the man back to the pavement one second before the car went blaring and buzzing by.

"If I had not been there," said her husband, who liked slang, "you would have got it where the chicken got the axe."

The two men grinned at each other; her husband smiling with good-fellowship, the other crinkling with amusement and gratitude.

They walked down the street and, on the strength of that adventure, they had lunch together.

They had sat for a long time after lunch, making each others'
acquaintance, smoking innumerable cigarettes, and engaged in a
conversation which she could never have believed her husband
would have shared in for ten minutes; and they had parted with a
wish, from her husband, that they should meet again on the following day, and a wordless smile from the man.

He had neither ratified nor negatived the arrangement.

"I hope he'll turn up," said her husband.

This conversation had excited her man, for it had drawn him into
an atmosphere to which he was a stranger, and he had found himself
moving there with such pleasure that he wished to get back to it
with as little delay as possible.

Briefly, as he explained it to her, the atmosphere was religious;
and while it was entirely intellectual it was more heady and ex-
hilarating than the emotional religion to which he had been accustomed, and from which he had silently lapsed.

He tried to describe his companion; but had such ill success in
the description that she could not remember afterwards whether he
was tall or short; fat or thin; fair or dark.

It was the man's eyes only that he succeeded in emphasizing; and
these, it appeared, were eyes such as he had never before seen in
a human face.

That also, he amended, was a wrong way of putting it, for his
eyes were exactly like everybody else's. It was the way he looked
through them that was different. Something, very steady, very
ardent, very quiet and powerful, was using these eyes for purposes
of vision. He had never met anyone who looked at him so . . . com-
prehendingly; so agreeably.

"You are in love," said she with a laugh.

After this her husband's explanations became more explanatory
but not less confused, until she found that they were both, with
curious unconsciousness, in the middle of a fairy-tale.

"He asked me," said her husband, "what was the thing I wished
for beyond all things.

"That was the most difficult question I have ever been invited to
answer," he went on; "and for nearly half an hour we sat thinking
it out, and discussing magnificences and possibilities.

"I had all the usual thoughts; and, of course, the first of them was wealth. We are more dominated by proverbial phrases than we conceive of, and, such a question being posed, the words 'healthy, wealthy, and wise' will come, unbidden, to answer it. To be alive is to be acquisitive, and so I mentioned wealth, tentatively, as a possibility; and he agreed that it was worth considering. But after a while I knew that I did not want money."

"One always has need of money," said his wife.

"In a way, that is true," he replied, "but not in this way; for, as I thought it over, I remembered that we have no children; and that our relatively few desires, or fancies, can be readily satisfied by the money we already have. Also we are fairly well off; we have enough in the stocking to last our time even if I ceased from business, which I am not going to do; and, in short, I discovered that money or its purchasing power had not any particular advantages to offer."

"All the same!" she murmured; and halted with her eyes fixed on purchasings far away in time and space.

"All the same!" he agreed with smile.

"I could not think of anything worth wishing for," he continued. "I mentioned health and wisdom, and we considered these; but, judging myself by the standard of the world in which we move, I concluded that both my health and knowledge were as good as the next man's; and I thought also that if I elected to become wiser than my contemporaries I might be a very lonely person for the rest of my days."

"Yes," said she thoughfully, "I am glad you did not ask to be made wise, unless you could have asked it for both of us."

"I asked him in the end what he would advise me to demand, but he replied that he could not advise me at all. 'Behind everything stands desire,' said he, 'and you must find out your desire.'

"I asked him then, if the conditions were reversed and if the opportunity had come to him instead of to me, what he should have asked for; not, as I explained to him, in order that I might copy his wish, but from sheer curiosity. He replied that he should not ask for anything. This reply astonished, almost alarmed me at first, but most curiously satisfied me on considering it, and I was about to adopt that attitude——"

"Oh," said his wife.

"When an idea came to me. 'Here I am,' I said to myself, 'forty-eight years of age: rich enough; sound enough in wind and limb; and as wise as I can afford to be. What is there now belonging to me, absolutely mine, but from which I must part, and which I should like to keep?' And I saw that the thing which was leaving me day by day; second by second; irretrievably and inevitably; was my forty-eighth year. I thought I should like to continue at the age of forty-eight until my time was up.

"I did not ask to live for ever, or any of that nonsense, for I saw that to live for ever is to be condemned to a misery of boredom more dreadful than anything else the mind can conceive of. But, while I do live, I wish to live competently, and so I asked to be allowed to stay at the age of forty-eight years with all the equipment of my present state unimpaired."

"You should not have asked for such a thing," said his wife, a little angrily. "It is not fair to me," she explained. "You are older than I am now, but in a few years this will mean that I shall be needlessly older than you. I think it was not a loyal wish."

"I thought of that objection," said he, "and I also thought that I was past the age at which certain things matter; and that both temperamentally and in the matter of years I am proof against sensual or such-like attractions. It seemed to me to be right; so I just registered my wish with him."

"What did he say?" she queried.

"He did not say anything; he just nodded; and began to talk again of other matters—religion, life, death, mind; a host of things, which, for all the diversity they seem to have when I enumerate them, were yet one single theme.

"I feel a more contented man tonight than I have ever felt," he continued, "and I feel in some curious way a different person from the man I was yesterday."

Here his wife awakened from the conversation and began to laugh.

"You are a foolish man," said she, "and I am just as bad. If anyone were to hear us talking this solemn silliness they would have a right to mock at us."

He laughed heartily with her, and after a light supper they went to bed.

2.

During the night his wife had a dream.

She dreamed that a ship set away for the Polar Seas on an expedition in which she was not sufficiently interested to find out its reason. The ship departed with her on board. All that she knew or cared was that she was greatly concerned with baggage, and with counting and going over the various articles that she had brought against arctic weather.

She had thick woollen stockings. She had skin boots all hairy inside, all pliable and wrinkled without. She had a great skin cap shaped like a helmet and fitting down in a cape over her shoulders. She had, and they did not astonish her, a pair of very baggy fur trousers. She had a sleeping sack.

She had an enormous quantity of things; and everybody in the expedition was equipped, if not with the same things, at least similarly.

These traps were a continuous subject of conversation aboard, and, although days and weeks passed, the talk of the ship hovered about and fell continually into the subject of warm clothing.

There came a day when the weather was perceptibly colder; so cold that she was tempted to draw on these wonderful breeches, and to fit her head into that most comfortable hat. But she did not do so; for, and everybody on the ship explained it to her, it was necessary that she should accustom herself to the feeling, the experience, of cold; and, she was further assured, that the chill which she was now resenting was nothing to the freezing she should presently have to bear.

It seemed good advice; and she decided that as long as she could bear the cold she would do so, and would not put on any protective covering; thus, when the cold became really intense, she would be in some measure inured to it, and would not suffer so much.

But steadily, and day by day, the weather grew colder.

For now they were in wild and whirling seas wherein great green and white icebergs went sailing by: and all about the ship little hummocks of ice bobbed and surged, and went under and came up; and the grey water slashed and hissed against and on top of these small hillocks.

Her hands were so cold that she had to put them under her armpits to keep any warmth in them; and her feet were in a worse condition. They had begun to pain her; so she decided that on the morrow she would put on her winter equipment, and would not mind what anybody said to the contrary.

"It is cold enough," said she, "for my arctic trousers, for my warm soft boots, and my great furry gloves. I will put them on in the morning," for it was then almost night and she meant to go to bed at once.

She did go to bed; and she lay there in a very misery of cold.

In the morning, she was yet colder; and immediately on rising she looked for the winter clothing which she had laid ready by the side of her bunk the night before; but she could not find them. She was forced to dress in her usual rather thin clothes; and, having done so, she went on deck.

When she got to the side of the vessel she found that the world about her had changed.

The sea had disappeared. Far as the eye could peer was a level plain of ice, not white, but dull grey; and over it there lowered a sky, grey as itself and of almost the same dullness.

Across this waste there blew a bitter, a piercing wind that her eyes winced from, and that caused her ears to tingle and sting.

Not a soul was moving on the ship, and the dead silence which brooded on the ice lay heavy and almost solid on the vessel.

She ran to the other side, and found that the whole ship's company had landed, and were staring at her from a little distance off the ship. And these people were as silent as the frozen air, as the frozen ship. They stared at her; they made no move; they made no sound.

She noticed that they were all dressed in their winter furs; and, while she stood, ice began to creep into her veins.

One of the ship's company strode forward a few paces and held up a bundle in his mittened hand. She was amazed to see that the bundle contained her clothes; her broad furry trousers; her great cosy helmet and gloves.

To get from the ship to the ice was painful but not impossible. A rope ladder was hanging against the side, and she went down this.

The rungs felt hard as iron, for they were frozen stiff; and the touch of those glassy surfaces bit into her tender hand like fire. But she got to the ice and went across it towards her companions.

Then, to her dismay, to her terror, all these, suddenly, with one unexpressed accord, turned and began to run away from her; and she, with a heart that shook once and could scarcely beat again, took after them.

Every few paces she fell, for her shoes could not grip on the ice; and each time that she fell those monsters stood and turned and watched her, and the man who had her clothes waved the bundle at her and danced grotesquely, silently.

She continued running, sliding, falling, picking herself up, until her breath went, and she came to a halt, unable to move a limb further and scarcely able to breathe; and this time they did not stay to look at her.

They continued running, but now with greater and greater speed, with the very speed of madmen; and she saw them become black specks away in the white distance; and she saw them disappear; and she saw that there was nothing where she stared but the long white miles, and the terrible silence, and the cold.

How cold it was!

And with that there arose a noiseless wind, keen as a razor.

It stung into her face; it swirled about her ankles like a lash; it stabbed under her armpits like a dagger.

"I am cold," she murmured.

She looked backwards whence she had come, but the ship was no longer in sight, and she could not remember from what direction she had come.

Then she began to run in any direction.

Indeed she ran in every direction to find the ship; for when she had taken a hundred steps in one way she thought, frantically, "this is not the way," and at once she began to run on the opposite road. But run as she might she could not get warm; it was colder she got. And then, on a steel-grey plane, she slipped, and slipped again, and went sliding down a hollow, faster and faster; she came to the brink of a cleft, and swished over this, and down into a hole of ice and there she lay.

"I shall die!" she said. "I shall fall asleep here and die. . . ."

Then she awakened.

She opened her eyes directly on the window and saw the ghost of dawn struggling with the ghoul of darkness. A greyish perceptibility framed the window without, but could not daunt the obscurity within; and she lay for a moment terrified at that grotesque adventure, and thanking God that it had only been a very horrible dream.

In another second she felt that she was cold. She pulled the clothes more tightly about her, and she spoke to her husband.

"How miserably cold it is!" she said.

She turned in the bed and snuggled against him for warmth; and she found that an atrocity of cold came from him; that he was icy.

She leaped from the bed with a scream. She switched on the light, and bent over her husband—

He was stone dead. He was stone cold. And she stood by him, shivering and whimpering.

Country Full of Swedes

BY

ERSKINE CALDWELL

THERE I was, standing in the middle of the chamber, trembling like I was coming down with the flu, and still not knowing what god-awful something had happened. In all my days in the Back Kingdom, I never heard such noises so early in the forenoon.

It was about half an hour after sun-rise, and a gun went off like a coffer-dam breaking up under ice at twenty below, and I'd swear it sounded like it wasn't any further away than my feet are from my head. That gun shot off, pitching me six-seven inches off the bed, and, before I could come down out of the air, there was another roar like somebody coughing through a megaphone, with a two weeks' cold, right in my ear. God-helping, I hope I never get waked up like that again until I can get myself home to the Back Kingdom where I rightfully belong to stay.

I must have stood there ten-fifteen minutes shivering in my night-shirt, my heart pounding inside of me like a ramrod working on a plugged-up bore, and listening for that gun again, if it was going to shoot some more. A man never knows what's going to happen next in the State of Maine; that's why I wish sometimes I'd never left the Back Kingdom to begin with. I was making sixty a month, with the best of bed and board, back there in the intervale; but like a God damn fool I had to jerk loose and come down here near the Bay. I'm going back where I came from, God-helping; I've never had a purely calm and peaceful day since I got here three-four years ago. This is the damnedest country for the unexpected raising of all kinds of unlooked-for hell a man is apt to run across in a life-time of traveling. If a man's born and raised in the Back Kingdom, he ought to stay there where he belongs; that's what I'd done if I'd had the sense to stay out of this down-country near the Bay, where you don't ever know, God-helping, what's going to happen next, where, or when.

But there I was, standing in the middle of the upstairs chamber, shaking like a rag weed in an August wind-storm, and not knowing what minute, maybe right at me, that gun was going to shoot off again, for all I knew. Just then, though, I heard Jim and Mrs. Frost trip-trapping around downstairs in their bare feet. Even if I didn't know what god-awful something had happened, I knew things around the place weren't calm and peaceful, like they generally were of a Sunday morning in May, because it took a stiff mixture of heaven and hell to get Jim and Mrs. Frost up and out of a warm bed before six of a forenoon, any of the days of the week.

I ran to the window and stuck my head out as far as I could get it, to hear what the trouble was. Everything out there was as quiet and peaceful as midnight on a backroad in middlemost winter. But I knew something was up, because Jim and Mrs. Frost didn't make a practice of getting up and out of a warm bed that time of forenoon in the chillish May-time.

There wasn't any sense in me standing there in the cold air shivering in my night-shirt, so I put on my clothes, whistling all the time through my teeth to drive away the chill, and trying to figure out what God damn fool was around so early shooting off a gun of a Sunday morning. Just then I heard the downstairs door open, and up the steps, two at a time, came Jim in his breeches and his shirt-tail flying out behind him.

He wasn't long in coming up the stairs, for a man sixty-seven, but before he reached the door to my room, that gun went off again: BOOM! Just like that; and the echo came rolling back through the open window from the hills: *Boom! Boom!* Like fireworks going off with your eyes shut. Jim had busted through the door already, but when he heard that *Boom!* sound he sort of spun around, like a cock-eyed weathervane, five-tix times, and ran out the door again like he had been shot in the hind parts with a moose gun. That *Boom!* so early in the forenoon was enough to scare the daylights out of any man, and Jim wasn't any different from me or anybody else in the town of East Joloppi. He just turned around and jumped through the door to the first tread on the stairway like his mind was made up to go somewhere else in a hurry, and no fooling around at the start.

COUNTRY FULL OF SWEDES

I'd been hired to Jim and Mrs. Frost for all of three-four years, and I was near about as much of a Frost, excepting name, as Jim himself was. Jim and me got along first-rate together, doing chores and haying and farm work in general, because neither one of us was ever trying to make the other do more of the work. We were hitched to make a fine team, and I never had a kick coming, and Jim said he didn't either. Jim had the name of Frost, to be sure, but I wouldn't ever hold that against a man.

The echo of that gun-shot was still rolling around in the hills and coming in through the window, when all at once that god-awful cough-like whoop through a megaphone sounded again right there in the room and everywhere else, like it might have been, in the whole town of East Joloppi. The man or beast or whatever animal he was who hollered like that ought to be locked up to keep him from scaring all the women and children to death, and it wasn't any stomach-comforting sound for a grown man who's used to the peaceful calm of the Back Kingdom all his life to hear so early of a Sunday forenoon, either.

I jumped to the door where Jim, just a minute before, leaped through. He didn't stop till he got clear to the bottom of the stairs. He stood there, looking up at me like a wild-eyed cow moose surprised in the sheriff's corn field.

"Who fired that god-awful shot, Jim?" I yelled at him, leaping down the stairs quicker than a man of my years ought to let himself do.

"Good God!" Jim said, his voice hoarse, and falling all to pieces like a stump of punk-wood. "The Swedes! The Swedes are shooting, Stan!"

"What Swedes, Jim—those Swedes who own the farm and buildings across the road over there?" I said, trying to find the button-holes in my shirt. "Have they come back here to live on that farm?"

"Good God, yes!" he said, his voice croaking deep down in his throat, like he had swallowed too much water. "The Swedes are all over the place. They're everywhere you can see, there's that many of them."

"What's their name, Jim?" I asked him. "You and Mrs. Frost never told me what their name is."

"Good God, I don't know. I never heard them called anything but Swedes, and that's what it is, I guess. It ought to be that, if it ain't."

I ran across the hall to look out a window, but it was on the wrong side of the house, and I couldn't see a thing. Mrs. Frost was stepping around in the downstairs chamber, locking things up in the drawers and closet and forgetting where she was hiding the keys. I could see her through the open door, and she was more scared-looking than Jim was. She was so scared of the Swedes she didn't know what she was doing, none of the time.

"What made those Swedes come back for, Jim?" I said to him. "I thought you said they were gone for good this time."

"Good God, Stan," he said, "I don't know what they came back for. I guess hard times are bringing everybody back to the land, and the Swedes are always in the front rush of everything. I don't know what brought them back, but they're all over the place, shooting and yelling and raising hell. There are thirty-forty of them, looks like to me, counting everything with heads."

"What are they doing now, Jim, except yelling and shooting?"

"Good God," Jim said, looking behind him to see what Mrs. Frost was doing with his things in the downstairs chamber. "I don't know what they're not doing. But I can hear them, Stan! You hurry out right now and lock up all the tools in the barn and bring in the cows and tie them up in the stalls. I've got to hurry out now, and bring in all of those new cedar fence posts across the front of the yard before they start pulling them up and carrying them off. Good God, Stan, the Swedes are everywhere you look outdoors! We've got to make haste, Stan!"

Jim ran to the side door and out the back of the house, but I took my time about going. I wasn't scared of the Swedes, like Jim and Mrs. Frost were, and I didn't aim to have Jim putting me to doing tasks and chores, or anything else, before breakfast and the proper time. I wasn't any more scared of the Swedes than I was of the Finns and Portuguese, anyway. It's god-awful shame for Americans to let Swedes and Finns and the Portuguese scare the daylights of them. God-helping, they are no different than us, and you never see a Finn or a Swede scared of an American. But people like Jim and Mrs. Frost are scared to death of Swedes and other people from the old countries; Jim and Mrs. Frost and people like that never stop to think that all of us Americans came over from the old countries, one time or another, to begin with.

But there wasn't any sense in trying to argue with Jim and Mrs.

Frost right then, when the Swedes, like a fired nest of yellow-headed
bumble bees, were swarming all over the place as far as the eye
could see, and when Mrs. Frost was scared to death that they were
coming into the house and carry out all of her and Jim's furniture
and household goods. So while Mrs. Frost was tying her and Jim's
shoes in pillow cases and putting them out of sight in closets and
behind beds, I went to the kitchen window and looked out to see
what was going on around that tall yellow house across the road.

Jim and Mrs. Frost both were right about there being Swedes all
over the place. God-helping, there were Swedes all over the country,
near about all over the whole town of East Joloppi, for what I could
see out the window. They were as thick around the barn and pump
and the woodpile as if they had been a nest of yellow-headed
bumble bees strewn over the countryside. There were Swedes everywhere a man could see, and the ones that couldn't be seen, could
be heard yelling their heads off inside the yellow clap-boarded house
across the road. There wasn't any mistake about their being Swedes
there, either; because I've never yet seen a man who mistakes a
Swede or a Finn for an American. Once you see a Finn or a Swede
you know, God-helping, that he is a Swede or a Finn, and not a
Portugee or an American.

There was a Swede everywhere a man could look. Some of them
were little Swedes, and women Swedes, to be sure; but little Swedes,
in the end, and women Swedes too, near about, grow up as big as
any of them. When you come right down to it, there's no sense in
counting out the little Swedes and the women Swedes.

Out in the road in front of their house were seven-eight autos
and trucks loaded down with furniture and household goods. All
around, everything was Swedes. The Swedes were yelling and shouting at one another, the little Swedes and the women Swedes just
as loud as the big Swedes, and it looked like none of them knew
what all the shouting and yelling was for, and when they found
out, they didn't give a damn about it. That was because all of them
were Swedes. It didn't make any difference what a Swede was yelling about; just as long as he had leave to open his mouth, he was
tickled to death about it.

I have never seen the like of so much yelling and shouting anywhere else before; but down here in the State of Maine, in the down-
country on the Bay, there's no sense in being taken-back at the

sights to be seen, because anything on God's green earth is likely and liable to happen between day and night, and the other way around, too.

Now, you take the Finns; there's any God's number of them in the woods, where you least expect to see them, logging and such. When a Finn crew breaks a woods camp, it looks like there's a Finn for every tree in the whole State, but you don't see them going around making the noise that Swedes do, with all their yelling and shouting and shooting off guns. Finns are quiet about their hell-raising. The Portuguese are quiet, too; you see them tramping around, minding their own business, and working hard on the river dam or something, but you never hear them shouting and yelling and shooting off guns at five-six of a Sunday morning. There's no known likeness to the noise that a houseful of Swedes can make when they get to yelling and shouting at one another early in the forenoon.

I was standing there all that time, looking out the window at the Swedes across the road, when Jim came into the kitchen with an armful of wood and threw it into the woodbox behind the range.

"Good God, Stan," Jim said, "the Swedes are everywhere you can look out-doors. They're not going to get that armful of wood, anyway, though."

Mrs. Frost came to the door and stood looking like she didn't know it was her business to cook breakfast for Jim and me. I made a fire in the range and put on a pan of water to boil for the coffee. Jim kept running to the window to look out, and there wasn't much use in expecting Mrs. Frost to start cooking unless somebody set her to it, in the shape she was in, with all the Swedes around the place. She was so up-set, it was a downright pity to look at her. But Jim and me had to eat, and I went and took her by the arm and brought her to the range and left her standing there so close she would get burned if she didn't stir around and make breakfast.

"Good God, Stan," Jim said, "those Swedes are into everything. They're in the barn, and in the pasture running the cows, and I don't know what else they're been into since I looked last. They'll take the tools and the horses and cows, and the cedar posts, too, if we don't get out there and put everything under lock and key."

"Now, hold on, Jim," I said, looking out the window. "Them

you see are little Swedes out there, and they're not going to make off with anything of yours and Mrs. Frost's. The big Swedes are busy carrying in furniture and household goods. Those Swedes aren't going to tamper with anything of yours and Mrs. Frost's. They're people just like us. They don't go around stealing everything in sight. Now, let's just sit here by the window and watch them while Mrs. Frost is getting breakfast ready."

"Good God, Stan, they're Swedes," Jim said, "and they're moving into the house across the road. I've got to put everything under lock and key before——"

"Hold on, Jim," I told him. "It's their house they're moving into. God-helping, they're not moving into your and Jim's house, are they, Mrs. Frost?"

"Jim," Mrs. Frost said, shaking her finger at him and looking at me wild-eyed and sort of flustered-like, "Jim, don't you sit there and let Stanley stop you from saving the stock and tools. Stanley doesn't know the Swedes like we do. Stanley came down here from the Back Kingdom, and he doesn't know anything about Swedes."

Mrs. Frost was partly right, because I've never seen the things in my whole life that I've seen down here near the Bay; but there wasn't any sense in Americans like Jim and Mrs. Frost being scared of Swedes. I've seen enough Finns and Portuguese in my time in the Back Kingdom, up in the intervale, to know that Americans are no different from the others.

"Now, you hold on a while, Jim," I said. "Swedes are no different than Finns. Finns don't go around stealing another man's stock and tools. Up in the Back Kingdom the Finns are the finest kind of neighbors."

"That may be so up in the Back Kingdom, Stan," Jim said, "but Swedes down here near the Bay are nothing like anything that's ever been before or since. Those Swedes over there across the road work in a pulp mill over to Waterville three-four years, and when they've got enough money saved up, or when they lose it all, as the case may be, they all move back here to East Joloppi on this farm of theirs for two-three years at a time. That's what they do. And they've been doing it for the past thirty-forty years, ever since I can remember, and they haven't changed none in all that time. I can recall the first time they came to East Joloppi; they built that house across the road then, and if you've ever seen a sight like

Swedes building a house in a hurry, you haven't got much else to live for. Why! Stan, those Swedes built that house in four-five days —just like that! I've never seen the equal to it. Of course now, Stan, it's the damnedest-looking house a man ever saw, because it's not a farmhouse, and it's not a city house, and it's no kind of a house an American would erect. Why! those Swedes threw that house together in four-five days—just like that! But whoever saw a house like that before, with three storeys to it, and only six rooms in the whole building! And painted yellow, too; Good God, Stan, white is the only color to paint a house, and those Swedes went and painted it yellow. Then on top of that, they went and painted the barn red. And of all of the shouting and yelling, at all times of the day and night, a man never saw or heard before. Those Swedes acted like they were purely crazy for the whole of four-five days, and they were, and they still are. But what gets me is the painting of it yellow, and the making of it three storeys high, with only six rooms in the whole building. Nobody but Swedes would go and do a thing like that; an American would have built a farm house, here in the country, resting square on the ground, with one storey, maybe a storey and a half, and then painted it lead-white. But Good God, Stan, those fool Swedes had to put up three storeys, to hold six rooms, and then went and painted the building yellow."

"Swedes are a little queer, sometimes," I said. "But Finns and Portuguese are too, Jim. And Americans sometimes——"

"A little queer!" Jim said. "Why! Good God, Stan, the Swedes are the queerest people on the earth, if that's the right word for them. You don't know Swedes, Stan. This is the first time you've ever seen those Swedes across the road, and that's why you don't know what they're like after being shut up in a pulpwood mill over to Waterville for four-five years. They're purely wild, I tell you, Stan. They don't stop for anything they set their heads on. If you was to walk out there now and tell them to move their autos and trucks off of the town road so the travelers could get past without having to drive through the brush, they'd tear you apart, they're that wild, after being shut up in the pulp mill over to Waterville these three-four, maybe four-five, years."

"Finns get that way, too," I tried to tell Jim. "After Finns have been shut up in a woods camp all winter, they make a lot of noise

when they get out. Everybody who has to stay close to the job
for three-four years likes to act free when he gets out from under
the job. Now, Jim, you take the Portuguese——"

"'Don't you sit there, Jim, and let Stanley keep you from putting
the tools away," Mrs. Frost said. "Stanley doesn't know the Swedes
like we do. He's lived up in the Back Kingdom most of his life,
tucked away in the intervale, and he's never seen Swedes——"

"Good God, Stan," Jim said, standing up, he was that nervous
and up-set, "the Swedes are over-running the whole country. I'll
bet there are more Swedes in the town of East Joloppi than there
are in the rest of the country. Everybody knows there's more Swedes
in the State of Maine than there are in the old country. Why! Jim,
they take to this State like potato bugs take to——"

"Don't you sit there and let Stanley keep you back, Jim," Mrs.
Frost put in again. "Stanley doesn't know the Swedes like we do.
Stanley's lived up there in the Back Kingdom most of his life."

Just then one of the big Swedes started yelling at some of the
little Swedes and women Swedes. I'll swear, those big Swedes
sounded like a pastureful of hoarse bulls, near the end of May, mad
about the black-flies. God-helping, they yelled like they were fixing
to kill all the little Swedes and women Swedes they could get their
hands on. It didn't amount to anything, though; because the little
Swedes and the women Swedes yelled right back at them just like
they had been big Swedes too. The little Swedes and women Swedes
couldn't yell hoarse bull bass, but it was close enough to it to make
a man who's lived most of his life up in the Back Kingdom, in the
intervale, think that the whole town of East Joloppi was full of big
Swedes.

Jim was all for getting out after the tools and stock right away,
but I pulled him back to the table. I wasn't going to let Jim and
Mrs. Frost set me to doing tasks and chores before breakfast and the
regular time. Forty dollars a month isn't much to pay a man for ten-
eleven hours' work a day, including Sundays, when the stock has to
be attended to like any other day, and I set myself that I wasn't going to work twelve-thirteen hours a day for them, even if I was practically one of the Frosts myself, except in name, by that time.

"Now, hold on a while, Jim," I said. "Let's just sit here by the
window and watch them carry their furniture and household goods
inside while Mrs. Frost's getting the cooking ready to eat. If they

start taking off any of you and Mrs. Frost's things, we can see
them just as good from here by the window as we could out there
in the yard and road."

"Now, Jim, I'm telling you," Mrs. Frost said, shaking all over,
and not even trying to cook us a meal, "don't you sit there and let
Stanley keep you from saving the stock and tools. Stanley doesn't
know the Swedes like we do. He thinks they're like everybody else."

Jim wasn't for staying in the house when all of his tools were
lying around in the yard, and while his cows were in the pasture
unprotected, but he saw how it would be better to wait where
we could hurry up Mrs. Frost with the cooking, if we were ever
going to eat breakfast that forenoon. She was so excited and nervous
about the Swedes moving back to East Joloppi from the pulp mill
in Waterville that she hadn't got the beans and brown bread fully
heated from the night before, and we had to sit and eat them cold.

We were sitting there by the window eating the cold beans and
brown bread, and watching the Swedes, when two of the little
Swedes started running across Jim and Mrs. Frost's lawn. They
were chasing one of their big yellow tom cats they had brought
with them from Waterville. The yellow tom was as large as an eight-
months collie puppy, and he ran like he was on fire and didn't
know how to put it out. His great bushy tail stuck straight up in
the air behind him, like a flag, and he was leaping over the lawn
like a devilish calf, new-born.

Jim and Mrs. Frost saw the little Swedes and the big yellow tom
cat at the same time I did.

"Good God," Jim shouted, raising himself part out of the chair.
"Here they come now!"

"Hold on now, Jim," I said, pulling him back to the table.
"They're only chasing one of their tom cats. They're not after taking anything that belongs to you and Mrs. Frost. Let's just sit here
and finish eating the beans, and watch them out the window."

"My crown in heaven!" Mrs. Frost cried out, running to the window and looking through. "Those Swedes are going to kill every
plant on the place. They'll dig up all the bulbs and pull up all the
vines in the flower bed."

"Now you just sit and calm yourself, Mrs. Frost," I told her.
"Those little Swedes are just chasing a tom cat. They're not after
doing hurt to your flowers."

The big Swedes were unloading the autos and trucks and carrying the furniture and household goods into their three storey, yellow clapboarded house. None of them was paying any attention to the little Swedes chasing the yellow tom over Jim and Mrs. Frost's lawn.

Just then the kitchen door burst open, and the two little Swedes stood there looking at us, panting and blowing their heads off.

Mrs. Frost took one look at them, and then she let out a yell, but the kids didn't notice her at all.

"Hey," one of them shouted, "come out here and help us get the cat. He climbed up in one of your trees."

By that time, Mrs. Frost was all for slamming the door in their faces, but I pushed in front of her and went out into the yard with them. Jim came right behind me, after he had finished calming Mrs. Frost, and telling her we wouldn't let the Swedes come and carry out her furniture and household goods.

The yellow tom was all the way up in one of Jim's young maple shade trees. The maple wasn't strong enough to support even the smallest of the little Swedes, if he should take it into his head to climb to the top after the cat, and neither Jim nor me was hurting ourselves trying to think of a way to get the feline down. We were all for letting the cat stay where he was, till he got ready to come down of his own free will, but the little Swedes couldn't wait for anything. They wanted the tom right away, then and there, and no wasting of time in getting him.

"You boys go home and wait for the cat to come down," Jim told them. "There's no way to make him come down now, till he gets ready to come down of his own mind."

But no, those two boys were little Swedes. They weren't thinking of going back home till they got the yellow tom down from the maple. One of them ran to the tree, before Jim or me could head him off, and started shinning up it like a pop-eyed squirrel. In no time, it seemed to me like, he was up amongst the limbs, jumping up there from one limb to another like he had been brought up in just such a tree.

"Good God, Stan," Jim said, "can't you keep them out of the trees?"

There was no answer for that, and Jim knew there wasn't.

There's no way of stopping a Swede from doing what he has set his head on doing.

The boy got almost to the top branch, where the yellow tom was clinging and spitting, when the tree began to bend towards the house. I knew what was coming, if something wasn't done about it pretty quick, and so did Jim. Jim saw his young maple shade tree begin to bend, and he almost had a fit looking at it. He ran to the lumber stack and came back dragging two lengths of two-by-fours. He got them set up against the tree before it had time to do any splitting, and then we stood there, like two damn fools, shoring up the tree and yelling at the little Swede to come down out of there before we broke his neck for being up in it.

The big Swedes across the road heard the fuss we were making, and they came running out of that three storey, six room house like it had been on fire inside.

"Good God, Stan," Jim shouted at me, "here comes the Swedes!"

"Don't turn and run off, Jim," I cautioned him, yanking him back by his coat-tail. "They're not wild beasts; we're not scared of them. Hold on where you are, Jim."

I could see Mrs. Frost's head almost breaking through the window-glass in the kitchen. She was all for coming out and driving the Swedes off her lawn and out of her flowers, but she was too scared to unlock the kitchen door and open it.

Jim was getting ready to run again, when he saw the Swedes coming toward us like a nest of yellowheaded bumble bees, but I wasn't scared of them, and I held on to Jim's coat-tail and told him I wasn't. Jim and me were shoring up the young maple, and I knew if one of us let go, the tree would bend to the ground right away and split wide open right up the middle. There was no sense in ruining a young maple shade tree like that, and I told Jim there wasn't.

"Hey," one of the big Swedes shouted at the little Swede up in the top of the maple, "come down out of that tree and go home to your mother."

"Ah, to hell with the old lady," the little Swede shouted down. "I'm getting the cat by the tail."

The big Swede looked at Jim and me. Jim was almost ready to run again by that time, but I wasn't, and I held him and told him

I wasn't. There was no sense in letting the Swedes scare the day-lights out of us.

"What in the hell can you do with kids when they get that age?" he asked Jim and me.

Jim was all for telling him to make the boy come down out of the maple before it bent over and split wide open, but I knew there was no sense in trying to make him come down out of there until he got good and ready to come, or else got the yellow tom by the tail.

Just then another big Swede came running out of that three storey, six room house across the road, holding a double-bladed ax out in front of him, like it was a red-hot poker, and yelling for all he was worth at the other Swedes.

"Good God, Stan," Jim said, "don't let those Swedes cut down my young maple!"

I had lots better sense than to try to make the Swedes stop doing what they had set their heads on doing. A man would be purely a fool to try to stop it from raining from above when it got ready to, even if he was trying to get his corn crop planted.

I looked around again, and there was Mrs. Frost all but popping through the window-glass. I could see what she was thinking, but I couldn't hear a word she was saying. It was good and plenty though, whatever it was.

"Come down out of that tree!" the Swede yelled at the boy up in Jim's maple.

Instead of starting to climb down, the little Swede reached up for the big yellow tom cat's tail. The tom reached out a big fat paw and harried the boy five-six times, just like that, quicker than the eye could follow. The kid let out a yell and a shout that must have been heard all the way to the other side of town, sounding like a whole houseful of Swedes up in the maple.

The big Swede covered the distance to the tree in one stride, push-ing everything behind him.

"Good God, Stan," Jim shouted at me, "we've got to do some-thing!"

There wasn't anything a man could do, unless he was either a Swede himself, or a man of prayer. Americans like Jim and me had no business getting in a Swede's way, especially when he was swinging a big double-bladed ax, and he just out of a pulp mill after being shut up making paper four-five years.

The big Swede grabbed the ax and let go at the trunk of the maple with it. There was no stopping him then, because he had the ax going, and it was whipping around his shoulders like a cow's tail in a swarm of black-flies. The little maple shook all over every time the ax-blade struck it, like wind blowing a corn stalk, and then it began to bend on the other side from Jim and me where we were shoring it up with the two-by-fours. Chips as big as dinner plates were flying across the lawn and pelting the house like a gang of boys stoning telephone insulators. One of those big dinner-plate chips crashed through the window where Mrs. Frost was, about that time. Both Jim and me thought at first she had fallen through the window, but when we looked again, we could see that she was still on the inside, and madder than ever at the Swedes.

The two-by-fours weren't any good any longer, because it was too late to get the other side of the maple in time to keep it from bending in that direction. The Swede with the double-bladed ax took one more swing, and the tree began to bend towards the ground.

The tree came down, the little Swede came down, and the big yellow tom came down on top of everything, holding for all he was worth to the top of the little Swede's head. Long before the tree and the boy struck the ground, the big yellow tom had sprung what looked like thirty feet, and landed in the middle of Mrs. Frost's flowers and bulbs. The little Swede let out a yell and a whoop when he hit the ground that brought out six-seven more Swedes from that three storey, six room house, piling out into the road like it was the first time they had ever heard a kid bawl. The women Swedes and the little Swedes and the big Swedes piled out on Jim and Mrs. Frost's front lawn like they had been dropped out of a dump-truck and didn't know which was straight up from straight down.

I thought Mrs. Frost was going to have a fit right then and there in the kitchen window. When she saw that swarm of Swedes coming across her lawn, and the big yellow tom cat in her flower bed among the tender plants and bulbs, digging up the things she had planted, and the Swedes with their No. 12 heels squashing the green shoots she had been nursing along—well, I guess she just sort of caved in, and fell out of sight for the time being. I didn't have time to run to see what was wrong with her, because Jim and me had to tear out behind the tom and the Swedes to try to save as much as we could.

"Good God, Stan," Jim shouted at me, "go run in the house and ring up all the neighbors on the line, and tell them to hurry over here and help us before the Swedes wreck my farm and buildings. There's no telling what they'll do next. They'll be setting fire to the house and barn the next thing, maybe. Hurry, Stan!"

I didn't have time to waste talking to the neighbors on the telephone line. I was right behind Jim and the Swedes to see what they were going to do next.

"I pay you good pay, Stan," Jim said, "and I want my money's worth. Now, you go ring up the neighbors and tell them to hurry."

The big yellow tom made one more spring when he hit the flower bed, and that leap landed him over the stone wall. He struck out for the deep woods with every Swede on the place behind him. When Jim and me got to the stone wall, I pulled up short and held Jim back.

"Well, Jim," I said, "if you want me to, I'll go down in the woods and raise hell with every Swede on the place for cutting down your young maple and tearing up Mrs. Frost's flower-bed."

We turned around and there was Mrs. Frost, right behind us. There was no knowing how she got there so quick after the Swedes had left for the woods.

"My crown in heaven," Mrs. Frost said, running up to Jim and holding on to him. "Jim, don't let Stanley make the Swedes mad. This is the only place we have got to live in, and they'll be here a year now this time, maybe two-three, if the hard times don't get better soon."

"That's right, Stan," he said. "You don't know the Swedes like we do. You would have to be a Swede yourself to know what to tell them. Don't go over there doing anything like that."

"God-helping, Jim," I said, "you and Mrs. Frost aren't scared of the Swedes, are you?"

"Good God, no," he said, his eyes popping out; "but don't go making them mad."

The Biscuit Eater

BY

JAMES STREET

LONNIE SET the greasy bag of table scraps on a hummock of wire grass and leaned over the branch, burying his face in the cool water. He wiped his mouth with the back of his hand. Hundreds of black, frisky water bugs, aroused at his invasion of their playground, scooted to the middle of the stream, swerved as though playing follow-the-leader, and scooted back to the bank.

The boy laughed at their capers. Slowly, he stooped over the water. His hands darted as a cottonmouth strikes and he snatched one of the bugs and smelled it. There was a sharp, sugary odor on the bug.

"A sweet stinker, sure as my name is Lonnie McNeil," the boy muttered. If you caught a sweet stinker among water bugs, it meant good luck, maybe. Everybody knew that. Lonnie held the bug behind him, closed his eyes, tilted his head and whispered, to the pine trees, the branch, the wire grass and anything else in the silence that wanted to hear him and would never tell his wish: "I hope Moreover is always a good dog."

Then Lonnie put the bug back in the branch. It darted in circles for a second and skedaddled across the creek, making a beeline for the other bugs. There were tiny ripples in its wake. The boy grinned. He was in for some good luck. If the sweet stinker had changed its course, it would have broken the charm.

He picked up his bag of scraps, crossed the branch on a log and moseyed to the edge of the woods where the cleared land began. He pursed his lower lip and whistled the call of the catbird, watching the cabin in the field where Text lived with his mother, Aunt Charity, and her brood. Old Charity had a heap of young'uns, but Text was the last. She had listened to her preacher for days during protracted meetings, seeking a fit'n name for her manchild. And because the evangelist took text from this and text from that, she named him Text and reckoned it was a name that God approved. Or else the preacher wouldn't have used it so much.

Lonnie saw Text run to the rickety front gallery of the cabin and listen. He whistled again. Text answered and ran around the house, and a minute later he was racing across the field with a big, brooding dog at his heels. The white boy opened his arms and the dog ran to him and tried to lick his face.

Text said, "Hydee, Lon, Ol' Morever is glad to see you. Me and him both."

Lonnie said, "Hi, Text. He looks slick as el-lem sap, don't he? Been working him?"

"A heap and whole lot," said Text. "Turned him loose in the wire grass yestiddy and he pointed two coveys 'fore I could say, 'Law 'a' mercy.' He's a prime superfine bird dawg, Lon. He ain't no no-'count biscuit eater."

Lonnie, the son of Harve McNeil, and Text had been friends long before they had got the dog on a mine-and-yours basis, but now they were inseparable. Moreover, the dog was community property between them, and their community was the piney woods of South Alabama, where Lonnie's father trained fine bird-dogs for Mr. Ames. The dog had wiped away all class and race barriers between the two.

Moreover's mother had run in the Grand National trials up at Grand Junction, Tennessee—the world series for bird-dogs. Then Mr. Ames had sold her. Moreover's father was a good dog until he killed one of Mr. Eben's sheep, and was shot, according to the code of the piney woods. Harve knew the pup, the outcast of the litter, had a bad streak in him, but had tried to train him only because Lonnie loved the pup. And Lonnie loved him only because nobody else did.

Harve never had been able to get close to the dog's affections. There had been no feeling between them, no understanding. The pup had cowered at Lonnie's feet when Harve had ordered him into the fields to hunt. And when Harve had caught him sucking eggs, he had given him away to a Negro across the ridge.

"He's a suck-egg biscuit eater," Harve had told the Negro. A biscuit eater was an ornery dog. Everybody knew that. A biscuit eater wouldn't hunt anything except his biscuits and wasn't worth the salt in his feed.

The Negro had accepted the dog because he knew he could swap him. That night the dog had stolen eggs from the Negro's henhouse and the Negro had beaten him and called him a low-life biscuit eater. The dog had run under the cabin and sulked.

When Lonnie learned what his father had done with the outcast, he went to Text, and together they went over the ridge to bargain for the dog.

The Negro man was wily. He sensed a good bargain and was trader enough to know that if he low-rated the dog, the boys would want him more than ever. The dog had a cotton rope around his neck and the rope was fastened to a block, and when the dog walked, his head was pulled sideways as he tugged the block. The dog walked to Lonnie and rubbed against his legs. The boy ignored him. He mustn't let the Negro man know he really wanted the dog. The man grabbed the rope and jerked the dog away.

"He's a biscuit eater!" The Negro nudged the dog with his foot. The animal looked sideways at his master and slunk away. "He ain't worth much."

"He's a suck-egg biscuit eater, ain't he?" Lonnie asked. The dog watched him, and when the boy said "biscuit eater" the dog ran under the cabin, pulling the block behind him. "He's scared." Lonnie said. "You been beating him. And ever' time you jump him and you call him 'biscuit eater.' That's how come he's scared. Whatcha take for him?"

The man said, "Whatcha gimme?"

"I'll give you my frog-sticker." Lonnie showed his knife. "And I got a pretty good automobile tire. Ain't but one patch in it. It'd make a prime superfine swing for your young'uns."

The Negro asked Text, "What'll you chip in to boot?"

Text said, "You done cussed out the dawg so far I don't want no share of him. You done low-rated him too much. If he sucks eggs at my house, my maw'll bust me in two halves. Whatcha want to boot?"

"Whatcha got?"

"Nothin'," said Text, "cep'n two big hands what can tote a heap of wood. Tote your shed full of light'r knots for boot."

"What else?"

Text thought for a minute, weighing the deal. "Lon wants that dawg. I know where there's a pas'l of May haws and a honeybee tree."

The Negro man said, "It's a deal, boys, if'n you pick me a lard bucket full of May haws and show me the bee tree."

Lonnie took the block from the dog and led him across the field. Then Text led him awhile. Out of sight of the Negro's shack, the boys stopped and examined their possession.

Text ran his hand over the dog, smoothing the fur. "He's a good dawg, ain't he, Lon? Look at them ol' eyes, and them big ol' feet, and that big ol' long tail. Bet he can point birds from here to yonder. Betcha if he tried, he can point partridge on light bread. What we gonna name him, Lon?"

Lonnie said, "Dunno, Text. But listen, don't ever call him—" He looked at the dog, then at Text. "You know." He held his fingers in the shape of a biscuit and pantomimed as though he were eating. The dog didn't understand. Neither did Text. So Lonnie whispered, "You know, 'biscuit eater.' Don't ever call him that. That's what's the matter with him. He expects a beating when he hears it."

"It's a go," Text whispered. "Let's name him Moreover. It's in the Bible."

"Where'bouts?"

"I heard the preacher say so. He said, 'Moreover, the dog,' and he was reading from the Bible."

Lonnie held the dog's chin with one hand and stroked his chest with the other. "He's Moreover then. He's a good dog, Text. And he's ours. You keep him and I'll furnish the rations. I can snitch 'em from papa. Will Aunt Charity raise Cain if you keep him?"

"Naw," said Text. "I 'member the time that big ol' brother of mine, ol' First-and-Second-Thessalonians, fetched a goat home, and maw didn't low-rate him. She just said she had so many young'uns, she didn't mind a goat. I spects she feels the same way 'bout a dawg, if'n he's got a Bible name."

"I reckon so too," said Lonnie, and ran home and told his father about the deal.

Harve told his son, "It's all right for you and Text to keep the dog, but keep him away from over here. I don't want him running around my good dogs."

Lonnie said, "He's a good dog, papa. He just ain't had no chance."

Harve looked at his son. The boy was growing, and the man was proud. "I'm going to work Silver Belle in the south forty," he said. "Want to come along?"

Lonnie shook his head. Harve knew then how much the boy loved his new dog; for, ordinarily, Lonnie would have surrendered any pleasure to accompany his father when he worked Silver Belle. She was the finest pointer in the Ames kennels and Harve had trained her since puppyhood. Already, she had won the Grand National twice. A third win would give his employer permanent possession of the Grand National trophy, and Harve wanted to win the prize for Mr. Ames more than he wanted anything in the world. He pampered Silver Belle. She was a small pointer—so small she had to wear a silver bell when hunting in the tall sage.

After his father and Silver Belle were gone, Lonnie collected the table scraps and went across the branch to Text's.

"Let's work him across the ridge today," Lonnie said. "Papa's got Silver Belle in the south forty and he won't want us and Moreover around."

Text said, "It's a go, Lon. I'll snitch ol' First-and-Second-Thessalonians' shotgun and meet you 'cross the ridge. But that there lan' over there is pow'ful close to Mr. Eben's place. I don't want no truck with that man."

"I ain't afraid of Mr. Eben," said Lonnie.

"Well, I am. And so are you! And so is your paw."

"Papa is not afraid of anything, and I'll bust you in two halves if you say so."

"Then how come he didn't whup Mr. Eben when Mr. Eben kicked his dawg about two years ago?"

Negroes heard everything and forgot nothing. Everybody in the county had wondered why Harve McNeil hadn't thrashed Eben, when the farmer kicked one of the McNeil dogs without cause.

Lonnie was ashamed. He said, "Papa didn't whip Mr. Eben 'cause mother asked him not to, that's why."

"Lady folks sho' are buttinskies," Text said. "All time trying to keep men folks from whupping each other. Lady folks sho' are scutters. All 'cept your maw and my maw, huh, Lon?"

Lonnie said, "Mr. Eben is just a crotchety man. Mother said so. He don't mean no harm."

"That's what you say," Text said. "But he's a scutter from way back. Maw says when he kills beeves he drinks the blood, and Ise popeyed scared of him. His lan' say, 'Posted. Keep off. Law.' And I ain't messin' around over there."

Lonnie often had worked dogs with his father and had seen the best run at field trials. He began training Moreover by inspiring confidence in him. The big dog was clumsy, but Lonnie never up- braided him. When Moreover showed a streak of good traits, Lon- nie and Text patted him. When he erred, they simply ignored him. The dog had a marvelous range, and moved through the saw grass at an easy gait, never tiring. He was not spectacular, but constant. He ran with a sort of awkward lope, twisting his head as though he still were tugging a block. But he covered ground. Day after day he trained and worked until the boys panted and stretched on the ground. Then he stood over them.

He had a strange point. He would cock his long head in the air, then turn it slowly toward Lonnie as he came to a point. His tail was like a ramrod. The first time Text shot over him, he cowered. The boys showed their displeasure by ignoring him. He soon was no longer gun-shy and he worked for the sheer joy of working.

"He sho' is a good dawg," Text said.

They were working him that day across the ridge near Eben's farm and Moreover, trailing a huge covey, raced through the stub- ble and disappeared in the sage. When the boys found him he was frozen on a point far inside Farmer Eben's posted land. And watch- ing Moreover from a pine thicket was Eben, a shotgun held loosely in the crook of his arm.

Text was terror-stricken and gaped at Eben as though the stubble-faced man were an ogre. Lonnie took one look at his dog, then at the man, and walked to the thicket. Text was in his shadow. "Please don't shoot him, Mr. Eben," Lonnie said.

The farmer said, "Huh?"

"Naw, suh, please don't shoot him." Text found his courage. "He couldn't read yo' posted sign."

Eben scowled. "I don't aim to shoot him. That is, less'n he gets round my sheep. I was watching his point. Right pretty, ain't it?"

Lonnie said, "Mighty pretty. He's a good dog, Mr. Eben. If you ever want a mess of birds, I'll give you the loan of him."

"Nothing shaking," Eben said. "He's that biscuit eater your paw gave that Negro over the ridge."

Text protested. "Don't go calling him biscuit eater, please, suh. He don't like it."

"He can't read my posted sign, but he can understand English, huh?" Eben laughed. "Well, get him off'n my land or I'll sprinkle him with bird shot."

Lonnie whistled and Moreover broke the point and followed him.

At supper, Lonnie asked his father, "How come you didn't whip Mr. Eben that time he kicked your dog?"

Harve said, "I've had my share of fighting, son. I don't fight for such foolishness any more. How come you ask?"

"Just 'cause," Lonnie said, and Harve knew his son wasn't satisfied with the reply. He frowned and glanced at his wife. He hadn't punished Eben simply because he didn't think the crime of kicking a dog justified a beating. There had been a time when he thought differently. But he was older now, and respected. He wondered if Lonnie thought he was afraid of Eben, and the thought bothered him.

"I wish we had the papers on Moreover," Lonnie changed the subject. "I want to register him."

Harve said, "I've got the papers, son. You can have 'em. What you gonna do, run your dog against my Belle in the county-seat trials?" He was joshing the boy.

"That's what I aim to do," Lonnie said.

The father laughed loudly, and his laughter trailed off into a chuckle. Lonnie enjoyed hearing his father laugh that way. "It's a great idea, son. So you have trained that biscuit eater for the trials! Where you going to get your entry fee?"

"He ain't no biscuit eater!" Lonnie said defiantly.

His mother was startled at his impudence to his father. But Harve shook his head at his wife and said, " 'Course he ain't, son. I'm sorry. And just to show that me and Belle ain't scared of you and Moreover, I'll give you and Text the job of painting around the kennels. You can earn your entry fee. Is it a go?"

"Yes-sirree, bob," Lonnie stuffed food in his mouth and hurried through his meal. "I'm going to high-tail it over and tell Text and Moreover."

Harve walked down the front path with his son. The boy reached to his shoulders. It was nice to walk down the path with his son. The father said simply and in man's talk, "Maybe I'm batty to stake you and your dog to your entry fee. You might whip me and Belle, and Mr. Ames might give you my job of training his dogs."

Lonnie didn't reply. But at the gate he paused and faced his father. "Papa, you ain't scared of Mr. Eben, are you?"

The trainer leaned against the gate and lit his pipe. "Son," he said, "I ain't scared of nothing but God. But don't tell your mother."

Mr. Ames, the Philadelphia sportsman, sat on the steps of the gun-club lodge and laughed when he saw his truck coming up the driveway. His cronies, who had come to the county seat for the trials —a sort of minor-league series—laughed too. Harve was driving. Silver Belle was beside him. Lonnie and Text were on the truck bed with dogs all around them, and behind the truck, tied with a cotton rope, loped Moreover. Mr. Ames shook hands with his trainer and met the boys.

"We got competition," Harve said, and nodded toward Moreover.

Ames studied the big dog. "By Joe, Harve! That used to be my dog. Is that the old bis—"

"Sh-h-h!" Harve commanded. "Don't say it. It hurts the dog's feelings. Or so the boys say."

Ames understood. He had a son at home. He walked around Moreover and looked at him. "Mighty fine dog, boys . . . If he beats Belle, I might hire you, Lonnie, and fire your father." He winked at Harve, but the boys didn't see him.

They took Moreover to the kennels. They had fetched their own feed. Text ran to the kitchen of the lodge, and soon had a job doing kitchen chores. Moreover's rations were assured, and the best. Lonnie bedded his dog down carefully and combed him and tried to make him look spruce. But Moreover would not be spruce. There was a quizzical look in his eyes. The other dogs took attention as though they expected it, but Moreover rubbed his head along the ground and scratched his ears against the kennel box and mussed himself up as fast as Lonnie cleaned him. But he seemed to know that Lonnie expected something of him.

All the other dogs were yelping and were nervous. But Moreover just flopped on his side and licked Lonnie's hands.

Inside the lodge, Ames asked Harve, "How's Belle?"

"Tiptop," said Harve. "She'll win hands down here, and I'm laying that she'll take the Grand National later. I'm gonna keep my boy with me, Mr. Ames. Text can stay with the help."

"What do those kids expect to do with that biscuit eater?" Ames laughed.

"You know how boys are. I'll bet this is the first time in history a colored boy and a white boy ever had a joint entry in a field trial. They get riled if anybody calls him a biscuit eater."

"Can't blame them, Harve," Ames said. "I get mad if anybody makes fun of my dogs. We are all alike, men and boys."

"You said it. Since the first, I reckon, boys have got mad if a fellow said anything against their mothers or dogs."

"Or fathers." Ames suggested.

"Depends on the father," said Harve. "Wish Lonnie could take his dog to the quarter finals, or thereabouts. Do the boy a heap of good."

They were having a drink by the big fireplace. Ames said, "I hope that big brute is not in a brace with Belle. She's a sensitive dog." Then he laughed. "Be funny, Harve, if that dog whipped us. I'd run you bowlegged."

All the men laughed, but when the waiter told the pantry maid the story, he neglected to say that the threat was a jest. The pantry maid told the barkeeper. The barkeeper told the cook, and by the time the story was circulated around the kitchen, the servants were whispering that rich Mr. Ames had threatened to fire poor Mr. Harve because his son had fetched a biscuit eater to the field trials.

The morning of the first run, Text met Lonnie at the kennels, and together they fed Moreover. "Let's put some good ol' gunpowder in his vittles," Text said. "Make him hunt better."

"Aw, that's superstition," said Lonnie.

"I don't care what it is, it helps," said Text.

Lonnie couldn't see any need of tempting luck, so Moreover was fed a sprinkling of gunpowder.

Text said, "I got my lucky buckeye along. We bound to have luck, Lon."

Lonnie was getting too big for such foolishness, but then he remembered. "I caught a sweet stinker not so long ago," he whispered. "And he swum the right way."

"A good ol' sweet-stinking mellow bug?" asked Text eagerly. "Lon, good luck gonna bust us in two halves."

Harve took Siver Belle out with an early brace and the pointer completely outclassed her rival. Her trainer sent her back to her kennel and went into the fields with Ames to watch Moreover in his first brace. He was braced with a rangy setter. Even the judges smiled at the two boys and their dog. Text, in keeping with rules of the sport, gave not an order. Lonnie put Moreover down on the edge of a clover field and the big dog rolled over, then jumped up and loped around the boy, leaping on him and licking his face. Lonnie and Text walked into the field, and Moreover followed. Lonnie whistled shrilly. The big dog jerked up his head, cocked it and began casting. He ranged to the edge of the field and worked in. He loped past a patch of saw grass, wheeled and pointed, his head cocked toward Lonnie, his right leg poised and his tail stiff as a poker.

Lonnie kept his dog on the point until the judges nodded, then whistled him off of it. He called Moreover to the far edge of the field and set him ranging again. He was on a point in a flash.

Ames looked at Harve. "That's a good dog, McNeil. He's trained beautifully. He'll go to the finals with us, sure as shooting."

Harve was beaming with pride. "It proves what I've always preached," Harve said; "that a bird dog will work for a man, if the man understands him. I couldn't do anything with that dog, but he will go to hell and back for my boy and Text."

Silver Belle and Moreover swept through the quarter and semifinals, and news that father and son would be matched in the finals, with the famous Belle and a biscuit eater, brought sportsmen and sports writers swarming to the county seat. Harve and Lonnie slept and ate together, but the man didn't discuss the contest with his son. He didn't want to make him nervous. He treated Lonnie as he would any other trainer. He knew that boys could sense condescension if adults eased up in games and that boys never want their fathers to make things too easy for them.

Harve took Silver Belle to the edge of a field of stubble, and she stood motionless as he snapped a tiny silver bell around her neck. He arose from his knees, patted her fondly and whispered, "Go get 'em girl."

The little pointer dashed into the stubble and soon was out of sight. Moreover rubbed against Lonnie's legs and watched her for a minute, then trotted along her path. There was no order between Lonnie and his dog, only understanding.

The men listened for the tingling of the silver bell that told them the champion was still casting. Through the brush the men sauntered, their sense alert. Suddenly the bell hushed.

Belle was on a point. The delicate little animal was rigid. Her trim body was thrown forward a bit, her nose, perfectly tilted, was aimed toward a clump of sage. She didn't fleck a muscle. She might have been made of marble.

The judges nodded approval. Harve motioned to Belle. She took two steps, stopped, then two more. A roar of wings, a whistle of flight, and the covey of partridge was away like feathered lightning. Guns thundered. Belle didn't bat an eye as the salvo cracked over her. When the echoes died, she began fetching, and when the last bird was laid at Harve's feet, she dashed into the sage again, seeking the singles.

Lonnie had held Moreover while Belle worked. Now he turned the big dog loose. Moreover swung along through the sage at an easy gait. He cast a bit to the right, stuck his nose almost to the ground and found the trail Belle had just made. Then he broke into an easy trot. He never depended on ground scents, but on body scents, and kept his nose high enough to catch any smells the wind blew his way.

About a hundred yards back up Belle's trail, Moreover suddenly broke his trot and eased his nose higher in the air. Then he jerked his head toward Lonnie and froze to a point. His right leg came up slowly, deliberately. He cocked his head in that strange fashion, and the quizzical, comical look came in his eyes. Moreover was a still hunter. He never waited for orders. He held the birds until Lonnie clicked the safety off of his gun. When Moreover heard the click, he began creeping toward the covey. He didn't budge as Lonnie began dropping the birds, and then, without orders, he fetched the dead birds and began casting for singles.

The judges whistled softly. "Most beautiful dog work I ever saw," whispered one. Ames' face took on a worried look. So did Harve's. The big dog had picked up a covey right under Belle's nose.

Belle settled down to hunt. She seemed everywhere. She dashed to a point on the fringe of a cornfield, then held another covey while Harve weeded out the first. She raced over the ridge, her nose picking up scents in almost impossible places. Moreover just loped along, but every time Belle got a covey, he would cast for a few minutes, point, fetch and wait for her to set the pace. She was hunting because she was bred to hunt. He was hunting from habit and because Lonnie expected him to.

It was exasperating. Belle tried every tirck of her training, but her skill was no match for his stamina. Her heart was pumping rapidly and she was tired when the men knocked off for lunch. Text ran back to the lodge to fetch food to the field. He strutted into the kitchen and told the servants that Moreover was running Silver Belle ragged.

The servants shook their heads, and one told him that Mr. Ames would fire Harve if Moreover beat Belle. Text couldn't swallow his food. He waited around the fringe of hunters until he caught Lonnie's eye, and motioned to him. "That Mr. Ames sho' is a scutter," said Text, after he told his story. "He's worse'n Mr. Eben. What we goin' do, Lon?"

Lonnie said, "He's half your dog, Text. What you say?"

"We can't let yo' paw get in no trouble on account of us, Lon. He got to have a job."

Lonnie nodded and bit his lip. He noticed that his father's face was drawn as the contest was renewed. Ames was nervous. The two men had worked for years to get Belle to perfection, and win the Grand National for the third time. And here an outcast dog was hunting her heart out at a minor meet. Lonnie thought his father was worried about his job and that Ames was angry.

His mind was made up. He watched Moreover leap across a creek, then race into a field of clover. He and Text were right behind him. Moreover came to his point, jerked his head toward his master and waited.

Lonnie cupped his hands and said hoarsely, "Hep!" It was an order Moreover never had heard. He turned and faced Lonnie. The judges gasped when the big dog left his point. Harve was puzzled.

Ames whispered, "He's breaking. That good-for-nothing streak is cropping out."

"Hep!" Lonnie said it again. The judges didn't hear. Moreover deserted the covey and walked to Lonnie and looked up. Lonnie shouted, "Back to your point, you low-life biscuit eater!"

Moreover tucked his tail between his legs and ran to the lodge and hid under it. Lonnie and Text followed him, without a word to the judges.

Ames looked at Harve for an explanation, and Harve said, "I don't get it. My son called his dog off. He quit."

It took Lonnie and Text a long time to coax Moreover from under the lodge. The dog crawled to Lonnie's feet and rolled over. Lonnie patted him, but Moreover didn't lick his face. The boys were with their dog in the kennel when the prize was awarded to Harve and Silver Belle.

"His feelings are hurt," Lonnie told Text as Moreover lay down and thumped his tail. . . . "I'm sorry I said it, Moreover. I had to."

Text said, "We sorry, puppy dawg. But us had to, didn't we, Lon?"

They loaded the truck, and Harve had his boy sit on the front seat by him. They said good-by and rolled away.

Harve said to Lonnie, "How come you did that, son?"

Lonnie didn't reply and the father didn't press the point. Finally, he said, "Don't ever quit, son, if you are winning or losing. It ain't fair to the dog."

"My dog is mad at me," Lonnie said.

"We'll give him a beef heart when we get home. His feelings are hurt because you threw him down. But he'll be all right. Dogs are not like folks. They'll forgive a fellow." He knew Lonnie had a reason for what he had done, and he knew that if his son wanted him to know the reason, he would tell him.

Back home, Lonnie cooked a beef heart for Moreover and took the plate to the back gallery where the dog was tied.

Harve said, "Untie him, son. You can let him run free over here. You don't ever have to keep him over at Text's house, unless you want to."

He untied his dog and put the food before him. Moreover sniffed the food and toyed with it. He never had had such good food before. Lonnie and his father went back into the house.

After supper, Lonnie went to see about his dog. The meat hadn't been touched and Moreover was gone.

Harve said, "He's probably gone back to Text's house."

Lonnie said, "I'm going after him."

"I'll go with you," said Harve, and got a lantern.

Text hadn't seen the dog. He joined the search and the three hunted through the woods for an hour or so, Lonnie whistling for Moreover, and Text calling him, "Heah, heah, fellow. Heah."

Harve sat on a stump, put the lantern down and called the boys to him. He had seen only a few dogs that would refuse to eat beef heart as Moreover had done.

"Text," he said sharply, "did Moreover ever suck eggs at your place?"

Text rolled his eyes and looked at Lonnie. "Yes, suh." He was afraid to lie to Harve. "But I didn't tell Lon. I didn't want to hurt his feelings. Moreover was a suck-egger, good and proper."

Harve said, "Go on, tell us about it."

"Maw put hot pepper in a raw egg, but it didn't break him. My ol' brother, ol' First-and-Second-Thessalonians, reckoned he'd kill Moreover less'n he quit suck-egging. So I got to snitching two eggs ever' night and feeding him with 'em. He sho' did like eggs, Mr. Harve, and we had plenty of eggs."

Lonnie said sharply, "You hadn't ought to have done that, Text."

Harve said, "Did you feed him eggs tonight?"

"Naw, suh," said Text. I reckoned he had vittles at yo' house. We had done gathered all the eggs and maw had counted them by nightfall."

Harve got up. "I'm worried. Let's walk up the branch. . . . Text, you take the left side. . . . Lonnie, you take the right side. I'll walk up the bank."

Lonnie found Moreover's body, still warm, only a few feet from the water. He stooped over his dog, put the lantern by his head, and opened his mouth. The dog had been poisoned. Lonnie straightened. He didn't cry. His emotions welled up within him, and, having no outlet, hurt him.

"I'm sorry I called him a biscuit eater," he said simply.

Text said, "He was trying to get to water. I sho hate to think of him dying, wanting just one swallow of good ol' water."

"Who killed him, papa?" Lonnie turned to his father.

The man picked up the lantern and walked away, the boys at his heels. They walked over the ridge to Eben's house, and Harve pounded on the front gallery until the farmer appeared.

"My boy's dog is dead," Harve said. "Reckoned you might know something about it."

Eben said, "If he was poisoned, I do. He's a suck-egg dog. I put poison in some eggs and left them in the field. Seems he must have committed suicide, McNeil."

"Seems you made it powerful easy for him to get those poisoned eggs," Harve said.

"Ain't no room round here for suck-egg dogs. His daddy was a sheep killer, too. It's good riddance. You ain't no cause to jump me, Harve McNeil."

Harve said, "He's right, boys. A man's got a right to poison eggs on his own land, and if a dog sucks 'em and dies, the dog's to blame."

Eben said, "Reckon you young'uns want to bury that dog. Buzzards will be thick tomorrow. You can have the loan of my shovel."

Lonnie looked at the man a long time. He bit his lip so he couldn't cry. "Me and Text will dig a hole with a stick," he said, and turned away.

"You boys go bury him," Harve said. "I'll be home in a few minutes."

Lonnie and Text walked silently into the woods. Text said, "He sho was a good dog, huh, Lon? You ain't mad at me 'cause I fed him eggs, are you, Lon?"

"No, Text. Let's wait up here and watch papa. He can't see us."

Back at Eben's gallery, Harve said, "I would have paid you for all the eggs the dog took, Eben. My boy loved that dog a heap."

"Looka heah!" Eben said. "I know my rights."

"I know mine," Harve said. "I always pay my debts, Eben. And I always collect them. I ain't got no cause to get riled because that dog stole poisoned eggs. You were mighty low-life to plant 'em, though. But two years ago you kicked one of my dogs."

"He barked at me and scared my team on the road," Eben said.

"A dog has a right to bark," Harve said, and reached up and grabbed Eben by the collar.

"I'll law you!" Eben shouted.

Harve didn't reply. He slapped the man with his open palm, and when Eben squared off to fight, Harve knocked him down.

In the shadows of the woods, Lonnie whispered to Text, "What did I tell you? My papa ain't scared of nothing cep'n God."

They buried their dog near the branch. Text poured water in the grave. "I can't stand to think of him wanting water when there's a heap of water so close. Reckon if he could have got to the ol' branch he could have washed out that poison? Reckon, Lon?"

"Maybe so."

They were walking to Lonnie's house. "My ol' buckeye and your sweet-stinking mellow bug ain't helped us much, eh, Lon? Luck is plumb mad at us, ain't it, Lon?"

Lonnie waited at the gate until his father arrived. "Me and Text saw the fight," he said. "I won't tell mother. Women are scutters, ain't they, papa? Always trying to keep men folks from fighting."

"I'll give you boys another dog, son," Harve said. He peered into the darkness and saw a car parked behind his house, then hurried inside. Mr. Ames was warming himself by the fire and talking with Mrs. McNeil. She went to the kitchen to brew coffee, and left the men alone, after calling for Lonnie and Text to follow her.

Ames said, "I heard why your boy called his dog off. Call him and that little colored boy in here. I can't go back East with those boys thinking what they do of me."

Lonnie and Text stood by the fire and Ames said, "That story you heard about me isn't so. I wouldn't have fired this man if your dog had won. We were joking about it and the servants got the story all wrong. I just wanted you boys to know that."

Harve said, "Yes. But even if Mr. Ames would have fired me, it wouldn't have made any difference. You did what you thought was right, but you were wrong. Don't ever quit a race, once you start it."

Lonnie told Mr. Ames, "My dog is dead. I'm sorry I called him a biscuit eater. He wasn't. I just want you to know that."

Ames lit his pipe and passed his tobacco pouch to Harve. He saw Harve's bloody hand as the trainer accepted the tobacco.

"Ran into some briers," Harve said.

"Lot of them around here." Ames' eyes twinkled. "Just been thinking, Harve. I got some fine pups coming along. You need help down here. Better hire a couple of good men. Know where you can get two good hands? They got to be men who can lose without grumbling and win without crowing."

Harve looked at Lonnie and Text, and smiled. "I know where I can get a couple of good men."

"All right," said Ames, and shook hands all around. "I've got to be going. Good night, men."

By the Waters of Babylon

BY

STEPHEN VINCENT BENÉT

THE NORTH and the west and the south are good hunting ground, but it is forbidden to go east. It is forbidden to go to any of the Dead Places except to search for metal and then he who touches the metal must be a priest or the son of a priest. Afterwards, both the man and the metal must be purified. These are the rules and the laws; they are well made. It is forbidden to cross the great river and look upon the place that was the Place of the Gods—this is most strictly forbidden. We do not even say its name though we know its name. It is there that spirits live, and demons—it is there that there are the ashes of the Great Burning. These things are forbidden —they have been forbidden since the beginning of time.

My father is a priest; I am the son of a priest. I have been in the Dead Places near us, with my father—at first, I was afraid. When my father went into the house to search for the metal, I stood by the door and my heart felt small and weak. It was a dead man's house, a spirit house. It did not have the smell of man, though there were old bones in a corner. But it is not fitting that a priest's son should show fear. I looked at the bones in the shadow and kept my voice still.

Then my father came out with the metal—a good, strong piece. He looked at me with both eyes but I had not run away. He gave me the metal to hold—I took it and did not die. So he knew that I was truly his son and would be a priest in my time. That was when I was very young—nevertheless my brothers would not have done it, though they are good hunters. After that, they gave me the good piece of meat and the warm corner by the fire. My father watched over me—he was glad that I should be a priest. But when I boasted or wept without a reason, he punished me more strictly than my brothers. That was right.

After a time, I myself was allowed to go into the dead houses and search for metal. So I learned the ways of those houses—and if I saw bones, I was no longer afraid. The bones are light and old—sometimes they will fall into dust if you touch them. But that is a great sin.

I was taught the chants and the spells—I was taught how to stop the running of blood from a wound and many secrets. A priest must know many secrets—that was what my father said. If the hunters think we do all things by chants and spells, they may believe so—it does not hurt them. I was taught how to read in the old books and how to make the old writings—that was hard and took a long time. My knowledge made me happy—it was like a fire in my heart. Most of all, I liked to hear of the Old Days and the stories of the gods. I asked myself many questions that I could not answer, but it was good to ask them. At night, I would lie awake and listen to the wind —it seemed to me that it was the voice of the gods as they flew through the air.

We are not ignorant like the Forest People—our women spin wool on the wheel, our priests wear a white robe. We do not eat grubs from the tree, we have not forgotten the old writings, although they are hard to understand. Nevertheless, my knowledge and my lack of knowledge burned in me—I wished to know more. When I was a man at last, I came to my father and said, "It is time for me to go on my journey. Give me your leave."

He looked at me for a long time, stroking his beard, then he said at last, "Yes. It is time." That night, in the house of the priesthood, I asked for and received purification. My body hurt but my spirit was a cool stone. It was my father himself who questioned me about my dreams.

He bade me look into the smoke of the fire and see—I saw and told what I saw. It was what I have always seen—a river, and, beyond it, a great Dead Place and in it the gods walking. I have always thought about that. His eyes were stern when I told him—he was no longer my father but a priest. He said, "This is a strong dream."

"It is mine," I said, while the smoke waved and my head felt light. They were singing the Star song in the outer chamber and it was like the buzzing of bees in my head.

He asked me how the gods were dressed and I told him how they were dressed. We know how they were dressed from the book, but I saw them as if they were before me. When I had finished, he threw the sticks three times and studied them as they fell.

"This is a very strong dream," he said. "It may eat you up."

"I am not afraid," I said and looked at him with both eyes. My voice sounded thin in my ears but that was because of the smoke.

He touched me on the breast and the forehead. He gave me the bow and the three arrows.

"Take them," he said. "It is forbidden to travel east. It is forbidden to cross the river. It is forbidden to go to the Place of the Gods. All these things are forbidden."

"All these things are forbidden," I said, but it was my voice that spoke and not my spirit. He looked at me again.

"My son," he said. "Once I had young dreams. If your dreams do not eat you up, you may be a great priest. If they eat you, you are still my son. Now go on your journey."

I went fasting, as is the law. My body hurt but not my heart. When the dawn came, I was out of sight of the village. I prayed and purified myself, waiting for a sign. The sign was an eagle. It flew east.

Sometimes signs are sent by bad spirits. I waited again on the flat rock, fasting, taking no food. I was very still—I could feel the sky above me and the earth beneath. I waited till the sun was beginning to sink. Then three deer passed in the valley, going east—they did not wind me or see me. There was a white fawn with them—a very great sign.

I followed them, at a distance, waiting for what would happen. My heart was troubled about going east, yet I knew that I must go. My head hummed with my fasting—I did not even see the panther spring upon the white fawn. But, before I knew it, the bow was in my hand. I shouted and the panther lifted his head from the fawn. It is not easy to kill a panther with one arrow but the arrow went through his eye and into his brain. He died as he tried to spring—he rolled over, tearing at the ground. Then I knew I was meant to go east—I knew that was my journey. When the night came, I made my fire and roasted meat.

It is eight suns' journey to the east and a man passes by many Dead Places. The Forest People are afraid of them but I am not. Once I made my fire on the edge of a Dead Place at night and, next morning, in the dead house, I found a good knife, little rusted. That was small to what came afterward but it made my heart feel big. Always when I looked for game, it was in front of my arrow, and twice I passed hunting parties of the Forest People without their knowing. So I knew my magic was strong and my journey clean, in spite of the law.

Toward the setting of the eighth sun, I came to the banks of the great river. It was half-a-day's journey after I had left the god-road —we do not use the god-roads now for they are falling apart into great blocks of stone, and the forest is safer going. A long way off, I had seen the water through trees but the trees were thick. At last, I came out upon an open place at the top of a cliff. There was the great river below, like a giant in the sun. It is very long, very wide. It could eat all the streams we know and still be thirsty. Its name is Ou-dis-sun, the Sacred, the Long. No man of my tribe had seen it, not even my father, the priest. It was magic and I prayed.

Then I raised my eyes and looked south. It was there, the Place of the Gods.

How can I tell what it was like—you do not know. It was there, in the red light, and they were too big to be houses. It was there with the red light upon it, mighty and ruined. I knew that in another moment the gods would see me. I covered my eyes with my hands and crept back into the forest.

Surely, that was enough to do, and live. Surely it was enough to spend the night upon the cliff. The Forest People themselves do not come near. Yet, all through the night, I knew that I should have to cross the river and walk in the places of the gods, although the gods ate me up. My magic did not help me at all and yet there was a fire in my bowels, a fire in my mind. When the sun rose, I thought, "My journey has been clean. Now I will go home from my journey." But, even as I thought so, I knew I could not. If I went to the place of the gods, I would surely die, but, if I did not go, I could never be at peace with my spirit again. It is better to lose one's life than one's spirit, if one is a priest and the son of a priest.

Nevertheless, as I made the raft, the tears ran out of my eyes. The Forest People could have killed me without fight, if they had come upon me then, but they did not come. When the raft was made, I said the sayings for the dead and painted myself for death. My heart was cold as a frog and my knees like water, but the burning in my mind would not let me have peace. As I pushed the raft from the shore, I began my death song—I had the right. It was a fine song.

"I am John, son of John," I sang. "My people are the Hill People. They are the men.
I go into the Dead Places but I am not slain.
I take the metal from the Dead Places but I am not blasted.
I travel upon the god-roads and am not afraid. E-yah! I have killed the panther, I have killed the fawn!
E-yah! I have come to the great river. No man has come there before.
It is forbidden to go east, but I have gone, forbidden to go on the great river, but I am there.
Open your hearts, you spirits, and hear my song.
Now I go to the place of the gods, I shall not return.
My body is painted for death and my limbs weak, but my heart is big as I go to the place of the gods!"

All the same, when I came to the Place of the Gods, I was afraid, afraid. The current of the great river is very strong—it gripped my raft with its hands. That was magic, for the river itself is wide and calm. I could feel evil spirits about me, in the bright morning; I could feel their breath on my neck as I was swept down the stream. Never have I been so much alone—I tried to think of my knowledge, but it was a squirrels' heap of winter nuts. There was no strength in my knowledge any more and I felt small and naked as a new-hatched bird—alone upon the great river, the servant of the gods.

Yet, after a while, my eyes were opened and I saw. I saw both banks of the river—I saw that once there had been god-roads across it, though now they were broken and fallen like broken vines. Very great they were, and wonderful and broken—broken in the time of the Great Burning when the fire fell out of the sky. And always the current took me nearer to the Place of the Gods, and the huge ruins rose before my eyes.

I do not know the customs of rivers—we are the People of the Hills. I tried to guide my raft with the pole but it spun around. I thought the river meant to take me past the Place of the Gods and out into the Bitter Water of the legends. I grew angry then—my heart felt strong. I said aloud, "I am a priest and the son of a priest!" The gods heard me—they showed me how to paddle with

the pole on one side of the raft. The current changed itself—I drew
near to the Place of the Gods.

When I was very near, my raft struck and turned over. I can swim
in our lakes—I swam to the shore. There was a great spike of rusted
metal sticking out into the river—I hauled myself up upon it and sat
there, panting. I had saved my bow and two arrows and the knife
I found in the Dead Place but that was all. My raft went whirling
downstream toward the Bitter Water. I looked after it, and thought
if it had trod me under, at least I would be safely dead. Nevertheless, when I had dried my bow-string and re-strung it, I walked
forward to the Place of the Gods.

It felt like ground underfoot; it did not burn me. It is not true
what some of the tales say, that the ground there burns forever, for
I have been there. Here and there were the marks and stains of the
Great Burning, on the ruins, that is true. But they were old marks
and old stains. It is not true either, what some of our priests say,
that it is an island covered with fogs and enchantments. It is not. It
is a great Dead Place—greater than any Dead Place we know. Everywhere in it there are god-roads, though most are cracked and
broken. Everywhere there are the ruins of the high towers of the
gods.

How shall I tell what I saw? I went carefully, my strung bow in
my hand, my skin ready for danger. There should have been the
wailings of spirits and the shrieks of demons, but there were not. It
was very silent and sunny where I had landed—the wind and the
rain and the birds that drop seeds had done their work—the grass
grew in the cracks of the broken stone. It is a fair island—no wonder
the gods built there. If I had come there, a god, I also would have
built.

How shall I tell what I saw? The towers are not all broken—here
and there one still stands, like a great tree in a forest, and the birds
nest high. But the towers themselves look blind, for the gods are
gone. I saw a fish-hawk, catching fish in the river. I saw a little dance
of white butterflies over a great heap of broken stones and columns.
I went there and looked about me—there was a carved stone with cut-
letters, broken in half. I can read letters but I could not understand
these. They said UBTREAS. There was also the shattered image
of a man or a god. It had been made of white stone and he wore his
hair tied back like a woman's. His name was ASHING, as I read on

the cracked half of a stone. I thought it wise to pray to ASHING, though I do not know that god.

How shall I tell what I saw? There was no smell of man left, on stone or metal. Nor were there many trees in that wilderness of stone. There are many pigeons, nesting and dropping in the towers —the gods must have loved them, or, perhaps, they used them for sacrifices. There are wild cats that roam the god-roads, green-eyed, unafraid of man. At night they wail like demons but they are not demons. The wild dogs are more dangerous, for they hunt in a pack, but them I did not meet till later. Everywhere there are the carved stones, carved with magical numbers or words.

I went North—I did not try to hide myself. When a god or a demon saw me, then I would die, but meanwhile I was no longer afraid. My hunger for knowledge burned in me—there was so much that I could not understand. After awhile, I knew that my belly was hungry. I could have hunted for my meat, but I did not hunt. It is known that the gods did not hunt as we do—they got their food from enchanted boxes and jars. Sometimes these are still found in the Dead Places—once, when I was a child and foolish, I opened such a jar and tasted it and found the food sweet. But my father found out and punished me for it strictly, for, often, that food is death. Now, though, I had long gone past what was forbidden, and I entered the likeliest towers, looking for the food of the gods.

I found it at last in the ruins of a great temple in the mid-city. A mighty temple it must have been, for the roof was painted like the sky at night with its stars—that much I could see, though the colors were faint and dim. It went down into great caves and tunnels—perhaps they kept their slaves there. But when I started to climb down, I heard the squeaking of rats, so I did not go—rats are unclean, and there must have been many tribes of them, from the squeaking. But near there, I found food, in the heart of a ruin, behind a door that still opened. I ate only the fruits from the jars—they had a very sweet taste. There was drink, too, in bottles of glass—the drink of the gods was strong and made my head swim. After I had eaten and drunk, I slept on the top of a stone, my bow at my side.

When I woke, the sun was low. Looking down from where I lay, I saw a dog sitting on his haunches. His tongue was hanging out of his mouth; he looked as if he were laughing. He was a big dog, with a grey-brown coat, as big as a wolf. I sprang up and shouted at him but he did not move—he just sat there as if he were laughing. I did not like that. When I reached for a stone to throw, he moved swiftly out of the way of the stone. He was not afraid of me; he looked at me as if I were meat. No doubt I could have killed him with an arrow, but I did not know if there were others. Moreover, night was falling.

I looked about me—not far away there was a great, broken god-road, leading North. The towers were high enough, but not so high, and while many of the dead-houses were wrecked, there were some that stood. I went toward this god-road, keeping to heights of the ruins, while the dog followed. When I had reached the god-road, I saw that there were others behind him. If I had slept later, they would have come upon me asleep and torn out my throat. As it was, they were sure enough of me; they did not hurry. When I went into the dead-house, they kept watch at the entrance—doubtless they thought they would have a fine hunt. But a dog cannot open a door and I knew, from the books, that the gods did not like to live on the ground but on high.

I had just found a door I could open when the dogs decided to rush. Ha! They were surprised when I shut the door in their faces—it was a good door, of strong metal. I could hear their foolish baying beyond it but I did not stop to answer them. I was in darkness—I found stairs and climbed. There were many stairs, turning around till my head was dizzy. At the top was another door—I found the knob and opened it. I was in a long small chamber—on one side of it was a bronze door that could not be opened, for it had no handle. Perhaps there was a magic word to open it but I did not have the word. I turned to the door in the opposite side of the wall. The lock of it was broken and I opened it and went in.

Within, there was a place of great riches. The god who lived there must have been a powerful god. The first room was a small ante-room—I waited there for some time, telling the spirits of the place that I came in peace and not as a robber. When it seemed to me that they had had time to hear me, I went on. Ah, what riches! Few, even, of the windows had been broken—it was all as it had been. The great windows that looked over the city had not been broken at all though they were dusty and streaked with many years. There were coverings on the floors, the colors not greatly faded, and the chairs were soft and deep. There were pictures upon the walls, very strange, very wonderful—I remember one of a bunch of flowers in a jar—if you came close to it, you could see nothing but bits of color, but if you stood away from it, the flowers might have been picked yesterday. It made my heart feel strange to look at this picture—and to look at the figure of a bird, in some hard clay, on a table and see it so like our birds. Everywhere there were books and writings, many in tongues that I could not read. The god who lived there must have been a wise god and full of knowledge. I felt I had right there, as I sought knowledge also.

Nevertheless, it was strange. There was a washing-place but no water—perhaps the gods washed in air. There was a cooking-place but no wood, and though there was a machine to cook food, there was no place to put fire in it. Nor were there candles or lamps—there were things that looked like lamps but they had neither oil nor wick. All these things were magic, but I touched them and lived—the magic had gone out of them. Let me tell one thing to show. In the washing-place, a thing said "Hot" but it was not hot to the touch—another thing said "Cold" but it was not cold. This must have been a strong magic but the magic was gone. I do not understand—they had ways—I wish that I knew.

It was close and dry and dusty in their house of the gods. I have said the magic was gone but that is not true—it had gone from the magic things but it had not gone from the place. I felt the spirits about me, weighing upon me. Nor had I ever slept in a Dead Place before—and yet, tonight, I must sleep there. When I thought of it, my tongue felt dry in my throat, in spite of my wish for knowledge. Almost I would have gone down again and faced the dogs, but I did not.

I had not gone through all the rooms when the darkness fell. When it fell, I went back to the big room looking over the city and made fire. There was a place to make fire and a box with wood in it, though I do not think they cooked there. I wrapped myself in a floor-covering and slept in front of the fire—I was very tired.

Now I tell what is very strong magic. I woke in the midst of the night. When I woke, the fire had gone out and I was cold. It seemed to me that all around me there were whisperings and voices. I closed my eyes to shut them out. Some will say that I slept again, but I do not think that I slept. I could feel the spirits drawing my spirit out of my body as a fish is drawn on a line.

Why should I lie about it? I am a priest and the son of a priest. If there are spirits, as they say, in the small Dead Places near us, what spirits must there not be in that great Place of the Gods? And would not they wish to speak? After such long years? I know that I felt myself drawn as a fish is drawn on a line. I had stepped out of my body—I could see my body asleep in front of the cold fire, but it was not I. I was drawn to look out upon the city of the gods.

It should have been dark, for it was night, but it was not dark. Everywhere there were lights—lines of light—circles and blurs of light—ten thousand torches would not have been the same. The sky itself was alight—you could barely see the stars for the glow in the sky. I thought to myself "This is strong magic" and trembled. There was a roaring in my ears like the rushing of rivers. Then my eyes grew used to the light and my ears to the sound. I knew that I was seeing the city as it had been when the gods were alive.

That was a sight indeed—yes, that was a sight: I could not have seen it in the body—my body would have died. Everywhere went the gods, on foot and in chariots—there were gods beyond number and counting and their chariots blocked the streets. They had turned night to day for their pleasure—they did not sleep with the sun. The noise of their coming and going was the noise of many waters. It was magic what they could do—it was magic what they did.

I looked out of another window—the great vines of their bridges were mended and the god-roads went East and West. Restless, restless, were the gods and always in motion! They burrowed tunnels under rivers—they flew in the air. With unbelievable tools they did giant works—no part of the earth was safe from them, for, if they wished for a thing, they summoned it from the other side of the world. And always, as they labored and rested, as they feasted and made love, there was a drum in their ears—the pulse of the giant city, beating and beating like a man's heart.

Were they happy? What is happiness to the gods? They were great, they were mighty, they were wonderful and terrible. As I looked upon them and their magic, I felt like a child—but a little more, it seemed to me, and they would pull down the moon from the sky. I saw them with wisdom beyond wisdom and knowledge beyond knowledge. And yet not all they did was well done—even I could see that—and yet their wisdom could not but grow until all was peace.

Then I saw their fate come upon them and that was terrible past speech. It came upon them as they walked the streets of their city. I have been in the fights with the Forest People—I have seen men die. But this was not like that. When gods war with gods, they use weapons we do not know. It was fire falling out of the sky and a mist that poisoned. It was the time of the Great Burning and the Destruction. They ran about like ants in the streets of their city—poor gods, poor gods! Then the towers began to fall. A few escaped—yes, a few. The legends tell it. But, even after the city had become a Dead Place, for many years the poison was still in the ground. I saw it happen, I saw the last of them die. It was darkness over the broken city and I wept.

All this, I saw. I saw it as I have told it, though not in the body. When I woke in the morning, I was hungry, but I did not think first of my hunger for my heart was perplexed and confused. I knew the reason for the Dead Places but I did not see why it had happened. It seemed to me it should not have happened, with all the magic they had. I went through the house looking for an answer. There was so much in the house I could not understand—and yet I am a priest and the son of a priest. It was like being on one side of the great river, at night, with no light to show the way.

Then I saw the dead god. He was sitting in his chair, by the window, in a room I had not entered before and, for the first moment, I thought that he was alive. Then I saw the skin on the back of his hand—it was like dry leather. The room was shut, hot and dry—no doubt that had kept him as he was. At first I was afraid to approach him—then the fear left me. He was sitting looking out over the city —he was dressed in the clothes of the gods. His age was neither young nor old—I could not tell his age. But there was wisdom in his face and great sadness. You could see that he would have not run away. He had sat at his window, watching his city die—then he himself had died. But it is better to lose one's life than one's spirit—and you could see from the face that his spirit had not been lost. I knew, that, if I touched him, he would fall into dust—and yet, there was something unconquered in the face.

That is all of my story, for then I knew he was a man—I knew then that they had been men, neither gods nor demons. It is a great knowledge, hard to tell and believe. They were men—they went a dark road, but they were men. I had no fear after that—I had no

fear going home, though twice I fought off the dogs and once I was
hunted for two days by the Forest People. When I saw my father
again, I prayed and was purified. He touched my lips and my breast,
he said, "You went away a boy. You come back a man and a priest."
I said, "Father, they were men! I have been in the Place of the Gods
and seen it! Now slay me, if it is the law—but still I know they
were men."

He looked at me out of both eyes. He said, "The law is not always
the same shape—you have done what you have done. I could not
have done it my time, but you come after me. Tell!"

I told and he listened. After that, I wished to tell all the people
but he showed me otherwise. He said, "Truth is a hard deer to hunt.
If you eat too much truth at once, you may die of the truth. It was
not idly that our fathers forbade the Dead Places." He was right—
it is better the truth should come little by little. I have learned that,
being a priest. Perhaps, in the old days, they ate knowledge too fast.

Nevertheless, we make a beginning. It is not for the metal alone
we go to the Dead Places now—there are the books and the writings.
They are hard to learn. And the magic tools are broken—but we can
look at them and wonder. At least, we make a beginning. And, when
I am chief priest we shall go beyond the great river. We shall go to
the Place of the Gods—the place new-york—not one man but a company. We shall look for the images of the gods and find the god
ASHING and the others—the gods Lincoln and Biltmore and Moses.
But they were men who built the city, not gods or demons. They
were men. I remember the dead man's face. They were men who
were here before us. We must build again.

The Lesson

BY

PEARL BUCK

"I HATE TO let Ru-lan go like this," said little Mrs. Stanley to her husband. "I don't believe she knows anything at all—she's not fit to be married."

She had just come in from the garden and her arms were full of roses, the swift-blooming, vivid roses of a Chinese May. Wyn Stanley looked at her, smiling, his heart caught in his throat at her loveliness. He and Mollie had been married five years but he never grew used to her. He saw her every day—how lucky it was that his work at the mission was to run the schools and not to be an itinerant evangelist! If he had had to go off on long preaching tours as Dr. Martin did, and be weeks away from Mollie, he could not have borne it. Sometimes in the night he woke to trouble and shivering, fearful lest God call him to such work, lest something happen that he and Mollie might have to be separated—suppose one of the children were to fall ill and have to be taken home across the sea to America like the Burgess child, and Mrs. Burgess away for nearly two years, or—he would put out his hand to touch Mollie's round little body lying deeply and healthfully asleep beside him. He would not wake her—but somehow she always woke and somehow he always told her his fears, and then wanted to hear her laugh her sweet contented laughter. "Oh Wyn, as if— Anyway, God hasn't called you to evangelistic work, has he? And if I had to go home you'd come too. We'd find another job. You suppose I'd *let* you stay here by yourself?" He was asleep before he knew it then.

Now he looked up at her from his desk, adoring her. She dimpled and put her hand on his cheek and pretended to pout. "You haven't heard a thing I've been saying. You never listen to me."

He caught her hand and held it to his lips, a little firm hand,

scratched with rose thorns. "It's because I can't keep from looking at you. What's going to happen to me if I keep loving you
more all the time?" He drew her to him and leaned his face against
her breast. Under his cheek he could feel the steady pounding of
her heart. "True heart—true heart—" he murmured to the rhythm
of her heart. She bent over his dark head, pressing it against her.
They both forgot the girl Ru-lan. They were swept back into the
summer morning five years ago in the little old churchyard behind the red brick church where her father had preached so many
years, and where Wyn had come as substitute for a month of vacation. She and her mother had sent her father off for the trip to
Palestine he had planned for a lifetime. What destiny it had been,
that on the summer when the family did not all go away together
Wyn had been the supply—just before he was to sail as a missionary
to China!

They had fallen in love at once. The first moment she saw his tall
young figure mounting the steps of the pulpit she knew him and
loved him. And he, when he looked over the congregation, saw her
and thereafter her only. And then in just a few weeks, that July
morning after church, when she was running home to the manse by
the short cut through the churchyard, he came striding after her,
still with his surplice on. He had, he said, meant only to ask her
to—to walk with him, perhaps, in the evening. But when she turned
and looked at him, under the deep shadows of the old elms and
hidden by the lilacs along the path, he had taken her into his arms
and enfolded her. There was no question asked and no answer
given, simply meeting. Whenever they came together it was the
same thing, the same deep union again—like this.

There was a small sound, and they jumped apart. The older mis-
sionaries always said, "The Chinese are not used to demonstration
between the sexes." Mrs. Burgess had taken her aside very soon and
said, "Try not to take your—Mr. Stanley's—hand in front of the
Chinese, dear. It is—they would consider it indelicate." So she and
Wyn had tried very hard to learn to wait until they were alone.
But hand went so instinctively to hand, his arm was around her so
naturally. Now they looked guiltily toward the door.

There she stood, Ru-lan, the girl she had come in to see Wyn
about, the poor stupid girl. She was standing there in the doorway, dressed in a clean blue cotton coat and trousers, with a blue

and white print handkerchief tied full of the books she never could learn. Her father had come for her to take her home to be married, and she was ready to go.

"Come in, Ru-lan," Mollie said. She smiled, her heart full of compassion. The girl's round placid face responded at once with a childlike pleasure. Above the large full cheeks her black eyes shone faintly. Mollie Stanley put down the roses and went over and took the girl's plump hand.

"I'm sorry you must go," she said in Chinese. "But your father will not consent to your staying longer. Sit down, child, and let me talk with you a little."

The girl sat down obediently, in silence. The smile had gone from her face now and she sat staring quietly at these two, observing all they did.

Mollie looked at her and was discouraged. She had so often in the school room faced that dense placidity.

"Wyn, what shall we do?" she asked, turning to him. "She's seventeen and she's been here ever since we came, and I don't believe she will ever learn much. She's been through all the classes—Bible and arithmetic and hygiene—she reads a few hundred characters and that's all you can say. She just isn't fit for marriage—such a good, faithful, kind, *stupid* girl! You know she came up for baptism twice, and she just can't remember enough to answer Dr. Martin's questions, however hard I coach her. I'm sometimes afraid she's still heathen."

"No, I know," answered Wyn. "It's no good her staying here. If she had any promise at all I'd try to persuade her father to let her finish at least the grades. But I haven't the heart to let him think she ever could finish. Maybe she'd better go on and be married."

"Wyn Stanley!" his wife cried out at him, "as if it weren't serious that a girl like that is to be married and have a lot of children! Of course she will have a lot of children!"

They both looked, troubled, at Ru-lan, who, meeting their eyes instantly broke into her great beaming smile, not understanding a word of their English. They were baffled by her smile.

"Do you know whom you are going to marry, Ru-lan?" asked Mollie gently in Chinese. The girl shook her head. "It is a landowner's son," she answered simply. "My father is a landowner, too. The son of another village landlord, it is."

She seemed to put the matter aside and continued to watch them intently. Mollie Stanley sighed. She put down the roses on the desk and went over to the girl and sat down on a chair next to her and took her hand again. "Try to remember," she said, "some of the things you have been taught. Remember about keeping things clean and remember how dangerous the flies and mosquitoes are, especially to little children—and how little children should not be given cucumbers and green melons to eat, and—remember about your prayers, and about the kind Christ, who came to save our souls—remember all the things we have tried to teach about being clean and good."

"Yes, teacher," the girl replied. She was looking closely at Mollie Stanley's wedding ring. Now she asked suddenly, "Did the other teacher give you the ring?"

Mollie dropped the hand she was holding and turned to her husband. "Oh dear—" she said.

"Don't worry, dear," said Wyn instantly. "I can't bear that look in your eyes. You mustn't, mustn't try to bear on your dear self all the troubles of everyone else. We've done the best we can for this child. Now she must go home. Come—" he stood and took up the roses. "Here are your roses, darling. Run along now. I'll see that Ru-lan gets away. Where *is* her father? In the school hall? I'll go, then."

"No, but, Wyn, I can't go so lightly. Tell her—tell him we'll come to see her sometime, anyway—Ru-lan"—she turned to the girl and changed her tongue quickly—"we shall come to see you some time— I'm coming to see if you remember everything—you must try—do not let yourself be like all the others who have never come to mission school."

"No, teacher," the girl said. She was staring at Wyn's hand resting unconsciously upon Mollie's shoulder, and he took it abruptly away.

Crossing the school lawn ahead of her, he thought to himself that Ru-lan was really a very tiresome girl. It was not only that she was so stupid, it was also that one could not be sure of what she was thinking. He would have said, for instance, that she was stolid and unfeeling; yet just now when she was about to follow

him out of his study she had made one of her great broad smiles
that seemed to enwrap him and Mollie, and she had taken Mollie's
hand and held it, and had said with simple utter gratitude, "You
have both taught me. Together you have taught me."

He remembered now how often they would find her staring at
them in her silent persevering way, that time at supper, for instance, when he had sat holding Mollie's hand as he ate—they always
sat side by side—and Ru-lan had come in with a note from one of
the teachers. She always contrived, he did believe, now that he
thought of it, to be the one to carry notes. He'd supposed it was
because she was such a faithful sort of person that they had sent
her. But perhaps it was because she wanted to come. There she
had stood, staring at them with that silent beaming look—slightly
feebleminded, undoubtedly. He sighed. Well, it was sad when years
went into teaching someone like that, someone who could never
learn, when there were so many who could, and had no chance.
But she had been there when he and Mollie came, and her father
had come twice a year with her fees, and so she had stayed. There
were not many fathers who paid full fees for a daughter.

He entered the hall, and there the father was, a plain brown-
faced countryman in a blue cotton gown cut a little too long and
too broad for him, but of good stout homewoven stuff. He was not
a poor man, it was evident, from his bearing. He rose politely as
the white man entered.

"Sit down, please, Mr. Yang. Do not be polite," said Wyn, seat-
ing himself also. The girl stood a little to one side, waiting.

"This girl," said the father nodding his head toward her, "I might
have left her with you to become a teacher for you out of gratitude
for all your efforts, but unfortunately she was early betrothed to the
son of a friend whom I do not care to offend, and now the family
demand the marriage. Otherwise I would give her to you to help
you in your school."

"I thank you certainly," said Wyn. He wondered uncomfortably
if in honesty he should tell the father that they could never have
used Ru-lan as a teacher because she was too stupid. He thrust an
apologetic thought toward God—it was difficult to be honest if it
hurt someone else. Mr. Yang was obviously so proud of his daughter.
He turned toward Wyn now saying, "She has had, you will remember, sir, eight years of schooling. It is not every man's son who has

such a wife. But I have treated her as though she were to be my own daughter-in-law and to remain in my family. I value my friend as myself."

"It is very honorable of you," murmured Wyn. At least he would not tell lies and say he was sorry that Ru-lan must go. He waited in courteous silence until the father rose, briskly dusting cake crumbs from his lap. "There—it is pleasant to sit drinking your tea and eating your cakes, but I have miles of country road to put beneath my beast's feet before night comes. Say good-by and give your gratitude to your teacher, Ru-lan."

"I thank you, teacher," murmured the girl. "I thank you for all I have learned."

They bowed to him together, father and daughter, and Wyn bowed, waiting at the door while they turned and bowed again. He watched them while they went out of the compound gate. "I suppose," he thought a little sadly, "that measured by any standard it must be said that we have wasted the church's substance upon that girl. Mollie's hours and mine, too! I wonder why they do not seem so important as dollars in the mission budget? Anyway, all waste! She's not even a church member."

He walked back, a little discouraged. It was so difficult to know what was worth while in the work. One was conscientious, did each day what it seemed should be done, should be taught, and then realized suddenly, as he and Mollie had today, that no fruit was possible. He sighed a little grimly. Well, Ru-lan was gone.

In the village of Long Peace the people were all very well content. They had just finished three days of great feasting entirely at the elder Liu's expense, since he was marrying his eldest son to Ru-lan, the daughter of his brother-friend Yang in the village of The Fighting Cocks. Everybody had eaten. First the tables were set for Mr. Liu's friends among the gentry, and the common people had waited their time, patiently and decently. Then the tables were set again and again, with pork and with fish, broiled with sugar and wine and vinegar, with beef and pork ground and stewed with cabbage and greens, with noodles and with sweet rice. In fact, nothing had been left undone, and everyone had drunk all the wine he could and had eaten far more than he could, and mothers had prudently tied into large blue and white handkerchiefs such tidbits as they could not eat or force their children to eat at table. Servants had been tipped, gifts had been given, and firecrackers exploded in immense volleys. The bride, moreover, had been exhibited and commented upon, and though after all she seemed to be nothing extraordinary, no one liked Elder Liu and Mr. Yang any the less for it.

There had been a great deal of curiosity to see her, because everybody knew Mr. Yang had sent his eldest daughter to a foreign school for eight years, and anything might have happened. She might even have changed the color of her eyes and hair, or the white women might have taught her how to bleach her skin, since it is well known the white people have magic. But she was nothing at all out of the ordinary. She was, in fact, a little more common than otherwise, a large lumpish girl with very plump round cheeks and small mild eyes. In addition her feet were large. Country wives nudged each other and whispered, "Look at her feet—big feet!" "Yes, but the foreigners do not allow their pupils to bind their feet!" "Ah, indeed! How lucky that the Elder Yang betrothed her in babyhood and to his best friend's son!" Young men glanced at the bride and made jokes concerning the width of her nose and the size of her mouth, and went home in high good humor because they need not be envious of the Elder Liu's son. Indeed, everybody was happy because for once the Elder Liu did not seem to be so very lucky, and one or two fathers whose daughters had been teasing to be allowed to go to a foreign school went home resolute for refusal. What—to waste eight years of fees and then have a daughter at the end who looked exactly as though she had never left the village! So everyone was happy. They went home by moonlight the night of the third day, full of cheerful vilifying talk.

In the house of the Elder Liu, in the court belonging to his eldest son, Ru-lan sat upon the edge of the large nuptial bed, hung with pictures of babies and pomegranates and mandarin ducks and every lucky sign for marriage, and waited for her husband. She had enjoyed everything very much, so much that she often forgot to keep her eyes downcast as she should. But this did not greatly trouble her. She had remembered enough, she thought comfortably, and tonight they had given her a good dinner. The more tedious part of the wedding was over. She had now come to the part which was her own affair.

This was the time, she knew, when maidens should feel shy and uncomfortable and even afraid. She knew because as a very small girl in the women's courts of her father's house she had squatted on her heels listening as all the little girls did to the women's talk. They listened while the women whispered loudly to each other, "I tell you, he was like a tiger—his great eyes—" "I tell you, nothing told is so terrible as—" "I tell you, I was like a chicken before a wolf—"

They all enjoyed telling each other of this hour when their unknown bridegrooms first appeared. She thought now, staring reflectively through the old-fashioned veil of beads that hung over her face, that it was natural they should be afraid of marriage. What they had seen of the thing between men and women was not comfortable. But she had been to school for eight years with the foreigners. There was the difference. Not that the first years she had been there were of any use to her at all. She could not see much use, for instance, in reading books. In the first place books told nothing interesting. If they were about God, there was no understanding them—how could humans understand gods? She had listened politely to Mrs. Burgess and been glad when Mrs. Burgess had been compelled to go to America. For then the dear little Stanley teacher had come, that little pretty round-faced teacher, whose eyes were also brown so that one liked to look at her. The Stanley teacher had worked so hard to teach her that sometimes she almost felt she should try to learn something, to listen perhaps to what the Stanley teacher was saying, but when she did it had seemed not valuable.

No, she had learned nothing until that day when she had observed the man Stanley place his arms about the woman Stanley. At first she thought with consternation that these were two wicked and unmannered people. But they were not punished if they were. In rapid succession they had two small sons, both healthy, both dark-eyed. Evidently their God was pleased with them. After that she had watched them many times. When they did not know it she had stolen in the night across the school campus, and had gazed steadily between the curtains of the room where they sat after the children were put to bed, and, watching them, had come to learn something from them. To this learning she applied her mind. So now she was not at all afraid. She waited peacefully for Yung-en, sitting at ease upon the bed, her hands folded in her red satin lap.

Everywhere through the courts quiet was descending after the noisy days of feasting. Children who had eaten too well ceased their crying and fell asleep, and servants yawned and barred the doors of courtyards and went to their own beds. Her own serving woman was only waiting until the master came in to spread her pallet down across the door to sleep. When everyone was still, when the young men had all gone home, wearied at last with their baiting and teasing of the bridegroom, then through the silent empty courts he would come. She had stolen her glances at him and she was pleased with his looks. He was an honest sturdy young man, with a square dark face, not too smiling. He was shy, she could see, not quick to speak. A woman could live with such a man. She was not afraid, having learned so much about a man and a woman.

Then suddenly the door creaked upon its wooden hinges and there he was, still in his bright blue wedding robes. He did not speak, nor did he look at her at once. He came in and sat down beside the table and began to crack watermelon seeds. She rose and poured out a cup of tea for him and he nodded and she sat down again. She was not impatient. He could not go on cracking watermelon seeds all night. Outside the door she heard a loud yawn and soon a muffled snore. Her serving woman was asleep. Now everyone slept except these two.

She waited, smiling a little, watching him through the beads of her veil, but he did not look at her. She waited and at last she caught his eyes, stealing toward her. She answered instantly, frankly, smiling her beam of a smile. He stared at her and coughed and after a second of surprise he grew very red and made haste to return to his watermelon seeds. She suddenly perceived that he was afraid of her.

"And why are you afraid of me?" she asked, making her voice soft as she had heard the little Stanley teacher's voice soft.

He turned his head from her's. "I am so ignorant," he said at last in a low voice. "You have been away to a foreign school and I have always lived in this village. You will laugh at me."

She watched him. How now would the Stanley teacher speak if the man Stanley had spoken like this? Once the man Stanley had put his head down upon the woman's shoulder and for some trouble had wept as a little boy weeps, and the woman had not laughed. She had taken him into her arms and pressed his head down and murmured to him as a mother murmurs to a suffering child, and soon he was quieted. Ru-lan had not understood the woman Stanley's words, but the sounds she understood, and the way she understood. It had made the man Stanley feel strong again and cease his weeping.

She looked demurely down at her hands and spoke in a small plaintive voice. "I have to confess to you," she said, "although I was so long in that school I have remained ignorant. You cannot be as ignorant as I am. I do believe there are a thousand things you know I do not know. There I remained for eight years shut behind walls, but my brain is too stupid to learn from books. So I am very ignorant. I have everything to learn from you."

He gazed at her now, forgetting that she was his bride and that he was afraid of her. "Did you not learn to read?" he demanded.

"Only a very little," she replied.

"Did you read to the end of the Four Books?" he asked again.

"Alas, I never read any of the Four Books," she answered.

"Then what did you do in all that time?" he inquired, astonished.

"I sat on benches in school rooms," she replied humbly, "and there were those who talked to me, but I could not understand them, being stupid from birth. They told me of gods and of magic, and of small insects that cause disease if eaten, but then who eats insects? At least we do not. So I learned nothing."

"Nothing at all?" he asked severely.

"Nothing at all," she answered sadly.

He was silent, but now he looked at her quite easily and he had stopped cracking watermelon seeds. She could see the shyness leaving him as he thought over what she had told him.

"I only learned one thing," she said after a long time. Now she leaned forward and looked at him and he looked at her.

"What is that one thing?" he asked.

"There was a white woman who was my teacher," she said, "and she was married to a white man, and they were very lucky, for one after the other they had two strong dark-eyed sons, and this when the other children of white people all have blue or green eyes. I learned from them something."

"What was the thing you learned?" he asked. "Certainly two dark-eyed sons are very lucky."

"I learned," she said considering, choosing some one thing among all she had learned, "that it is lucky when a man and his wife speak together freely and always with kind voices, as though they were friends speaking easily together and not as they do in our houses, where it seems shameful so to speak."

"Do you mean speak together anywhere?"

"Yes, I mean that."

He gazed at her steadily. "What then?"

"And then it is lucky if the husband helps the wife if there is a thing to be done, such as to carry a basket or a bundle, if there is not a servant near."

"What does the wife do?" he asked, astonished.

"She also wishes to carry the things, and so they try mutually to help each other."

"And who wins?" he asked.

"They share the thing," she replied simply.

She waited a little, thinking, remembering. . . . Once she had seen the man Stanley lift his wife over a pool of mud in the road, and carry her through and set her down on the other side, one afternoon, when they thought none saw them. But before he set her down he had held her hard and placed his cheek against hers, and then they had gone on hand in hand until they saw her. But she had seen them long since. She had wanted to say, "Do not drop your hands apart. I know it is your pleasure to walk thus." But she had not spoken. . . .

"What else have you learned?" he asked.

"It is lucky," she said slowly, "for a man and his wife to clasp their hands together sometimes—it is not shameful."

He coughed and looked away and she went on quickly. "There are many things not shameful that we have thought shameful—they are lucky between man and wife. But I cannot speak them—they are things to be done rather than to be spoken."

He looked down and did not answer. He did not answer for quite a long time. Then he said a little gruffly, "Then do them—do what you have learned."

She rose slowly and went over to him. She knelt down on the floor before him as often she had seen the woman Stanley do. But she could not go on, although she knew quite well what came next.

Next was to put her head down upon his knees and clasp her arms about his waist. But she could not do it. Now it was she who was shy. It had looked so easy when the woman Stanley did it.

"I cannot do it all at once," she faltered. "A little every day. But perhaps—at least take my hands."

He sat quite still and then he lifted her hands in his own. Something rushed between them through their hands, and suddenly her heart began to pound. Did the woman Stanley's heart pound like this also? What was the matter with her?

"What next did you learn?" he asked.

She could not answer. She drew their hands together and laid her head down upon their knotted hands. She should have asked the woman Stanley about this pounding heart.

"Lift up your head," he said. How gentle his voice was, as gentle as the man Stanley's voice was! "Lift up your head and let me take away your veil that I may see you."

She lifted up her head, and he drew his hands away and took off the headdress and the veil and set them on the table and then he looked at her. And then he went on speaking in that same gentle voice, "And did you learn it was lucky for a man to like very well the woman chosen for him?" He had taken her hands again. He was gazing at her, smiling, happy, as the man Stanley gazed at that woman who knelt to him. The man Stanley had also asked something of the woman in that strange tongue of theirs and she had answered. Oh, what was the answer to the gentle question? There must be an answer—she should have learned the answer—Then suddenly it came to her. It came to her, not out of her brain which was so slow and stupid and never quick to speak. It came from her pounding heart. "Yes, it is a lucky thing, I know, and the luck is perfect if the woman likes also very well the man to whom she is given."

She felt his cheek against hers, even as she had learned.

If Ru-lan had been able to write she would long ago have written to her teacher Stanley to ask her why, when she had said she would come to see her, she had not yet come, although it had been now nearly five years since Ru-lan had left the school. In the five years she had grown heavier, as what woman would not who had given birth to three large strong sons and now a small pretty daughter, so pretty that the child's father went against all nature and loved her twice as well, apparently, as even he loved his sons.

But then there was of course no man on the earth's surface like Yung-en. The man Stanley was never better to his wife than Yung-en was to Ru-lan. Bit by bit, through the five years, she had told him what she had seen those two white ones do, how they looked at each other, how they spoke, and with the telling new comprehension had come to them of what those looks and words meant. She was now sure that when those two spoke to each other in that strong soft fashion they said in their own tongue what came welling up from her own heart and Yung-en's. It was wonderful to think how alike were hearts. She knew this because it was so soon instinct to move freely with Yung-en, walking beside him freely, moving toward him freely and fully when they were alone. She knew that the women in the courts were often disapproving. She knew they said, "It is the boldness she learned in the foreign school—it is the freedom of the modern ways." She smiled, knowing there was a truth in what they said.

She pondered a good deal on her own ease. It did not occur to her, for instance, to share the anxiety of the other women lest their husbands take concubines. Did she not know Yung-en's heart? That was what she had learned, how to know his heart. They talked together sometimes about it, and how their life was different from those about them, and Yung-en said gratefully always, "If the man and woman Stanley should ever come to see us, there would not be enough I could do for them to thank them for what you learned from them. If you had not seen and learned, my life would not have been above any other man's. As it is, you have contented me so that all other women in the world might die and I should not know it." She smiled, knowing she had never been beautiful and now was less so than ever, if one should measure her by a beautiful woman. But she feared none of them.

So when suddenly one August morning a letter came from the school she could hardly wait for Yung-en to come home to read it. She had long given up any pretense at reading. The characters she had once known had quite slipped out of her memory. If some woman asked her in curiosity sometimes what a character was on a bit of paper found, she laughed comfortably and said, "If once I knew, that once is long gone. I have so little use for letters these days." Or if her elder son, now beginning to learn, ran to ask her the meaning of a word she would say, always laughing, "You must go ignorant if you ask learning of me, my son!"

She put the letter by until she heard Yung-en come and then she went to him and waited while he opened it, her hand upon his arm. After those five years it was more than ever necessary to her to put her hand upon his arm, and he moved toward her when he felt her touch, understanding.

"It is a letter from the man Stanley," he said after murmuring the letters aloud awhile. "They wish to open a chapel here in our village and preach their religion, and there will be also a school, and he is coming and with him the woman Stanley."

"Of course they would not be separated," she said gently.

"No," he said, folding the letter. He was planning rapidly. "We shall have them here in our own house. There is the south room upon the old peony terrace where I have my few books and where I never go. Prepare it with the best bed and with the blackwood furniture my father gave us from the south. And I shall invite guests —all my friends. I do not care to invite guests for the religion, but it is a way to repay these two if I show myself a friend. Now I can thank them for all they taught you."

"Yes," she said. "And we can show them our sons—"

"And we can send our daughter to their school," he cried, smiling. They sat down together in simple pleasure, holding each other's hands, laughing a little. "Everything is lucky in our life," he said.

"Everything," she echoed fervently.

So it was that on a certain morning in August, nearly at the end of summer, she welcomed those two. There they were at the door, standing together, a little thinner than she remembered them, a little gray in their hair. "You are tired," she cried, her heart rushing out to them. "Come in—rest and eat. Oh, how welcome you are!"

Yung-en gave up his work when they came and stayed at home, running hither and thither, himself carrying trays of sweetmeats and keeping plates full and pouring tea and going to see what quilts were rolled upon the bed and if the mosquito net was properly drawn. "I can never do enough for them," he said to her in passing.

Well, there it was. The two Stanleys stayed three days and into the days Yung-en and Ru-lan heaped all that they had, all the years of their happy life together, all their luck in the three sons and the little girl. Ru-lan had meant to dress the children in their best, but then it was so hot that she let it go. It was better that they be comfortable. Besides, they were so beautiful and so healthy it must be a pleasure for anyone to see their little brown bodies bare to the waist. She had meant, too, to clean the house a little more, to wipe the dust from the table legs and from the gilt crevices of the family gods. But the summer days passed so quickly until the guests came, and once they were come there was no time for anything except urging them to eat, to talk, to rest themselves, to enjoy the huge feast and the lanterns hung to welcome them, to see the fireworks Yung-en bought and bade the servants fire for their amusement.

She had planned to try to tell the dear teachers Stanley a little about her own life and how much she owed them. She had planned to say at least that she had been very happy. But there was no time for anything. They were busy about the new school, planning, working hard as they always did.

But they were still happy. She knew that. They still paused as they used to pause, to look at each other deeply. When they went away, so soon, so far too soon, she loved them more than ever. She stood beside Yung-en at the gate waving to them, crying to them to go slowly, to return quickly. And then when Yung-en shouted after them, "Our daughter shall be your first girl pupil!" her heart overflowed toward them and she cried after them, "Yes—teach her, for you taught me so much!" That was all she had the time to say. But she did not worry—they would understand. She went back into her house with Yung-en. His hand sought hers comfortably, and they sauntered across their courtyard, well content.

Rocking down the road in their rickety mission Ford, Mollie leaned back against Wyn, grateful to be alone again with him. Now, as always, when she sat beside Wyn she began to feel warm deep peace welling up in her. They were going home, they were together. They were going back to the children. She crept more closely to him, and he put his arm about her. He drove very expertly one-armed.

"Sweetheart!" he said gently. "It was wonderful of you to leave the children and make this trip with me. I shouldn't have blamed you, you know, if you hadn't."

"I can't be away from you, Wyn."

"No, I know." They fell into intimate, peaceful silence.

Over the Chinese landscape twilight was beginning to fall, creeping up in small mists from the ponds and the canals, darkening over the hills from the sky. From the thatched roofs the blue lines of smoke of fires kindled for the evening meal rose straightly into the still air. How strange, how different the scene was from the rough hills of her own home country, from the sharp angular American towns! And yet how little strange, how little different! These were homes, too, and these were people, living together in their families. And here was her home. Wherever Wyn was, was her home. She was instantly deeply content, content with everything, with everybody.

Then suddenly she thought of Ru-lan.

"Wyn!" she said.

"Yes?" he answered.

"What did you really think of Ru-lan?"

"Well?" asked Wyn, twinkling at her a little. "What did you really think?"

"It was just exactly as I was afraid it would be," she answered dolefully. "She's lost even the little she had. Wyn, you wouldn't have known, now would you honestly, that Ru-lan had ever been outside that village? Did you see the slightest difference between her house and any other ignorant village woman's house?"

"No," said Wyn thoughtfully. He guided the car skillfully between two deep wheelbarrow ruts.

Mollie stared mournfully over the landscape, the valleys tawny with ripening rice, the hills browning with ending summer, the willow-encircled villages. "No," she continued, "the house was dusty and not very clean, and the children were eating just anything. I saw that little girl chewing on a cucumber, skin and all."

"So did I," he said briefly.

"And Ru-lan is just like an amiable cow. She just sits and smiles and smiles. She doesn't read, she doesn't seem to do anything in the village, she's just an ordinary woman—after all those years away. I don't believe she does one thing different in her home for all the hours I tried to teach her."

"Mollie, did you see those idols?" Wyn said gravely.

"Yes," said Mollie reluctantly.

They rolled along in silence for a moment, remembering the row of gilt figures with the guttered candles before them. They had taught Ru-lan so patiently to say over and over again, "Thou shall have no other gods before Me. . . ." "Ru-lan, what are gods?" she used to ask. Ru-lan had smiled apologetically. "Teacher, tell me, for I do not know."

"They are idols, Ru-lan."

"Yes, Teacher, it is what I thought."

"You must not worship them, Ru-lan."

"No, Teacher."

And then when Dr. Martin had once asked her in the catechism class what God was, she had said, "Sir, God is an idol." Poor stupid Ru-lan! There was no telling how she would learn a thing. . . .

She thought over the two crowded days, days full of too much food and too much noise and many children and curious neighbors coming in and out to see the newcomers. But Ru-lan had not seemed to mind anything. She had sat tranquil in the midst of the confusion, smiling and smiling. And everybody had seemed fond of her—her children ran to her often, and the neighbors called to her cheerfully, and Yung-en . . . She was struck now, remembering Yung-en.

"Wyn!" she said suddenly, looking up at him.

"Yes, darling?"

He turned and smiled down at her. There she was snuggled down by him like a kitten, looking not a day older . . .

"There was one thing about Ru-lan—her husband really seemed to like her."

"I believe he does," he said slowly. "Yes—I don't know why exactly—she certainly doesn't remember anything we ever taught her!"

The Bear

BY

WILLIAM FAULKNER

H<small>E WAS TEN.</small> But it had already begun, long before that day when at last he wrote his age in two figures and he saw for the first time the camp where his father and Major de Spain and old General Compson and the others spent two weeks each November and two weeks again each June. He had already inherited then, without ever having seen it, the tremendous bear with one trap-ruined foot which, in an area almost a hundred miles deep, had earned itself a name, a definite designation like a living man.

He had listened to it for years: the long legend of corncribs rifled, of shotes and grown pigs and even calves carried bodily into the woods and devoured, of traps and dead-falls overthrown and dogs mangled and slain, and shotgun and even rifle charges delivered at point-blank range and with no more effect than so many peas blown through a tube by a boy—a corridor of wreckage and destruction beginning back before he was born, through which sped, not fast but rather with the ruthless and irresistible deliberation of a locomotive, the shaggy tremendous shape.

It ran in his knowledge before he ever saw it. It looked and towered in his dreams before he even saw the unaxed woods where it left its crooked print, shaggy, huge, red-eyed, not malevolent but just big—too big for the dogs which tried to bay it, for the horses which tried to ride it down, for the men and the bullets they fired into it, too big for the very country which was its constricting scope. He seemed to see it entire with a child's complete divination before he ever laid eyes on either—the doomed wilderness whose edges were being constantly and punily gnawed at by men with axes and plows who feared it because it was wilderness, men myriad and nameless even to one another in the land where the old bear had earned a

name, through which ran not even a mortal animal but an anachro-
nism, indomitable and invincible, out of an old dead time, a phan-
tom, epitome and apotheosis of the old wild life at which the puny
humans swarmed and hacked in a fury of abhorrence and fear, like
pygmies about the ankles of a drowsing elephant: the old bear solitary, indomitable and alone, widowered, childless, and absolved of
mortality—old Priam reft of his old wife and having outlived all
his sons.

Until he was ten, each November he would watch the wagon containing the dogs and the bedding and food and guns and his father
and Tennie's Jim, the Negro, and Sam Fathers, the Indian, son of a
slave woman and a Chickasaw chief, depart on the road to town, to
Jefferson, where Major de Spain and the others would join them.
To the boy, at seven, eight, and nine, they were not going into the
Big Bottom to hunt bear and deer, but to keep yearly rendezvous
with the bear which they did not even intend to kill. Two weeks
later they would return, with no trophy, no head and skin. He had
not expected it. He had not even been afraid it would be in the
wagon. He believed that even after he was ten and his father would
let him go too, for those two weeks in November, he would merely
make another one, along with his father and Major de Spain and
General Compson and the others, the dogs which feared to bay at it
and the rifles and shotguns which failed even to bleed it, in the
yearly pageant of the old bear's furious immortality.

Then he heard the dogs. It was in the second week of his first time
in the camp. He stood with Sam Fathers against a big oak beside the
faint crossing where they had stood each dawn for nine days now,
hearing the dogs. He had heard them once before, one morning last
week—a murmur, sourceless, echoing through the wet woods, swelling presently into separate voices which he could recognize and call
by name. He had raised and cocked the gun as Sam told him and
stood motionless again while the uproar, the invisible course, swept
up and past and faded; it seemed to him that he could actually see
the deer, the buck, blond, smoke-colored, elongated with speed,
fleeing, vanishing, the woods, the gray solitude, still ringing even
when the cries of the dogs had died away.

"Now let the hammers down," Sam said.

"You knew they were not coming here too," he said.

"Yes," Sam said. "I want you to learn how to do when you

didn't shoot. It's after the chance for the bear or the deer has done already come and gone that men and dogs get killed."

"Anyway," he said, "it was just a deer."

Then on the tenth morning he heard the dogs again. And he readied the too-long, too-heavy gun as Sam had taught him, before Sam even spoke. But this time it was no deer, no ringing chorus of dogs running strong on a free scent, but a moiling yapping an octave too high, with something more than indecision and even abjectness in it, not even moving very fast, taking a long time to pass completely out of hearing, leaving then somewhere in the air that echo, thin, slightly hysterical, abject, almost grieving, with no sense of a fleeing, unseen, smoke-colored, grass-eating shape ahead of it, and Sam, who had taught him first of all to cock the gun and take position where he could see everywhere and then never move again, had himself moved up beside him; he could hear Sam breathing at his shoulder, and he could see the arched curve of the old man's inhaling nostrils.

"Hah," Sam said. "Not even running. Walking."

"Old Ben!" the boy said. "But up here!" he cried. "Way up here!"

"He do it every year," Sam said. "Once. Maybe to see who in camp this time, if he can shoot or not. Whether we got the dog yet that can bay and hold him. He'll take them to the river, then he'll send them back home. We may as well go back too; see how they look when they come back to camp."

When they reached the camp the hounds were already there, ten of them crouching back under the kitchen, the boy and Sam squatting to peer back into the obscurity where they had huddled, quiet, the eyes luminous, glowing at them and vanishing, and no sound, only that effluvium of something more than dog, stronger than dog and not just animal, just beast, because still there had been nothing in front of that abject and almost painful yapping save the solitude, the wilderness, so that when the eleventh hound came in at noon and with all the others watching—even old Uncle Ash, who called himself first a cook—Sam daubed the tattered ear and the raked shoulder with turpentine and axle grease, to the boy it was still no living creature, but the wilderness which, leaning for the moment down, had patted lightly once the hound's temerity.

"Just like a man," Sam said. "Just like folks. Put off as long as she could having to be brave, knowing all the time that sooner or later she would have to be brave to keep on living with herself, and knowing all the time beforehand what was going to happen to her when she done it."

That afternoon, himself on the one-eyed wagon mule which did not mind the smell of blood nor, as they told him, of bear, and with Sam on the other one, they rode for more than three hours through the rapid, shortening winter day. They followed no path, no trial even that he could see; almost at once they were in a country which he had never seen before. Then he knew why Sam had made him ride the mule which would not spook. The sound one stopped short and tried to whirl and bolt even as Sam got down, blowing its breath, jerking and wrenching at the rein, while Sam held it, coaxing it forward with his voice, since he could not risk trying it, drawing it forward while the boy got down from the marred one.

Then, standing beside Sam in the gloom of the dying afternoon, he looked down at the rotted over-turned log, gutted and scored with claw marks and, in the wet earth beside it, the print of the enormous warped two-toed foot. He knew now what he had smelled when he peered under the kitchen where the dogs huddled. He realized for the first time that the bear which had run in his listening and loomed in his dreams since before he could remember to the contrary, and which, therefore, must have existed in the listening and dreams of his father and Major de Spain and even old General Compson, too, before they began to remember in their turn, was a mortal animal, and that if they had departed for the camp each November without any actual hope of bringing its trophy back, it was not because it could not be slain, but because so far they had had no actual hope to.

"Tomorrow," he said.

"We'll try tomorrow," Sam said. "We ain't got the dog yet."

"We've got eleven. They ran him this morning."

"It won't need but one," Sam said. "He ain't here. Maybe he ain't nowhere. The only other way will be for him to run by accident over somebody that has a gun."

"That wouldn't be me," the boy said. "It will be Walter or Major or—"

"It might," Sam said. "You watch close in the morning. Because he's smart. That's how come he has lived this long. If he gets hemmed up and has to pick out somebody to run over, he will pick out you."

"How?" the boy said. "How will he know—" He ceased. "You mean he already knows me, that I ain't never been here before, ain't had time to find out yet whether I—" He ceased again, looking at Sam, the old man whose face revealed nothing until it smiled. He said humbly, not even amazed, "It was me he was watching. I don't reckon he did need to come but once."

The next morning they left the camp three hours before daylight. They rode this time because it was too far to walk, even the dogs in the wagon; again the first gray light found him in a place which he had never seen before, where Sam had placed him and told him to stay and then departed. With the gun which was too big for him, which did not even belong to him, but to Major de Spain, and which he had fired only once—at a stump on the first day, to learn the recoil and how to reload it—he stood against a gum tree beside a little bayou whose black still water crept without movement out of a canebrake and crossed a small clearing and into cane again, where, invisible, a bird—the big woodpecker called Lord-to-God by Negroes—clattered at a dead limb.

It was a stand like any other, dissimilar only in incidentals to the one where he had stood each morning for ten days; a territory new to him, yet no less familiar than that other one which, after almost two weeks, he had come to believe he knew a little—the same solitude, the same loneliness through which human beings had merely passed without altering it, leaving no mark, no scar, which looked exactly as it must have looked when the first ancestor of Sam Fathers' Chickasaw predecessors crept into it and looked about, club or stone ax or bone arrow drawn and poised; different only because, squatting at the edge of the kitchen, he smelled the hounds huddled and cringing beneath it and saw the raked ear and shoulder of the one who, Sam said, had had to be brave once in order to live with herself, and saw yesterday in the earth beside the gutted log the print of the living foot.

He heard no dogs at all. He never did hear them. He only heard the drumming of the woodpecker stop short off and knew that the bear was looking at him. He never saw it. He did not know whether it was in front of him or behind him. He did not move, holding the useless gun, which he had not even had warning to cock and which even now he did not cock, tasting in his saliva that taint as of brass which he knew now because he had smelled it when he peered under the kitchen at the huddled dogs.

Then it was gone. As abruptly as it had ceased, the woodpecker's dry, monotonous clatter set up again, and after a while he even believed he could hear the dogs—a murmur, scarce a sound even, which he had probably been hearing for some time before he even remarked it, drifting into hearing and then out again, dying away. They came nowhere near him. If it was a bear they ran, it was another bear. It was Sam himself who came out of the cane and crossed the bayou, followed by the injured bitch of yesterday. She was almost at heel, like a bird dog, making no sound. She came and crouched against his leg, trembling, staring off into the cane.

"I didn't see him," he said. "I didn't, Sam!"

"I know it," Sam said. "He done the looking. You didn't hear him neither, did you?"

"No," the boy said. "I—"

"He's smart," Sam said. "Too smart." He looked down at the hound, trembling faintly and steadily against the boy's knee. From the raked shoulder a few drops of fresh blood oozed and clung. "Too big. We ain't got the dog yet. But maybe someday. Maybe not next time. But someday."

So I must see him, he thought. *I must look at him.* Otherwise, it seemed to him that it would go on like this forever, as it had gone on with his father and Major de Spain, who was older than his father, and even with old General Compson, who had been old enough to be a brigade commander in 1865. Otherwise, it would go on so forever, next time and next time, after and after and after. It seemed to him that he could never see the two of them, himself and the bear, shadowy in the limbo from which time emerged, becoming time; the old bear absolved of mortality and himself partaking, sharing a little of it, enough of it. And he knew now what he had smelled in the huddled dogs and tasted in his saliva. He recognized fear. *So I will have to see him,* he thought, without dread or even hope. *I will have to look at him.*

It was in June of the next year. He was eleven. They were in camp again, celebrating Major de Spain's and General Compson's birthdays. Although the one had been born in September and the other in the depth of winter and in another decade, they had met for two weeks to fish and shoot squirrels and turkey and run coons and wildcats with the dogs at night. That is, he and Boon Hoggenbeck and the Negroes fished and shot squirrels and ran the coons and cats, because the proved hunters, not only Major de Spain and old General Compson, who spent those two weeks sitting in a rocking chair before a tremendous iron pot of Brunswick stew, stirring and tasting, with old Ash to quarrel with about how he was making it and Tennie's Jim to pour whiskey from the demijohn into the tin dipper from which he drank it, but even the boy's father and Walter Ewell, who were still young enough, scorned such, other than shooting the wild gobblers with pistols for wagers on their marksmanship.

Or, that is, his father and the others believed he was hunting squirrels. Until the third day, he thought that Sam Fathers believed that too. Each morning he would leave the camp right after breakfast. He had his own gun now, a Christmas present. He went back to the tree beside the bayou where he had stood that morning. Using the compass which old General Compson had given him, he ranged from that point; he was teaching himself to be a better-than-fair woodsman without knowing he was doing it. On the second day he even found the gutted log where he had first seen the crooked print. It was almost completely crumbled now, healing with unbelievable speed, a passionate and almost visible relinquishment, back into the earth from which the tree had grown.

He ranged the summer woods now, green with gloom; if anything, actually dimmer than in November's gray dissolution, where, even at noon, the sun fell only in intermittent dappling upon the earth, which never completely dried out and which crawled with snakes—moccasins and water snakes and rattlers, themselves the color of the dappling gloom, so that he would not always see them until they moved, returning later and later, first day, second day, passing in the twilight of the third evening the little log pen enclosing the log stable where Sam was putting up the horses for the night.

"You ain't looked right yet," Sam said.

He stopped. For a moment he didn't answer. Then he said

peacefully, in a peaceful rushing burst as when a boy's miniature
dam in a little brook gives way, "All right. But how? I went to the
bayou. I even found that log again. I—"

"I reckon that was all right. Likely he's been watching you.
You never saw his foot?"

"I," the boy said—"I didn't—I never thought—"

"It's the gun," Sam said. He stood beside the fence motionless—
the old man, the Indian, in the battered faded overalls and the
five-cent straw hat which in the Negro's race had been the badge
of his enslavement and was now the regalia of his freedom. The
camp—the clearing, the house, the barn and its tiny lot with which
Major de Spain in his turn had scratched punily and evanescently
at the wilderness—faded in the dusk, back into the immemorial
darkness of the woods. *The gun,* the boy thought. *The gun.*

"Be scared," Sam said. "You can't help that. But don't be afraid.
Ain't nothing in the woods going to hurt you unless you corner it,
or it smells that you are afraid. A bear or a deer, too, has got to
be scared of a coward the same as a brave man has got to be."

The gun, the boy thought.

"You will have to choose," Sam said.

He left the camp before daylight, long before Uncle Ash would
wake in his quilts on the kitchen floor and start the fire for breakfast. He had only the compass and a stick for snakes. He could
go almost a mile before he would begin to need the compass. He
sat on a log, the invisible compass in his invisible hand, while
the secret night sounds, fallen still at his movements, scurried
again and then ceased for good, and the owls ceased and gave
over to the waking of day birds, and he could see the compass.
Then he went fast yet still quietly; he was becoming better and
better as a woodsman, still without having yet realized it.

He jumped a doe and a fawn at sunrise, walked them out of
the bed, close enough to see them—the crash of undergrowth, the
white scut, the fawn scudding behind her faster than he had believed it could run. He was hunting right, upwind, as Sam had
taught him; not that it mattered now. He had left the gun; of
his own will and relinquishment he had accepted not a gambit, not
a choice, but a condition in which not only the bear's heretofore
inviolable anonymity but all the old rules and balances of hunter
and hunted had been abrogated. He would not even be afraid, not

even in the moment when the fear would take him completely—blood, skin, bowels, bones, memory from the long time before it became his memory—all save that thin, clear, immortal lucidity which alone differed him from this bear and from all the other bear and deer he would ever kill in the humility and pride of his skill and endurance, to which Sam had spoken when he leaned in the twilight on the lot fence yesterday.

By noon he was far beyond the little bayou, farther into the new and alien country than he had ever been. He was traveling now not only by the old, heavy, biscuit-thick silver watch which had belonged to his grandfather. When he stopped at last, it was for the first time since he had risen from the log at dawn when he could see the compass. It was far enough. He had left the camp nine hours ago; nine hours from now, dark would have already been an hour old. But he didn't think that. He thought, *All right. Yes. But what?* and stood for a moment, alien and small in the green and topless solitude, answering his own question before it had formed and ceased. It was the watch, the compass, the stick—the three lifeless mechanicals with which for nine hours he had fended the wilderness off; he hung the watch and compass carefully on a bush and leaned the stick beside them and relinquished completely to it.

He had not been going very fast for the last two or three hours. He went no faster now, since distance would not matter even if he could have gone fast. And he was trying to keep a bearing on the tree where he had left the compass, trying to complete a circle which would bring him back to it or at least intersect itself, since direction would not matter now either. But the tree was not there, and he did as Sam had schooled him—made the next circle in the opposite direction, so that the two patterns would bisect somewhere, but crossing no print of his own feet, finding the tree at last, but in the wrong place—no bush, no compass, no watch—and the tree not even the tree, because there was a down log beside it and he did what Sam Fathers had told him was the next thing and the last.

As he sat down on the log he saw the crooked print—the warped, tremendous, two-toed indentation which, even as he watched it, filled with water. As he looked up, the wilderness coalesced, solidified—the glade, the tree he sought, the bush, the watch and the

compass glinting where a ray of sunshine touched them. Then he
saw the bear. It did not emerge, appear; it was just there, immo-
bile, solid, fixed in the hot dappling of the green and windless noon,
not as big as he had dreamed it, but as big as he had expected it,
bigger, dimensionless, against the dappled obscurity, looking at
him where he sat quietly on the log and looked back at it.

Then it moved. It made no sound. It did not hurry. It crossed
the glade, walking for an instant into the full glare of the sun; when
it reached the other side it stopped again and looked back at him
across one shoulder while his quiet breathing inhaled and exhaled
three times.

Then it was gone. It didn't walk into the woods, the undergrowth. It faded, sank back into the wilderness as he had watched
a fish, a huge old bass, sink and vanish into the dark depths of
its pool without even any movement of its fins.

He thought, *It will be next fall.* But it was not next fall, nor
the next nor the next. He was fourteen then. He had killed his
buck, and Sam Fathers had marked his face with the hot blood,
and in the next year he killed a bear. But even before that accolade
he had become as competent in the woods as many grown men
with the same experience; by his fourteenth year he was a better
woodsman than most grown men with more. There was no territory
within thirty miles of the camp that he did not know—bayou, ridge,
brake, landmark, tree and path. He could have led anyone to any
point in it without deviation, and brought them out again. He
knew the game trails that even Sam Fathers did not know; in his
thirteenth year he found a buck's bedding place, and unbeknown to
his father he borrowed Walter Ewell's rifle and lay in wait at dawn
and killed the buck when it walked back to the bed, as Sam had told
him how the old Chickasaw fathers did.

But not the old bear, although by now he knew its footprints
better than he did his own, and not only the crooked one. He could
see any one of the three sound ones and distinguish it from any
other, and not only by its size. There were other bears within these
thirty miles which left tracks almost as large, but this was more
than that. If Sam Fathers had been his mentor and the back-yard
rabbits and squirrels at home his kindergarten, then the wilderness
the old bear ran was his college, the old male bear itself, so long un-

wifed and childless as to have become its own ungendered progenitor, was his alma mater. But he never saw it.

He could find the crooked print now almost whenever he liked, fifteen or ten or five miles, or sometimes nearer the camp than that. Twice while on stand during the three years he heard the dogs strike its trail by accident; on the second time they jumped it seemingly, the voices high, abject, almost human in hysteria, as on that first morning two years ago. But not the bear itself. He would remember that noon three years ago, the glade, himself and the bear fixed during that moment in the windless and dappled blaze, and it would seem to him that it had never happened, that he had dreamed that too. But it had happened. They had looked at each other, they had emerged from the wilderness old as earth, synchronized to the instant by something more than the blood that moved the flesh and bones which bore them, and touched, pledged something, affirmed something more lasting than the frail web of bones and flesh which any accident could obliterate.

Then he saw it again. Because of the very fact that he thought of nothing else, he had forgotten to look for it. He was still hunting with Walter Ewell's rifle. He saw it cross the end of a long blowdown, a corridor where a tornado had swept, rushing through rather than over the tangle of trunks and branches as a locomotive would have, faster than he had ever believed it could move, almost as fast as a deer even, because a deer would have spent most of that time in the air, faster than he could bring the rifle sights up with it. And now he knew what had been wrong during all the three years. He sat on a log, shaking and trembling as if he had never seen the woods before nor anything that ran them, wondering with incredulous amazement how he could have forgotten the very thing which Sam Fathers had told him and which the bear itself had proved the next day and had now returned after three years to reaffirm.

And now he knew what Sam Fathers had meant about the right dog, a dog in which size would mean less than nothing. So when he returned alone in April—school was out then, so that the sons of farmers could help with the land's planting, and at last his father had granted him permission, on his promise to be back in four days—he had the dog. It was his own, a mongrel of the sort called by Negroes a fyce, a ratter, itself not much bigger than a rat and possessing that bravery which had long since stopped being courage and had become foolhardiness.

It did not take four days. Alone again, he found the trail on the first morning. It was not a stalk; it was an ambush. He timed the meeting almost as if it were an appointment with a human being. Himself holding the fyce muffled in a feed sack and Sam Fathers with two of the hounds on a piece of a piowline rope, they lay down wind of the trail at dawn of the second morning. They were so close that the bear turned without even running, as if in surprised amazement at the shrill and frantic uproar of the released fyce, turning at bay against the trunk of a tree, on its hind feet; it seemed to the boy that it would never stop rising, taller and taller, and even the two hounds seemed to take a desperate and despairing courage from the fyce, following it as it went in.

Then he realized that the fyce was actually not going to stop. He flung, threw the gun away, and ran; when he overtook and grasped the frantically pin-wheeling little dog, it seemed to him that he was directly under the bear.

He could smell it, strong and hot and rank. Sprawling, he looked up to where it loomed and towered over him like a cloudburst and colored like a thunderclap, quite familiar, peacefully and even lucidly familiar, until he remembered: This was the way he had used to dream about it. Then it was gone. He didn't see it go. He knelt, holding the frantic fyce with both hands, hearing the abashed wailing of the hounds drawing farther and farther away, until Sam came up. He carried the gun. He laid it down quietly beside the boy and stood looking down at him.

"You've done seed him twice now with a gun in your hands," he said. "This time you couldn't have missed him."

The boy rose. He still held the fyce. Even in his arms and clear of the ground, it yapped frantically, straining and surging after the fading uproar of the two hounds like a tangle of wire springs. He was panting a little, but he was neither shaking nor trembling now.

"Neither could you!" he said. "You had the gun! Neither did you!"

"And you didn't shoot," his father said. "How close were you?"
"I don't know, sir," he said. "There was a big wood tick inside his right hind leg. I saw that. But I didn't have the gun then."

"But you didn't shoot when you had the gun," his father said. "Why?"

But he didn't answer, and his father didn't wait for him to, rising and crossing the room, across the pelt of the bear which the boy had killed two years ago and the larger one which his father had killed before he was born, to the bookcase beneath the mounted head of the boy's first buck. It was the room which his father called the office, from which all the plantation business was transacted; in it for the fourteen years of his life he had heard the best of all talking. Major de Spain would be there and sometimes old General Compson, and Walter Ewell and Boon Hoggenback and Sam Fathers and Tennie's Jim, too, were hunters, knew the woods and what ran them.

He would hear it, not talking himself but listening—the wilderness, the big woods, bigger and older than any recorded document of white man fatuous enough to believe he had bought any fragment of it or Indian ruthless enough to pretend that any fragment of it had been his to convey. It was of the men, not white nor black nor red, but men, hunters with the will and hardihood to endure and the humility and skill to survive, and the dogs and the bear and deer juxtaposed and reliefed against it, ordered and compelled by and within the wilderness in the ancient and unremitting contest by the ancient and immitigable rules which voided all regrets and brooked no quarter, the voices quiet and weighty and deliberate for retrospection and recollection and exact remembering, while he squatted in the blazing firelight as Tennie's Jim squatted, who stirred only to put more wood on the fire and to pass the bottle from one glass to another. Because the bottle was always present, so that after a while it seemed to him that those fierce instants of heart and brain and courage and wiliness and speed were concentrated and distilled into that brown liquor which not women, not boys and children, but only hunters drank, drinking not of the blood they had spilled but some condensation of the wild immortal spirit, drinking it moderately, humbly even, not with the pagan's base hope of acquiring the virtues of cunning and strength and speed, but in salute to them.

His father returned with the book and sat down again and opened it. "Listen," he said. He read the five stanzas aloud, his voice quiet and deliberate in the room where there was no fire

now because it was already spring. Then he looked up. The boy
watched him. "All right," his father said. "Listen." He read again,
but only the second stanza this time, to the end of it, the last two
lines, and closed the book and put it on the table beside him.
"She cannot fade, though thou hast not thy bliss, for ever wilt
thou love, and she be fair," he said.

"He's talking about a girl," the boy said.

"He had to talk about something," his father said. Then he
said, "He was talking about truth. Truth doesn't change. Truth
is one thing. It covers all things which touch the heart—honor
and pride and pity and justice and courage and love. Do you see
now?"

He didn't know. Somehow it was simpler than that. There was
an old bear, fierce and ruthless, not merely just to stay alive, but
with the fierce pride of liberty and freedom, proud enough of the
liberty and freedom to see it threatened without fear or even alarm;
nay, who at times even seemed deliberately to put that freedom and
liberty in jeopardy in order to savor them, to remind his old strong
bones and flesh to keep supple and quick to defend and preserve
them. There was an old man, son of a Negro slave and an Indian
king, inheritor on the one side of the long chronicle of a people
who had learned humility through suffering, and pride through
the endurance which survived the suffering and injustice, and on
the other side, the chronicle of a people even longer in the land
than the first, yet who no longer existed in the land at all save in the
solitary brotherhood of an old Negro's alien blood and the wild
and invincible spirit of an old bear. There was a boy who wished
to learn humility and pride in order to become skillful and worthy
in the woods, who suddenly found himself becoming so skillful so
rapidly that he feared he would never become worthy because
he had not learned humility and pride, although he had tried to,
until one day and as suddenly he discovered that an old man who
could not have defined either had led him, as though by the hand,
to that point where an old bear and a little mongrel of a dog
showed him that, by possessing one thing other, he would possess
them both.

And a little dog, nameless and mongrel and many-fathered,
grown, yet weighing less than six pounds, saying as if to itself,
"I can't be dangerous, because there's nothing much smaller than

I am; I can't be fierce, because they would call it just a noise; I can't be humble, because I'm already too close to the ground to genuflect; I can't be proud, because I wouldn't be near enough to it for anyone to know who was casting the shadow, and I don't even know that I'm not going to heaven, because they have already decided that I don't possess an immortal soul. So all I can be is brave. But it's all right. I can be that, even if they still call it just noise."

That was all. It was simple, much simpler than somebody talking in a book about youth and a girl he would never need to grieve over, because he could never approach any nearer her and would never have to get any farther away. He had heard about a bear, and finally got big enough to trail it, and he trailed it four years and at last met it with a gun in his hands and he didn't shoot. Because a little dog— But he could have shot long before the little dog covered the twenty yards to where the bear waited, and Sam Fathers could have shot at any time during that interminable minute while Old Ben stood on his hind feet over them. He stopped. His father was watching him gravely across the spring-rife twilight of the room; when he spoke, his words were as quiet as the twilight, too, not loud, because they did not need to be because they would last, "Courage, and honor, and pride," his father said, "and pity, and love of justice and of liberty. They all touch the heart, and what the heart holds to becomes truth, as far as we know the truth. Do you see now?"

Sam, and Old Ben, and Nip, he thought. And himself too. He had been all right too. His father had said so. "Yes, sir," he said.

The Knife

BY

JOHN RUSSELL

THE THING that saved Jimmy Lee was his finding the knife. This is certain. If he had not found it he must have curled up and died of sheer helplessness with the sea-slugs and jellyfish and the other stranded specimens that festered in the sun on Rose Island beach. But while he was crawling along a coral ledge beside the lagoon, whimpering feebly and searching with vague notions of salvage from the wreck, he chanced to peer down into a purple-green pool. And there he caught the familiar shimmer of a knife-blade, silver and shadow alternately two fathom deep.

It is possible that much abler individuals than Jimmy Lee would have derived no consolation whatever from the discovery. Crusoe, for example. Crusoe would have scorned it. But then, that bloke Crusoe, he was blooming careful to get hisself cast away with all manner of fixings proper to a man-size shipwreck—wasn't he? Muskets and swords and bags of biscuit and kegs of rum. Crikey! Why couldn't it have happened to Jimmy Lee that way?

Jimmy knew about that bloke Crusoe. There had been some tattered pages of a book aboard the *Dundee,* pilfered from a Sailors' Mission in Auckland, on which he had feasted word by word at furtive moments of delight behind the galley stove. And as a matter of fact—talk of knowing things—he knew perfectly well why such splendid luck had not happened and never could have happened to him. . . . Not being man-size Jimmy Lee was aware of it.

Like all the failures of his oppressed and drudging life, this was just another failure—humiliating, self-convicting and thumb-handed, as usual—that now he had fallen into a real adventure, now his actual turn had come to be shipwrecked himself, he had neither food nor tool nor weapon of any kind.

175

Nothing—literally—except his six-penny shirt and the ragged trousers he stood in.

And even the trousers were an out-worn pair of Cookie Anderson's, flung at him by that dreaded tyrant months before—"so y' won't 'ave to pig it with the niggers in the foc'sle, quite. . . ."

"Not as y're any ways too good fer it, y' dirty wharf-rat," was Cookie's amiable method of presenting the gift. "Gawd knows y' got less spirit than the blackest woolly-head kanaka of the lot. But y're white-coloured—or might be if y' ever washed!" Here he twisted Jimmy's ears until Jimmy yelled, then kicked him out through the galley door and the trousers after him. "Whoopee: whee-whee-whee!" It was Cookie's warcry: something between a crow and a squeal: a hateful sound. "Skinny-legs. Pie-face. Left-over shank o' soup-meat!" he shrilled. "Get aht o' this, and don't show back till y're dressed like the bleedin' image of a man!"

Afterward he had the infernal inspiration to make an issue of those trousers. There was a pocket in them—the first pocket Jimmy had ever owned. It pleased a morbid streak in the cook's nature to point the possibilities of that pocket, on the theory—tacitly supposed if never admitted—that his victim might be meditating a desperate revenge.

"Nar then—nar then, wot y' 'iding in them britches?" he would nag, making painful inquisition with the toe of his boot or the flat of his hand. "A knife? Don't tell me y' gone and 'id a knife abaht y'!" Jimmy never risked hiding so much as a crust of bread, but Cookie would thrust forward his whittled, chinless face and lower his voice with subtly evil suggestion. "Count 'em out—d' y' 'ear? Count the knives out and let me see y' do it. Lord 'elp you if I ever catch y' sneaking one—mind that!"

For the most part of Jimmy's weary round had to do with knives. Hours and hours he spent on them, with pumice and whetstone.

There were the knives of the galley, first of all: butcher knives and carving knives and the knives for meals. They hung in gleaming ranks against the bulkhead—all kinds of knives, from the great two-foot cleaver that could unjoint an ox to the tiny, accurate blade designed for surgical operations on a potato. There were the broad and heavy oyster knives, brought into hard usage when the *Dundee* struck a strictly-preserved pearl bank and did a rare stroke of business while the shell rotted out through a hurried and smell-some week. There were the sheath-knives of the men—even the black deck-hands were privileged to carry their own, belted in swagger fashion against their lean rumps as a badge of independence and of manhood.

And every one of those knives had to pass under Jimmy's anxious care, to be kept bright and shiny and razor-keen. Cookie Anderson saw to that, though the best Jimmy could do never satisfied him. It was the man's obsession.

To the other whites on the schooner, naturally, the thing became in time an accepted jest, as any such current ugliness tends to be among tough and tarry minds. They witnessed this little drama of master and slave with a detached humour. And when the big mate, Gulbranson, might poke his shaggy head in at the scuttle, Jimmy would be whetting steadily away. Cookie at his own work would be keeping a watchful, malignant eye. Gulbranson would chuckle his warning in a hoarse aside:

"Look out for that young coot, Anderson. Look out he don't turn on y', some time. I see it in his eye—he'll get even on y' sure, some day!"

"Get aht! 'Im? I'd skin 'im like one of these 'ere spuds. Like to see 'im try it. Yes, or you either, y' big tripe. Or anyone." And the cook would flap his arms and crow excitedly only at the thought of it. "Whee-whee-whee! . . . My word, if anybody 'as a 'ankering, let 'im turn on me—that's all!"

Then Gulbranson would grin half contemptuously at the febrile creature, and half speculatively at the thin, yellow-haired, unformed youngster who sat so humbly by. Gulbranson never interfered. None of the others, from Cap'n Joe Brett down, ever interfered. They were open-air, unfanciful men, neither better nor worse than the run of island trading crews. They had served their own apprenticeships. If he survived, the lad must win his rightful rating for himself: meanwhile his net value lay in valeting the knives.

This was the age-old law of the sea that governed the case of Jimmy Lee: and this was the particular reason why Jimmy took his first effective impulse from a mere flickering reflection.

Through the water, churned by a wash of ground swell over the rocks, he could not see the thing clearly. But he made out its flat, clean, metallic lustre. A knife. Being a knife it was the thing he knew: a thing of daily use and habit. Being a knife it offered an object and a means—the whole difference between life and death.

It came in good time for Jimmy. •

Rose Island, to which his fate had drifted him, is one of the innumerable left-over remnants of the Pacific: a hummock of rock about the bigness of a battleship, ringed with shattered beach and the enclosing coral reef—the whole no more than a pinprick on any chart. Nobody goes to Rose Island. Messrs. Cook do not sell tickets to it. It lies on no route of trader or fisherman. . . . According to official legend it was visited once by a Naval Governor to set up an imposing notice:

ROSE ISLAND

AMERICAN SAMOA

NO TRESPASSING

Why any person should trespass, how he was to keep alive or in what manner go about removing himself if cast up as an unwilling trespasser, the Governor did not state. There stood his defiance amid the wastes of ocean: a stern reminder to marauding frigate birds and the piratical sea turtle.

By the time of the *Dundee's* venture hereabouts, however, this triumph of human prescience must have disappeared. The *Dundee* came on a fortune hunt, in hope of tracing a certain valuable lumber derelict, the *Yackarra,* last reported somewhere near the Manua group. She sighted Rose Island on the fourteenth of April. But it was no signboard that warned her off. She came close enough to observe how poor was the picking and to drop a comment in the higher criticism.

"They say Gawd made such places with the rest," remarked Cap'n Joe Brett. "Just as well for 'Im 'E didn't 'ave to put in no bill for this job. . . . What's the good of it, Gulbranson?"

To which the mate, a philosopher of sorts: "Well, you can't never tell, Cap'n. It maybe might come useful yet for some poor soul."

Three days later and some twelve miles further south they could have used the shelter of that isle themselves—poor souls!—and thankful. This occurred on the seventeenth of April: a date to be memorable throughout that region below the Line where history is counted in devastating storms. . . .

They had found their derelict, right enough: an old three-master kept afloat by her cargo of deals and tin-bound stacks of cedar shingles. They were in the act of passing a hawser aboard when a squall swept upon them like the black wings of Azrael. The kanaka at the wheel promptly lost his head, the *Dundee's* fore-boom jibbed and carried away its tackle, and the fore-mast snapped short.

Cookie Anderson, eager with the promise of loot, had been the first man overside. He was standing in the dinghy with Jimmy Lee to bear a hand at the moment all hell broke loose. The dinghy smashed against the channels. Cookie grabbed for a rope. Jimmie was in the way. With a shriek, Cookie snatched him back and sprang to safety on his sprawling body just as the dinghy went under.

What happened after that: how he was borne up in wreckage and flung to leeward on the *Yackarra's* rail; how he lay partly stunned and nearly drowned while the *Dundee* disappeared like a draggle-winged bird in the smother, how the derelict finally crashed on Rose Island reef and he came ashore among the "shingles"—serviceable life preservers with their binding of tin strips—these events were mercifully dim.

The first dependable fact he gripped was the presence of that knife.

As he crouched there by the ledge he had reached the fever stage of thirst. He began to think (a queer process for Jimmy) and he thought that if he had the knife he might slash the sappy vines and young trees that grew so thickly round about. In one place, too, were things like big green melons, hanging high up. With the knife fixed to a branch he might hack them loose. They might be good to suck. Crickey! He had the feel of cool juice squashing out and trickling down his throat, and he made puppy noises and bit his fingers in desire and despair.

For Jimmy could not swim. Worse than that his ingrained terror of the water had been most horridly confirmed. Worse than all, he was aware of dreadful dangers lurking down yonder, in the pool—he glimpsed their wavering fins and slow, snaky tentacles: mysterious and unnameable monsters.

. . . No. He dared not plunge in after the knife. Still, it was there; something to strive for. So instead of dying just yet, he stumbled along where the big fruits grew and tried to climb a tree.

He never had learned how to climb a tree. He slipped and floundered and very grievously barked his nose and his shins, and sat down and wept. But nobody being on hand to kick him and the process of thought continuing, after a while he took off his sixpenny shirt and tied it between his ankles as a loose bandage. And therewith when he tried again he hiked himself up, topside of a leaning trunk, exactly as the island natives do—the trick they have used time out of mind.

He knocked off a fruit. It proved unreasonably tough, but he managed to worry the fibre apart at one end. He jabbed into the core with a stick: something spurted, and he clapped his salt-tortured mouth to the most delicious, vivifying, heart-lifting draught that ever rejoiced an amateur castaway. A miracle to Jimmy, it might pass as a very fair miracle anyhow. He had discovered the aerial fountain of half the tropical world—the common green cocoanut!

Such was Jimmy's immediate salvation. Actually, he had broken the spell of horror, of loneliness, of hopelessness. Actually, he had derived motive and accomplishment from the one simple cause. And he continued to derive.

That night he had his first rest, undisturbed by lions and bears and other noxious beasts. By day he could see that there was no such game and scant cover to hide a cat. But in the dark, roaring with voices of wind and reef: who could be sure? He felt much safer to spread his dry seaweed beside the ledge, handy to a weapon which he might perhaps reach in desperate need—if he could ever bring himself to the risk.

Next day he tried to fork it out with a length of splintered bamboo. He nearly lost it altogether, but prodding around he chanced to impale a curious arrangement like a bunch of wriggling, soft, semi-translucent ribbons. Jimmy was mortally hungry. He tore the creature apart. He bit into it—with shrinkings, at first, and then with gusto. Later he improved his spear by wedging the splinters apart and sharpening them on the coral: and about the same time he began to regard the doings of the late Mr. Crusoe with rather less awe.

Again he blundered on a lucky discovery when he twisted some threads of cocoanut fibre into a crude net, weighted with pebbles. The clumsy device was no good as a dredge: it would not catch the knife at all. But when he buzzed it about his head and threw it at a

huddle of seabirds on the beach it brought down one ensnared, so
that he made an easy captive, and might have gone into the poultry
business on a large scale if he had been able to stomach raw fowl
as readily as raw rock-squid.

The matter of cookery, however, was reserved for his best performance. . . .

It came to an issue weeks afterward—after he had contrived his
hut of pandanus thatch, his cocohusk sandals for wading the sharp
reefs and his little coral hammer for gathering shell-fish at low tide;
his throwing stones and his sling and his dagger of cane. After he
had domesticated himself.

He still dwelt on the ledge above the purple-green pool. Between
flaming sunrise and blazing sunset, under fierce noons that made
the rocks dance in the heat haze, within the whole thunderous ring
of his prison was no other refuge for the poor wharf-rat. The
Yackarra had broken up long since, dispersed as flotsam. But there
was no help in battered planks and shingle bundles. Whereas he was
always conscious of the knife as a piece of man's handiwork: a comfort and a prize to be struggled for: a vision that enforced the trembling will to live.

Once, as he sat brooding and glooming over it, he pictured how
he might get at it with a hook of some sort. Hooks would be useful
for his fishing, too. They might be carved of clamshell, he imagined,
and he remembered how Cookie Anderson through quiet evenings
had used cunningly and patiently to drill out shell bracelets with
an instrument he called a "Yankee fiddle."

Now a hook after all, is nothing but the segment of a bracelet,
and a Yankee fiddle is nothing in the world but a stout bow and
arrow, with two loops of string to twirl the shaft. Jimmy had already made rude experiments in that direction, so he took his own
bow and arrow and put his weight to them as he had seen Cookie
do, and set to work.

First he tried on shell, and then he noticed what surprising heat
sprang up under his fingers, on slips of wood. He failed many times.
But there came a moment when he started a curling blue wisp, and
then a live spark from the bamboo dust. . . .

On all accounts, this marks the climax of Jimmy's adventure. It
is the point for wonder, and for pride in human potential, that
alone and unaided by any Crusoe fixings whatever the cook's-boy

had wrested from a howling wilderness food, shelter, tools and finally—fire. No mean achievement, it may be said: the sort of achievement easily doubted by a generation too wise to believe in desert islands. But the fact stands indubitably attested—the sole cause and the direct cause of Jimmy's rescue.

> *June 6—Friday.* 14° 30″ S. 68° 11″ W. *Fresh breeze out of S. E. No sign of derelict which likely drifted too far or smashed up. If not sighted to-morrow we shape for Butaritari. . . . Afternoon, smoke observed to south. Supposing it might be wreckers or ship on fire, bore up toward Rose Island.*

Thus the log of the schooner *Dundee.*

The log of the *Dundee* was, and it continues to be, a strictly unfanciful, open-air chronicle: and that is why it contains no mention of a missing cook's-boy—regretful or otherwise—between the dates of his tragic disappearance and his most unexpected recovery. The *Dundee* herself had been laying up for repairs these last two months in Apia roadstead. Once more at sea, she had put in some few days in perfunctory search. Not for Jimmy, of course, but for the lost *Yackarra.* Not for Jimmy, whose existence had never occurred as a possibility until the *Dundee's* surf-boat entered the lagoon and her crew blinked toward the beach. . . . Even then they were slow enough about it.

"Now what t' Sam Hill sort of guy would you take that to be?" inquired Gulbranson.

At the edge of the rocks popped up a figure, squinting through the slanted sunlight. A stalwart figure, nearly naked, with the remnant of ragged trousers about its waist. Weathered to a ruddy bronze, with a skin fine-drawn on the coiling muscles—startled and alert as he stood at gaze—the fellow might have seemed some able young native on the isles. But no native ever wore a great shock of blonde hair—yellow as corn-silk! And certainly no native would ever have given the curious, wild shout of recognition he loosed across at them.

"Whee-whee-whee!" So it sounded.

Cap'n Joe Brett was sitting in the stern sheets: Gulbranson beside him. On the next thwart sat Cookie Anderson, a volunteer under the pious plea of gathering turtles' eggs for dinner. Two white sailors were rowing—for Cap'n Joe, not knowing what he might find, had not cared to bring the blacks.

All hands stared beachward, and stared at each other. "Good gosh!" remarked Gulbranson. "It's Jimmy Lee!"

They were close enough to be sure, for all the mad improbability of it. They could see it was Jimmy Lee. And they saw more. . . . Suddenly the little brown apparition broke into the strangest activity. It began to leap: it began to dance. It hammered its chest and flapped its arms and crowed abroad like a game-cock.

" 'E's gone crazy!" opined Cap'n Joe.

Gulbranson put up a hand.

"Listen——"

"Whoopee!" came the amazing challenge: a voice harsh with disuse, and with something else—sheer exultation. "I see you there: I'm talkin' to you, y' dirty sea-cook!" Followed the name of Cookie Anderson, three times running. "You 'ear me? Kettle-scraper. 'Ash-slinger. I'm lookin' for you. I been waitin' for you! . . . Whoopee-whee-whee!"

They listened, all of them, dumbly, while comprehension began to creep over each bewildered face. . . . But the figure on the rock still held them in its singular demonstration. It turned. It paused. It poised for an instant with an indefinable last gesture of suspense and hesitation: then with a triumphant yell it sprang forward, cleaving the water in a clean, deep dive. When it reappeared and climbed the rock again it held an object that flashed in the sun.

The four others in the boat glanced around at Cookie Anderson. They remembered. They had a perfectly clear sequence of that little galley drama aboard the *Dundee* between master and slave: the misery, the cruelty and the crowning treachery. And with the simple humour of tough and tarry minds, they understood: that is to say, they got the situation well enough—the essential justice of it as Cap'n Joe Brett summed up for them, grimly:

"Not so bloomin' crazy, after all!"

The boat had drawn very near the ledge. Cookie Anderson sat crouched like a thing of venom. His lips were lifted on the yellow teeth: his little eyes showed red. " 'E's got a knife!" he squealed.

All the evil of his twisted nature spat in the word. He bunched himself eagerly toward the gunwale, and swiftly his own dirk was

out and gleaming. . . . But Gulbranson knocked it from his grip
and overboard with one contemptuous sweep.

"No, he ain't. Look there!"

For Jimmy Lee had cast his own weapon aside. He was coming
to meet the boat, and coming empty-handed. "Knife be damned!"
said Gulbranson.

"I tol' you how it would be," he chuckled. "I tol' you he'd turn
on y'! The young coot was bound to get square some day. . . . Man
to man, Even Stephen—and we'll all see fair play!"

He laughed: they all laughed. Cookie was like a snake deprived
of its sting. He would have shrunk away, but they boosted him forward. At the last he would have begged and cringed, but they
booted him out on the strand and stood round him as a ring, until
for mere shame he took position. As Gulbranson stepped over to
referee, his foot caught in something so that he almost tripped. It
was the thing that Jimmy had plunged for: the thing he had finally
thrown away—a thin band of shimmery metal—one of those tin
strips in which shingle bundles are bound. . . . But it meant nothing
to Gulbranson. And it meant nothing to Jimmy Lee. Smiling, confident—hard and able—he came up to settle his score and to take his
rightful rating at last with nothing but his two fists, man-fashion,
in the age-old way of the sea.

Crime Without Passion

BY

BEN HECHT

M<small>R. L</small>OU H<small>ENDRIX</small> looked at the lady he had been pretending to love for the past six months and, being a lawyer, said nothing. Mr. Hendrix was a gentleman who could listen longer to female hysterics without unbending than was normal. This, he would have said, was due to his aloof and analytical mind. Then, also, the events which were taking place in this boudoir at the moment were of a familiar pattern. Some eight or nine times Mr. Hendrix had been the hero of just such climaxes as this, when new love had entered his life, and necessitated similar farewells.

The young lady who, this time, was doing the screaming was a nymph of the cabarets, known as Brownie. Her full name was Carmen Browne. She danced, and very effectively, at the El Bravo Club where, devoid of plumage as an eel, she led the Birds of Paradise number. In this she was ravishing as a Dream of Fair Women.

Why so young and delicious a siren as Brownie should be so disturbed over the amorous defections of Mr. Hendrix would have confused anyone who knew this gentleman or merely took a one minute look at him. He was not Romeo nor was he Adonis, nor was he even such a male as one associates with the general practise of seduction. He was a little man with that objectionable immaculateness which reminds one, instanter, of sheep's clothing. He was one of those popinjays of the flesh pots with the face of a tired and sarcastic boy. His sideburns were a wee too long, his smile unduly persistent (like a ballet dancer's), his voice far too gentle to have deceived anyone, except perhaps a woman, as to his spiritual composition. But one can always depend on the ladies to misunderstand the combination of gentleness and sideburns.

Brownie, who among her own kind was considered not only quite a reader of books but a sort of practical authority on masculine characteristics, had misunderstood Lou Hendrix, amazingly. Carry on as she would now she was no match for this *caballero* of the law who, out of a clear sky, was engaged in giving her what she called "the go-by." As her monologue of screams, epithets and sobs progressed the lovely and muscular girl understod it all. She perceived, much too late for any use, that she had to do with as purring a hypocrite, rogue and underhanded soul as one might flush in a seven-day hunt on Broadway, which, according to the chroniclers Brownie most admired, is the world's leading water hole for human beasts of prey.

Looking around at the pretty apartment in which Mr. Hendrix had installed her and in which she had lorded it over her friends for the six months and from which she must now exit—love's dream being ended, Brownie spread herself on the couch and filled her Sybaritic diggings with a truly romantic din. From the more coherent utterances of this tearstained beauty it seemed that she was innocent of all dallyings with a certain Eddie White, an ex-college hero, and that since leaving this same Mr. White whose love interest she had been before the Birds of Paradise number was staged, she had never once permitted him to lay a finger on her. She was, wailed Brownie, being wrongly accused. Then, sitting up, her greenish eyes popping with rage until they looked like a pair of snake heads, Brownie laughed, as she would have said, scornfully, and declared that she could see through Mr. Hendrix and his so-called jealousy. He was getting rid of her because he didn't love her any more. He was tiring of her and putting her on the escalator—that was all there was to it.

To this, Mr. Hendrix, thoroughly seen through, made no reply and Brownie, announcing that she was not going to be made a sucker of, fell back on the couch, beat some cushions with her fists and shook with grief. The telephone rang. Brownie straightened on the couch.

"It's probably for you," she said.

"More likely it's Mr. White," said Mr. Hendrix.

The taunt brought Brownie to her feet.

"If it's for me, by any mischance," said Mr. Hendrix, "say I'm not here."

Brownie spoke into the phone.

"Who?" she asked. "No, he's not here. No, I don't know when he'll be here. No, no, I don't expect him." Hanging up she looked bitterly at Mr. Hendrix. "Your office," she said. "Always making me lie for you."

"You might have been a bit more polite," said Mr. Hendrix.

The heartlessness of this suggestion sent Brownie back to the couch and her grief. She resumed her sobs. Mr. Hendrix continued to regard her with creditable, if villainous, detachment. His heart was in the highlands with another lassie. But even discounting that factor Mr. Hendrix felt he was pursuing a wise course in ridding himself of so obstreperous an admirer as lay howling here. He had no use for over-emotional types. They were inclined to drive diversion, which was Mr. Hendrix' notion of Cupid, out of the window with their caterwauling.

Mr. Hendrix' soul, in fact, was a sort of china closet and he was firm in his aversion to flying hooves. He belonged to that tribe of Don Juans, rather numerous at the Broadway hole, who never hang themselves for love. Tears he regarded as bad sportsmanship and heartbreak was to him plain blackmail. Beauty—and by beauty Mr. Hendrix meant chiefly those delicious and agile Venuses of the cabaret floor-shows—beauty had been put into Broadway (if not into the world) for man's delight; certainly not for his confusion and despair. And this little barrister lived elegantly, if rather villainously, by this conception.

A number of things, all obvious to the analytical Mr. Hendrix, were now operating in Brownie's mind and making her wail— Eddie's vengeful delight at her getting the go-by from his successor; the tittering of the little group of columnists, hoofers, waiters and good-time Charlies whom she called the World; the lessening of her status as a siren—she might even be demoted from leading the Birds of Paradise Number, and through all these considerations—the Nerve of the Man, throwing her down as if she were some Nobody! As for the more passional side of the business, the pain in her heart at losing someone she had so stupidly loved and misunderstood and at losing the foolish Broadwayish dream of wedlock she had cherished for half a year, Brownie chose not to mention these in her ravings, being too proud.

Mr. Hendrix, still preserving his finest courtroom manner of Reason and Superiority, watched on in silence and fell to wondering

what he had even seen in this red-headed, almost illiterate creature
with her muscular legs and childish face to have ever considered
her charming or desirable. But he was given small time to meditate
this problem of idealization. Brownie, with a yell that set the base
of his spine tingling, leaped from the couch, stared wildly around
and then, emitting a series of shrill sounds, had at the furnishings
of the Love Nest. She pulled a portière down, hurled two vases to
the floor, swung a chair against the wall and smashed it, beat Mr.
Hendrix' framed photograph to bits against the edge of the piano,
seized a clock from the mantelpiece and bounced it on the floor and
was making for Mr. Hendrix' derby, which he had placed on a
chair near the door, when he, with an unexpected shout, headed
her off.

The barrister defending his derby received a blow on the side of
his face that sent him spinning. A thrown object caught him behind
the ear. Brownie's pointed shoes belabored his shins. He retreated.
But the hysteria to which he had been coolly and analytically listening seemed suddenly to have been injected, like a virus, into his
bloodstream. It had started with the tingling in the base of his spine.
Smarting from blows and full of some sort of electric current which
gave off oaths in his head, the little lawyer began to out-bellow his
now ex-paramour. He came at the lady and in his hand he held,
almost unaware of the fact, a large brass candlestick.

What it was that made this popinjay, so renowned for coolness,
strategy and cynicism in his twin professions of amour and the law,
so completely shed his character, God alone, who was not at Mr.
Hendrix' elbow at the moment, could have told; and perhaps a psy-
chiatrist or two might also have made a guess at. But here he was
much too far gone for analysis, his own or anyone else's, charging
at the lovely Carmen Browne like a bantam cave man, screaming
and swinging the heavy piece of brass in the air.

There was no precedent in Mr. Hendrix' life for such a turn of
events and no hint in any of his former love doings that passion
could so blind his faculties and hate so fill his heart. Yet blind he
was and full of a clamorous hate that demanded something of him.
From the oaths which escaped Mr. Hendrix during this preliminary
skirmish with the brass candlestick, it seemed that what he hated
was women; loathed and hated them with a fury out of the Pit.
Announcing this he swung the piece of brass and the second swing

exhilarated him the more. It had struck squarely against Brownie's head, dropping her to the carpet. Mr. Hendrix, out of breath, stood cursing and grimacing over her like a murderer.

Slowly the little lawyer's rage melted. His heart swelled with terror and the nape of his neck grew warm. Brownie lay as she had fallen. He leaned over. Her skull was cracked. Blood was running. Her eyes were closed. Her legs, exposed in an incongruously graceful sprawl, were inert. He put his ear to her bosom. There was no heart beating. He stood for several minutes holding his breath and listening automatically for sounds outside the door. The choking sensation in his lungs subsided and the cool, analytical mind that was Mr. Hendrix returned like some errant accomplice tiptoeing back to the scene of the crime.

Carmen Browne lay dead on her hearthstone. No more would she lead the Birds of Paradise number at the El Bravo Club. But Mr. Hendrix wasted no time considering this sentimental phase of the matter. He had committed a murder, without intent, to be sure, even in self-defense, looked at factually. But no, self-defense wouldn't hold, Mr. Hendrix was thinking swiftly. There rushed through his mind all the angles, holes, difficulties, improbabilities and prejudices of his case and in less than a minute the little lawyer had put himself on trial on a plea of self-defense and found himself guilty.

Since a young man, Mr. Hendrix had always been close to crime. He had had that unmoral and intellectual understanding of it which helps make one type of excellent lawyer. In action, defending a criminal, Mr. Hendrix had always been like some imperturbable surgeon. Guilt was a disease that could be cured, not by any operation on the soul of its victim, but by a process of legerdemain which convinced a jury that no guilt existed. Mr. Hendrix might have said that he served a cause beyond good and evil, that of extricating the victims of fleeting misadvanture from the unjustly permanent results of their deeds.

Thus, far beyond most men who might have found themselves confronted by the strange and ugly dilemma of having unexpectedly committed a murder, Mr. Hendrix was prepared for his new role of criminal. He knew all the ropes, he knew all the pitfalls of the defense of such a case as this. He knew the psychology of the prosecution. And with an expert, if slightly still fevered mind, he knew the perfect details by which his guilt might be cured, the ideal evidence, persuasive and circumstantial, by which a jury could be cajoled to the verdict of not guilty.

In less than a minute, Mr. Hendrix had a full grasp of his case, seeing far into its convolutions and difficulties. He set about straightening these out.

But like some dramatic critic who, after observing plays for years with subtle and intimate understanding of them, is summoned suddenly on the stage and with the strange footlights glaring in his eyes told to perform the part whose words he knows, whose ideal gesture and intonation he has always dreamed about, Mr. Hendrix felt the panic of debut. To know and to act were phenomena surprisingly separate. This was what delayed the cautious barrister for another minute, a minute during which Mr. Hendrix' client, with beating heart and white face, mumbled for speed, chattered even of flight.

But at the end of this second minute Mr. Hendrix had elbowed this ignominious client into a far corner of his mind, seated him as it were at the counsel's table with orders to keep his mouth shut— and taken charge of the case. He leaned over and looked at the clock on the floor. The dial glass was broken. The clock had stopped, its hands at two minutes of four. Mr. Hendrix' thoughts were rapid, almost as if he were not thinking at all but knowing. He could move the hands forward to five o'clock. He could leave the premises undetected, if possible, and attach himself for the next two hours to a group of prospective alibi witnesses, remain with them during the hours between four-ten and seven and this would be the proof he had not been in the apartment at the time of the murder. Mr. Hendrix examined the watch on Carmen Browne's wrist. It too had stopped. It registered one minute after four. The two time pieces, evidently synchronized by their owner, told a graphic and substantially correct tale. At 3:58 the struggle had begun. At 4:01 the woman was killed. He would have to set the wrist-watch forward a ful hour to preserve this interesting discrepancy in the stopped clocks.

The telephone rang. Mr. Hendrix straightened, not having touched either of the hour hands. He had actually anticipated a telephone ringing, and in this anticipation known the ruse of the forwarded time hands was stupid. At 3:50 Carmen Browne had answered a phone call, a record of which was with the switchboard man in the lobby. Now at 4:03—he consulted his own watch—she

failed to answer. Other phone calls might likewise come before five
o'clock, all of which Carmen Browne would fail to answer, thus
establishing an important series of witnesses against the fact that
the murdered woman had been alive between four and five o'clock;
thus rendering his alibi of his own whereabouts during that time
practically futile. There was also the possibility that the neighbors
had heard their quarrel and noted the time of the screaming. And
more than all these the chance that someone, a maid or the building agent (Carmen Browne had been consulting him about sublet-
ting her place) might enter the room before five o'clock.

It was the hour preceding 4:01 for which Mr. Hendrix needed an
alibi. He already knew its vital ground work. At 3:50 Carmen
Browne, alive, had told someone on the phone—probably Tom
Healey of his own law firm—that he was not in her apartment. Mr.
Hendrix' eyes had remained on his own wrist watch as his thought
slipped through these pros and cons. It was 4:04. He glanced at the
sprawled figure on the floor, shivered, but stood his ground. Another phase of his case had overcome him. He smiled palely, shocked
at what had almost been an oversight. He must not only provide
an alibi for himself but fortify it with evidence tending to prove
someone other than he had done the deed. He must invent a mythical murderer—leave a trail of evidence for the sharp eyes and wits
of the prosecution leading to Another—a never to be found another,
but yet one always present in the Case.

Carmen Browne's fingerprints were on the broken clock, the
smashed chair, the battered photo frame. This was wrong. It would
reveal that it was Carmen who had been in the rage, smashing
things, demanding something that had resulted in her murder—and
this sort of a situation, brought out by the prosecution, might easily
point to Lou Hendrix, known to have been her lover. No, said
Lawyer Hendrix swiftly, it must have been her assailant, demanding
something of Carmen Browne, who had been in the rage and done
the smashing and struck the fatal blow. Mr. Hendrix established
this fact circumstantially by wiping Carmen Browne's fingerprints
from the objects in question with a silk handkerchief. The absence
of fingerprints pointed to a certain self-consciousness on the part of
the assailant after the deed but that was both legitimate and normal.
Men of the deepest passion, and there was precedence for this, remembered to obliterate evidence.

At the door Mr. Hendrix, in his hat, overcoat and gloves, paused. He repeated to himself carefully, Carmen Browne had been attacked by some suitor, jealous of her real sweetheart, Mr. Hendrix, as witness the destroyed photograph of the latter. But why hadn't she used the gun the police would find in the desk drawer two feet from the spot where her body lay? There were, of course, normal explanations to be put forward. But Mr. Hendrix did not admire them legally. For fifteen seconds Lawyer Hendrix balanced the issue. During this space Mr. Hendrix listened rather than thought. He listened to the prosecution pointing out to the jury that the reason Carmen Browne had not reached for this available weapon with which to defend herself was because she had not expected an attack from her assailant, because the assailant was one familiar to her against whom she had no thought of arming herself; and even further, because the assailant, all too familiar with the premises, knew where this gun was as well as did Carmen Browne, and prevented her from reaching it. All these values pointed shadowly, Mr. Hendrix perceived, at his client. He removed the gun from the drawer and dropped it into his coat pocket. He must be careful in disposing of the weapon and Mr. Hendrix' mind dwelt stubbornly on a dozen cases in which an attempt at post-crime-evidence disposal had been the connecting link with guilt. But Mr. Hendrix assured his client firmly that he would be more cautious in this regard than any of his previous defendants had been.

With the gun in his coat pocket Mr. Hendrix stepped out of the apartment. Now he was, he knew, purely in the hands of luck. A door opening, a neighbor appearing would ruin his case instantly. But no untoward event happened. He had three floors to descend. He listened at the ornamental elevator doors. Both cages were going up. Mr. Hendrix walked quickiy down the three flights and coolly, now, like a gambler rather than a lawyer, rehearsed the possible permutations of Luck.

He had entered the apartment at three o'clock that morning with Carmen Browne. But because it was his habit to preserve a surface air of respectability toward the attendants of the place, though he fancied they knew well enough what was going on, he had walked up to the apartment with Brownie. The switchboard operator concealed in an alcove in the lobby had not seen them come in, nor had the elevator boy on duty, as both were out of sight at the moment. If now he could leave the building with the equal but vitally more important luck of not being seen, his case would be more than launched.

The lobby was empty, but Mr. Hendrix did not make the mistake of slipping out too quickly, and coddling the presumption that no eyes had observed him. He knew too well the possibility of the unexpected witness and he paused to study the premises. The switchboard attendant, half hidden in the alcove, had his back to the lobby and was reading a newspaper. Both elevator cages were out of sight. There was no one else. Mr. Hendrix stepped into the street.

Here again he stopped to look for that unexpected witness. How often, he remembered grimly, had the best of his cases been tumbled by the appearance on the stand of those aimless, incalculable human strays who had "Seen the Defendant." Mr. Hendrix saw two of just that type. Two women were walking, but with their backs to him and away from the apartment. A delivery truck was passing. Mr. Hendrix noticed that the driver was talking to a companion and that neither of these passers looked in his direction. There was no one else. Mr. Hendrix turned his attention to the windows across the street. Only the first three floors mattered. Identification was impossible, or at least could be sufficiently challenged, from any great height. The windows were empty. As for the windows of the building directly over him, if he kept close to the wall none could see him from these.

Satisfied with this rapid but concentrated scrutiny, Mr. Hendrix started walking toward the corner. If the triumph of intellect over nerves, of reason over the impulses of the senses may be called heroism, then this smiling, casually moving little popinjay in the black derby and snug overcoat might well be called a hero. Innocence, even aimlessness, was in his every movement; and in his refusal, despite a driving curiosity to look at the time on his wrist—a telltale gesture were it recorded by anyone—there was something approaching the loftiness of purpose which distinguished the ancient Ascetics. As he turned the corner, Mr. Hendrix, still unruffled, still amiably rhythmic in his movements, looked back to make sure no taxicabs had entered the street. None had.

He was now on 6th Avenue and he moved more briskly. He had four blocks to walk and habit sent his eyes looking for a taxicab. But alert to every variety of witness, he shook his head and stayed afoot.

He smiled, remembering that his own bed in his own apartment was unmade. He had just turned in the night before when Brownie had telephoned and asked to meet him. Thus his housekeeper, who never arrived before noon, would establish simply the fact that he had slept at home. This was unnecessary, to be sure, unless some passerby had seen Brownie and a man enter the former's apartment at three this morning.

Mr. Hendrix arrived now at a 6th Avenue cinema palace. He looked carefully over the small crowd, waiting for tickets and then joined the line. In a few minutes he was being ushered into the roped enclosure at the rear of the auditorium. He slipped away quickly, however, and walked in the dark to the other side of the theatre. He approached one of the ushers and demanded to know where he could report the loss of a pair of gloves. After a brief colloquy he was led to the office of the lost and found department and here Mr. Hendrix, very voluble and affable, explained his mishap. He was not, he smiled, usually so careless with his belongings but the picture had been so engrossing that he had forgotten all about his haberdashery. Then Mr. Hendrix gave his name, address, a description of the missing gloves and watched with a glow of deep creative satisfaction the time being written down on the blank form used for cataloguing such matters. "Four-eighteen," the man wrote and Mr. Hendrix, consulting his watch, pretended to be startled. Was it that late, he demanded, good Lord! he had had no idea of the time. It was quite a long picture. And the Lost and Found official, drawn into chumminess by Mr. Hendrix' affability, agreed that the film was a little longer than most, but well worth sitting through—to which Mr. Hendrix heartily assented.

Emerging from the movie palace, Mr. Hendrix rehearsed his case to date. The main body of his alibi was achieved. He had spent the time between two-thirty and four watching a movie. His continued presence at four-eighteen in this theatre was written down in black and white. He had also taken care that it should be a movie he had already seen so as to be able to recite its plot were he questioned in the next few hours. And he had also provided a motive for seeing this particular movie. The film had to do with the character and career of a mythical state's attorney, and a newspaper friend of Mr. Hendrix who conducted a gossip column had asked him to contribute a few paragraphs from a legal point of view carping at the improbabilities of the scenario.

Mr. Hendrix' next port of call was an elegant speakeasy. Here he had a drink, engaged in an exchange of views with the bartender, who knew him, asked the correct time so he might adjust his watch. At 4:50 he stepped into a phone booth in the place and called his office. He inquired whether anybody had been trying to reach him that afternoon. The law clerk on duty for the firm, Tom Healey, answered as Mr. Hendrix had expected. Mr. Healey said he had been trying to find him in relation to a disposition but had been unable to locate him. At this Mr. Hendrix feigned a light anger. Where had the incompetent youth called? He had, said Mr. Healey, tried everywhere, even Miss Carmen Browne's apartment.

At this bit of information Mr. Hendrix, in his mind's eye addressing one of his future star witnesses, changed his voice. He grew angry and very obviously so, for he knew the laziness of people's memory and their slipshod powers of observation. He inquired sourly if Mr. Healey had spoken to Miss Browne. On hearing that he had, Mr. Hendrix said:

"Do you mind telling me how she seemed when you asked if I was there?"

"Well, I don't know," Mr. Healey said.

"Try and think," said Mr. Hendrix, "I'd like to know."

"Well," said Mr. Healey, "come to think of it, she struck me as a little curt or upset about something."

"Ha!" said Mr. Hendrix and, to the surprise of his office underling, called the young lady a villainous name.

"I don't want you to call me up at her place any more." He raised his voice. The clerk, Mr. Healey, said he would never do it again, but Mr. Hendrix, as though too enraged to notice his promise continued. "I'm all washed up at that telephone number. Understand what I mean? You can just forget about it. Any other calls?"

"No," said Mr. Healey.

"O.K.," said Mr. Hendrix and hung up the phone with an angry bang.

He walked from the speakeasy with the light step which to Mr. Hendrix' office colleagues always characterized a Not Guilty ver-

dict in sight. Now that the tingling at the base of his spine as well
as the annoying warmth on the nape of his neck, as if a Prosecuting
Staff were actually breathing on him, had gone entirely, Mr. Hendrix was beginning to feel not only relaxed but even amused. He
could hear the Prosecution falling into this little trap he had just
laid.

Question: So Mr. Hendrix told you that you needn't try to reach
him at Miss Browne's apartment any more?

Answer: Yes, sir.

And Lawyer Hendrix looked winningly at the jury that sat in his
mind's eye. Gentlemen of the Jury, consider this. As if, having committed a crime the defendant would be so gauche as to give himself away by some such oafish remark to a law-clerk—a type of person trained to remember what he hears. Not a casual stranger, mind
you, but a man with sharp and practiced wits.

Mr. Hendrix, skittering happily along the street, cleared his
throat, beamed, felt a desire to laugh. He had never quite so enjoyed a case. What subtle and yet vital psychological proof of his
innocence was the fact that he had just said to Tom Healey what
he had; what perfect proof of the fact that he had been the victim
of an obvious coincidence in saying he was washed up with Carmen
Browne when she lay dead in her apartment. No guilty man would
ever have said that.

From a drug store he was passing, Mr. Hendrix made another
telephone call. He called Carmen Browne. Inquiring for her of the
apartment switchboard operator a sharp excitement stirred him.
Before his eyes the image of her body sprawled gracefully and awfully on the floor at his feet swayed for a moment. He hoped the
crime had been discovered, although there were still chances to improve his Case. But the switchboard man calmly plugged in for
Carmen Browne's apartment.

"She doesn't answer," he said after a pause.

"This is Mr. Hendrix calling," said Mr. Hendrix. "Has she been
in at all? I've been trying to get her all day."

"Hasn't come in while I've been here," said the man.

"How long is that?" said Mr. Hendrix.

"Oh, about three hours," said the man.

"Thank you," said Mr. Hendrix and hung up.

He had told Tom Healey he was washed up with Carmen Browne

and now he was trying to reach her, and Mr. Hendrix considered this paradox, in behalf of his client, with a smile. It revealed, Gentlemen of the Jury, a distracted man; a lover full of confusion as a result of—what? Of the fact, gentlemen, Mr. Hendrix purred to himself, that my client was jealous of the attentions he had found out someone was paying to Carmen Browne; that he did not believe the poor girl's protestations of innocence and, driven from her side by suspicions, was yet lured back to her by his deep love. Jealous, Gentlemen of the Jury, of the attentions being paid to Carmen Browne by this creature who that very afternoon had entered her apartment and against whom Carmen Browne had defended herself until struck down and killed.

To augment this phase of the case, Mr. Hendrix returned now to the apartment building in which Carmen Browne lay murdered. He approached the switchboard operator, who greeted him by name. Here Mr. Hendrix controlled a curious impulse that whitened the skin around his mouth. He felt impelled to ask this man whether he had noticed Mr. Hendrix in the building before, whether he had seen him during the few moments he had walked from the lobby an hour ago. Astonished at this impulse, Mr. Hendrix held his tongue for a space, aware that the switchboard man was looking at him with curiosity.

Question: How did the defendant seem?

Answer: Confused.

Gentlemen of the Jury, and how would a man, consumed with jealousy, seen while inquiring, against all his pride, if the woman he thought was wronging him, was home?

"Has Miss Browne come in since I called?" asked Mr. Hendrix.

"I haven't seen her," said the man. "I'll try her apartment again."

There was no response.

"Give her this note when she comes back," said Mr. Hendrix.

He wrote on the lower part of a business letter from his pocket.

"Darling, if you are innocent, don't torture me any more. Give me a chance to believe you. I'm willing to forget what I heard or thought I heard over the phone. As ever, Lou."

He placed this in a used envelope, scribbled her name on it, and sealed it.

Gentlemen of the Jury, can you imagine any man who had killed a woman he loved or had loved, so lost to all human reaction, so fiendishly wanton as to have written that little plea when he knew she was lying dead at his hands?

That was merely a rhetorical overtone, the human rather than evidential side of the note, but Mr. Hendrix filed it away in his memory as a bit of decoration. His alibi, Lawyer Hendrix murmured to himself, was now complete. But the secondary phase of the case needed further effort. The beauty of a case lay always in the elaborateness of diverse but corroborating detail—as if the world were crying the defendant's innocence from every nook and cranny. And happily at work, Mr. Hendrix had lawyer-like so far forgotten the human existence of his client as to whistle cheerily the while he turned over and re-turned over the major psychological problem in his mind.

Defense—Carmen Browne had been murdered by a man to whom she refused, after perhaps leading him on, to surrender herself. Also it might be that the killing had been one of those passional accidents which the sex instinct, run amok, precipitates. It might be that Carmen Browne had led a double life and was discovered in this double life by her slayer.

Ergo—Lou Hendrix, sharp-witted, observant, a veritable connoisseur of women, must suspect the existence of this other man. And Defendant Hendrix must also be jealous of him.

Witness to this—his talk to Tom Healey; his note to Carmen Browne now in the hands of the switchboard operator.

And Lawyer Hendrix, with the thrill of a gambler rolling a third lucky seven, remembered at this point a third witness—a veritable star witness, beautifully, if unwittingly, prepared for her role a few days ago. This was Peggy Moore.

Miss Moore danced at the El Bravo Club as a member of the ensemble. She had been Brownie's confidante for a year. Mr. Hendrix smiled blissfully recalling his conversation with Miss Moore less than a week ago and recalling also her general character, one made to order for the part he was to assign her.

This young lady was a tall, dark-haired Irish lassie with slightly bulging eyes and an expression of adenoidal and not unpleasing vacuity about her face. She was, as Brownie had frequently confined to him, a veritable love slave, a dithering creature incapable of thinking or talking on any subject other than the emotions stirred in her bosom by love or jealousy.

Some days ago Mr. Hendrix had selected this almost congenital idiot as the opening pawn in his decision to rid himself of Brownie. He had confided to Miss Moore's ears, so perfectly attuned to all tales of amorous agony, that he suspected Brownie of being still in love with his predecessor, Eddie White. Miss Moore's eyes had bulged, her mouth opened as if to disgorge a fish hook and simultaneously a shrewd, if transparent emotion, had overcome her. Miss Moore, the victim of so much perfidy, had been convinced instanter of her chum's guilt and had launched at once into a series of lies, all defending Brownie's integrity and offering idiotic details of her devotion to her lawyer lover. Mr. Hendrix, intent on laying some foolish groundwork for his subsequent defection, had persisted, however, and, for no other reason than that he delighted in playing the human fraud whenever he could, had feigned sorrow and talked of woe.

Now Mr. Hendrix summoned Miss Moore on the telephone to meet him at the speakeasy he had recently quitted. He spoke guardedly, hinting at a lovers' quarrel, and pretending he needed her to verify some evidences of Brownie's guilt, just unearthed. Miss Moore, full of a laudable and loyal ambition to lie her head off in Brownie's behalf, as Mr. Hendrix had foreseen, arrived in a rush. And the two sat down at a table in a corner, Miss Moore to invent innocent explanations and alibis for her chum, at which like all over-tearful addicts of passion she was amazingly expert; and Mr. Hendrix to weave her artfully into his case.

But first Mr. Hendrix, aware of the lady's sensitivity toward all matters pertaining to love, proceeded to get himself drunk. He must be the lover stricken with jealousy and seeking to drown his pains in liquor, a characterization which this simple child and student of amour would remember only too vividly on the witness stand. Three drinks were consumed and then, honestly befuddled from such an unaccutomed dose, Mr. Hendrix launched into cross examination. And despite his thickened tongue and touch of genuine physical paralysis, Lawyer Hendrix remained as cool and analytical as if he were in a courtroom. He was not one to betray a client by any human weaknesses.

He put himself at Miss Moore's mercy. He must know the truth and she alone could tell him. Otherwise with too much brooding and uncertainty he would be sure to go out of his mind. His law practice was already suffering. He would lose all his money. Miss Moore nodded tenderly and understandingly at this saga of love woes. In reply she could assure Mr. Hendrix that he was being very foolish to be jealous of Eddie White because Mr. White wasn't even in town and besides Mr. White was engaged to marry a society girl in Newport. Mr. Hendrix sighed appreciatively at this walloping lie.

"It's not Eddie," said Mr. Hendrix, "it's somebody else. You know that as well as I. You're in her confidence. Don't try to lie to me, dearie. I caught her red handed, talking over the phone. She hung up when I came into the room. She was making a date—and not with Eddie White."

Miss Moore paled at the thought of this dreadful contretemps, but kept her wits. Her chum's guilt frightened her but at the same time she saw through Mr. Hendrix' effort to lead her astray. Of course it was Eddie White of whom he was jealous. Miss Moore was certain of this and Mr. Hendrix, listening to her somewhat hysterical defense of Brownie, sufficient to have convicted that young lady of a hundred infidelities had he been interested, realized exactly what was in his companion's mind. He considered for a moment the plan of involving Eddie White in his case. He had thought of it before—Brownie's previous lover, a known hot-headed young gentleman given to nocturnal fisticuffs in public places. But for the second time he dismissed this phase. Eddie would have an alibi and the establishing of Eddie's physical innocence, however psychologically promising his guilt might have looked, would embarrass his client's case.

For the next hour Mr. Hendrix drank and discussed his jealousy, pleading with Miss Moore to be kind to him and reveal what she knew; and hinting at gifts in return for such service. But Miss Moore only increased the scope of her lies.

"Have you seen Brownie today?" Miss Moore finally broke off, winded.

Mr. Hendrix weaved in his seat and looked at her with bleary, drunken eyes.

"No," he said. "I don't trust myself to see her. God knows what I would do—feeling this way."

"You're just worked up about absolutely nothing," said Miss Moore and rose. She had to toddle off to the El Bravo where she performed during the dinner hour. Mr. Hendrix accompanied her to the door.

"Tell Brownie," he whispered, "I'll be over to the club tonight. And . . . and give her a last chance to prove her innocence."

"I'll give her the message," said Miss Moore and sighed.

Alone, Mr. Hendrix returned to the phone booth. He sat down heavily and put in a call for Carmen Browne. His case was ready. He desired to hear the news of the finding of the body. And annoying tingle touched the base of his spine as he waited for the apartment switchboard to answer. He wondered how drunk he was. Drunk, to be sure, but sober enough to know exactly every phase and weigh every nuance. The moment he heard of the crime he would rush over, be detained by the police and with the aid of his intoxicated condition act thoroughly irrational and grief stricken. He would hint at no alibis, reveal not a shred of his case until the coroner's inquest.

The switchboard operator finally answered. Mr. Hendrix inquired thickly for Miss Browne. He was told Miss Browne was not in. He hung up. Rising and swaying for a moment, Mr. Hendrix, thoroughly at peace with the world, except for this intermittent tingle, decided on the best course. He would go to the El Bravo Club, order his dinner and wait there till Brownie's absence was noticed and a search started.

The El Bravo orchestra was rendering a dance number. The dance floor was crowded, Mr. Hendrix looked dizzily at the circling figures. He had selected a table far to the side, one of those at which the performers and their friends grouped themselves during the evening. The stuffiness of the air made Mr. Hendrix feel drowsy. Looking up, he beheld a familiar figure approaching. It was Eddie White, whom he had pleased to style the ignorant drop kicker. Mr. Hendrix smiled. He noticed tiredly that Mr. White seemed a little drunk.

The ex-college hero, still a sturdy, tanned and muscular product of the Higher Education, greeted Mr. Hendrix calmly. He dropped into a chair at the table and inquired, with an eye roving over the place, how tricks were. Mr. Hendrix said they were fine.

There was a pause during which the music filled the cafe with glamorous and exciting sounds.

"Didn't know you were such a movie fan," said Mr. White apropos of nothing and Mr. Hendrix felt himself sobering up as if in a cold shower.

"Just what do you mean?" Mr. Hendrix managed to inquire and very casually.

His companion was busy looking them over on the dance floor and offering a roguish eye to a few of the tastier numbers. Mr. Hendrix stared at him in silence and felt the tingle return to his spine.

"Saw you going into the Roxy this afternoon," Mr. White resumed.

"You did?" said Mr. Hendrix, and then added, as if he were looping the loop, "what time was that?"

"What time?" Mr. White repeated, looking at the little lawyer with a dull, athlete's stare. "Oh, a little after four, I should say."

"You're crazy," said Mr. Hendrix, "if you think you saw me going into the Roxy after four. Why I came out about twenty after four, after seeing the whole show."

"I don't care what you saw," said Mr. White, "I saw you going in at about a quarter after. I was gonna say hello but I thought the hell with it. How'd you like the picture? Ought to be in your line—all about one of those crooked legal sharks."

In the brief space during which Mr. Hendrix was now silent his thoughts were very rapid. Mr. White, God help Mr. Hendrix, was that most objectionable of all humans known to a legal case—the aimless stray that the Prosecution was wont to drag, rabbit fashion, out of its hat with which to confound the guilty. And Mr. Hendrix knew without thinking the full significance of this witness, Eddie White. If the defendant had been seen entering the movie theater after four, he had been seen entering after the murder had been committed. But that was the least damaging phase. The defendant had left the movie theater at 4:20, having lied to the attendant and told them he had spent an hour and a half in the place. With the fact of this lie established, the prosecution could take apart piece by piece the obvious mechanism of his alibi. There was no abili. There was no case. In fact, to the contrary, Eddie White's simple statement of the time of day—after four—revealed all of the defendant's subsequent actions as those of a thoroughly guilty man, and Mr. Hendrix leaned across the table and put a hand on the athlete's arm.

"It must have been somebody else you saw," he purred.

"Listen, don't tell me," said Mr. White. "I saw you looking around, buying your ticket and ducking in."

Mr. Hendrix winced at the damning phraseology.

"I know it was about a quarter after four," pursued Mr. White, "because I had a date outside. And don't get so excited. It wasn't with Brownie."

The tingle at the base of the Hendrix spine was almost lifting him out of his seat.

"That's a lie," said Mr. Hendrix thickly.

"What's that?" Mr. White demanded.

"I said you're lying," Mr. Hendrix repeated slowly. "You didn't see me."

"Oh, that's what you said, is it?" Mr. White was unexpectedly grim. "Listen, I never liked you and I don't take talk off a guy I got no use for. Get that."

And for the second time that day an unprecedented mood overcame the little lawyer. He made an effort to stop the words which suddenly filled his head but he heard himself saying them and wondering confusedly who it was who was drunk—he who was listening or he who was speaking. He was telling Mr. White what a liar, numbskull and oaf he was and Mr. White stood up. Words continued, Mr. Hendrix aware that he and Mr. White were both talking at once. But the music made a blur in his ears and the El Bravo Club swayed in front of his eyes. Then Mr. Hendrix realized, and darkly, that the towering Mr. White's hand was on his collar and that he was being lifted out of his seat. The El Bravo orchestra was rolling out a jazz finale and nobody seemed to have noticed as yet the fracas taking place at this side table. As Mr. Hendrix felt himself being hoisted to his feet, a sense of nausea and helplessness overcame him. He thrust his hand into his coat pocket.

"Calling me a liar, eh?" Mr. White was growling in the Hendrix ear. He added a number of epithets.

The little lawyer saw for an instant a fist pull back that never landed. Mr. Hendrix had removed a gun from his coat pocket, a gun of whose existence in his hand he was as unaware as he had been of the brass candlestick. The gun exploded and Mr. White, with a look of suddenly sober astonishment, fell back into a chair. The music at this moment finished with a nanny goat blare of trumpets. No heads turned. No waiters came rushing. Shaking as if his bones had turned into castanets, Mr. Hendrix stood looking at the crumpled athlete and watched his head sink over the table. The mouth was open. The athlete's fingers hanging near the floor were rigid.

Music started again and Mr. Hendrix turned his eyes automatically toward the dance floor. Blue and pink flood lights were shining on it and out from behind the orchestra shell came a line of almost naked girls. White legs kicked, smiles filled the air. Leading this chorus line Mr. Hendrix saw Carmen Browne. She was dancing.

The little lawyer grew sick. He shut his eyes. Then he opened them. They were full of pain and bewilderment. It was no hallucination. It was Brownie. Extending under her ear at the back of her head he saw strips of court plaster. She was alive and restored.

Mr. Hendrix knew exactly what had happened. The last time he had called her apartment, the switchboard man, failing to recognize his liquor-thickened voice, had withheld the information he might have offered Mr. Hendrix—that Carmen Browne was alive, that she had summoned a doctor, that she had left the apartment.

And even as he was thinking of this tiny detail, a hundred other details crowded into the Hendrix mind. He remembered his accusations to Brownie that she still loved Eddie White; his statement to Peggy Moore last week and this afternoon that he was too jealous to trust himself; his attack on Carmen Browne, his subsequent drunkenness, his idiotic antics in the movie theater—as if he were shadowing Eddie White—what else could his rushing in and rushing out mean? Everything Mr. Hendrix had accomplished since 4:02 this afternoon pointed only at one conclusion—that he hated Eddie White, that he had almost killed his sweetheart out of jealousy over White, that, still burning with this emotion he had tracked White down and murdered him in cold blood.

Mr. Hendrix, during these brief moments staring at the crumpled athlete, wanted to scream, so macabre did all these events strike him, but his voice trailed off into a moan. What was this insane thing he had done for his client! Exonerated him! Mr. Hendrix, still shaking, slipped down into his chair. He, Lou Hendrix, the shining legal intelligence, had like some Nemesis convicted himself—and not of manslaughter, which might have been the verdict otherwise—but of premeditated murder in the first degree. There was no case. No defense was possible. There was nothing left to do but to flee like some thug.

Mr. Hendrix looked at his wrist. He had twenty minutes to make the ten o'clock train for Chicago. From Chicago he would travel to New Orleans and thence into Mexico. He had a wallet full of bills. The side exit of the El Bravo was ten feet away. But Mr. Hendrix, struggling to get to his feet, swayed and fell forward. The dozen drinks he had so shrewdly tossed down his gullet to help him act his part, joined the hideous plot he had hatched against himself. He was too drunk, too dizzy to stand up and move quickly.

They found the little barrister hunched in his seat staring at the murdered athlete. The gun was still in his hand, Mr. Hendrix was mumbling passionlessly.

"Guilty. Guilty. Guilty."

2
HUMOR

A. V. Laider

BY

MAX BEERBOHM

I UNPACKED MY THINGS and went down to await luncheon.
It was good to be here again in this little old sleepy hostel by
the sea. Hostel I say, though it spelt itself without an s and even
placed a circumflex above the o. It made no other pretension. It was
very cosy indeed.

I had been here just a year before, in mid-February, after an
attack of influenza. And now I had returned, after an attack of influenza. Nothing was changed. It had been raining when I left, and
the waiter—there was but a single, a very old waiter—had told me it
was only a shower. That waiter was still here, not a day older. And
the shower had not ceased.

Steadfastly it fell on to the sands, steadfastly into the iron-grey
sea. I stood looking out at it from the windows of the hall, admiring
it very much. There seemed to be little else to do. What little there
was I did. I mastered the contents of a blue handbill which, pinned
to the wall just beneath the framed engraving of Queen Victoria's
Coronation, gave token of a concert that was to be held—or rather,
was to have been held some weeks ago—in the Town Hall, for the
benefit of the Life-Boat Fund. I looked at the barometer, tapped it,
was not the wiser. I glanced at a pamphlet about Our Dying Indus-
tries (a theme on which Mr. Joseph Chamberlain was at that time
trying to alarm us). I wandered to the letter-board.

These letter-boards always fascinate me. Usually some two or
three of the envelopes stuck into the cross-garterings have a certain
newness and freshness. They seem sure they will yet be claimed.
Why not? Why *shouldn't* John Doe, Esq., or Mrs. Richard Roe,
turn up at any moment? I do not know. I can only say that nothing
in the world seems to me more unlikely. Thus it is that these young

bright envelopes touch my heart even more than do their dusty and sallow seniors. Sour resignation is less touching than impatience for what will not be, than the eagerness that has to wane and wither. Soured beyond measure these old envelopes are. They are not nearly so nice as they should be to the young ones. They lose no chance of sneering and discouraging. Such dialogues as this are only too frequent:

A VERY YOUNG ENVELOPE. Something in me whispers that he will come to-day!

A VERY OLD ENVELOPE. He? Well, that's good! Ha, ha, ha! Why didn't he come last week, when you came? What reason have you for supposing he'll ever come now? It isn't as if he were a frequenter of the place. He's never been here. His name is utterly unknown here. You don't suppose he's coming on the chance of finding you?

A V. Y. E. It may seem silly, but—something in me whispers——

A V. O. E. Something in you? One has only to look at you to see there's nothing in you but a note scribbled to him by a cousin. Look at me! There are three sheets, closely written, in me. The lady to whom I am addressed——

A V. Y. E. Yes, sir, yes; you told me all about her yesterday.

A V. O. E. And I shall do so to-day and to-morrow and every day and all day long. That young lady was a widow. She stayed here many times. She was delicate, and the air suited her. She was poor, and the tariff was just within her means. She was lonely, and had need of love. I have in me for her a passionate avowal and strictly honourable proposal, written to her, after many rough copies, by a gentleman who had made her acquaintance under this very roof. He was rich, he was charming, he was in the prime of life. He had asked if he might write to her. She had flutteringly granted his request. He posted me to her the day after his return to London. I looked forward to being torn open by her. I was very sure she would wear me and my contents next to her bosom. She was gone. She had left no address. She never returned . . . This I tell you, and shall continue to tell you, not because I want any of your callow sympathy,—no, thank you!—but that you may judge how much less than slight are the chances that you yourself——

But my reader has overheard these dialogues as often as I. He wants to know what was odd about this particular letter-board before which I was standing. At first glance I saw nothing odd about

it. But presently I distinguished a handwriting that was vaguely
familiar. It was mine. I stared, I wondered. There is always a slight
shock in seeing an envelope of one's own after it has gone through
the post. It looks as if it had gone through so much. But this was
the first time I had ever seen an envelope of mine eating its heart
out in bondage on a letter-board. This was outrageous. This was
hardly to be believed. Sheer kindness had impelled me to write to
'A. V. Laider, Esq.', and this was the result! I hadn't minded receiving no answer. Only now, indeed, did I remember that I hadn't
received one. In multitudinous London the memory of A. V. Laider
and his trouble had soon passed from my mind. But—well, what a
lesson not to go out of one's way to write to casual acquaintances!

My envelope seemed not to recognise me as its writer. Its gaze was
the more piteous for being blank. Even so had I once been gazed at
by a dog that I had lost and, after many days, found in the Batter-
sea Home. 'I don't know who you are, but whoever you are, claim
me, take me out of this!' That was my dog's appeal. This was the
appeal of my envelope.

I raised my hand to the letter-board, meaning to effect a swift
and lawless rescue, but paused at sound of a footstep behind me.
The old waiter had come to tell me that my luncheon was ready. I
followed him out of the hall, not, however, without a bright glance
across my shoulder to reassure the little captive that I should come
back.

I had the sharp appetite of the convalescent, and this the sea-air
had whetted already to a finer edge. In touch with a dozen oysters,
and with stout, I soon shed away the unreasoning anger I had felt
against A. V. Laider. I became merely sorry for him that he had not
received a letter which might perhaps have comforted him. In touch
with cutlets, I felt how sorely he had needed comfort. And anon,
by the big bright fireside of that small dark smoking-room where,
a year ago, on the last evening of my stay here, he and I had at
length spoken to each other, I reviewed in detail the tragic experience he had told me; and I fairly revelled in reminiscent sympathy
with him. . . .

A. V. LAIDER—I had looked him up in the visitors' book on the
night of his arrival. I myself had arrived the day before, and had
been rather sorry there was no one else staying here. A convalescent

by the sea likes to have some one to observe, to wonder about, at meal-time. I was glad when, on my second evening, I found seated at the table opposite to mine another guest. I was the gladder because he was just the right kind of quest. He was enigmatic. By this I mean that he did not look soldierly nor financial nor artistic nor anything definite at all. He offered a clean slate for speculation. And thank heaven! he evidently wasn't going to spoil the fun by engaging me in conversation later on. A decently unsociable man, anxious to be left alone.

The heartiness of his appetite, in contrast with his extreme fragility of aspect and limpness of demeanour, assured me that he, too, had just had influenza. I liked him for that. Now and again our eyes met and were instantly parted. We managed, as a rule, to observe each other indirectly. I was sure it was not merely because he had been ill that he looked interesting. Nor did it seem to me that a spiritual melancholy, though I imagined him sad at the best of times, was his sole asset. I conjectured that he was clever. I thought he might also be imaginative. At first glance I had mistrusted him. A shock of white hair, combined with a young face and dark eyebrows, does somehow make a man look like a charlatan. But it is foolish to be guided by an accident of colour. I had soon rejected my first impression of my fellow-diner. I found him very sympathetic.

Anywhere but in England it would be impossible for two solitary men, howsoever much reduced by influenza, to spend five or six days in the same hostel and not exchange a single word. That is one of the charms of England. Had Laider and I been born and bred in any other land we should have become acquainted before the end of our first evening in the small smoking-room, and have found ourselves irrevocably committed to go on talking to each other throughout the rest of our visit. We might, it is true, have happened to like each other more than any one we had ever met. This off-chance may have occurred to us both. But it counted for nothing as against the certain surrender of quietude and liberty. We slightly bowed to each other as we entered or left the dining-room or smoking-room, and as we met on the widespread sands or in the shop that had a small and faded circulating library. That was all. Our mutual aloofness was a positive bond between us.

Had he been much older than I, the responsibility for our silence would of course have been his alone. But he was not, I judged, more than five or six years ahead of me, and thus I might without impropriety have taken it on myself to perform that hard and peril- ous feat which English people call, with a shiver, 'breaking the ice.' He had reason, therefore, to be as grateful to me as I to him. Each of us, not the less frankly because silently, recognised his obligation to the other. And when, on the last evening of my stay, the ice actu- ally was broken no ill-will rose between us: neither of us was to blame.

It was a Sunday evening. I had been out for a long last walk and had come in very late to dinner. Laider left his table almost imme- diately after I sat down to mine. When I entered the smoking-room I found him reading a weekly review which I had bought the day before. It was a crisis. He could not silently offer, nor could I have silently accepted, sixpence. It was a crisis. We faced it like men. He made, by word of mouth, a graceful apology. Verbally, not by signs, I besought him to go on reading. But this, of course, was a vain counsel of perfection. The social code forced us to talk now. We obeyed it like men. To reassure him that our position was not so desperate as it might seem, I took the earliest opportunity to men- tion that I was going away early next morning. In the tone of his 'Oh, are you?' he tried bravely to imply that he was sorry, even now, to hear that. In a way, perhaps, he really was sorry. We had got on so well together, he and I. Nothing could efface the memory of that. Nay, we seemed to be hitting it off even now. Influenza was not our sole theme. We passed from that to the aforesaid weekly re- view, and to a correspondence that was raging therein on Faith and Reason.

This correspondence had now reached its fourth and penultimate stage—its Australian stage. It is hard to see why these correspond- ences spring up; one only knows that they do spring up, suddenly, like street crowds. There comes, it would seem, a moment when the whole English-speaking race is unconsciously bursting to have its say about some one thing—the split infinitive, or the habits of migratory birds, or faith and reason, or what-not. Whatever weekly review happens at such a moment to contain a reference, however remote, to the theme in question reaps the storm. Gusts of letters blow in from all corners of the British Isles. These are presently reinforced by Canada in full blast. A few weeks later the Anglo-

Indians weigh in. In due course we have the help of our Australian cousins. By that time, however, we of the Mother Country have got our second wind, and so determined are we to make the most of it that at last even the Editor suddenly loses patience and says 'This correspondence must now cease.—Ed.' and wonders why on earth he ever allowed anything so tedious and idiotic to begin.

I pointed out to Laider one of the Australian letters that had especially pleased me in the current issue. It was from 'A Melbourne Man,' and was of the abrupt kind which declares that 'all your correspondents have been groping in the dark' and then settles the whole matter in one short sharp flash. The flash in this instance was 'Reason is faith, faith reason—that is all we know on earth and all we need to know.' The writer then inclosed his card and was, etc., 'A Melbourne Man.' I said to Laider how very restful it was, after influenza, to read anything that meant nothing whatsoever. Laider was inclined to take the letter more seriously than I, and to be mildly metaphysical. I said that for me faith and reason were two separate things, and (as I am no good at metaphysics, however mild) I offered a definite example, to coax the talk on to ground where I should be safer. 'Palmistry, for example,' I said. 'Deep down in my heart I believe in palmistry.'

Laider turned in his chair. 'You believe in palmistry?'

I hesitated. 'Yes, somehow I do. Why? I haven't the slightest notion. I can give myself all sorts of reasons for laughing it to scorn. My common sense utterly rejects it. Of course the shape of the hand means something—is more or less an index of character. But the idea that my past and future are neatly mapped out on my palms——' I shrugged my shoulders.

"You don't like that idea?' asked Laider in his gentle, rather academic voice.

'I only say it's a grotesque idea.'

'Yet you do believe in it?'

'I've a grotesque belief in it, yes.'

'Are you sure your reason for calling this idea "grotesque" isn't merely that you dislike it?'

'Well,' I said, with the thrilling hope that he was a companion in absurdity, 'doesn't it seem grotesque to *you?*'

'It seems strange.'

'You believe in it?'

'Oh, absolutely.'

'Hurrah!'

He smiled at my pleasure, and I, at the risk of re-entanglement in
metaphysics, claimed him as standing shoulder to shoulder with me
against 'A Melbourne Man.' This claim he gently disputed. 'You
may think me very prosaic,' he said, 'but I can't believe without
evidence.'

'Well, I'm equally prosaic and equally at a disadvantage: I can't
take my own belief as evidence, and I've no other evidence to
go on.'

He asked me if I had ever made a study of palmistry. I said I had
read one of Desbarolles' books years ago, and one of Heron-Allen's.
But, he asked, had I tried to test them by the lines on my own
hands or on the hands of my friends? I confessed that my actual
practice in palmistry had been of a merely passive kind—the prompt
extension of my palm to any one who would be so good as to 'read'
it and truckle for a few minutes to my egoism. (I hoped Laider
might do this.)

'Then I almost wonder,' he said, with his sad smile, 'that you
haven't lost your belief, after all the nonsense you must have heard.
There are so many young girls who go in for palmistry. I am sure
all the five foolish virgins were "awfully keen on it" and used to say
"You can be led, but not driven," and "You are likely to have a
serious illness between the ages of forty and forty-five," and "You
are by nature rather lazy, but can be very energetic by fits and
starts." And most of the professionals, I'm told, are as silly as the
young girls.'

For the honour of the profession, I named three practitioners
whom I had found really good at reading character. He asked
whether any of them had been right about past events. I confessed
that, as a matter of fact, all three of them had been right in the
main. This seemed to amuse him. He asked whether any of them
had predicted anything which had since come true. I confessed that
all three had predicted that I should do several things which I had
since done rather unexpectedly. He asked if I didn't accept this as
at any rate a scrap of evidence. I said I could only regard it as a
fluke—a rather remarkable fluke.

The superiority of his sad smile was beginning to get on my
nerves. I wanted him to see that he was as absurd as I. 'Suppose,' I

said, 'suppose for sake of argument that you and I are nothing but helpless automata created to do just this and that, and to have just that and this done to us. Suppose, in fact, we *haven't* any free will whatsoever. Is it likely or conceivable that the Power that fashioned us would take the trouble to jot down in cipher on our hands just what was in store for us?'

Laider did not answer this question, he did but annoyingly ask me another. 'You believe in free will?'

'Yes, of course. I'll be hanged if I'm an automaton.'

'And you believe in free will just as in palmistry—without any reason?'

'Oh, no. Everything points to our having free will.'

'Everything? What, for instance?'

This rather cornered me. I dodged out, as lightly as I could, by saying 'I suppose *you* would say it was written in my hand that I should be a believer in free will.'

'Ah, I've no doubt it is.'

I held out my palms. But, to my great disappointment, he looked quickly away from them. He had ceased to smile. There was agitation in his voice as he explained that he never looked at people's hands now. 'Never now—never again.' He shook his head as though to beat off some memory.

I was much embarrassed by my indiscretion. I hastened to tide over the awkward moment by saying that if *I* could read hands I wouldn't, for fear of the awful things I might see there.

'Awful things, yes,' he whispered, nodding at the fire.

'Not,' I said in self-defence, 'that there's anything very awful, so far as I know, to be read in *my* hands.'

He turned his gaze from the fire to me. 'You aren't a murderer, for example?'

'Oh, no,' I replied, with a nervous laugh.

'*I* am.'

This was a more than awkward, it was a painful, moment for me; and I am afraid I must have started or winced, for he instantly begged my pardon. 'I don't know,' he exclaimed, 'why I said it. I'm usually a very reticent man. But sometimes—' He pressed his brow. 'What you must think of me!'

I begged him to dismiss the matter from his mind.

'It's very good of you to say that; but—I've placed myself as well as you in a false position. I ask you to believe that I'm not the sort of man who is "wanted" or ever was "wanted" by the police. I should be bowed out of any police-station at which I gave myself up. I'm not a murderer in any bald sense of the word. No.'

My face must have perceptibly brightened, for 'Ah,' he said, 'don't imagine I'm not a murderer at all. Morally, I am.' He looked at the clock. I pointed out that the night was young. He assured me that his story was not a long one. I assured him that I hoped it was. He said I was very kind. I denied this. He warned me that what he had to tell might rather tend to stiffen my unwilling faith in palmistry, and to shake my opposite and cherished faith in free will. I said 'Never mind.' He stretched his hands pensively toward the fire. I settled myself back in my chair.

'My hands,' he said, staring at the backs of them, 'are the hands of a very weak man. I dare say you know enough of palmistry to see that for yourself. You notice the slightness of the thumbs and of the two "little" fingers. They are the hands of a weak and over-sensitive man—a man without confidence, a man who would certainly waver in an emergency. Rather Hamlet-ish hands,' he mused. 'And I'm like Hamlet in other respects, too: I'm no fool, and I've rather a noble disposition, and I'm unlucky. But Hamlet was luckier than I in one thing: he was a murderer by accident, whereas the murders that I committed one day fourteen years ago—for I must tell you it wasn't one murder, but many murders that I committed— were all of them due to the wretched inherent weakness of my own wretched self.

'I was twenty-six—no, twenty-seven years old, and rather a nondescript person, as I am now. I was supposed to have been called to the Bar. In fact, I believe I *had* been called to the Bar. I hadn't listened to the call. I never intended to practise, and I never did practise. I only wanted an excuse in the eyes of the world for existing. I suppose the nearest I have ever come to practising is now at this moment: I am defending a murderer. My father had left me well enough provided with money. I was able to go my own desultory way, riding my hobbies where I would. I had a good stableful of hobbies. Palmistry was one of them. I was rather ashamed of this one. It seemed to me absurd, as it seems to you. Like you, though, I believed in it. Unlike you, I had done more than merely read a book or so about it. I had read innumerable books about it. I had taken casts of all my friends' hands. I had tested and tested again the points at which Desbarolles dissented from the gypsies, and—well, enough that I had gone into it all rather thoroughly, and was as sound a palmist as a man may be without giving his whole life to palmistry.

'One of the first things I had seen in my own hand, as soon as I had learned to read it, was that at about the age of twenty-six I should have a narrow escape from death—from a violent death. There was a clean break in the life-line, and a square joining it—the protective square, you know. The markings were precisely the same in both hands. It was to be the narrowest escape possible. And I wasn't going to escape without injury, either. That is what bothered me. There was a faint line connecting the break in the life-line with a star on the line of health. Against that star was another square. I was to recover from the injury, whatever it might be. Still, I didn't exactly look forward to it. Soon after I had reached the age of twenty-five, I began to feel uncomfortable. The thing might be going to happen at any moment. In palmistry, you know, it is impossible to pin an event down hard and fast to one year. This particular event was to be when I was *about* twenty-six; it mightn't be till I was twenty-seven; it might be while I was only twenty-five.

'And I used to tell myself that it mightn't be at all. My reason rebelled against the whole notion of palmistry, just as yours does. I despised my faith in the thing, just as you despise yours. I used to try not to be so ridiculously careful as I was whenever I crossed a street. I lived in London at that time. Motor-cars had not yet come in, but—what hours, all told, I must have spent standing on curbs, very circumspect, very lamentable! It was a pity, I suppose, that I had no definite occupation—something to take me out of myself. I was one of the victims of private means. There came a time when I drove in four-wheelers rather than in hansoms, and was doubtful of four-wheelers. Oh, I assure you, I was very lamentable indeed.

'If a railway-journey could be avoided, I avoided it. My uncle had a place in Hampshire. I was very fond of him and of his wife. Theirs was the only house I ever went to stay in now. I was there for a week in November, not long after my twenty-seventh birthday. There were other people staying there, and at the end of the week we all travelled back to London together. There were six of us in the carriage: Colonel Elbourn and his wife and their daughter, a girl of seventeen; and another married couple, the Blakes. I had been at Winchester with Blake, but had hardly seen him since that time. He was in the Indian Civil, and was home on leave. He was sailing for India next week. His wife was to remain in England for some months, and then join him out there. They had been married five years. She was now just twenty-four years old. He told me that this was her age.

'The Elbourns I had never met before. They were charming people. We had all been very happy together. The only trouble had been that on the last night, at dinner, my uncle asked me if I still went in for "the gypsy business," as he always called it; and of course the three ladies were immensely excited, and implored me to "do" their hands. I told them it was all nonsense, I said I had forgotten all I once knew, I made various excuses; and the matter dropped. It was quite true that I had given up reading hands. I avoided anything that might remind me of what was in my own hands. And so, next morning, it was a great bore to me when, soon after the train started, Mrs. Elbourn said it would be "too cruel" of me if I refused to do their hands now. Her daughter and Mrs. Blake also said it would be "brutal"; and they were all taking off their gloves, and—well, of course I had to give in.

'I went to work methodically on Mrs. Elbourn's hands, in the usual way, you know, first sketching the character from the backs of them; and there was the usual hush, broken by the usual little noises—grunts of assent from the husband, cooings of recognition from the daughter. Presently I asked to see the palms, and from them I filled in the details of Mrs. Elbourn's character before going on to the events in her life. But while I talked I was calculating how old Mrs. Elbourn might be. In my first glance at her palms I had seen that she could not have been less than twenty-five when she married. The daughter was seventeen. Suppose the daughter had been born a year later—how old would the mother be? Forty-three, yes. Not less than that, poor woman!'

Laider looked at me. 'Why "poor woman," you wonder? Well, in that first glance I had seen other things than her marriage-line. I had seen a very complete break in the lines of life and of fate. I had seen violent death there. At what age? Not later, not possibly *later*, than forty-three. While I talked to her about the things that had happened in her girlhood, the back of my brain was hard at work

on those marks of catastrophe. I was horribly wondering that she
was still alive. It was impossible that between her and that catastrophe there could be more than a few short months. And all the
time I was talking; and I suppose I acquitted myself well, for I remember that when I ceased I had a sort of ovation from the Elbourns.

'It was a relief to turn to another pair of hands. Mrs. Blake was
an amusing young creature, and her hands were very characteristic,
and prettily odd in form. I allowed myself to be rather whimsical
about her nature, and, having begun in that vein, I went on in it—
somehow—even after she had turned her palms. In those palms
were reduplicated the signs I had seen in Mrs. Elbourn's. It was as
though they had been copied neatly out. The only difference was in
the placing of them; and it was this difference that was the most
horrible point. The fatal age in Mrs. Blake's hands was—not past,
no, for here *she* was. But she might have died when she was twenty-
one. Twenty-three seemed to be the utmost span. She was twenty-
four, you know.

'I have said that I am a weak man. And you will have good proof
of that directly. Yet I showed a certain amount of strength that day
—yes, even on that day which has humiliated and saddened the rest
of my life. Neither my face nor my voice betrayed me when in the
palms of Dorothy Elbourn I was again confronted with those same
signs. She was all for knowing the future, poor child! I believe I
told her all manner of things that were to be. And she had no
future—none, none in in *this* world except——

'And then, while I talked, there came to me suddenly a suspicion.
I wondered it hadn't come before. You guess what it was? It made
me feel very cold and strange. I went on talking. But, also, I went
on—quite separately—thinking. The suspicion wasn't a certainty.
This mother and daughter were always together. What was to befall
the one might anywhere—anywhere—befall the other. But a like
fate, in an equally near future, was in store for that other lady. The
coincidence was curious, very. Here we all were together—here, they
and I—I who was narrowly to escape, so soon now, what they, so
soon now, were to suffer. Oh, there was an inference to be drawn.
Not a *sure* inference, I told myself. And always I was talking, talking, and the train was swinging and swaying noisily along—to what?
It was a fast train. Our carriage was near the engine. I was talking

loudly. Full well I had known what I should see in the Colonel's hands. I told myself I had not known. I told myself that even now the thing I dreaded was not sure to be. Don't think I was dreading it for myself. I wasn't so "lamentable" as all that—now. It was only of them that I thought—only for them. I hurried over the Colonel's character and career; I was perfunctory. It was Blake's hands that I wanted. *They* were the hands that mattered. If *they* had the marks—— Remember, Blake was to start for India in the coming week, his wife was to remain in England. They would be apart. Therefore——

'And the marks were there. And I did nothing—nothing but hold forth on the subtleties of Blake's character. There was a thing for me to do. I wanted to do it. I wanted to spring to the window and pull the communication-cord. Quite a simple thing to do. Nothing easier than to stop a train. You just give a sharp pull, and the train slows down, comes to a standstill. And the Guard appears at your window. You explain to the Guard.

'Nothing easier than to tell him there is going to be a collision. Nothing easier than to insist that you and your friends and every other passenger in the train must get out at once . . . There *are* easier things than this? Things that need less courage than this? Some of *them* I could have done, I daresay. This thing I was going to do. Oh, I was determined that I would do it—directly.

'I had said all I had to say about Blake's hands. I had brought my entertainment to an end. I had been thanked and complimented all round. I was quite at liberty. I was going to do what I had to do. I was determined, yes.

'We were near the outskirts of London. The air was grey, thickening; and Dorothy Elbourn had said, "Oh, this horrible old London! I suppose there's the same old fog!" And presently I heard her father saying something about "prevention" and "a short act of Parliament" and "anthracite." And I sat and listened and agreed and——'

Laider closed his eyes. He passed his hand slowly through the air.

'I had a racking headache. And when I said so, I was told not to talk. I was in bed, and the nurses were always telling me not to talk. I was in a hospital. I knew that. But I didn't know why I was there. One day I thought I should like to know why, and so I asked. I was feeling much better now. They told me, by degrees, that I had concussion of the brain. I had been brought there unconscious, and had remained unconscious for forty-eight hours. I had been in an accident—a railway accident. This seemed to me odd. I had arrived quite safely at my uncle's place, and I had no memory of any journey since that. In cases of concussion, you know, it's not uncommon for the patient to forget all that happened just before the accident; there may be a blank of several hours. So it was in my case. One day my uncle was allowed to come and see me. And somehow, suddenly, at sight of him, the blank was filled in. I remembered, in a flash, everything. I was quite calm, though. Or I made myself seem so, for I wanted to know how the collision had happened. My uncle told me that the engine-driver had failed to see a signal because of the fog, and our train had crashed into a goods-train. I didn't ask him about the people who were with me. You see, there was no need to ask. Very gently my uncle began to tell me, but—I had begun to talk strangely, I suppose. I remember the frightened look of my uncle's face, and the nurse scolding him in whispers.

'After that, all a blur. It seems that I became very ill indeed, wasn't expected to live. However, I live.'

There was a long silence. Laider did not look at me, nor I at him. The fire was burning low, and he watched it.

At length he spoke. 'You despise me. Naturally. I despise myself.'

'No, I don't despise you; but——'

'You blame me.' I did not meet his gaze. 'You blame me,' he repeated.

'Yes.'

'And there, if I may say so, you are a little unjust. It isn't my fault that I was born weak.'

'But a man may conquer weakness.'

'Yes, if he is endowed with the strength for that.'

His fatalism drew from me a gesture of disgust. 'Do you really mean,' I asked, 'that because you didn't pull that cord, you *couldn't* have pulled it?'

'Yes.'

'And it's written in your hands that you couldn't?'

He looked at the palms of his hands. 'They are the hands of a very weak man,' he said.

'A man so weak that he cannot believe in the possibility of free will for himself or for any one?'

'They are the hands of an intelligent man, who can weigh evidence and see things as they are.'

'But answer me: Was it fore-ordained that you should not pull that cord?'

'It was fore-ordained.'

'And was it actually marked in your hands that you were not going to pull it?'

'Ah, well, you see, it is rather the things one *is* going to do that are actually marked. The things one *isn't* going to do,—the innumerable negative things,—how could one expect *them* to be marked?'

'But the consequences of what one leaves undone may be positive?'

'Horribly positive,' he winced. 'My hand is the hand of a man who has suffered a great deal in later life.'

'And was it the hand of a man *destined* to suffer?'

'Oh, yes. I thought I told you that.'

There was a pause.

'Well,' I said, with awkward sympathy, 'I suppose all hands are the hands of people destined to suffer.'

'Not of people destined to suffer so much as *I* have suffered—as I still suffer.'

The insistence of his self-pity chilled me, and I harked back to a question he had not straightly answered. 'Tell me: Was it marked in your hands that you were not going to pull that cord?'

Again he looked at his hands, and then, having pressed them for a moment to his face, 'It was marked very clearly,' he answered, 'in *their* hands.'

Two or three days after this colloquy there had occurred to me in London an idea—an ingenious and comfortable doubt. How was Laider to be sure that his brain, recovering from concussion, had *remembered* what happened in the course of that railway-journey? How was he to know that his brain hadn't simply, in its abeyance, *invented* all this for him? It might be that he had never seen those signs in those hands. Assuredly, here was a bright loop-hole. I had forthwith written to Laider, pointing it out.

This was the letter which now, at my second visit, I had found miserably pent on the letter-board. I remembered my promise to rescue it. I arose from the retaining fireside, stretched my arms,

yawned, and went forth to fulfil my Christian purpose. There was
no one in the hall. The 'shower' had at length ceased. The sun had
positively come out, and the front door had been thrown open in
its honour. Everything along the sea-front was beautifully gleaming,
drying, shimmering. But I was not to be diverted from my errand.
I went to the letter-board. And—my letter was not there! Resourceful and plucky little thing—it had escaped! I did hope it would not
be captured and brought back. Perhaps the alarm had already been
raised by the tolling of that great bell which warns the inhabitants
for miles around that a letter has broken loose from the letter-
board. I had a vision of my envelope skimming wildly along the
coastline, pursued by the old but active waiter and a breathless pack
of local worthies. I saw it out-distancing them all, dodging past
coast-guards, doubling on its tracks, leaping breakwaters, unluckily
injuring itself, losing speed, and at last, in a splendour of despera-
tion, taking to the open sea. But suddenly I had another idea. Perhaps Laider had returned?

He had. I espied afar on the sands a form that was recognisably,
by the listless droop of it, his. I was glad and sorry—rather glad, because he completed the scene of last year; and very sorry, because
this time we should be at each other's mercy: no restful silence and
liberty, for either of us, this time. Perhaps he had been told I was
here, and had gone out to avoid me while he yet could. Oh, weak,
weak! Why palter? I put on my hat and coat, and marched out to
meet him.

'Influenza, of course?' we asked simultaneously.

There is a limit to the time which one man may spend in talking
to another about his own influenza; and presently, as we paced the
sands, I felt that Laider had passed this limit. I wondered that he
didn't break off and thank me now for my letter. He must have
read it. He ought to have thanked me for it at once. It was a very
good letter, a remarkable letter. But surely he wasn't waiting to answer it by post? His silence about it gave me the absurd sense of
having taken a liberty, confound him! He was evidently ill at ease
while he talked. But it wasn't for me to help him out of his difficulty, whatever that might be. It was for him to remove the strain
imposed on myself.

Abruptly, after a long pause, he did now manage to say, 'It was—
very good of you to—to write me that letter.' He told me he had

only just got it, and he drifted away into otiose explanations of this
fact. I thought he might at least say it was a remarkable letter; and
you can imagine my annoyance when he said, after another interval, 'I was very much touched indeed.' I had wished to be convinc-
ing, not touching. I can't bear to be called touching.

'Don't you,' I asked, 'think it *is* quite possible that your brain invented all those memories of what—what happened before that accident?'

He drew a sharp sigh. 'You make me feel very guilty.'

'That's exactly what I tried to make you *not* feel!'

'I know, yes. That's why I feel so guilty.'

We had paused in our walk. He stood nervously prodding the
hard wet sand with his walking-stick. 'In a way,' he said, 'your
theory was quite right. But—it didn't go far enough. It's not only
possible, it's a fact, that I didn't see those signs in those hands. I
never examined those hands. They weren't there. *I* wasn't there. I
haven't an uncle in Hampshire, even. I never had.'

I, too, prodded the sand. 'Well,' I said at length, 'I do feel rather
a fool.'

'I've no right even to beg your pardon, but——'

'Oh, I'm not vexed. Only—I rather wish you hadn't told me this.'

'I wish I hadn't had to. It was your kindness, you see, that forced
me. By trying to take an imaginary load off my conscience, you laid
a very real one on it.'

'I'm sorry. But you, of your own free will, you know, exposed
your conscience to me last year. I don't yet quite understand why
you did that.'

'No, of course not. I don't deserve that you should. But I think
you will. May I explain? I'm afraid I've talked a great deal already
about my influenza, and I shan't be able to keep it out of my explanation. Well, my weakest point—I told you this last year, but it
happens to be perfectly true that my weakest point—is my will. Influenza, as you know, fastens unerringly on one's weakest point.
It doesn't attempt to undermine my imagination. That would be a
forlorn hope. I have, alas! a very strong imagination. At ordinary
times my imagination allows itself to be governed by my will. My
will keeps it in check by constant nagging. But when my will isn't
strong enough even to nag, then my imagination stampedes. I become even as a little child. I tell myself the most preposterous

fables, and—the trouble is—I can't help telling them to my friends. Until I've thoroughly shaken off influenza, I'm not fit company for any one. I perfectly realize this, and I have the good sense to go right away till I'm quite well again. I come here usually. It seems absurd, but I must confess I was sorry last year when we fell into conversation. I knew I should very soon be letting myself go, or rather, very soon be swept away. Perhaps I ought to have warned you; but—I'm a rather shy man. And then you mentioned the subject of palmistry. You said you believed in it. I wondered at that. I had once read Desbarolles' book about it, but I am bound to say I thought the whole thing very great nonsense indeed.'

'Then,' I gasped, 'it isn't even true that you believe in palmistry?'

'Oh, no. But I wasn't able to tell you that. You had begun by saying that you believed in palmistry, and then you proceeded to scoff at it. While you scoffed I saw myself as a man with a terribly good reason for *not* scoffing; and in a flash I saw the terribly good reason; I had the whole story—at least I had the broad outlines of it—clear before me.'

'You hadn't ever thought of it before?' He shook his head. My eyes beamed. 'The whole thing was a sheer improvisation?'

'Yes,' said Laider, humbly, 'I am as bad as all that. I don't say that all the details of the story I told you that evening were filled in at the very instant of its conception. I was filling them in while we talked about palmistry in general, and while I was waiting for the moment when the story would come in most effectively. And I've no doubt I added some extra touches in the course of the actual telling. Don't imagine that I took the slightest pleasure in deceiving you. It's only my will, not my conscience, that is weakened after influenza. I simply can't help telling what I've made up, and telling it to the best of my ability. But I'm thoroughly ashamed all the time.'

'Not of your ability, surely?'

'Yes, of that, too,' he said with his sad smile. 'I always feel that I'm not doing justice to my idea.'

'You are too stern a critic, believe me.'

'It is very kind of you to say that. You are very kind altogether. Had I known that you were so essentially a man of the world— in the best sense of that term—I shouldn't have so much dreaded seeing you just now and having to confess to you. But I'm not going

to take advantage of your urbanity and your easy-going ways. I hope
that some day we may meet somewhere when I haven't had influenza and am a not wholly undesirable acquaintance. As it is, I refuse to let you associate with me. I am an older man than you, and
so I may without impertinence warn you against having anything
to do with me.'

I deprecated this advice, of course; but, for a man of weakened
will, he showed great firmness. 'You,' he said, 'in your heart of
hearts don't want to have to walk and talk continually with a person who might at any moment try to bamboozle you with some
ridiculous tale. And I, for my part, don't want to degrade myself
by trying to bamboozle anyone—especially one whom I have taught
to see through me. Let the two talks we have had be as though
they had not been. Let us bow to each other, as last year, but
let that be all. Let us follow in all things the precedent of last year.'

With a smile that was almost gay he turned on his heel, and
moved away with a step that was almost brisk. I was a little disconcerted. But I was also more than a little glad. The restfulness of
silence, the charm of liberty—these things were not, after all, forfeit.
My heart thanked Laider for that; and throughout the week I
loyally seconded him in the system he had laid down for us. All was
as it had been last year. We did not smile to each other, we merely
bowed, when we entered or left the dining-room or smoking-room,
and when we met on the widespread sands or in that shop which
had a small and faded, but circulating, library.

Once or twice in the course of the week it did occur to me that
perhaps Laider had told the simple truth at our first interview
and an ingenious lie at our second. I frowned at this possibility.
The idea of any one wishing to be quit of me was most distasteful.
However, I was to find reassurance. On the last evening of my stay,
I suggested, in the small smoking-room, that he and I should, as
sticklers for precedent, converse. We did so, very pleasantly. And
after a while I happened to say that I had seen this afternoon a great
number of sea-gulls flying close to the shore.

'Sea-gulls?' said Laider, turning in his chair.

'Yes. And I don't think I had ever realized how extraordinarily
beautiful they are when their wings catch the light.'

'Beautiful?' Laider threw a quick glance at me and away from me.
'You think them beautiful?'

'Surely.

'Well, perhaps they are, yes; I suppose they are. But—I don't like seeing them. They always remind me of something—rather an awful thing—that once happened to me.' . . .

It was a very awful thing indeed.

Mother and Pug Dogs and Rubber Trees

BY

CLARENCE DAY

T HERE WERE two special things that it was considered chic to
have, in good New York homes, in the eighties. One of these
was a fat pug dog with a ribbon around his neck, tied in a bow.
The other was a rubber tree.

Father's instinct was to do the right thing, and to live in the
right way, according to the ideas of his times, but he drew the line
at pug dogs. He said he had owned dogs himself as a boy, and he
wasn't fussy about their breeds either, but "I must positively de-
cline," he told Mother, "to begin domesticating monstrosities." He
said he doubted whether pugs were dogs anyhow. They looked too
Chinese. He said that quite possibly in China they filled a niche of
their own, though he couldn't guess what, but no pop-eyed pug
dog would ever be permitted to waddle around Father's home.

As to rubber trees, he was still more emphatic. He said he liked
to be cheerful himself and to live in cheerful surroundings, and of
all the disconsolate plants in the world a rubber tree was the most
dismal. A rubber tree wasn't a tree, it was nothing but a stick with
three leaves on it, and why or how such an unsightly plant had
ever become a craze was a mystery.

The trouble was that Mother felt a longing for these two things,
she didn't know why. She saw pug dogs and rubber trees everywhere
but in her own home, and gradually her home came to seem bare.
When visitors looked around the parlor it embarrassed her. They
were too polite to say, "Where's your rubber tree?" but she was sure
they were thinking it.

On Christmas morning Father found one of his socks fastened
with a bent pin to his mantel-piece. It had a small china dish in it.
His one hope and prayer was not to be given anything whatever on

Christmas, but he recognized this thing. "Why, this is my soap-dish," he said. "What's it doing here, damn it?"

Mother's eyes were sparkling with mischief. "I thought you might need it, Clare dear," she said sweetly, "when you were feeding your nice new pug dog."

She pointed to what looked like a hat box, done up in red ribbons. Father opened it and took out the tissue paper. A life-sized pug dog, made of china, was sitting inside.

"Ha!" Father said in relief. This objet d'art wasn't beautiful by any means, it was in the way and it was awkwardly large, but it wasn't alive. He could stand it.

Mother adored that pug dog. And as it was such a handsome piece of china, she said, and had cost her so much, she had to think carefully where would be the best place to put it. After trying several sites she decided on a place in the parlor, facing the door as you came in. For years and years there it sat on the floor, where it deceived and amazed Mother's visitors. They exclaimed in delight at its lifelike appearance and its big bulging eyes. Mother added to the effect by tying a broad red satin bow round its neck.

A rubber tree followed. A real one. It was hidden in the narrow hall bedroom next to Mother's, at first, and spoken of as "the new plant," and by the time that Father became suspicious enough to investigate, it was practically a member of the family, the way Mother felt, and she couldn't be parted from it. After a battle or two, Father made up his mind that he needn't bother because the lanky thing would soon die, and until then he might as well ignore it, as he did the imitation pug dog.

That rubber tree seemed to me a most lugubrious object to look at. It had had five dark green leaves when it came, but three of these soon turned a horrible mottled yellow and dried up and died. After that nothing happened to it for weeks. It just stood there, with its thin, twisty stem tied for support to the bookcase, sullenly drinking up all the water Mother poured into its pot, and looking more utterly forlorn and sick of this world every day.

Mother however had plenty of determination and spirit, whether her tree had or not, and her will at last prevailed. The rubber tree still looked to me quite as doleful as ever, but it took up the burden of existence once more and put out a new leaf. A more tedious and deliberate unfolding of a bud I'd never seen. Mother didn't mind how slow it was. It was responding to her, and that made her happy. As soon as the new leaf had uncurled itself and spread itself out, the rubber tree was borne downstairs in state to the parlor, to stand on an Empire table by the china pug dog.

After dinner, Mother took Father's arm, coaxingly, and led him in there to look at it. He stood, smoking his cigar, and watching her as she cooed over it and patted its little new leaf. "Don't smoke too near it, Clare dear," she said, over her shoulder. Father stroked his mustache, said "Humph," and walked thoughtfully back to the dining-room. He winked at me presently and said, "Your mother has a very warm heart."

A year or two later, when the rubber tree began to get tall, it was replanted in a much larger flower pot, and put in a tray on the floor; and as time passed by and as it kept growing, it was given a green wooden tub. It went with us to the country every summer and came back in the fall. It was as much trouble and worry, almost, as a baby.

The only possible way to transport it on these two annual trips was to entrust it to Morgan, the coachman, to take in the dog-cart. Morgan hated that rubber tree. It had a good many leaves on it now, but if even one fell off Mother missed it. Morgan explained that neither he nor all the angels could keep a dog-cart from joggling, but Mother said she knew that very well, and that was why she had reminded him specially that he must walk the horse, and three large leaves were missing from the bottom this time and two from the top.

I was sorry for Mother because I knew how she watched over that tree and loved every leaf, but I also felt sorry for Morgan. I had heard other coachmen make fun of him. On these trips he had to drive one horse in the dog-cart and lead two others behind. He had to stow quite a sizeable cargo on and under the seats. His livery, his high hat, his bedding, light and heavy blankets for each of the horses, curry-combs, cloths and brushes, buckets, hoof-picks, two saddles, several bridles, a bag full of bits of old harness, and Topsy, the cat. Morgan used to arrive at our front door in town with everything on board except the rubber tree and old Topsy, find room for these too, and unhappily drive off down Madison Avenue, feeling very conspicuous. Topsy, who didn't like Morgan, yowled and wailed in her basket, and the rubber tree, sitting beside him, was now eight feet high.

His destination, and ours, every summer was New London, a hundred and twenty-five miles away. We went on the train of course. Morgan and the horses and Topsy went on the night boat. I never knew, nor could I manage to picture to myself, what kind of a time Morgan had. A veil was drawn over those dark experiences. All I knew was that Morgan and his caravan arrived a day after we did, the animals dejected and dingy, and Morgan dejected and drunk.

If it hadn't been for the rubber tree, which according to Mother's orders he had to deliver at once, Morgan wouldn't have had to exhibit himself to us in this state. He could have gone direct to the large boarding stables and slept himself sober. As it was, he was faced with a problem that he could never quite solve, the problem of how a man in his cups could get a rubber tree out of a dog-cart and carry it up a tar path and into a cottage, without self-betrayal.

He tried being jaunty about it. He tried being hearty and jolly. But as he was in reality profoundly depressed, by what he had gone through on the boat, his attempts to be pleasant rang hollow. They sounded slightly insane. When he tried being grave and judicial instead, he alarmed Mother dreadfully by his sweeping gestures and his important-looking nods of the head. "For Heaven's sake, Morgan," she would cry, "do get out of this cottage. Don't stand there by my poor rubber tree wagging your head at me that way."

The next day Morgan always had to go through a long, trying session. It began with his being discharged, and it ended with his taking the pledge. This consisted of his solemn assurance that he would never again touch a drop. He freely invoked on himself the most picturesque dooms if he did. "May the Mother of God tear the gullet out of me, bless her sweet heart, the very next drop I take, Mrs. Day, and I won't take it neither." He would continue in a loud, rising scale with his eyes fixed upon Mother's, until he reached a crescendo of fervor that convinced her, and that I think convinced him.

"Morgan," she said, at the end of one such interview.

Morgan respectfully touched his hat. "Yes, mum?"

"You don't deserve it, but I'll try to believe you once more."

"Yes mum, thank you, Mrs. Day," Morgan replied, looking brighter.

"But if you should ever *dare*," Mother vehemently added, "to take another drink of that wicked stuff I hope it will *choke* you!"

Morgan paled. "I hope not, mum," he hastily muttered, again touching his hat.

After we got a place of our own in the country where the tree had more room to grow than ever, it grew far too much. It stood on the piazza, in the one place that wasn't roofed over, and it became so tall that its upper branches reached to the second-floor window. This window unfortunately was Father's. He began to complain. He said that damned tree was too noisy. He said he had built himself a home in the country, at great expense, so as to have some peace and quiet, instead of which here was an outlandish rubber tree tapping on his window all night.

Mother got prouder and prouder of it, the taller it grew. She began busily cutting slips from it and planting numbers of these in new pots, all the way around the piazza. These slips were tall but weedy and weak. Every one of them had to be tied to one of the piazza's square wooden pillars.

The old original tree was now far too big to go into our city home any more. It had to be left in a greenhouse belonging to Mr. Fremd in the winters, and it lived with us only in summer. It would have been out of place in town anyhow. The rubber tree craze had ended long since, and all the pug dogs of New York were gone, too. Those once popular animals had completely disappeared from the city, even our china one, which one of us boys had broken. New fads had sprung up. One was for "favrile glass" which Louis Tiffany made lamps of, and another was for old-fashioned warming-pans. Mother of course had one of each. Her favrile lamp was in the shape of a swollen and adipose lily, glittering with curious hues, far more hues and more glitter than Solomon had in all his glory. Her warming-pan, which she had bought somewhere in New England, had been fixed up to match. Its honest old oaken handle had been stained to look like polished mahogany, and a broad red satin ribbon was tied in a bowknot around it, like that which the pug dog had worn.

Mother was not one to be fickle, however, and she was faithful to her rubber tree still. It was on her mind all the time. When we moved up to the country each spring, that tree was the first thing she greeted.

It was becoming quite a job for her to water it sufficiently, on account of its size, and this was particularly difficult when there was a drought. What made it so hard at such times, at least in Mother's eyes, was Father's bath. Drought or no drought, he said, he had to have his cold bath every morning. Mother said that her tree would die and he wouldn't, and what was his answer to that? His answer was that he had always taken a bath every day of his life.

For years he had tried to get Mother to take an icy plunge too. As he grew older he said less about it, but he took a tubbing himself just the same. Mother said that if he insisted on a daily bath, even in droughts, he must leave the water standing in his tub so that it could be used for her rubber tree.

Father let her use it but he didn't like it. He said Mother was messy. She tracked water all over his floor, he said, when she walked back and forth, filling her pitcher from his tub and then pouring it out of his bedroom window to splash it on top of that tree. Mother said she didn't splash the water, and had not tracked up his floor, and when Father pointed indignantly to the pools and wet spots by his sofa, she said that those were just a few drops from the outside of the pitcher.

One cold, dark autumn morning, Father was longer than usual taking his bath. The water was icy, and things hadn't been going well with him, and altogether he wasn't feeling as vigorous as usual that morning. When Mother dipped her pitcher into his bathtub she found that it wasn't cold. He had secretly warmed it a little to take off some of its chill.

"Why, Clare!" she laughed. "I thought you were such a stickler for taking cold baths!"

"Damnation!" said Father. "Get out of my bathroom. Leave my bathtub alone! I swear to God no man ever had so much to bear from a rubber tree."

Mr. Fremd, although he was a professional nursery-man, felt the same way. He was getting tired of the rubber tree too. One winter, without telling Mother, he cut off its top. In May, when his wagon climbed our hill again, bringing back his maimed victim, and when Mother expressed the grief and fury she felt at his conduct, Mr. Fremd was defiant. He had simply had to do it, he said. The roof of his greenhouse wasn't high enough for that tree any more. Mother quarreled with him about this. She warned him that he must never again behave like that to her plants, and that summer she helped the old tree to regain its full height. Mr. Fremd retaliated, the following winter, by keeping it lying flat on its side for the seven or eight months that he had it. He said, what else could he do. That was the only way he could get it indoors. From that time on the tree spent over half of each year lying down, never standing up except in the summers, and it gradually became rather towzled.

When this strange pet of Mother's had finally completely outgrown her, and when she had vainly appealed for help to all of her friends, she happened one evening to hear my brother George speak of the Marsh Botanical Garden at Yale. The next I knew she had presented the Botanical Garden with her rubber tree. They tried to explain to her that they didn't have any rubber trees, but this did them no good, it only made Mother the prouder to bestow hers upon them. Her one stipulation was that as the coachman couldn't very well drive it all the way up to New Haven, the Marsh Botanical Garden must come down to Harrison and get it themselves. To my private astonishment they apparently did so. Although years later George told me that he had hired a truck for the purpose, letting Mother believe that the University had done so, as he knew that Mother would never have been willing to let George do it—or to do it herself. And George was unwilling to have the University pay. The last I saw of our tree was its top sticking way out of the rear of a Forestry truck, rounding a turn down the road.

Women

BY

RING LARDNER

YOUNG JAKE UTTERED a few words which it would pain me to repeat.

"And what are *you* crabbin' about?" asked Mike Healy from his corner of the bench.

"Oh, nothin'!" said Jake. "Nothin' except that I'm sick of it!"

"Sick of what?" demanded Healy.

"Of settin' here!" Jake replied.

"You!" said Mike Healy, with a short laugh. "You've got a fine license to squawk! Why, let's see: what is it? The third of June, and your first June in the league. You ain't even *begin* to sit! Look at me! Been on this bench since catchers started wearin' a mast, or anyway it seems that long. And you never hear me crab, do you, Lefty?"

"Only when you talk," answered the athlete addressed. "And that's only at table or between meals."

"But if this kid's hollerin' already," said Mike, "what'll he be doin' along in August or September, to say nothin' about next August and the August after that?"

"Don't worry!" said Young Jake. "I'll either be a regular by the end of this season or I won't be on this ball club at all!"

"That-a-boy!" said Healy. "Threaten 'em!"

"I mean what I say!" retorted Jake. "I ain't goin' to spend my life on no bench! I come here to play baseball!"

"Oh, you did!" said Healy. "And what do you think I come here for, to fish?"

"I ain't talkin' about you," said Young Jake. "I'm talkin' about myself."

"Thats' a novelty in a ball player," remarked Lefty.

236

"And what I'm sayin'," Jake went on, "is that I'm sick of settin' on this bench."

"This ain't a bad bench," said Healy. "They's a hell of a lot worse places you might sit."

"And a hell of a lot better places!" said Jake. "I can think of one right now. I'm lookin' right at it."

"Where at?"

"Right up in the old stand; the third—no, the fourth row, next to the aisle, the first aisle beyond where the screen leaves off."

"I noticed her myself!" put in Lefty. "Damn cute! Too damn cute for a busher like you to get smoked up over."

"Oh, I don't know!" said Young Jake. "I didn't get along so bad with them dames down South."

"Down South ain't here!" replied Lefty. "Those dames in some of those swamps, they lose their head when they see a man with shoes on. But up here you've got to have something. If you pulled that Calhoun County stuff of yours on a gal like that gal in the stand she'd yell for the dog catcher. She'd——"

"They're all alike!" interrupted Mike Healy. "South, or here, or anywheres, they're all the same, and all poison!"

"What's poison?" asked Jake.

"Women!" said Healy. "And the more you have to do with 'em the better chance you've got of spendin' your life on this bench. Why—— That's pitchin', Joe!" he shouted when the third of the enemy batters had popped out and left a runner stranded at second base. "You look good in there today," he added to Joe as the big pitcher approached the dugout.

"I'm all right, I guess," said Joe, pulling on his sweater and moving toward the water bottle. "I wished that wind'd die down."

The manager had come in.

"All right! Let's get at 'em!" he said. "Nice work, Joe. Was that a fast one Meusel hit?"

"No," said Joe. "A hook, but it didn't break."

"A couple of runs will beat 'em the way you're going," said the manager, stooping over to select his bat. "Make this fella pitch, boys," he said. "He was hog wild in Philly the other day."

The half inning wore on to its close, and the noncombatants were again left in possession of the bench. Young Jake addressed Healy.

"What's women done to you, Mike?"

"Only broke me. That's all!" said Healy.

"What do you mean, broke you! The boys tells me you ain't spent nothin' but the summer since you been in the league."

"Oh, I've got a little money," said Healy. "I don't throw it away. I don't go around payin' ten smackers a quart for liquid catnip. But they's more kinds of broke than money broke, a damn sight worse kinds, too. And when I say women has broke me, I mean they've made a bum out of my life; they've wrecked my—what-do-you-call-it?"

"Your career," supplied Lefty.

"Yes, sir," said Healy. "And I ain't kiddin', neither. Why say, listen: Do you know where I'd be if it wasn't for a woman? Right out there in that infield, playin' that old third sack."

"What about Smitty?" asked Young Jake.

"He'd be where I am—on this bench."

"Aw, come on, Mike! Be yourself! You don't claim you're as good as him!" Jake remonstrated.

"I do claim it, but it don't make no difference if I am or I ain't. He shouldn't never ought to of had a chance, not on this club, anyway. You'd say the same if you knowed the facts."

"Well, let's hear 'em."

"It's a long story, and these boys has heard it before."

"That's all right, Mike," said Gephart, a spare catcher. "We ain't listened the last twelve times."

"Well, it was the year I come in this league, four years ago this spring. I'd been with the Toledo club a couple of years. I was the best hitter on the Toledo club. I hit .332 the first year and .354 the next year. And I led the third basemen in fieldin'."

"It would be hard not to," interposed Lefty. "Anything a third baseman don't get they call it a base hit. A third baseman ought to pay to get in the park."

Healy glanced coldly at the speaker, and resumed:

"This club had Johnnie Lambert. He was still about the best third baseman in this league, but he was thirty-five years old and had a bad knee. It had slipped out on him and cost this club the pennant. They didn't have no other third baseman. They lose sixteen out of twenty games. So that learned 'em a lesson, and they bought me. Their idear was to start Johnnie in the spring, but they didn't expect his knee to hold up. And then it was goin' to be my turn.

"But durin' the winter Johnnie got a hold of some specialist somewheres that fixed his knee, and he come South with a new lease of life. He hit good and was as fast as ever on the bases. Meanw'ile I had been on a huntin' trip up in Michigan that winter and froze my dogs, and they ailed me so that I couldn't do myself justice all spring."

"I suppose it was some woman made you go huntin'," said Gephart, but Healy continued without replying:

"They was a gal from a town named Ligonier, Indiana, that had visited in Toledo the second year I played ball there. The people where she was visitin' was great baseball fans, and they brought her out to the game with them, and she got stuck on me."

"Ligonier can't be a town! It must be an asylum!" said Lefty.

"She got stuck on me," Healy repeated, "and the people where she was stayin' asked me to their house to supper. After supper the man and his wife said how about goin' to the picture show, and the gal said she was tired and rather stay home. So the man and woman excused themselves. They said it was a picture they wanted to see and would I excuse them runnin' off and leavin' we two together. They were clubbin' on me, see?

"Well, I thought to myself, I'll give this dame an unpleasant surprise, so I didn't even hold her hand all evenin'. When I got up to go she says she supposed it would be the last time she seen me as she expected to go back to Ligonier the next day. She didn't have no more intentions of goin' back the next day than crossin' Lake Erie in a hollow tooth. But she knowed if I thought it was good-by I'd kiss her. Well, I knowed it wasn't good-by, but what the hell! So that's how it started, and I went Ligonier that fall to see her, and we got engaged to be married. At least she seemed to think so."

"Look at that!" interrupted Young Jake, his eyes on the field of action. "What could Sam of been thinkin'!"

"Thinkin'!" said Gephart. "Him!"

"What would Sam do," wondered Lefty, "if they played baseball with only one base? He wouldn't enjoy the game if he couldn't throw to the wrong one."

"That play's liable to cost us somethin'," said Gephart.

"I went up in Michigan on a huntin' trip with some friends

of mine," Healy continued. "I froze my feet and was laid up all through January and February and shouldn't of never went South. It was all as I could do to wear shoes, let alone play baseball. I wasn't really myself till along the first of May. But, as I say, Johnnie Lambert had a new least of life and was lookin' better than he'd looked for years. His knee wasn't troublin' him at all.

"Well, that's how things went till around the last part of June. I didn't get no action except five or six times goin' up to hit for somebody. And I was like a young colt crazy to be let loose. I knowed that if I once got in there and showed what I could do Judge Landis himself couldn't keep me on the bench. I used to kneel down every night and pray to God to get to work on Lambert's knee.

"The gal kept writin' me letters and I answered 'em once in a w'ile, but we hadn't saw each other since before Christmas. She hinted once or twice about when was we goin' to get married, but I told her I didn't want to even disgust the subject till I was somethin' besides a bench warmer.

"We had a serious in Chi the tail-end of June, and the first night we was there I got a long-distance call from Ligonier. It was the gal's sister, sayin' the gal was sick. She was delirious part of the time and hollerin' for me, and the doctor said if she could see me, it'd probably do her more good than medicine.

"So I said that's all right, but they ain't no off days in the schedule right now and I can't get away. But they had looked up the time table and seen where I could leave Chi after the ball game, spend the night in Ligonier and get back for the game the next day.

"So I took a train from Englewood in the evenin' and when I got off at Ligonier, there was my gal to meet me. She was the picture of health and no more delirious than usual. They said she had been just about ready to pass out when she learned I was comin' and it cured her. They didn't tell me what disease she'd had, but I suppose it was a grasshopper bite or somethin'.

"When I left next mornin', the weddin' date was set for that fall.

"Somewheres between South Bend and Laporte, the train stopped and liked it so well that we stayed there over three hours. We hit Englewood after four o'clock and I got to the park just in time to see them loadin' Lambert into a machine to take him away. His knee had broke down on him in the first innin's. He ain't never played ball since. And Smitty, who's always been a natural second baseman, he had my job."

"He filled it pretty good," said Lefty.

"That's either here or there," retorted Healy. "If I'd been around, nobody'd ever knowed if he could play third base or not. And the worst of him is," he added, "that he never gets hurt."

"Maybe you ain't prayed for him like you done for Lambert," said Young Jake. "What happened to the gal? Did you give her the air?"

"No, I didn't," said Healy. "When I give my word, I keep it. I simply wrote and told her that I'd agreed to marry her and I wouldn't go back on it. But that my feelin's towards her was the same as if she was an advanced case of spinal meningitis. She never answered the letter, so I don't know if we're still engaged or not."

The inning was over and the boys were coming in.

"Joe was lucky to get out of that with only two runs," remarked Lefty. "But of course it was Sam that put him in bad."

"I'm goin' to see if he'll leave me get up on the lines," said Young Jake, "so I can get a better look at that dame."

The manager waited for Sam to catch up.

"What the hell was the matter with you, Sam?" he demanded.

Sam looked silly.

"I thought—"

"That's where you make your mistake!" the manager broke in. "Tough luck, Joe! But two runs are nothing. We'll get 'em back."

"Shall I go up on the lines?" asked Young Jake, hopefully.

"You? No!" said the manager. "You, Mike," turning to Healy, "go over and coach at third base. You brought us luck yesterday."

So it was Mike who was held partly responsible a few moments later when Smitty, who had tripled, was caught napping off the bag.

"Nice coachin', Mike!" said Lefty, as Healy came back to the bench.

"Why don't he watch hisself!" growled Mike. "And besides, I did yell at him!"

"You're a liar!" said Lefty. "Your back was to the ball game. You were lookin' up in the stand."

"Why would I be lookin' at the stand!" demanded Healy.

But nobody answered him. There was silence for a time. The boys were depressed; in their own language, their dauber was down. Finally Young Jake spoke.

"She's starin' right over this way!" he said.

"Who?" asked Gephart.

"That dame I pointed out. In the tan suit. 'Way over behind third base, the other side of the screen, in the fourth row."

"I see her. Not bad!"

"I'll say she's not bad!" said Jake.

"Women!" said Healy. "You better get your mind on baseball or you'll be back in that silo league, jumpin' from town to town in a wheelbarrow."

"I don't see why you should be off all women just because one of them brought you a little hard luck."

"She wasn't the only one! Why, say, if it wasn't for women I'd be playin' regular third base for McGraw right now and cuttin' in on the big money every fall."

"I didn't know you was ever with McGraw."

"I wasn't," said Healy, "but I ought to been, and would of been only for a woman. It was when I was playin' with the Dayton club; my first year in baseball. Boy, I was fast as a streak! I was peggin' bunts to first base before the guy could drop his bat. I covered so much ground to my left that I was always knockin' the shortshop down and bumpin' heads with the right fielder. Everybody was marvelin' at me. Some of the old timers said I reminded them of Bill Bradley at his best, only that I made Bradley look like he was out of the game for a few days.

"Baldy Pierce was umpirin' in our league that year. He wasn't a bad umps, but he never left business interfere with pleasure. Many's the time he called the last fella out in the last innin's when the fella was safer than a hot chocolate at the Elks' convention—just because Baldy was hungry for supper.

"He was so homely that dogs wouldn't live in the same town, and his friends used to try and make him wear his mask off the field as well as on. And yet he grabbed some of the prettiest gals you ever see. He said to me once, he said, 'Mike,' he said, 'you tell me I'm homelier than Railroad Street, but I can cop more pips than you can with all your good looks!'"

At this point there were unprintable comments by Lefty, Gephart, and other occupants of the bench.

"One of these gals of his," Healy went on, "was a gal named Helen Buck from Hamiliton, Ohio. She was visitin' in Dayton and come out to the ball game. The first day she was there a lot of the boys was hit in the face by thrown balls, and every time a foul went to the stand the whole infield run in to shag it. But she wouldn't look at nobody but Pierce.

"Well, McGraw had heard about me, and he sent a fella named McDonald, that was scoutin' for him, to look me over. It was in September and we was just about through. How the games come out didn't make no difference, but I knowed this McDonald was there and what he was there for, so I wanted to make a showin'. He had came intendin' to stay two days, but he'd overlooked a skip in the schedule that left us without no game the second day, so he said one game would have to be enough, as he had to go somewheres else.

"We was playin' the Springfield club. I had a good day in the field, but Bill Hutton, who started pitchin' for them, he was hog wild and walked me the first two times up. The third time they was a man on third and I had to follow orders and squeeze him home. So I hadn't had no chance to really show what I could do up there at the plate.

"Well, we come into the ninth innin's with the score tied and it was gettin' pretty dark. We got two of them out, and then their first baseman, Jansen, he got a base on balls. Bill Boone caught a hold of one just right and cracked it to the fence and it looked like Jansen would score, but he was a slow runner. Davy Shaw, our short-stop thought he must of scored and when the ball was thrown to him he throwed it to me to get Boone, who was tryin' for three bases.

"Well, I had took in the situation at a glance; I seen that Jansen hadn't scored and if I put the ball on Boone, quick enough, why the run wouldn't count. So I lunged at Boone and tagged him before Jansen had crossed the plate. But Pierce said the score counted and that Boone wasn't out because I'd missed him. Missed him! Say, I bet that where I tagged him they had to take stitches!

"Anyway, that give 'em a one run lead, and when the first two fellas got out in our half everybody thought it was over. But

Davy Shaw hit one to right center that a man like I could of ran around twice on it, but they held Davy at third base. And it was up to me to bring him in.

"By this time Jim Preston was pitchin' for Springfield, and Jim was always a mark for me. I left the first one go by, as it was outside, but Pierce called it a strike. Then they was a couple of balls that he couldn't call strikes. I cracked the next one over the left-field fence, but it was a few inches foul. That made it two and two, and the next ball he throwed, well, if I hadn't ducked my head just when I did they'd of been brains scattered all over Montgomery County. And what does Pierce do but yell "Batter out!" and run for the clubhouse!

"Well, I run after him and asked him what the hell, and here is what he said. He said, 'Mike,' he said, 'these games don't mean nothin', but if this here game had of wound up a tie it would of meant a game tomorrow, when we got a off day. And I made a date for tomorrow to go on a picnic with my little gal in Hamilton. You wouldn't want me to miss that, would you?' "

"Why," inquired Young Jake, "didn't you break his nose or bust him in the chin?"

"His nose was already broke," said Healy, "and he didn't have no chin. I tried to get a hold of McDonald, the fella that was there scoutin' me. I was going' to explain the thing to him. But he'd left town before I could catch him. It seems, though, that he'd set over to the side where he couldn't see what a lousy strike it was and he told a friend of mine that he couldn't recommend a man that would take a third strike when a base hit would of tied up the game; that on top of me 'missin' ' Boone at third——"

Another half inning was over and Healy started for the third-base coaching line without waiting for the manager to reach the bench. His teammates were not in a position to see the glance he threw at a certain spot in the stand as he walked to his "work." When the side was retired scoreless and he had returned to his corner of the dugout he looked more desolate than ever.

"Women!" he said. "Why, if it wasn't for women I'd be playin' third base for Huggins; I'd have Joe Dugan's job; I'd be livin' right here in the capital of the world."

"How do you make that out?" asked Young Jake.

"It's a long story," said Healy, "but I can tell you in a few words. We was playin' the New York Club out home. Frank Baker had began to slip and Huggins was lookin' for a good young fella to take his place. He was crazy to get me, but he had heard that I didn't want to play in New York. This had came from me kiddin' with some of the boys on the New York Club, tellin' 'em I wouldn't play here if they give me the town. So Huggins wanted to make sure before he started a trade. And he didn't want no one to see him talkin' to me. So he came around one night to the hotel where I was livin' at the time. I was up in my room waitin' for the phone gal to be off duty. She was stuck on me and I had a date to take her for a drive. So when Huggins come to see me she said I was out. She was afraid her date was goin' to be interfered with. So Huggins went away and his club left town that night."

"What did you do to her?" asked Jake.

"Oh, I couldn't do nothin' to her," said Healy. "She claimed she didn't know who it was."

"Didn't he give his name?"

"No."

"Then how do you know it was Huggins?"

"She said it was a little fella."

"He ain't the only little fella."

"He's the littlest fella I know," said Healy.

"But you ain't sure what he wanted to see you for."

"What *would* Huggins want to see me for—to scratch my back? But as I say, she didn't know who it was, so I couldn't do nothin' to her except ignore her from then on, and they couldn't of been no worse punishment as far as she was concerned."

"All and all," summed up Lefty, "if it wasn't for women, you'd of been playin' third base for McGraw and Huggins and this club, all at the same time."

"Yes," said Healy, "and with Washin'ton, too. Why——"

"Mike Healy!" interrupted the voice of Dick Trude, veteran usher. "Here's a mash note and it wants an answer."

Healy read the note and crumpled it in his hand.

"Who is she?" he asked.

"Look where I point," said Trude. "It's that good-lookin' dame in the tan suit, in the fourth row, back of third base. There! She asked me who you was when you was out there coachin'. So I told her, and she give me that note. She said you could answer yes or no."

"Make it 'yes,'" said Healy, and Trude went away.

Healy threw the crumpled note under the water bottle and addressed Young Jake.

"What I want you to get through your head, boy——"

"Oh, for God's sake, shut up!" said Young Jake.

You Should Live So, Walden Pond

BY

S. J. PERELMAN

UP THE rolling ridge of Giggles Hill, a mile back from the Pennsylvania bank of the Delaware River, stands a modest stone house, pretty much as it stood during the last century. It is approached through a majestic avenue of large yellow signboards, placed there at ruinous expense and with no conviction whatever that he who runs will read. Beginning gently enough with the silky admonition "Fortified Area—Stay Off," the tone changes abruptly to a sinister "Communicable Diseases— Proceed at Your Own Risk." Should this prove inadequate, and it always does, the next two hundred feet are devoted to some choice billingsgate culled from Restoration plays, calculated to make a mule skinner flush to the roots of his hair. Unfortunately, since very few mule skinners pass that way, and those mostly bald, the effect is negligible, and by the time you top the rise beyond the persimmon trees, the signs culminate on a note of sheer hopelessness in a pair of 24-sheet billboards reading "County Life: A Mockery" and "Solitude, My Foot."

Naturally enough I have been called everything from an old crosspatch to a modern Timothy Dexter of Newburyport. Indeed, whenever I drive my gig into the county seat for a pound of wire brads, of which I am inordinately fond, a troop of small boys invariably forms at my heels with taunts of "Oh, you modern Timothy Dexter of Newburyport!" So if I take the stand now in my own defense, it is only because Thoreau has had it long enough. Privacy in the country? Don't make me laugh, I've got a split personality.

Back in 1932, just before That Man came in and destroyed business confidence by reopening the banks, I belonged to a little group of profound thinkers who spent their evenings doing embroidery. The embroidery was on the theme, "If you have a small piece of dirt somewhere, you can always raise enough to keep you going." There was also a corollary which specified, "Nobody bothers you in the country. You can sleep as late as you like." Well, Sal's in a brothel, Pat's in jail, and I'm the one to tell the tale. I raised enough to keep myself going, all right, but my stomach never really became adjusted to ferns and hot water. Now I eat and drink whatever I like and sleep like a top—till shortly before dawn. Then the parade begins.

It is usually headed by a snaggle-toothed old bit player over-picturesquely made up as a hired man, who follows a well-worn routine. After sneaking around the house a few times to set the dogs in an uproar, he stations himself beneath my bedroom window and bawls out some obscene farrago, which presumably is a request for instructions about the chores. Properly keyed up on several brandies and armed with a pony, I can feel my way through Pennsylvania German dialect, but pluck me out of a sound slumber and I present a pitiable sight. Experience has taught me that to keep the respect of this man, whom I have never seen after five o'clock in the morning, I must pretend to give the matter deep thought. So for the next five minutes we both remain *en tableau:* he with an oily grin on his face, as though butter wouldn't melt in his mouth (he has even held up lumps of unmelted butter to me on occasion), and the young master swaying against the window, eyes closed and forefinger to temple in an attitude of profound concentration. In the end I give the fellow carte blanche and reel back to my crib, only to discover later, on arising again, that he has chopped down all the Chinese elms I planted last fall. Who pays the man to do this type of work I have no idea, unless it can be the War Office in Tokio.

Hardly am I back in the Taj Mahal, surrounded by Madeleine Carroll and five hundred million billion trillion dollars, when the masons, carpenters and assorted technicians arrive, minus tools but with plenty of noisemakers and confetti. After a brief warmup, which includes morris dancing on the green and feats of strength, one of their number, who is either eighteen feet high or uses a ladder, leans in at my window for a series of those highly complex questions you love to wake up to: "Hey, Mister, does the bushing fit over or under the flange on the cam?" or "Shall we put the differential on the housing or whitelead the gaskets? You haven't got a pound of sixpenny nails in there, have you?" Ignoring with con-

siderable hauteur the implication that I am the sort of man who
sleeps with sixpenny nails, I now rise and stand up in a clothes
closet until time for breakfast.

Belowstairs, preparations have gone forward briskly to welcome
the laird to his morning meal. Compared to my dining room, the
floor of the Stock Exchange is a cloistered dell. The family motto
seems to be "Let's tell him now, he'll only find out anyway." Bubbling with infectious laughter, the staff greets me with the news that
the hot-water system has gone to hell and rabbits have been at the
lettuce. Gramps, a lovable old white-haired character who fought
with Meade at Shiloh—he and Meade just never got along—has been
up since six, making his usual inspection of the premises, and
things look pretty black. A large bird, cousin to the giant condor
of the Andes, has mysteriously wedged itself into the chimney during the night; it might be cheaper to tear down the whole kitchen
wing while we're about it. None of the lespedeza he planted yesterday is up yet, and the old gentleman shouldn't wonder if they sold
him last year's seed. With the orange juice and coffee scarcely more
than a hot ball in my throat, instant decisions are now in order regarding the dinner menu. What about roast-beef hash with gravy
and browned potatoes? Or a few salmon croquettes followed by
boiled beef with horseradish and capers? Yes, but don't put so much
flour in the sauce. Well, you try and cook with that oven. Nothing
wrong with the oven; we just bought it. Nothing wrong with the
oven? *Didn't we tell you?* This morning, just as Freda went to light
the burner. . . .

83 ROLLING ACRES—Quaint old stone house—completely restored—summer kitchen, guest house—historic maple shade—
orchard, never-failing creek, artesian well—30 acres in timber—
huge bank barn stabling 21 head—poultry houses, garage, work-
shop, all farm implements—owner will exchange for 9×6 city
apt. above 15th fl.—must have air shaft and no view—apply
immediately.

The Schartz-Metterklume Method

BY

"SAKI" (H. H. MUNRO)

LADY CARLOTTA stepped out on the platform of the small way-side station and took a turn or two up and down its unin-teresting length, to kill time till the train should be pleased to proceed on its way. Then, in the roadway beyond, she saw a horse struggling with a more than ample load, and a carter of the sort that seems to bear a sullen hatred against the animal that helps him to earn a living. Lady Carlotta promptly betook her to the road-way, and put rather a different complexion on the struggle. Certain of her acquaintances were wont to give her plentiful admonition as to the undesirability of interfering on behalf of a distressed ani-mal, such interference being "none of her business." Only once had she put the doctrine of non-interference into practice, when one of its most eloquent exponents had been besieged for nearly three hours in a small and extremely uncomfortable may-tree by an angry boar-pig, while Lady Carlotta, on the other side of the fence, had proceeded with the water-colour sketch she was engaged on, and refused to interfere between the boar and his prisoner. It is to be feared that she lost the friendship of the ultimately rescued lady. On this occasion she merely lost the train, which gave way to the first sign of impatience it had shown throughout the journey, and steamed off without her. She bore the desertion with philosophical indifference; her friends and relations were thoroughly well used to the fact of her luggage arriving without her. She wired a vague non-committal message to her destination to say that she was com-ing on "by another train." Before she had time to think what her next move might be she was confronted by an imposingly at-tired lady, who seemed to be taking a prolonged mental inventory of her clothes and looks.

"You must be Miss Hope, the governess I've come to meet," said the apparition, in a tone that admitted of very little argument.

"Very well, if I must I must," said Lady Carlotta to herself with dangerous meekness.

"I am Mrs. Quabarl," continued the lady; "and where, pray, is your luggage?"

"It's gone astray," said the alleged governess, falling in with the excellent rule of life that the absent are always to blame; the luggage had, in point of fact, behaved with perfect correctitude. "I've just telegraphed about it," she added, with a nearer approach to truth.

"How provoking," said Mrs. Quabarl; "these railway companies are so careless. However, my maid can lend you things for the night," and she led the way to her car.

During the drive to the Quabarl mansion Lady Carlotta was impressively introduced to the nature of the charge that had been thrust upon her; she learned that Claude and Wilfred were delicate, sensitive young people, that Irene had the artistic temperament highly developed, and that Viola was something or other else of a mould equally commonplace among children of that class and type in the twentieth century.

"I wish them not only to be *taught*," said Mrs. Quabarl, "but *interested* in what they learn. In their history lessons, for instance, you must try to make them feel that they are being introduced to the life-stories of men and women who really lived, not merely committing a mass of names and dates to memory. French, of course, I shall expect you to talk at mealtimes several days in the week."

"I shall talk French four days of the week and Russian on the remaining three."

"Russian? My dear Miss Hope, no one in the house speaks or understands Russian."

"That will not embarrass me in the least," said Lady Carlotta coldly.

Mrs. Quabarl, to use a colloquial expression, was knocked off her perch. She was one of those imperfectly self-assured individuals who are magnificent and autocratic as long as they are not seriously opposed. The least show of unexpected resistance goes a long way towards rendering them cowed and apologetic. When the new governess failed to express wondering admiration of the large, newly purchased and expensive car, and lightly alluded to the superior advantages of one or two makes which had just been put on the market, the discomfiture of her patroness became almost abject. Her feelings were those which might have animated a general of ancient warfaring days, on beholding his heaviest battle-elephant ignominiously driven off the field by slingers and javelin throwers.

At dinner that evening, although reinforced by her husband, who usually duplicated her opinions and lent her moral support generally, Mrs. Quabarl regained none of her lost ground. The governess not only helped herself well and truly to wine, but held forth with considerable show of critical knowledge on various vintage matters, concerning which the Quabarls were in no wise able to pose as authorities. Previous governesses had limited their conversation on the wine topic to a respectful and doubtless sincere expression of a preference for water. When this one went as far as to recommend a wine firm in whose hands you could not go very far wrong Mrs. Quabarl thought it time to turn the conversation into more usual channels.

"We got very satisfactory references about you from Canon Teep," she observed; "a very estimable man, I should think."

"Drinks like a fish and beats his wife, otherwise a very lovable character," said the governess imperturbably.

"My *dear* Miss Hope! I trust you are exaggerating," exclaimed the Quabarls in unison.

"One must in justice admit that there is some provocation," continued the romancer. "Mrs. Teep is quite the most irritating bridge-player that I have ever sat down with; her leads and declarations would condone a certain amount of brutality in her partner, but to souse her with the contents of the only soda-water syphon in the house on a Sunday afternoon, when one couldn't get another, argues an indifference to the comfort of others which I cannot altogether overlook. You may think me hasty in my judgments, but it was practically on account of the syphon incident that I left."

"We will talk of this some other time," said Mrs. Quabarl hastily.

"I shall never allude to it again," said the governess with decision.

Mr. Quabarl made a welcome diversion by asking what studies the new instructress proposed to inaugurate on the morrow.

"History to begin with," she informed him.

"Ah, history," he observed sagely; "now, in teaching them history you must take care to interest them in what they learn. You must make them feel that they are being introduced to the life-stories of men and women who really lived—"

"I've told her all that," interposed Mrs. Quabarl.

"I teach history on the Schartz-Metterklume method," said the governess loftily.

"Ah, yes," said her listeners, thinking it expedient to assume an acquaintance at least with the name.

"What are you children doing out here?" demanded Mrs. Quabarl the next morning, on finding Irene sitting rather glumly at the head of the stairs, while her sister was perched in an attitude of depressed discomfort on the window-seat behind her, with a wolf-skin rug almost covering her.

"We are having a history lesson," came the unexpected reply. "I am supposed to be Rome, and Viola up there is the she-wolf; not a real wolf, but the figure of one that the Romans used to set store by—I forgot why. Claude and Wilfred have gone to fetch the shabby women."

"The shabby women?"

"Yes, they've got to carry them off. They didn't want to, but Miss Hope got one of father's fives-bats and said she'd give them a number nine spanking if they didn't, so they've gone to do it."

A loud, angry screaming from the direction of the lawn drew Mrs. Quabarl thither in hot haste, fearful lest the threatened castigation might even now be in process of infliction. The outcry, how-ever, came principally from the two small daughters of the lodge-keeper, who were being hauled and pushed towards the house by the panting and dishevelled Claude and Wilfred, whose task was rendered even more arduous by the incessant, if not very effectual, attacks of the captured maidens' small brother. The governess, fives-bat in hand, sat negligently on the stone balustrade, presiding over the scene with the cold impartiality of a Goddess of Battles. A furious and repeated chorus of "I'll tell muvver" rose from the lodge children, but the lodge-mother, who was hard of hearing, was for the moment immersed in the preoccupation of her wash-tub. After an apprehensive glance in the direction of the lodge (the good woman was gifted with the highly militant temper which

is sometimes the privilege of deafness) Mrs. Quabarl flew indignantly to the rescue of the struggling captives.

"Wilfred! Claude! Let those children go at once. Miss Hope, what
on earth is the meaning of this scene?"

"Early Roman history; the Sabine women, don't you know? It's
the Schartz-Metterklume method to make children understand history by acting it themselves; fixes it in their memory, you know.
Of course, if, thanks to your interference, your boys go through
life thinking that the Sabine women ultimately escaped, I really
cannot be held responsible."

"You may be very clever and modern, Miss Hope," said Mrs.
Quabarl firmly, "but I should like you to leave here by the next
train. Your luggage will be sent after you as soon as it arrives."

"I'm not certain exactly where I shall be for the next few days,"
said the dismissed instructress of youth; "you might keep my luggage till I wire my address. There are only a couple of trunks and
some golf-clubs and a leopard cub."

"A leopard cub!" gasped Mrs. Quabarl. Even in her departure
this extraordinary person seemed destined to leave a trail of embarrassment behind her.

"Well, it's rather left off being a cub; it's more than half-
grown, you know. A fowl every day and a rabbit on Sundays is
what it usually gets. Raw beef makes it too excitable. Don't trouble
about getting the car for me, I'm rather inclined for a walk."

And Lady Carlotta strode out of the Quabarl horizon.

The advent of the genuine Miss Hope, who had made a mistake
as to the day on which she was due to arrive, caused a turmoil
which that good lady was quite unused to inspiring. Obviously the
Quabarl family had been woefully befooled, but a certain amount
of relief came with the knowledge.

"How tiresome for you, dear Carlotta," said her hostess, when the
overdue guest ultimately arrived; "how very tiresome losing your
train and having to stop overnight in a strange place."

"Oh, dear, no," said Lady Carlotta; "not at all tiresome—for me."

Farewell, My Lovely

BY

LEE STROUT WHITE

I SEE BY the new Sears Roebuck catalogue that it is still possible to
buy an axle for a 1909 Model T Ford, but I am not deceived. The
great days have faded, the end is in sight. Only one page in the current catalogue is devoted to parts and accessories for the Model T;
yet everyone remembers springtimes when the Ford gadget section
was larger than men's clothing, almost as large as household furnishings. The last Model T was built in 1927, and the car is fading from
what scholars call the American scene—which is an understatement,
because to a few million people who grew up with it, the old Ford
practically *was* the American scene.

It was the miracle God had wrought. And it was patently the sort
of thing that could only happen once. Mechanically uncanny, it was
like nothing that had ever come to the world before. Flourishing in-
dustries rose and fell with it. As a vehicle, it was hard-working, commonplace, heroic; and it often seemed to transmit those qualities to
the persons who rode in it. My own generation identifies it with
Youth, with its gaudy, irretrievable excitements; before it fades into
the mist, I would like to pay it the tribute of the sigh that is not
a sob, and set down random entries in a shape somewhat less cum-
bersome than a Sears Roebuck catalogue.

The Model T was distinguished from all other makes of cars by
the fact that its transmission was of a type known as planetary—
which was half metaphysics, half sheer friction. Engineers accepted
the word "planetary" in its epicyclic sense, but I was always conscious that it also meant "wandering," "erratic." Because of the
peculiar nature of this planetary element, there was always, in
Model T, a certain dull rapport between engine and wheels, and
even when the car was in a state known as neutral, it trembled with

a deep imperative and tended to inch forward. There was never a moment when the bands were not faintly egging the machine on. In this respect it was like a horse, rolling the bit on its tongue, and country people brought to it the same technique they used with draft animals.

Its most remarkable quality was its rate of acceleration. In its palmy days the Model T could take off faster than anything on the road. The reason was simple. To get under way, you simply hooked the third finger of the right hand around a lever on the steering column, pulled down hard, and shoved your left foot forcibly against the low-speed pedal. These were simple, positive motions; the car responded by lunging forward with a roar. After a few seconds of this turmoil, you took your toe off the pedal, eased up a mite on the throttle, and the car, possessed of only two forward speeds, catapulted directly into high with a series of ugly jerks and was off on its glorious errand. The abruptness of this departure was never equalled in other cars of the period. The human leg was (and still is) incapable of letting in a clutch with anything like the forthright abandon that used to send Model T on its way. Letting in a clutch is a negative, hesitant motion, depending on delicate nervous control; pushing down the Ford pedal was a simple, country motion—an expansive act, which came as natural as kicking an old door to make it budge.

The driver of the old Model T was a man enthroned. The car, with top up, stood seven feet high. The driver sat on top of the gas tank, brooding it with his own body. When he wanted gasoline, he alighted, along with everything else in the front seat; the seat was pulled off, the metal cap unscrewed, and a wooden stick thrust down to sound the liquid in the well. There were always a couple of these sounding sticks kicking around in the ratty sub-cushion regions of a flivver. Refueling was more of a social function then, because the driver had to unbend, whether he wanted to or not. Directly in front of the driver was the windshield—high, uncompromisingly erect. Nobody talked about air resistance, and the four cylinders pushed the car through the atmosphere with a simple disregard of physical law.

There was this about a Model T: the purchaser never regarded his purchase as a complete, finished product. When you bought a Ford, you figured you had a start—a vibrant, spirited framework to which could be screwed an almost limitless assortment of decorative and functional hardware. Driving away from the agency, hugging the new wheel between your knees, you were already full of creative worry. A Ford was born naked as a baby, and a flourishing industry grew up out of correcting its rare deficiencies and combatting its fascinating diseases. Those were the great days of lily-painting. I have been looking at some old Sears Roebuck catalogues, and they bring everything back so clear.

First you bought a Ruby Safety Reflector for the rear, so that your posterior would glow in another car's brilliance. Then you invested thirty-nine cents in some radiator Moto Wings, a popular ornament which gave the Pegasus touch to the machine and did something god-like to the owner. For nine cents you bought a fan-felt guide to keep the belt from slipping off the pulley.

You bought a radiator compound to stop leaks. This was as much a part of everybody's equipment as aspirin tablets are of a medicine cabinet. You bought special oil to prevent chattering, a clamp-on dash light, a patching outfit, a tool box which you bolted to the running board, a sun visor, a steering-column brace to keep the column rigid, and a set of emergency containers for gas, oil, and water—three thin, disc-like cans which reposed in a case on the running board during long, important journeys—red for gas, gray for water, green for oil. It was only a beginning. After the car was about a year old, steps were taken to check the alarming disintegration. (Model T was full of tumors, but they were benign.) A set of anti-rattlers (98c) was a popular panacea. You hooked them on to the gas and spark rods, to the brake pull rod, and to the steering-rod connections. Hood silencers, of black rubber, were applied to the fluttering hood. Shock-absorbers and snubbers gave "complete relaxation." Some people bought rubber pedal pads, to fit over the standard metal pedals. (I didn't like these, I remember.) Persons of a suspicious or pugnacious turn of mind bought a rear-view mirror; but most Model T owners weren't worried by what was coming from behind because they would soon enough see it out in front. They rode in a state of cheerful catalepsy. Quite a large mutinous clique among Ford owners went over to a foot accelerator (you could buy one and screw it to the floor board), but there was a certain madness in these people, because the Model T, just as she stood, had a choice of three foot pedals to push, and there were plenty of moments when both feet were occupied in the routine performance of duty and when the only way to speed up the engine was with the hand throttle.

Gadget bred gadget. Owners not only bought ready-made gadgets, they invented gadgets to meet special needs. I myself drove my car directly from the agency to the blacksmith's, and had the smith affix two enormous iron brackets to the port running board to support an army trunk.

People who owned closed models builded along different lines: they bought ball grip handles for opening doors, window anti-rattlers, and deluxe flower vases of the cut-glass anti-splash type. People with delicate sensibilities garnished their car with a device called the Donna Lee Automobile Disseminator—a porous vase guaranteed, according to Sears, to fill the car with a "faint clean odor of lavender." The gap between open cars and closed cars was not as great then as it is now: for $11.95, Sears Roebuck converted your touring car into a sedan and you went forth renewed. One agreeable quality of the old Fords was that they had no bumpers, and their fenders softened and wilted with the years and permitted the driver to squeeze in and out of tight places.

Tires were 30 x 3½, cost about twelve dollars, and punctured readily. Everybody carried a Jiffy patching set, with a nutmeg grater to roughen the tube before the goo was spread on. Everybody was capable of putting on a patch, expected to have to, and did have to.

During my association with Model T's, self-starters were not a prevalent accessory. They were expensive and under suspicion. Your car came equipped with a serviceable crank, and the first thing you learned was how to Get Results. It was a special trick, and until you learned it (usually from another Ford owner, but sometimes by a period of appalling experimentation) you might as well have been winding up an awning. The trick was to leave the ignition switch off, proceed to the animal's head, pull the choke (which was a little wire protruding through the radiator), and give the crank two or three nonchalant upward lifts. Then, whistling as though thinking about something else, you would saunter back to the driver's cabin, turn the ignition on, return to the crank, and this time, catching it on the down stroke, give it a quick spin with plenty of That. If this procedure was followed, the engine almost always responded—first with a few scattered explosions, then with a tumultuous gunfire, which you checked by racing around to the driver's seat and retarding the throttle. Often, if the emergency brake hadn't been pulled all the way back, the car advanced on you the instant the first explosion occurred and you would hold it back by leaning your weight against it. I can still feel my old Ford nuzzling me at the curb, as though looking for an apple in my pocket.

In zero weather, ordinary cranking became an impossibility, except for giants. The oil thickened, and it became necessary to jack up the rear wheels, which, for some planetary reason, eased the throw.

The lore and legend that governed the Ford were boundless. Owners had their own theories about everything; they discussed mutual problems in that wise, infinitely resourceful way old women discuss rheumatism. Exact knowledge was pretty scarce, and often proved less effective than superstition. Dropping a camphor ball into the gas tank was a popular expedient; it seemd to have a tonic effect on both man and machine. There wasn't much to base exact knowledge on. The Ford driver flew blind. He didn't know the temperature of his engine, the speed of his car, the amount of his fuel, or the pressure of his oil (the old Ford lubricated itself by what was amiably described as the "splash system"). A speedometer cost money and was an extra, like a windshield-wiper. The dashboard of the early models was bare save for an ignition key; later models, grown effete, boasted an ammeter which pulsated alarmingly with the throbbing of the car. Under the dash was a box of coils, with vibrators which you adjusted, or thought you adjusted. Whatever the driver learned of his motor, he learned not through instruments but through sudden developments. I remember that the timer was one of the vital organs about which there was ample doctrine. When everything else had been checked, you "had a look" at the timer. It was an extravagantly odd little device, simple in construction, mysterious in function. It contained a roller, held by a spring, and there were four contact points on the inside of the case against which, many people believed, the roller rolled. I have had a timer apart on a sick Ford many times, but I never really knew what I was up to—I was just showing off before God. There were almost as many schools of thought as there were timers. Some people, when things went wrong, just clenched their teeth and gave the timer a smart crack with a wrench. Other people opened it up

and blew on it. There was a school that held that the timer needed
large amounts of oil; they fixed it by frequent baptism. And there
was a school that was positive it was meant to run dry as a bone;
these people were continually taking it off and wiping it. I remember once spitting into a timer; not in anger, but in a spirit of
research. You see, the Model T driver moved in the realm of metaphysics. He believed his car could be hexed.

One reason the Ford anatomy was never reduced to an exact
science was that, having "fixed" it, the owner couldn't honestly
claim that the treatment had brought about the cure. There were
too many authenticated cases of Fords fixing themselves—restored
naturally to health after a short rest. Farmers soon discovered this,
and it fitted nicely with their draft-horse philosophy: "Let 'er cool
off and she'll snap into it again."

A Ford owner had Number One Bearing constantly in mind. This
bearing, being at the front end of the motor, was the one that always
burned out, because the oil didn't reach it when the car was climbing hills. (That's what I was always told, anyway.) The oil used to
recede and leave Number One dry as a clam flat; you had to watch
that bearing like a hawk. It was like a weak heart—you could hear
it start knocking, and that was when you stopped and let her cool
off. Try as you would to keep the oil supply right, in the end
Number One always went out. "Number One Bearing burned out
on me and I had to have her replaced," you would say, wisely; and
your companions always had a lot to tell about how to protect and
pamper Number One to keep her alive.

Sprinkled not too liberally among the millions of amateur witch
doctors who drove Fords and applied their own abominable cures
were the heaven-sent mechanics who could really make the car
talk. These professionals turned up in undreamed-of spots. One
time, on the banks of the Columbia River in Washington, I heard
the rear end go out of my Model T when I was trying to whip it
up a steep incline onto the deck of a ferry. Something snapped; the
car slid backward into the mud. It seemed to me like the end of
the trail. But the captain of the ferry, observing the withered remnant, spoke up.

"What's got her?" he asked.

"I guess it's the rear end," I replied, listlessly. The captain leaned over the rail and stared. Then I saw that there was a hunger in his eyes that set him off from other men.

"Tell you what," he said, carelessly, trying to cover up his eagerness, "let's pull the son of a bitch up onto the boat, and I'll help you fix her while we're going back and forth on the river."

We did just this. All that day I plied between the towns of Pasco and Kennewick, while the skipper (who had once worked in a Ford garage) directed the amazing work of resetting the bones of my car.

Springtime in the heyday of the Model T was a delirious season. Owning a car was still a major excitement, roads were still wonderful and bad. The Fords were obviously conceived in madness: any car which was capable of going from forward into reverse without any perceptible mechanical hiatus was bound to be a mighty challenging thing to the human imagination. Boys used to veer them off the highway into a level pasture and run wild with them, as though they were cutting up with a girl.

Most everybody used the reverse pedal quite as much as the regular foot brake—it distributed the wear over the bands and wore them all down evenly. That was the big trick, to wear all the bands down evenly, so that the final chattering would be total and the whole unit scream for renewal.

The days were golden, the nights were dim and strange. I still recall with trembling those loud, nocturnal crises when you drew up to a signpost and raced the engine so the lights would be bright enough to read destinations by. I have never been really planetary since. I suppose it's time to say goodbye. Farewell, my lovely!

Camp Nomopo

BY

LUDWIG BEMELMANS

AFTER HER FIRST walk through the city, Barbara came back to the Hotel Metropolitano in Quito with her lips blue and her little fists clenched. Mimi put her to bed and I went out to look for a garment that would shield her against the cold wind that blows down from Pichincha. There was no snow suit to be had; it's not cold enough for that, and the coats for little girls which I found and brought back to the hotel Barbara waved away. Four and a half years old, she knew exactly what she wanted. She sat up in bed with the first measles spots on her chest and said she would rather freeze to death than wear anything like the samples she had seen.

During the next weeks while she was in bed, I had to design coats for her. I exhausted myself making a stack of fashion drawings, designs of dramatic coats, and hats to go with them, and I cut paper dolls out of old fashion magazines and pasted my coats on them. The design that found favor with Barbara was a three-storied kind of pelerine, a garment such as Viennese fiacre drivers of the time of Franz Josef used to wear.

"This is it," she said. "That's the bestest good one."

As soon as Barbara was well, we went to a tailor with the design. The shop of Señor Pablo Duque Arias faces the square of San Francisco. It is like an indoor farm. Chickens run around among the sewing machines and over the low podium on which Mr. Arias's chief cutter sits with crossed legs; a cat, a dog with offspring, and a parrot complete the fauna; the flora consist of artificial paper roses stuck in a dry vase that stands on a small shelf between an oil print of the Madonna and a picture of the Temptation of St. Anthony.

Barbara eyed this *salon de couture* with alarm and suspicion, but she let Señor Arias measure her. He studied my design and then we went to the store of Don Alfonso Perez Pallares to buy the cloth —the tailor, Barbara, Madame, and myself. We found something that looked like the lining of a good English traveling bag. It was made in Ecuador and it was agreeable to everyone.

The coat was in work for a week, and on each day we inspected progress of the garment. At the end, Barbara looked into a mirror and was delighted with the results. It cost $7.50, not counting my time and talent. The coat was a very warm and useful garment on the return trip to New York in February.

Barbara is one of the seventy-five or a hundred over-privileged children who are allowed to play inside the cast-iron confines of Gramercy Park. Another little girl, equally well fixed, is an earnest, dark-haired, five-year-old whose name is Ruthie. Ruthie played with Barbara one day and they became friends—and at their third meeting, on a day in March, when Barbara was dressed in my creation, little Ruthie said to Barbara, "You look like Oliver Twister in that coat. That's a coat like orphans wear. I think it's terrible. I don't see how you can wear it."

On a visit to Ruthie's house that afternoon, Barbara inspected Ruthie's wardrobe. She did not wear the "Oliver Twister" coat when she came back, but carried it in her arms and hid it in the closet of her room.

She succeeded by a week of ceaseless cajolery and little-girl appeal in wangling a new winter outfit from me when it was already spring and all the Gramercy Park trees were breaking out with small green buds. Of course, it was an outfit exactly like something that Ruthie had, only newer.

Barbara and Ruthie were now bosom friends. They sat together on a bench facing a stone urn, to the left of the statue of Mr. Booth, and there they hatched another plot. The plan was to go to a summer camp together. Little Ruthie had been at this camp the year before and she described the sylvan, rugged beauty of that life to Barbara. Barbara said to Ruthie that she'd love to go but that she was afraid she would be lonesome, that she never had gone anywhere without her parents.

"Oh," said Ruthie, "after the third day you forget you ever had a father or mother."

Barbara came home with this bit of grim wisdom.

The camp we chose took care of a hundred girls. It was in the upper Adirondacks. The water came from artesian wells, the children slept in semi-bungalows and washed themselves at ten taps that spouted cold artesian water. The taps were conveniently located in front of the bungalows, the prospectus said, and the children got up to the sound of a bugle at 7:30 a.m. and did their own housework.

When I came to this part of the booklet I was convinced that nothing was better for our darling than to rise in the upper Adirondacks at seven-thirty and scrub herself at a cold-water tap.

Barbara hopped on one foot and on the other and clasped her hands with joy when I told her that she would be one of the lucky members of Camp Nomopo, which in the language of the Indians means Land That Is Bright.

The equipment needed for this simple life had to be marked with the name of the child and was as follows:

Bathing suits, 2
Bathing sandals, 1 pair
Heavy bathing caps, 2
Cotton ankle socks, 4 pairs
Cotton underwear, 4 suits
Pajamas, 3 pairs
Bathrobe, 1
Tennis sneakers, 1 pair
Handkerchiefs, 6
Play suits, 2
Bedroom slippers, 1 pair
Rubbers, 1 pair
Tennis racquet, 1
Tennis balls, 3
Toilet articles
Poncho, 1
Rain hat, 1
Riding breeches, 1 pair
Bed sheets, 3
Pillow cases, 3

Dark blankets, 3
Bath towels, 3
Face towels, 3
Mattress protector, 1
Laundry bag, 1
Duffel bag, 1
Folding knife and spoon, 1 each
Drinking cup with handle, 1
Sewing material
Bible, 1
In addition, there was this special equipment:
1 pair Nomopo gabardine shorts
1 pair Nomopo brown oxfords
2 white Nomopo shirts
2 Nomopo suits
1 Nomopo green tie
1 Nomopo green sweater
2 pairs Nomopo ankle socks

The whole thing went into a green army trunk and was stowed in the back seat of the car.

The cost of going to the camp for two months was a healthy figure, about what it would take to stay at a good hotel for that time. There was a canteen. There were, besides, provisions for pocket money to buy extra things at the canteen and an additional charge for the materials used in the arts and crafts building of Camp Nomopo.

The camp was full of cheer and gladness when we arrived. The Madame who ran it received her guests with the intense charm and cordiality of a Howard Johnson hostess; the counselors hopped around, and little Ruthie, who had arrived the day before, took Barbara by the hand and led her down to their semi-bungalow, Number 5. I checked on the waterspout which was right next to it. The cabin was a loose shelter built on stilts, open to the north and south, with no windows, but large shutters that were held up by pieces of wood. In it stood six little cast-iron cots such as you see in orphanages; birds sang outside and the branches of the trees were the curtains.

In this room the floor was a row of unpainted boards through which, here and there, you could see the good earth. We also inspected the Mess Hall and the Infirmary. The counselor that had Barbara in charge showed her how to make her bed, how to sweep the floor, and how to empty the rubbish bin—three duties that were her part of the housekeeping. Barbara did it all with gusto.

The Madame came around at about 3 p.m. and said, "Please leave before it gets dark. It's easier for the child that way."

So we said good-by to Barbara. She was brave. She said, "Good-by," and walked away with her back to the car waving as she walked. Halfway down to shack Number 5, at the cold-water tap, she suddenly turned. The small face was streaked with tears and she came back and got a grip on her mother and announced that she would not stay in the camp.

I don't know where I got the courage because my heart was breaking, but I took Barbara, handed her to the Madame, who pressed her to her ample bosom. I got Mimi into the car, and drove off. We called the camp an hour later on the phone and the Madame announced that Barbara's grief had lasted for a quarter of an hour. "Now she's in the recreation hall having the time of her life, the little darling. She's sitting in front of the big fire with little Ruthie, listening to 'Peter and the Wolf.' Don't you worry a minute about her—and please, please don't come visiting her until ten days from now."

The next day, while staying at a hotel, I reflected what a wonderful racket a children's camp is, how much better it is than owning a hotel, for example.

Imagine if the guests of a hotel like the Savoy-Plaza arrived bringing their own three dark blankets and sheets, towels, and pillow cases, made their own beds, emptied their garbage, went down to the cold-water taps in Central Park to scrub themselves, and without murmur ate the healthy, strength-giving diet you put before them! If instead of going out in the evening and spending their money in rival establishments, they would quietly sit around the bar listening to "Peter and the Wolf" or do arty-crafty things in the ballroom—all of them dressed in hats, shoes, and sweaters marked Savoy-Plaza!

We came back after ten days in which we wrote nine letters and received four cards written by Barbara's counselor. After a glowing report on how glad and happy and what a fine girl she was, the Madame sent for her.

She came in the rain, between the wet dripping trees, in the Nomopo rain hat, the Nomopo green sweater and poncho, alone and much sadder looking than "Oliver Twister" ever was. She broke out in streams of tears when she saw us and she kept crying even after it stopped raining outside. She blinked red-eyed in the sun that shone above rays of floating mist.

We went out to a play field, and, at one moment when we stepped aside to discuss what to do, Barbara found herself surrounded by her comrades. Madame looked down at her with reproach and her counselor, a maiden from whose Nomopo sweater I could hardly take my eyes, said, "You're not going to be a sissy now, are you, and run away from us?"

Barbara was the most complete portrait of misery I have ever seen, not excepting the work of El Greco. She cried, "I don't like it here. I want to go home with Mummy and Pappy. I want to go home; I don't like it here. I want to go home."

We took her into the car with us and I said in French to Mimi that I thought under the circumstances it would be the best thing to take her home with us. While I spoke, she took hold of the leather straps that are attached to the convertible top of the car as if to anchor herself, and said, "You don't have to speak French, I know what you were saying. You said, 'Let's start the car and push Barbara out and drive away like the last time' "—and then she continued, "I dream about you at night and when I wake up you're not there, and in the morning, another little girl next to me cries and that makes me cry too.

"Ruthie said she cried too the first time last year, but her mother just left her there and never came to see her and now she's used to it, but I won't get used to it because I dream of you every night. And it's so cold in the morning, and I have to empty the pail and sweep."

The washing at the tap she had got around, apparently. She was streaked with dirt and her hair was a mess. She said, "We take a bath twice a week, down at the lake, and the water is cold. I want to go home. I don't like it here. I want to go home with Mummy and Pappy."

A man came to the car and smiled and said, "I'm only the husband of Mrs. Van Cortland who runs the camp and I can assure you that Barbara's the happiest little girl when you're not here. She sings and plays all day long. I think it would be a great mistake for you to take her away."

I told him that we would take her away. Barbara let go of the straps and the man said, "Well, all I can say is that in my twenty-seven years this has happened only once before."

Barbara smelled of garlic and unwashed hair. They had had meat loaf for lunch. It was dark by the time we had made the decision and we stayed for supper. It began to rain again and there is nothing more wet and desolate than Adirondack camps in the rain. The meal was served on a drafty porch, a piece of canvas blew in with every gust of wind. The menu consisted of melted cheese poured over toast and a lukewarm rice pudding that tasted like glue; a glass of milk was served to each diner.

We left poor Ruthie behind, and the Madame and her husband assured us again that it was only the second time in twenty-seven years that such a thing had happened.

Le Scandale International

BY

RUTH McKENNEY

ONCE, while in the prime, not to say the first blush, of my early youth in Cleveland, Ohio, during those stirring days when I led the Shaw High School debating team from one intoxicating triumph to another, I was, I am still sorry to say, the cause and author of a fearful international scandal.

The whole disreputable mess had its roots in the deplorable fact that I was Shaw High School's champion debater, in spite of the fact that I stuttered. I was, in fact, a sort of local Demosthenes. "Take the Marines out of Nicaragua!" I used to thunder to a fairly spellbound audience. "Redeem America's g-g-good n-n-name."

I was a big success with my teachers and my doting family but, alas, a complete failure with my fellow-pupils. In fact, I was a moral leper, an outcast, among my contemporaries. Eileen shook her curly head over my career. No boy in his right mind would have been caught dead within ten miles of me. Girls regarded me with a kindly and patronizing charity.

"I don't see how you do it," Mary Tenor said one day in the washroom, as she put on a layer of forbidden lipstick. "You certainly are smart. I said to Johnnikins last night at the Mayfair—you know, Johnny German, only I call him Johnnikins—Ruth certainly is smart. . . ."

Johnny German was the handsomest boy in high school and played right end on the football team. The Mayfair was a Chinese dine-and-dance place much favored for an after-the-movies snack by the selecter few at Shaw High. I had never been there in my life. I would have cut off my right hand, the one I used to make my most telling gestures with, to have had the delirious pleasure of calling Johnny German "Johnnikins" at the Mayfair.

Of course, to be perfectly honest, I would never have been asked to the Mayfair by young Master German, even if I had not been a peerless public speaker. I took to Nicaragua as a last resort. For I was, in the first place, exactly two years and seven months younger than most of the maidens in my class. While they were bootlegging their first lipsticks and wangling high heels out of their doting mothers, I was still in the Growing Girl oxford stage. They had their hair marceled for parties, while mine hung in twin braids down the back of my disgusting middy blouse.

But it wasn't only my youth, it was my looks that marked me down as a social failure. After all, Eileen was a whole year younger than I was, and already she figured as the belle of the Epworth League and the sensation of the Eighth Grade. The bitter truth of the matter was that I was homely as a mud fence. I looked like exactly what I was, the ex-star of an all-boy (except me) baseball team and the current sensation of the Northern Ohio Debating League. I don't see how, looking back on that awful period of my life, I stood it at all.

I did, though. I endured my fourteenth year somehow, until suddenly one day a ray of sunlight came to brighten the sodden gloom of my despair.

The whole thing started in French class, of all places. I was simply terrible in French. Oh, I could read French well enough and I was a positive whizz at translating the French classics cut down to high-school size, but my teacher, Miss Parrish, used to tell me frankly that I had probably the worst French accent she had ever heard, even in Shaw High School, where French accents reached remarkable lows. Because of my stuttering, I could simply never learn how to say the most elementary French sentence. I sat in the back of the class, and Miss Parrish didn't even bother about me any more.

That particular day, though, I was reading a magazine hidden under my desk when Miss Parrish interrupted my wandering thoughts to announce, "And, Ruth, your correspondent will be Alfonse Donater." I pricked up my ears. It appeared that all the boys and girls of the advanced-French class in Shaw High School were going to write letters to the pupils in an advanced-English class in some faraway *lycée* in France. Miss Parrish apologized to the young ladies among her students. She knew, she said, we would rather correspond with girls our own ages, but unfortunately the

school with which she had made the arrangements for the hands-
across-the-sea gesture had only boy pupils. Miss Parrish's girl students lowered their eyes, ready, apparently, to make the best of this
disappointing situation. A few quiet giggles broke our brave silence.

Writing to strange young men in France sounded romantic, but
at first it was just terribly dull. We had to write in French, in the
first place, which severely handicapped dopes like Mary Tenor.
Then our first few letters were regular school exercises. We had to
write them in class, and have them corrected, and then copy them
off in our best handwriting before we could ship them across the
Atlantic.

Alfonse's first few letters seemed also to have been written under
the eagle eyes of his teacher. Alfonse discussed in quaint but im-
peccable English the weather, the books he read, and his passionate
desire to become a construction engineer and make a great deal of
money. Alfonse sounded like a fearful prig to me. I began to lose
interest. Then he sent me his picture. He was quite handsome.

Just after Alfonse's picture arrived, Miss Parrish announced that
from now on correspondence with our dear little French friends
was optional. She hoped we would continue writing to our faraway
fellow-students and asked us kindly to be careful of our grammar.

I rushed home from school that night lugging a huge French dic-
tionary and my French grammar. *"Cher Alfonse,"* I began. Shortly
before midnight I wound up, *"Votre amie, Ruth."* In between these
two phrases were three pages of the most dreadful lies I had ever
told. I let Alfonse think I lived in a positive whirlwind of mad
pleasure. I said his picture reminded me of my fourth best beau,
who was on the football team.

"I will give you a picture of a day in my life," I wrote. *"Je vous
donnerai un tableau de la jour dans ma vie [sic]."* My day, as I described it, was composed of a gay series of social events—a tea dance,
a dinner engagement, a Junior Prom, and a bit of dancing at the
Mayfair to wind it all up. One became, I said, rather bored with
such a constant round of dances, but what could one do when one
was so popular? I couldn't find a French word for that, so I finally
compromised on *"bien-aimée,"* which sounded well, I thought.

I mailed this letter without a qualm and spent two dreamy weeks
thinking about Alfonse. Then, really before I expected it, Alfonse's
reply arrived, a pleasantly thick envelope studded with foreign

stamps. I tore up the stairs, locked my bedroom door, opened the window, lit an absolutely forbidden cigarette, and settled down in comfort to read the letter from *mon cher* Alfonse. I tore open the flap. To my surprise, I found inside three closely written pages of French. Alfonse was supposed to write in English, the dope. I looked inside the envelope again. Perhaps there was a translation.

And so I saw the picture. It was a postcard-size affair, glossy and smooth. To the right was a lady whose style of hairdress indicated she had reached the prime of her youth in about 1910. She was clad in fluttering garments, cut much too low at the bosom, at least for my Puritan eyes. On the left was a gentleman with slick hair, clad in full evening dress, and reclining on one elegant knee. The photographer had caught the gentleman in the very act of passionately embracing the lady, who was, I supposed at first glance, his fiancée. Certainly there could be no other excuse for the way she was carrying on.

I regarded the picture with surprise. Perhaps this was Alfonse's none-too-delicate way of telling me he was engaged. I examined the figure of the gentleman with great care. No, I felt sure that this bemused stranger was not Alfonse. He looked too old and a touch too carefree to be a student at a respectable *lycée*.

Feeling slightly uneasy, I put the picture aside and took up the letter. Here I met complete defeat. Nothing I had ever learned in advanced French at Shaw High School helped in the least. All I could make out was the salutation, "Dear, dearest Ruth." This brought a faint blush and a further feeling of alarm. Alfonse seemed to be taking a lot for granted. I brooded over the French scrawl. Here and there I could make out a familiar word, such as *"l'amour."* The rest was lost in a deep obscurity. Victor Hugo (high-school-text edition) was never like this.

For days I burned with curiosity. If I had had any sense at all, I would have tossed Alfonse's pretty picture and Alfonse's mysterious billet-doux into the nearest wastepaper basket, but after all, this was the first letter from a boy I had ever received in my entire life—along personal lines, I mean—and I felt the outlook for getting another was none too bright.

I carried Alfonse's letter in my history book, and one day while the rest of Miss Teester's pupils were dully considering what General Grant said to General Lee, I trotted out the now somewhat worn pages and again tried to decipher my dear French fellow-student's fearful alien scrawl.

Lost in happy concentration, I did not, unfortunately, notice that Buster Lockmonton, who sat next to me, was also trying to make out Alfonse's handwriting. Buster Lockmonton was, in my opinion, the most revolting student at Shaw High School. In the first place, he was exactly my own age, a bare fifteen, while the rest of the boys in my class were seventeen going on eighteen. He was a disgusting child. He wore, for precisely the same reasons that I wore Growing Girl oxfords, knee pants. His very name, Buster, indicated his hopeless immaturity.

But young Master Lockmonton was not only young, he was rich, and nauseatingly proud of it. His parents had given dear Buster advantages. He had lived in France for four solid years, attending French schools. Miss Parrish said he spoke French better than some Frenchmen. He was constantly bringing souvenirs of his fascinating sojourn in France to school and every one of us at Shaw High had been liberally favored with Buster's memories of *la belle France*.

"Psssst," the horrid boy now signaled. I jumped and turned a slow but bright purple.

"Who's the letter from?" Buster muttered.

"None of your business," I replied.

"Buster!" Miss Teester warned.

Buster was momentarily reduced to silence, but his blood was up. The moment Miss Teester turned her back to write a few dates on the blackboard, Buster returned to his prey.

"It was in French," he whispered. "I can read French better than you can."

"Go fry an egg," I growled, but Buster had planted the germ of an idea in my harried mind.

All that evening during debating-team practice I toyed with the notion of letting Buster translate the letter. Could I trust him? Reason, instinct, and solid practical experience said no. Finally I decided that if Buster knew the Scout oath, I would make him swear eternal secrecy and have him copy out Alfonse's letter in English for me. I should have known better, of course, but by this time I was ready to throw reason to the winds.

Buster swore. He was so anxious to get hold of the letter that he rushed through the Scout oath, mumbling along at a rapid pace. I made him say it again slowly and I handed him the letter, complete with the picture, for I hoped there was an explanation somewhere in Alfonse's bad handwriting of my fellow-student's taste in art. Buster promised to give me a written translation in history class the next morning.

Mr. Lockmonton was nearly late for class that terrible day. He came in hurriedly and sat down without a word.

"Where is it?" I hissed as Miss Teester started off, "Good morning, class. Today we are to consider the closing Federal campaign in Georgia."

Buster pretended to be absorbed in Miss Teester's kittenish remarks about the origin of the song "Marching Through Georgia."

"Hand it over," I muttered.

"I can't," whispered Buster.

"You couldn't read it, then," I said, very nasty.

Buster shook his odious head. "I read it, but I can't tell you what's in it," he stage-whispered.

"Why not?" I demanded furiously, and lapsed into forced silence. Miss Teester was staring at me, full of reproach.

"Because," Buster growled when the danger was over, "it was too terrible. Boy, what was in that letter! And the picture! Wow!"

I began to feel very, very sick, and stared helplessly at Buster, appealing, I hoped, to his sense of chivalry. It was no use. Then the class bell rang.

"Hot diggety dog," Buster continued with enthusiasm, now that he could speak out loud. "Boy, you must have written that guy plenty!"

"I did not," I replied with dignity. "Give the letter back."

Buster handed the letter over. "And the picture," I snapped.

"I lost the picture by mistake," Buster answered blandly.

"You did not!" I cried hysterically. "Buster Lockmonton, if you have any Boy Scout honor, you will give that picture back!"

Buster scorned a reply. He walked out of the room, murmuring, "What I know about Ruth, oh, boy, oh, boy, oh, boy!"

I went through the corridors of dear old Shaw High School for days in a kind of fevered sweat. Alfonse's letter, which I had reduced to ashes, could never be used as evidence against me, but the thought of Buster showing around that awful picture filled me with a shuddering horror.

It took Buster's Boy Scout honor rather longer to break down than I thought it would. Three days, to be exact. On the morning of the fourth day, Johnny German gave a long, low whistle as I walked into French class. I thought I would faint. I hoped I would faint. Nothing happened, though. I walked, my face purple red, to my desk. Mary Tenor immediately wrote me a note and slipped it over. "What I heard about you!" it read. From Buster to Johnny German to Mary Tenor to Miss Parrish was, I knew, a matter of days or even hours. I waited, the cold hand of death on my heart.

Miss Parrish was very brutal about it, I thought. "From now on," she announced in class a day or two later, "every letter written to France will first be brought to me for approval. I do not care to discuss the reason for this change in procedure. Ruth, will you see me after class, and also Buster Lockmonton?"

The class had minor convulsions. Johnny German whistled again. I waited to die of shame.

Miss Parrish began by making Buster produce the picture, after I said, with truth, that I had burned the letter. For a long time Buster and Miss Parrish and I stood in silence, regarding the gentleman in evening clothes embracing the lady in the low-cut fluttering garments.

"Well," Miss Parrish said at last. She tore the picture up with slow finality, made a neat pile of the scraps, and threw them carefully into her wastepaper basket. Buster and I watched this operation in heavy quiet.

"Now, Buster," she said, "you will please tell me, as nearly as you can remember, what was in that letter."

"I can't," Buster said desperately, "it's too terrible." A faint spot of color came to Miss Parrish's maiden cheek. I turned my ordinary high purple.

"Nevertheless, Buster," Miss Parrish said bravely, "I must know in order to report Alfonse to his teacher. No French boy can be allowed to insult a nice American girl, even on paper."

I wished passionately that I were dead, stone-dead, in a peaceful graveyard, where people would come and be sorry for me.

"Speak, Buster!" said Miss Parrish sharply.

"Miss Parrish," Buster cried in agony, "I don't know. I couldn't translate it. I just made up what I said." Then the insufferable boy burst into tears.

I have often wondered, in later years, now that I can bear to think about it, what was really in Alfonse's letter. After all, it *was* the first letter I ever got from a boy—of a personal nature, that is.

Bottoms Up!

BY

JACK GOODMAN AND ALAN GREEN

THIS is the true story of how one dauntless man—I—went out to do battle singlehanded with man's ancient enemy, the sea. It is also the story of how I lost, and of how the sea never knew it had been in a fight at all.

But never mind that. The important thing is: if you own a boat or hope to—even if you have a friend with a little catboat he may take you out in—then read carefully. You will profit by knowing just what happened when I bought a secondhand sailboat and, with the tiller in my hand, the salt spray in my hair, the end of the boom banging my forehead, and the anchor rope inextricably entangled with my leg, I put out to sea.

We'd better get one thing straight at the beginning. When I use the term "the sea," I refer to a tiny, island-sheltered corner of Long Island Sound whose briny fighting spirit has long ago been broken by countless small children in cockleshell sailing dinghies. But never mind that either. Just remember to do nothing that I did. Do just the opposite, in fact, and within the next ten minutes you will have learned as much as you could have in a two-year cruise in an old whaling ship.

Why get a boat anyway? you may ask yourself. Many a time, sitting on the deck of my little sloop with nothing between me and the ocean floor but the boat's hull, which was stuck fast in it, I, too, have asked myself that question.

It's probably the books that make you want a boat. Those books by Joseph Conrad, John Masefield, Herman Melville—books full of towering white canvas, trade winds, and gleaming decks. I wanted all that. I also wanted the unparalleled sensation of being at one with my vessel, a creature of the wind and wave. Also, the equally unparalleled sensation, unmentioned in the books, of traveling without paying anyone for fares or gasoline.

Maybe you will get what I wanted. I didn't. Except the part about being a creature of the wind and wave. My boat's canvas didn't tower, I never got close to a trade wind, and the deck didn't gleam because it was only a decklet and generally knee-deep in water. As far as traveling without paying goes, I estimate that it has cost me so far about a dollar a mile, or fifty times as much as train tickets. True, this will go down as I travel more, but then, so may the boat.

Let us assume that you buy your little boat, as I did. It is only fifteen feet long, or thereabouts, but that doesn't matter. It has a hull and a mast, a sail and a rudder. Those are the essentials. It differs from the greatest of the China clippers only in superficial details of size and unimportant accessories. You can get into just as much trouble aboard it.

Now you must get a mooring. This is because you have chosen the one means of transportation that flatly refuses to hold still and will, unless tied firmly to something, immediately start off for somewhere else. It will always do this except occasionally when you are in it and want it to go somewhere else, at which time it assumes a state known as "becalmed," in which it might just as well be riveted down. This state will be discussed later.

You have already noticed that all the other sailboats in front of the yacht club are neatly tied up to floating tin buoys at which they tug and scold with every puff of wind. You buy one of these tin buoys and discover that, like an iceberg, the most important part of the mooring is beneath the water. You are therefore loaded up with a seventy-five pound mushroom anchor, which is a large piece of iron resembling an inverted umbrella—and lots and lots of rope.

All right. Now you load anchor, rope, and buoy into your rowboat and pull stanchly for the spot, fifty or so yards from shore, where you have decided to drop your mooring. It is hard work, because you are, of course, towing your sailboat behind the rowboat, and the water is choppy. It is a rule of the sea that it is choppy whenever this sort of work has to be done.

Finally you reach the spot and, with a heave of your massive back muscles, plop the anchor overboard. You watch it sink to the muddy bottom, a satisfied smile on your face. This smile disappears as it suddenly occurs to you that you should have attached the floating buoy to the end of the rope, which is just barely visible as it sinks.

You are now sitting in a rowboat to which is attached a sailboat for which there should be a mooring but isn't.

It is at this point that you will find out whether there is iron in your soul or meringue. I wasn't discouraged and I hope you won't be either. The mushroom anchor still has that long rope attached to it. You can dive down, grab the rope, bring it back to the surface, and attach it to the little tin buoy just as if no mistake had ever been committed.

It is but the work of a moment to strip to your shorts and dive. You scrape your scalp on the anchor the very first dive. This is beginner's luck. Pushing up to the surface with the rope in one hand, you keep the other hand carefully above your head in case you come up under the boats.

This is a needless precaution because the boats have now drifted about forty feet downstream, which is their inalienable right because they are not attached to anything.

It takes you no time at all to swim to the boats, for you are a powerful swimmer. As you climb into the rowboat and pull back, you congratulate yourself on this fact, then stop suddenly, realizing you have again lost the rope attached to the mushroom anchor.

You hurry back to the approximate spot you dropped it. This time you take no chances, holding the rowboat's painter (or "rope") in your hand as you dive. You have no luck. This is because each time you dive the painter (or "rope"), being too short, brings you up sharply every time you are within a couple of feet from the bottom.

You try this several times, feeling more and more like a well-hooked tarpon. You decide it is a losing game. You get in the rowboat and lie there awhile, deciding whether or not you should howl like a wolf if you ever get your breath back. You go home and buy a new mushroom anchor.

Next day you manage to get the mooring down correctly. You will have to change its location only twice, first when you discover you have placed it too close to shore, leaving it and the sailboat high and dry when the tide goes out, and the second time when you discover your sailboat with its nose tucked in the water and its stern (or "behind") brazenly exposed, like a duck looking for food. This has happened because you used only a twelve-foot rope and the water subsequently rose to sixteen feet.

But at last you row out for your first sail. Eagerly you think of the moment when you will be skimming across the water, lolling by the tiller with the sheet (or "rope"—this is the one attached to the boom) in your hand. You catch a glimpse of your little beauty of a boat, sitting low in the water as if she were just about to jump out of it, so anxious is she to get going.

You draw alongside and discover that this is not the reason she is sitting low. She has eight inches of water in her. You realize that it rained last night and that your boat must be bailed.

Let us pass hurriedly over the art of bailing. I don't like it. Nobody likes it, except perhaps a psychiatric case, if you could find one, with a "there's-buried-treasure-just-under-this-water-and-all-I-have-to-do-is-scoop-it-away!" complex.

Eventually your boat is emptied of water and you are ready to Raise the Sail. This consists of the following stages:

1. You seize the halyard (or "rope") hanging down the mast from the pulley at the top, saying "Yeo-heave-ho!" merrily to whoever is with you. They ask coldly why you are delaying. You heave.

2. Nothing happens.

3. You discover that the other end of the rope is still lashed around a cleat at the bottom of the mast.

4. You free the rope, standing on the boat's edge to do so, and pull the sail up. The sail rises majestically. A gust of wind catches it and the boom swings your way, forcing you to step back.

5. You are now gasping in water eight feet deep.

Before you are ready for the final step, you must now climb back in the boat, preserve a dignified silence at any comments that may be made, and dry yourself off.

Ready? Well, then, we can at last take up the final and most important phase—Putting to Sea.

1. You grasp the tiller firmly and pull it toward you.
2. Nothing happens.
3. You push the tiller away from you.
4. Nothing happens.
5. You remember to untie the boat from the mooring.

6. The boat slides crabwise across the inlet and is about to bump into another boat moored between you and the shore.

7. You twist around quickly and stick out one leg, bracing it against the other boat to fend it off.

8. Your knee comes up and smacks you in the chin as the two boats grind together.

9. A man comes out of a house onshore and asks loudly what in hell you think you are doing to his boat.

10. You stand up to apologize and your boom swings over again, knocking you from your boat to his.

11. The man shouts that if you don't get out of his boat he will tell the harbor master.

12. You climb back to your boat, deciding that you need more space than the inlet provides for your first sail. You lower the sail and, using an oar, paddle out of the inlet.

By now your companion has jumped off and swum to shore and you have no one to talk to. But as you paddle out you can amuse yourself by thinking about what makes a sailboat go.

And don't answer blithely, "Why, the wind, of course!" Why should a wind blowing sideways onto a sail make a boat go *forward?* Oh, so you can't answer that? Well, neither can I, and all my intelligent friends look very wise and mutter something about "parallelogram of forces." Then they spend the rest of the evening with a pencil and paper, trying to figure it out.

Furthermore, I always worried about those beautiful old square-riggers. It seemed to me that they must inevitably have gone backwards in the wind—straight backwards. Although this sounded silly to me, I have consulted a lot of people about it and no one has given me any reason to change my mind. This, of course, accounts for the disappearance of the square-rigger.

Well, at last you have a lot of clear space, your sail is up, and, wonder of wonders, you are actually sailing! The boat is boiling right along! You change your course slightly. The wind seems to be farther in back of you. Look out, you are jibing!

I must now leave you for a moment in the act of ducking the boom and explain just what jibing is. It occurs when the wind gets behind your sail and shifts it from one side to the other—fast. It is considered very shameful, just why, I don't know.

Before we were married, Phyllis was a sailing fiend. During one of my first week ends at her place, I found her smiling tolerantly when I upset a bowl of rare goldfish onto an even rarer Chinese rug. She urged me to think no more of it when I stripped the gears of her new car while attempting to extricate it from the side of the garage into which I had plunged it. She even chuckled amusedly when I set fire to the kitchen while burning some brandy over my oatmeal.

Yet when I took over the tiller of her sailboat and jibed almost immediately, she made me feel like a small child who simply wasn't, after that, going to be permitted to have any liquid at all within three hours before retiring.

When you jibe, the boom swings over so quickly that it may fracture a skull or, worse still, put a bad strain on the mast. It can upset the boat, too, but fortunately this has not happened to you.

You now experiment, going this way and that. You try to "tack." This means that you go in a different direction from the place you want to get to so as to get to it. It is only understood by hardened sailors. It is the principle that the shortest distance beween two points is the letter Z.

You will now discover that you can see only on the side that the sail isn't, as if you were driving a car with a curtain over half the windshield. An ocean liner could be coming at you from the blind side and you wouldn't see it.

Watch out, an ocean liner *is* coming at you!

We now have an interesting situation. You have the right of way. Even the Chief Officer of that liner, gnawing his nails on the bridge, knows that sail always has the right of way over power. The Chief Officer is eager to relieve the tedium of his vigil by engaging in a guessing game with you, deciding whether or not he should run aground if you decide at the last minute against changing your course. Nevertheless, you will not care to toy with him too long. Right of way or no right of way, you will always change your course, though to fail to postpone doing this until the last possible moment is to fail to uphold the dignity of the sailing vessel.

Such harmless fun is not dependent upon the occasional ocean liner. It is possible to involve many more people in your sailing affairs. Coast guardsmen, for instance, like nothing better than to be called from an overwarm fireside to struggle through gale or surf to your rescue when you're out seeing how your cat-boat or sailing canoe handles in a bad blow. Other yachtsmen will have excellent opportunities to test the speed of their reflexes if you cut suddenly across their bows. And fishermen, anchored in their small boats, weary of sitting sluggishly for hour after hour without results, must welcome the excitement and the outpouring of their adrenalin as you sail in small circles around them, frightening the fish away and making their sport less one-sided.

There comes a time, though, when you have even less control than usual over your boat. This is about an hour after you have been trying to get home but not making any headway. The wind, tired of playing its cat-and-mouse game with you, simply goes away.

You are now Becalmed.

I have found that this generally happens about three miles off-shore when all the powerboats which might have towed you home have gone in for the day. Do not bother trying to row home, for the current will have just shifted and you won't be able to pull against it. Do not complain either. You have always wanted to commune with the sea and you are about to commune with it until you are blue in the face.

The one thing to do is to appreciate the chance for solitude, to lie back, light a cigarette, and give yourself over to thought. There are, experience taught me, many things to think about:

1. That the cigarette you just lit is your last.
2. That the current is rapidly taking you into a steamer lane.
3. What to do in case of pirates.
4. That the sea water you have suddenly noticed in the bottom of the boat doesn't seem to have splashed in.
5. That last week a man tried to inveigle you into buying an outboard motor.
6. That you have a cocktail date with a girl who has the habit of checking the hospitals and the morgue when you are fifteen minutes late.
7. That this time she will probably get results.

But most of all, you can think about what you used to do before you owned a boat. About how slavishly dependent you were for entertainment on such things as golf, bridge, and the company of charming people. About the money you now spend on the boat, money that used to be tossed away on food, clothing, and shelter. About how you used to risk curvature of the spine curled up reading about sailing.

All of this takes a long time. The sun goes down. It gets colder.

And then a wonderful thing occurs. The moon comes up and the sea sparkles into life. You feel the veriest whisper of a breeze. It rapidly matures into a full-bodied wind. Your sail begins to billow again. Your lee rail is awash and the happy little boat leaps ahead like a chamois.

You are off! You are headed for the open sea. All the little trials and tribulations are forgotten. Forgotten too is the cocktail date. This is worth everything (and it really is, what's more). You want to go on, on, on, drenched in spray and moonlight, your sail proudly spread like an eagle's wing.

It is a good thing that you want to go on, on, on, because your tiller has jammed and you can't turn homewards. It is silly to continue trying to tell you how to do practically anything, because from now on you will be unable to do anything, even impractically. *Bon voyage,* dear reader, *bon voyage!* It was nice to have known you!

Johnny One-Eye

BY

DAMON RUNYON

THIS CAT I am going to tell you about is a very small cat, and in fact it is only a few weeks old, consequently it is really nothing but an infant cat. To tell the truth, it is just a kitten.

It is gray and white and very dirty and its fur is all frowzled up, so it is a very miserable-looking little kitten to be sure the day it crawls through a broken basement window into an old house in East Fifty-third Street over near Third Avenue in the city of New York and goes from room to room saying merouw, merouw in a low, weak voice until it comes to a room at the head of the stairs on the second story where a guy by the name of Rudolph is sitting on the floor thinking of not much.

One reason Rudolph is sitting on the floor is because there is nothing else to sit on as this is an empty house that is all boarded up for years and there is no furniture whatever in it, and another reason is that Rudolph has a .38 slug in his side and really does not feel like doing much of anything but sitting. He is wearing a derby hat and his overcoat as it is in the wintertime and very cold and he has an automatic Betsy on the floor beside him and naturally he is surprised quite some when the little kitten comes merouwing into the room and he picks up the Betsy and points it at the door in case anyone he does not wish to see is with the kitten. But when he observes that it is all alone, Rudolph puts the Betsy down again and speaks to the kitten as follows:

"Hello, cat," he says.

Of course the kitten does not say anything in reply except merouw but it walks right up to Rudolph and climbs on his lap, although the chances are if it knows who Rudolph is it will hightail it out of there quicker than anybody can say scat. There is enough

284

daylight coming through the chinks in the boards over the windows for Rudolph to see that the kitten's right eye is in bad shape, and in fact it is bulged half out of its head in a most distressing manner and it is plain to be seen that the sight is gone from this eye. It is also plain to be seen that the injury happens recently and Rudolph gazes at the kitten a while and starts to laugh and says like this:

"Well, cat," he says, "you seem to be scuffed up almost as much as I am. We make a fine pair of invalids here together. What is your name, cat?"

Naturally the kitten does not state its name but only goes merouw and Rudolph says, "All right, I will call you Johnny. Yes," he says, "your tag is now Johnny One-Eye."

Then he puts the kitten in under his overcoat and pretty soon it gets warm and starts to purr and Rudolph says:

"Johnny," he says, "I will say one thing for you and that is you are plenty game to be able to sing when you are hurt as bad as you are. It is more than I can do."

But Johnny only goes merouw again and keeps on purring and by and by it falls sound asleep under Rudolph's coat and Rudolph is wishing the pain in his side will let up long enough for him to do the same.

Well, I suppose you are saying to yourself, what is this Rudolph doing in an old empty house with a slug in his side, so I will explain that the district attorney is responsible for this situation. It seems that the D.A. appears before the grand jury and tells it that Rudolph is an extortion guy and a killer and I do not know what all else, though some of these statements are without doubt a great injustice to Rudolph as, up to the time the D.A. makes them, Rudolph does not kill anybody of any consequence in years.

It is true that at one period of his life he is considered a little wild but this is in the 1920's when everybody else is, too, and for seven or eight years he is all settled down and is engaged in business organization work, which is very respectable work, indeed. He organizes quite a number of businesses on a large scale and is doing very good for himself. He is living quietly in a big hotel all alone, as Rudolph is by no means a family guy, and he is highly spoken of by one and all when the D.A. starts poking his nose into his affairs, claiming that Rudolph has no right to be making money out of the businesses, even though Rudolph gives these businesses plenty of first-class protection.

In fact, the D.A. claims that Rudolph is nothing but a racket guy and a great knock to the community, and all this upsets Rudolph no little when it comes to his ears in a roundabout way. So he calls up his lawbooks and requests legal advice on the subject and lawbooks says the best thing he can think of for Rudolph to do is to become as inconspicuous as possible right away but to please not mention to anyone that he gives this advice.

Lawbooks says he understands the D.A. is requesting indictments and is likely to get them and furthermore that he is rounding up certain parties that Rudolph is once associated with and trying to get them to remember incidents in Rudolph's early career that may not be entirely to his credit. Lawbooks says he hears that one of these parties is a guy by the name of Cute Freddy and that Freddy makes a deal with the D.A. to lay off of him if he tells everything he knows about Rudolph, so under the circumstances a long journey by Rudolph will be in the interest of everybody concerned.

So Rudolph decides to go on a journey but then he gets to thinking that maybe Freddy will remember a little matter that Rudolph long since dismisses from his mind and does not wish to have recalled again, which is the time he and Freddy do a job on a guy by the name of The Icelander in Troy years ago and he drops around to Freddy's house to remind him to be sure not to remember this.

But it seems that Freddy, who is an important guy in business organization work himself, though in a different part of the city than Rudolph, mistakes the purpose of Rudolph's visit and starts to out with his rooty-toot-toot and in order to protect himself it is necessary for Rudolph to take his Betsy and give Freddy a little tattooing. In fact, Rudolph practically crochets his monogram on Freddy's chest and leaves him exceptionally deceased.

But as Rudolph is departing from the neighborhood, who bobs up but a young guy by the name of Buttsy Fagan, who works for Freddy as a chauffeur and one thing and another, and who is also said to be able to put a slug through a keyhole at forty paces without touching the sides though I suppose it will have to be a pretty good-sized keyhole. Anyway, he takes a long-distance crack at Rudolph as Rudolph is rounding a corner but all Buttsy can see of

Rudolph at the moment is a little piece of his left side and this is what Buttsy hits, although no one knows it at the time, except of course Rudolph, who just keeps on departing.

Now this incident causes quite a stir in police circles, and the D.A. is very indignant over losing a valuable witness and when they are unable to locate Rudolph at once, a reward of five thousand dollars is offered for information leading to his capture alive or dead and some think they really mean dead. Indeed, it is publicly stated that it is not a good idea for anyone to take any chances with Rudolph as he is known to be armed and is such a character as will be sure to resent being captured, but they do not explain that this is only because Rudolph knows the D.A. wishes to place him in the old rocking chair at Sing Sing and that Rudolph is quite allergic to the idea.

Anyway, the cops go looking for Rudolph in Hot Springs and Miami and every other place except where he is, which is right in New York wandering around town with the slug in his side, knocking at the doors of old friends requesting assistance. But all the old friends do for him is to slam the doors in his face and forget they ever see him, as the D.A. is very tough on parties who assist guys he is looking for, claiming that this is something most illegal called harboring fugitives. Besides Rudolph is never any too popular at best with his old friends as he always plays pretty much of a lone duke and takes the big end of everything for his.

He cannot even consult a doctor about the slug in his side as he knows that nowadays the first thing a doctor will do about a guy with a gunshot wound is to report him to the cops, although Rudolph can remember when there is always a sure-footed doctor around who will consider it a privilege and a pleasure to treat him and keep his trap closed about it. But of course this is in the good old days and Rudolph can see they are gone forever. So he just does the best he can about the slug and goes on wandering here and there and around and about and the blats keep printing his picture and saying, where is Rudolph?

Where he is some of the time is in Central Park trying to get some sleep, but of course even the blats will consider it foolish to go looking for Rudolph there in such cold weather, as he is known as a guy who enjoys his comfort at all times. In fact, it is comfort that Rudolph misses more than anything as the slug is commencing to cause him great pain and naturally the pain turns Rudolph's thoughts to the author of same and he remembers that he once hears somebody say that Buttsy lives over in East Fifty-third Street.

So one night Rudolph decides to look Buttsy up and cause him a little pain in return and he is moseying through Fifty-third when he gets so weak he falls down on the sidewalk in front of the old house and rolls down a short flight of steps that lead from the street level to a little railed-in areaway and ground floor or basement door and before he stops rolling he brings up against the door itself and it creaks open inward as he bumps it. After he lays there a while Rudolph can see that the house is empty and he crawls on inside.

Then when he feels stronger, Rudolph makes his way upstairs because the basement is damp and mice keep trotting back and forth over him and eventually he winds up in the room where Johnny One-Eye finds him the following afternoon and the reason Rudolph settles down in this room is because it commands the stairs. Naturally, this is important to a guy in Rudolph's situation, though after he is sitting there for about fourteen hours before Johnny comes along he can see that he is not going to be much disturbed by traffic. But he considers it a very fine place, indeed, to remain planted until he is able to resume his search for Buttsy.

Well, after a while Johnny One-Eye wakes up and comes from under the coat and looks at Rudolph out of his good eye and Rudolph waggles his fingers and Johnny plays with them, catching one finger in his front paws and biting it gently and this pleases Rudolph no little as he never before has any personal experience with a kitten. However, he remembers observing one when he is a boy down in Houston Street, so he takes a piece of paper out of his pocket and makes a little ball of it and rolls it along the floor and Johnny bounces after it very lively indeed. But Rudolph can see that the bad eye is getting worse and finally he says to Johnny like this:

"Johnny," he says, "I guess you must be suffering more than I am. I remember there are some pet shops over on Lexington Avenue not far from here and when it gets good and dark I am going to take you out and see if we can find a cat croaker to do something about your eye. Yes, Johnny," Rudolph says, "I will also get you something to eat. You must be starved."

Johnny One-Eye says merouw to this and keeps on playing with the paper ball but soon it comes on dark outside and inside, too, and in fact, it is so dark inside that Rudolph cannot see his hand before him. Then he puts his Betsy in a side pocket of his overcoat and picks up Johnny and goes downstairs, feeling his way in the dark and easing along a step at a time until he gets to the basement door. Naturally, Rudolph does not wish to strike any matches because he is afraid someone outside may see the light and get nosey.

By moving very slowly, Rudolph finally gets to Lexington Avenue and while he is going along he remembers the time he walks from 125th Street in Harlem down to 110th with six slugs in him and never feels as bad as he does now. He gets to thinking that maybe he is not the guy he used to be, which of course is very true as Rudolph is now forty-odd years of age and is fat around the middle and getting bald, and he also does some thinking about what a pleasure it will be to him to find this Buttsy and cause him the pain he is personally suffering.

There are not many people in the streets and those that are go hurrying along because it is so cold and none of them pay any attention to Rudolph or Johnny One-Eye either, even though Rudolph staggers a little now and then like a guy who is rummed up, although of course it is only weakness. The chances are he is also getting a little feverish and lightheaded because finally he stops a cop who is going along swinging his arms to keep warm and asks him if he knows where there is a pet shop and it is really most indiscreet of such a guy as Rudolph to be interviewing cops. But the cop just points up the street and goes on without looking twice at Rudolph and Rudolph laughs and pokes Johnny with a finger and says:

"No, Johnny One-Eye," he says, "the cop is not a dope for not recognizing Rudolph. Who can figure the hottest guy in forty-eight states to be going along a street with a little cat in his arms? Can you, Johnny?"

Johnny says merouw and pretty soon Rudolph comes to the pet shop the cop points out. Rudolph goes inside and says to the guy like this:

"Are you a cat croaker?" Rudolph says. "Do you know what to do about a little cat that has a hurt eye?"

"I am a kind of a vet," the guy says.

"Then take a glaum at Johnny One-Eye here and see what you can do for him," Rudolph says.

Then he hands Johnny over to the guy and the guy looks at Johnny a while and says:

"Mister," he says, "the best thing I can do for this cat is to put it out of its misery. You better let me give it something right now. It will just go to sleep and never know what happens."

Well, at this, Rudolph grabs Johnny One-Eye out of the guy's hands and puts him under his coat and drops a duke on the Betsy in his pocket as if he is afraid the guy will take Johnny away from him again and he says to the guy like this:

"No, no, no," Rudolph says. "I cannot bear to think of such a thing. What about some kind of an operation? I remember they take a bum lamp out of Joe the Goat at Bellevue one time and he is okay now."

"Nothing will do your cat any good," the guy says. "It is a goner. It will start having fits pretty soon and die sure. What is the idea of trying to save such a cat as this? It is no kind of a cat to begin with. It is just a cat. You can get a million like it for a nickel."

"No," Rudolph says, "this is not just a cat. This is Johnny One-Eye. He is my only friend in the world. He is the only living thing that ever comes pushing up against me warm and friendly and trusts me in my whole life. I feel sorry for him."

"I feel sorry for him, too," the guy says. "I always feel sorry for animals that get hurt and for people."

"I do not feel sorry for people," Rudolph says. "I only feel sorry for Johnny One-Eye. Give me some kind of stuff that Johnny will eat."

"Your cat wants milk," the guy says. "You can get some at the delicatessen store down at the corner. Mister," he says, "you look sick yourself. Can I do anything for you?"

But Rudolph only shakes his head and goes on out and down to the delicatessen joint where he buys a bottle of milk and this transaction reminds him that he is very short in the moo department. In fact, he can find only a five-dollar note in his pockets and he remembers that he has no way of getting any more when this runs out, which is a very sad predicament indeed for a guy who is accustomed to plenty of moo at all times.

Then Rudolph returns to the old house and sits down on the floor again and gives Johnny One-Eye some of the milk in his derby hat as he neglects buying something for Johnny to drink out of. But Johnny offers no complaint. He laps up the milk and curls himself into a wad in Rudolph's lap and purrs.

Rudolph takes a swig of the milk himself but it makes him sick for by this time Rudolph is really far from being in the pink of condition. He not only has the pain in his side but he has a heavy cold which he probably catches from lying on the basement floor or maybe sleeping in the park and he is wheezing no little. He commences to worry that he may get too ill to continue looking for Buttsy, as he can see that if it is not for Buttsy he will not be in this situation, suffering the way he is, but on a long journey to some place.

He takes to going off into long stretches of a kind of stupor and every time he comes out of one of these stupors the first thing he does is to look around for Johnny One-Eye and Johnny is always right there either playing with the paper ball or purring in Rudolph's lap. He is a great comfort to Rudolph but after a while Rudolph notices that Johnny seems to be running out of zip and he also notices that he is running out of zip himself especially when he discovers that he is no longer able to get to his feet.

It is along in the late afternoon of the day following the night Rudolph goes out of the house that he hears someone coming up the stairs and naturally he picks up his Betsy and gets ready for action when he also hears a very small voice calling kitty, kitty, kitty, and he realizes that the party that is coming can be nobody but a child. In fact, a minute later a little pretty of maybe six years of age comes into the room all out of breath and says to Rudolph like this:

"How do you do?" she says. "Have you seen my kitty?"

Then she spots Johnny One-Eye in Rudolph's lap and runs over and sits down beside Rudolph and takes Johnny in her arms and at first Rudolph is inclined to resent this and has a notion to give her a good boffing but he is too weak to exert himself in such a manner.

"Who are you?" Rudolph says to the little pretty, "and," he says, "where do you live and how do you get in this house?"

"Why," she says, "I am Elsie, and I live down the street and I am looking everywhere for my kitty for three days and the door is open downstairs and I know kitty likes to go in doors that are open so I came to find her and here she is."

"I guess I forgot to close it last night," Rudolph says. "I seem to be very forgetful lately."

"What is your name?" Elsie asks, "and why are you sitting on the floor in the cold and where are all your chairs? Do you have any little girls like me and do you love them dearly?"

"No," Rudolph says. "By no means and not at all."

"Well," Elsie says, "I think you are a nice man for taking care of my kitty. Do you love kitty?"

"Look," Rudolph says, "his name is not kitty. His name is Johnny One-Eye, because he has only one eye."

"I call her kitty," Elsie says. "But," she says, "Johnny One-Eye is a nice name too and if you like it best I will call her Johnny and I will leave her here with you to take care of always and I will come to see her every day. You see," she says, "if I take Johnny home Buttsy will only kick her again."

"Buttsy?" Rudolph says. "Do I hear you say Buttsy? Is his other name Fagan?"

"Why, yes," Elsie says. "Do you know him?"

"No," Rudolph says, "but I hear of him. What is he to you?"

"He is my new daddy," Elsie says. "My other one and my best one is dead and so my mamma makes Buttsy my new one. My mamma says Buttsy is her mistake. He is very mean. He kicks Johnny and hurts her eye and makes her run away. He kicks my mamma too. Buttsy kicks everybody and everything when he is mad and he is always mad."

"He is a louse to kick a little cat," Rudolph says.

"Yes," Elsie says, "that is what Mr. O'Toole says he is for kicking my mamma but my mamma says it is not a nice word and I am never to say it out loud."

"Who is Mr. O'Toole?" Rudolph says.

"He is the policeman," Elsie says. "He lives across the street from us and he is very nice to me. He says Buttsy is the word you say just now, not only for kicking my mamma but for taking her money when she brings it home from work and spending it so she cannot buy me nice things to wear. But do you know what?" Elsie says. "My mamma says some day Buttsy is going far away and then she will buy me lots of things and send me to school and make me a lady."

Then Elsie begins skipping around the room with Johnny One-Eye in her arms and singing I am going to be a lady, I am going to be a lady, until Rudolph has to tell her to pipe down because he is afraid somebody may hear her. And all the time Rudolph is thinking of Buttsy and regretting that he is unable to get on his pins and go out of the house.

"Now I must go home," Elsie says, "because this is a night Buttsy comes in for his supper and I have to be in bed before he gets there so I will not bother him. Buttsy does not like little girls. Buttsy does not like little kittens. Buttsy does not like little anythings. My mamma is afraid of Buttsy and so am I. But," she says, "I will leave Johnny here with you and come back tomorrow to see her."

"Listen, Elsie," Rudolph says, "does Mr. O'Toole come home to-night to his house for his supper, too?"

"Oh, yes," Elsie says. "He comes home every night. Sometimes when there is a night Buttsy is not coming in for his supper my mamma lets me go over to Mr. O'Toole's and I play with his dog Charley but you must never tell Buttsy this because he does not like O'Toole either. But this is a night Buttsy is coming and that is why my mamma tells me to get in early."

Now Rudolph takes an old letter out of his inside pocket and a pencil out of another pocket and he scribbles a few lines on the envelope and stretches himself out on the floor and begins groaning oh, oh, oh, and then he says to Elsie like this:

"Look, Elsie," he says, "you are a smart little kid and you pay strict attention to what I am going to say to you. Do not go to bed tonight until Buttsy gets in. Then," Rudolph says, "you tell him you come in this old house looking for your cat and that you hear somebody groaning like I do just now in the room at the head of the stairs and that you find a guy who says his name is Rudolph lying on the floor so sick he cannot move. Tell him the front door of the basement is open. But," Rudolph says, "you must not tell him that Rudolph tells you to say these things. Do you understand?"

"Oh," Elsie says, "do you want him to come here? He will kick Johnny again if he does."

"He will come here, but he will not kick Johnny," Rudolph says. "He will come here, or I am the worst guesser in the world. Tell

him what I look like, Elsie. Maybe he will ask you if you see a
gun. Tell him you do not see one. You do not see a gun, do you,
Elsie?"

"No," Elsie says, "only the one in your hand when I come in but
you put it under your coat. Buttsy has a gun and Mr. O'Toole has
a gun but Buttsy says I am never, never to tell anybody about this
or he will kick me the way he does my mamma."

"Well," Rudolph says, "you must not remember seeing mine,
either. It is a secret between you and me and Johnny One-Eye.
Now," he says, "if Buttsy leaves the house to come and see me, as I
am pretty sure he will, you run over to Mr. O'Toole's house and
give him this note, but do not tell Buttsy or your mamma either
about the note. If Buttsy does not leave, it is my hard luck but you
give the note to Mr. O'Toole anyway. Now tell me what you are
to do, Elsie," Rudolph says, "so I can see if you have got everything
correct."

"I am to go on home and wait for Buttsy," she says, "and I am
to tell him Rudolph is lying on the floor of this dirty old house with
a fat stomach and a big nose making noises and that he is very sick
and the basement door is open and there is no gun if he asks me,
and when Buttsy comes to see you I am to take this note to Mr.
O'Toole but Buttsy and my mamma are not to know I have the
note and if Buttsy does not leave I am to give it to Mr. O'Toole
anyway and you are to stay here and take care of Johnny my kitten."

"That is swell," Rudolph says. "Now you run along."

So Elsie leaves and Rudolph sits up again against the wall because
his side feels easier this way and Johnny One-Eye is in his lap
purring very low and the dark comes on until it is blacker inside
the room than in the middle of a tunnel and Rudolph feels that
he is going into another stupor and he has a tough time fighting
it off.

Afterward some of the neighbors claim they remember hearing a
shot inside the house and then two more in quick succession and
then all is quiet until a little later when Officer O'Toole and half a
dozen other cops and an ambulance with a doctor come busting into
the street and swarm into the joint with their guns out and their
flashlights going. The first thing they find is Buttsy at the foot of
the stairs with two bullet wounds close together in his throat, and
naturally he is real dead.

Rudolph is still sitting against the wall with what seems to be a small bundle of bloody fur in his lap but which turns out to be what is left of this little cat I am telling you about, although nobody pays any attention to it at first. They are more interested in getting the come-alongs on Rudolph's wrists but before they move him he pulls his clothes aside and shows the doctor where the slug is in his side and the doctor takes one glaum and shakes his head and says:

"Gangrene," he says. "I think you have pneumonia, too, from the way you are blowing."

"I know," Rudolph says. "I know this morning. Not much chance, hey, croaker?"

"Not much," the doctor says.

"Well, cops," Rudolph says, "load me in. I do not suppose you want Johnny, seeing that he is dead."

"Johnny who?" one of the cops says.

"Johnny One-Eye," Rudolph says. "This little cat here in my lap. Buttsy shoots Johnny's only good eye out and takes most of his noodle with it. I never see a more wonderful shot. Well, Johnny is better off but I feel sorry about him as he is my best friend down to the last."

Then he begins to laugh and the cop asks him what tickles him so much and Rudolph says:

"Oh," he says, "I am thinking of the joke on Buttsy. I am positive he will come looking for me, all right, not only because of the little altercation between Cute Freddy and me but because the chances are Buttsy is greatly embarrassed by not tilting me over the first time, as of course he never knows he wings me. Furthermore," Rudolph says, "and this is the best reason of all, Buttsy will realize that if I am in his neighborhood it is by no means a good sign for him, even if he hears I am sick.

"Well," Rudolph says, "I figure that with any kind of a square rattle I will have a better chance of nailing him than he has of nailing me, but that even if he happens to nail me, O'Toole will get my note in time to arrive here and nab Buttsy on the spot with his gun on him. And," Rudolph says, "I know it will be a great pleasure to the D.A. to settle Buttsy for having a gun on him.

"But," Rudolph says, "as soon as I hear Buttsy coming on the sneaksby up the stairs, I can see I am taking all the worst of it because I am now wheezing like a busted valve and you can hear me a block away except when I hold my breath, which is very difficult indeed, considering the way I am already greatly tuckered out. No," Rudolph says, "it does not look any too good for me as Buttsy keeps coming up the stairs, as I can tell he is doing by a little faint creak in the boards now and then. I am in no shape to maneuver around the room and pretty soon he will be on the landing and then all he will have to do is to wait there until he hears me which he is bound to do unless I stop breathing altogether. Naturally," Rudolph says, "I do not care to risk a blast in the dark without knowing where he is as something tells me Buttsy is not a guy you can miss in safety.

"Well," Rudolph says, "I notice several times before this that in the dark Johnny One-Eye's good glim shines like a big spark, so when I feel Buttsy is about to hit the landing, although of course I cannot see him, I flip Johnny's ball of paper across the room to the wall just opposite the door and tough as he must be feeling Johnny chases after it when he hears it light. I figure Buttsy will hear Johnny playing with the paper and see his eye shining and think it is me and take a pop at it and that his gun flash will give me a crack at him.

"It all works out just like I dope it," Rudolph says, "but," he says, "I never give Buttsy credit for being such a marksman as to be able to hit a cat's eye in the dark. If I know this, maybe I will never stick Johnny out in front the way I do. It is a good thing I never give Buttsy a second shot. He is a lily. Yes," Rudolph says, "I can remember when I can use a guy like him."

"Buttsy is no account," the cop says. "He is a good riddance. He is the makings of a worse guy than you."

"Well," Rudolph says, "it is a good lesson to him for kicking a little cat."

Then they take Rudolph to a hospital and this is where I see him and piece out this story of Johnny One-Eye, and Officer O'Toole is at Rudolph's bedside keeping guard over him, and I remember that not long before Rudolph chalks out he looks at O'Toole and says to him like this:

"Copper," he says, "there is no chance of them out-juggling the kid on the reward moo, is there?"

"No," O'Toole says, "no chance. I keep the note you send me by Elsie saying she will tell me where you are. It is information leading to your capture just as the reward offer states. Rudolph," he says, "it is a nice thing you do for Elsie and her mother, although," he says, "it is not nearly as nice as icing Buttsy for them."

"By the way, copper," Rudolph says, "there is the remainders of a pound note in my pants pocket when I am brought here. I want you to do me a favor. Get it from the desk and buy Elsie another cat and name it Johnny, will you?"

"Sure," O'Toole says. "Anything else?"

"Yes," Rudolph says, "be sure it has two good eyes."

One Kind Word for Hollywood

BY

H. ALLEN SMITH

IT BECAME my pleasant duty one day ten or twelve years ago to interview Ernst Lubitsch. Mr. Lubitsch undertook to explain for me why the motion picture is superior to the legitimate theater. He demonstrated how the camera can extract drama from the slow turning of a doorknob, the slight movement of an actor's finger—things that are impossible on the stage. Mr. Lubitsch didn't need to convince me. I was already a movie man.

Your hidebound theatergoer usually sneers at motion pictures and in so doing afflicts me with all the symptoms of hydrophobia. I go to the legitimate theater two or three times a year, not to look at the people on the stage but to contemplate the deodorized ladies of the audience and the silk-hatted weregoats who serve those ladies as escorts. Thus the most interesting part of an evening at the theater, to me anyway, is intermission, when the customers gather in the lobby to smoke and to smell up the premises with their conversation.

I've never had a real hot yen to see but one stage play and it was never produced. It was written by a pleasant man named Frank White, who used to hang around the Denver Press Club. Frank White was a former newspaperman who played a good game of poker and, if pressed, would recite the play he had written. I don't remember the title of the opus but I do remember the way the script goes. Of it, Frank White used to say:

"No matter what anybody else has accomplished, I can always lay claim to one distinction. I am the author of the shortest play ever written."

The White drama has a single stage setting: the dreary living room of a New England farmhouse. As the curtain rises two characters are on stage. Lying in front of the fireplace is Eb, the son of the family. He is writing with chalk on the back of a shovel. Seated in the rocking chair is the daughter of the family, Marybelle.

Suddenly the door is flung open, revealing at one and the same time a blizzard and Paw. Paw holds the door open long enough for the audience to recognize the full fury of the storm outside. He is a tall geezer with chin whiskers. He slams the door, stamps the snow from his feet, crosses the room, and confronts Marybelle. He stares down at her a moment, then lifts his arm, points to the door, and says:

"Git out!"

Eb looks up from his shovel and says:

"Whatsa matter, Paw? She ain't done nuthin'."

And Paw replies:

"I know she ain't done nuthin', but it's a-snowin' out, an' out she goes!"

Curtain.

There's a play I could enjoy, though given my choice of seeing it on the stage or on the screen, I'd take it on the screen.

People who are stage daffy strike me as being of the same caliber as autograph bugs. If they ever go to a movie I have an idea they sit for ninety minutes, saying to themselves: "That's not really Joan Crawford up there. That's not anybody at all. Nobody. Only a bunch of photographs. No more Joan Crawford than I am. Joan Crawford's out in Hollywood." If they were seeing Joan Crawford on the stage, they'd apparently get a tingle from the fact of their being within a few yards of Joan Crawford in the flesh. I think such people suffer from the disease called Vicarious Vertigo. I know all about that disease because I've had it for years.

I am personally acquainted with Irving Berlin through Vicarious Vertigo. Know him well. I'll prove it as soon as I explain the disease. Vicarious Vertigo is a malady endemic in the United States of America and is characterized by pleasurable dizzy spells, swollen tongue, and, in some cases, loin twitch. Something also happens to the head. Both children and grownups suffer from Vicarious Vertigo, which is contagious, and the pill hasn't yet been pestled that will cure it.

Perhaps the most common manifestation of the disease is to be

observed outside stage doors. Here the Vicarious Vertigo germ is
joined by bacillus autograph, causing the victim to see spots before
the eyes as big as basketballs.

If you are an observing person, you may see evidence of the
disease all around you. Not long ago I was riding in a subway
train when the chance arose to study an interesting case. The victim
was a girl in her middle teens. The train was crowded and the girl
was standing. Across the car was a middle-aged woman, occupying a
vacant look. As it developed, the middle-aged woman was the dam
of the teen-age girl. I was busy reading the works of Keats (Fred)
when the girl, in that loud and unself-conscious manner of New
Yorkers, yelled:

"Mommer!"

Mommer looked up.

"Mommer," yelled the girl, "you rememba that putchy kid lives
uppen th' next block over tords Margie's name Freddie got the
freckles all over him?"

"Yehr," said Mommer. "So what about?"

"Jus' think," yelled the girl. "You rememba that they had this
memorial surface to Lou Gehrig up the Polo Grounds or somewheres and LaGardy and all them was there?"

"Where at?" Mommer called out.

"Well," said the girl, ignoring the question, "this Freddie he was
the one played the taps on the bugle. Right there at the memorial
surface to Lou Gehrig. Frunta all them people and LaGardy. Freddie, that lives over tords . . . You know, Freddie, got all them freckles
on him."

"No!" said Mommer.

"Swearta God!" said the girl. "Margie told me he was the one."

The girl looked around at the other people in the car, smiling
proudly.

There is a case of Vicarious Vertigo. Knowing the course usually
taken by the malady, I realized that this girl would go around for
weeks and months and maybe years, bragging about how she was
"personly acquainnit with Freddie that played the bugle at the
Lou Gehrig memorial surface in front of LaGardy." She was enjoying a sort of three-cushion celebrity herself and, no doubt, the
disease soon took hold of Mommer. Mommer could now brag
about how her own daughter knew Freddie that played . . . etc.

I have already confessed that the V. V. germ has had possession of my own carcass for years and I fear I have passed the disease along to my children. My daughter, who is in her teens, came dashing into the house a while back, crying:

"I think I saw Billy Gilbert!"

"Billy Who?" I asked.

"Billy Gilbert," she answered breathlessly. "You know, Billy Gilbert, the big fat movie star, the one that sneezes, got a little mustache."

"Where'd you see him?"

"Well," she said, "I was crossing the street, Northern Boulevard, and the light was red and this car was stopped and just as I got across I looked up and there were two men in this car, the driver and this other man, and it was Billy Gilbert. Honest it was! And he was looking *straight at me*. And he *grinned* at me. It was Billy Gilbert. It couldn't have been anybody else. And he acted like he almost *knew* me!"

Then she flew out of the house, headed for the homes of all her girl friends, to brag about this earth-shaking thing that had happened to her. I was left to sit alone and brood over the appalling evidence. The fact stared me in the face. My daughter had inherited V. V.

When I was a little heel around eleven or twelve I lived in an Illinois town and was learning to swim at the Y.M.C.A. One afternoon I was on my way to the "Y" pool and was walking across a strip of ground back of the tennis courts. Suddenly a tennis ball rolled across my path. I picked it up and looked toward the court and saw a tall guy with a racquet. Apparently he was alone and had been batting the ball against the side of a building. He held his hand up and smiled and I threw the ball at him and then I went on toward the building housing the pool. At the door one of the "Y" attendants stopped me and said:

"Hey, son. Know who that was you throwed the ball to? That was none other than the great Bill Tilden."

Sure enough, it was Bill Tilden—not so great at that moment as he later became but already a famous personality. The hell with going swimming after that. I headed for home and, arriving there, set off on a bragging tour of the neighborhood. The V. V. germ had me. At first I told a story of having retrieved a ball for the great

Bill Tilden, of how I walked up and handed him the ball and chatted with him about the weather. Within a few days I was telling how I had joined Bill Tilden in a little game of batting the ball against a building. By the time two weeks had passed I was remarking, quite casually, that I had played a regulation game of tennis with Tilden. And thereafter, for half-a-dozen years, I went around talking about how I had engaged Bill Tilden in an impromptu *set* and had BEATEN THE LIVING HELL OUT OF HIM!

That's the way the insidious malady works. The frightful thing about it is that people listen to its victims. Let me cite just one more instance before I get to Irving Berlin. As you doubtless know, the late O. O. McIntyre was, to millions of outland Americans, the First Citizen of New York. They worshiped him, particularly through the Middle West where he had his origin. Now, it happens that I had occasion to telephone O. O. McIntyre one day in connection with a newspaper story I was writing. I talked to him about thirty-eight seconds.

Some months later I was visiting my home town in the Middle West (I have at least four home towns) and was talking to a fellow at the Elks Club.

"Live in New York now, eh?" he said.

"Yep."

"Know people there purty well?"

"Well, I know some people."

"Know O. O. McIntyre?"

"Only slightly," I said. "Just slightly, is all. Talked to him not long ago on the telephone."

He was full of eagerness for the details—wanted to know how McIntyre's voice sounded, what he said, how he said it. And then he spread it all over town like this:

"Knows O. O. McIntyre, he does! Spoke to him on the phone. Says he talks regular, just like anybody else! Told me all about it at ten-eighteen by the clock last night at the third card table from the door on the left-hand side in the Elks Club."

By now you know Vicarious Vertigo and how it works, and I can demonstrate how intimately I know Irving Berlin.

One evening I was a guest in the home of the Carters in Greenwich Village. Mrs. Carter is employed by a large firm of interior decorators and has worked on many important jobs. Some time during the evening she began talking about her Easter bonnet. She had constructed it herself and it was unique beyond being simply a woman's hat. She had fashioned it of materials left over from three recent decorating jobs.

The main part of the hat was built from a slab of straw matting. This was left over from a table mat on the huge liner *America,* which Mrs. Carter had helped decorate. She had taken the fragment of matting and formed it into a shallow crown, and around the edges she had tacked on some yellow silk stuff that was left over from the bandstand of a leading New York night club.

Hanging down the side of the homemade hat was a small black tassel. This came from—here's the pay-off—this came from the home of Irving Berlin. Mrs. Carter had helped redecorate the Berlin home and had preserved a tassel left over from the drapes.

She got the hat out and let me look at it, even let me hold it. I held it in my lap for, well, maybe ten minutes all told. And I *fondled* the tassel that was left over from the drapes that were hung in Irving Berlin's house when Irving Berlin's house was redecorated.

Do I know Irving Berlin? Know him well. Known him for years. Practically pals, me and Irving. Know him almost as well as I know Bill Tilden.

* * *

By hoary tradition newspapermen are supposed to be supercilious in the presence of fame. If I were a glittering Hollywood star, twice as big as I am now and possessing three times my present courage, and if I were subjected to periodic interviewing at the hands of newspapermen I would soon conclude my career on the gallows for mass murder. The ordinary reporter, when interviewing a movie celebrity, generally out-hams the ham. He puts on a pose of insolent superiority when, in actual fact, he's more than a trifle thrilled, even though thumbscrews would never bring him to admit it.

I used to be that way. I'd act haughty and superior in the presence of interviewees when I didn't really mean it. Right now I can confess that I get a wallop out of meeting most celebrities. That's why I enjoy visiting in Hollywood as a member of the press —a person with rare privileges, constantly being introduced to movie stars and even being invited to their homes. A visiting newspaperman, particularly one who has "circulation," is treated as royalty by the picture studios.

A newspaperman I know told me about his arrival in Hollywood and how he was taken at once into the presence of Louis B. Mayer. Mr. Mayer talked with him a while, made some discreet inquiries respecting the guy's following among newspaper readers, then informed him that he could have anything he wanted. As the visitor was leaving, Mr. Mayer glanced at the publicity man who had accompanied him and said:

"A."

Outside the door the newspaperman asked what he meant by "A."

"That means," said the publicity man, "that you're in luck. You get the 'A' treatment. You get a private car with chauffeur, always at your disposal. You get all the restaurants and night spots you want, on the cuff. And you get to date any of our actresses who are available. How would Linda Darnell suit you tonight?"

During my own two visits in Hollywood I never got the "A" treatment but I got better than that. I got Rufus Blair. Rufus Blair is a publicity man at Paramount. He is a master of invective, oral and written. He talks a good deal like H. L. Mencken writes. He is bitter and contemptuous toward most of Hollywood's institutions and never hesitates to express himself in that direction. When I come into Hollywood Rufus Blair is there to meet me. He was there at the airport when I came out of the plane and saw him for the first time. He stepped up, his hand extended, and said:

"You resemble a terrible baboon named Smith, so described to me by my New York office."

He stays with me for the duration, and we make a determined effort to keep away from such places as the Brown Derby and Dave Chasen's and Slapsie Maxie's. We simply settle down in the Blair hillside residence, which is called Baskerville because of the presence of an entire herd of police dogs. Occasionally we invite Lou Smith or Blake McVeigh or Harry Flannery or Eddie Albert in to join us and we have a good time.

On the last visit I spent three weeks in Hollywood and I had a schedule of work laid out that was more exhausting than the love life of a galloping goose. I was appearing once a week on a sad radio program called "Swop Night," which required script conferences and interviews with yucks. *Yuck* is a word introduced into the language by Fred Allen. A yuck is a dope who makes a practice of going around appearing on quiz programs. That was its original definition; it now means a dope of any description.

In addition to the radio show I was supposed to be collecting material for some magazine pieces about Bing Crosby. That was, in fact, my chief purpose in going to Movietown, although I also had to turn out a daily column containing, theoretically, something more than random thoughts on sunshine.

In writing the column from Hollywood I undertook an experiment in which I sought to avoid interviewing a single movie actor or actress during the entire three weeks. The publicity men kept my phone ringing constantly, offering appointments with the stars. One man wanted me to interview Gene Autry's horse on the subject of what a nice fellow Gene Autry is. I turned them all down because I knew that if I interviewed a star at Warner's, then I'd be compelled, in fairness, to interview stars at all the other studios, and I didn't have time for that. It amuses me to think back about the attention I got from the studios then. I was a columnist, an outlet for valuable publicity, and they courted me and sent gifts to my hotel and offered to take me to the fights and offered automobile service and all that. The next time I go out I won't be a newspaperman and they'll shun me as they'd shun a meat-eating Staphylococcus.

I intend to go out again, not alone for the pleasure of being ignored, but to achieve three small ambitions. I didn't have time for them before.

First, I want to visit Harry Carey's thumb. Harry Carey's thumb was my favorite movie actor when I was a kid. I went to all his Westerns and I was always fascinated by his thumb. He employed it dramatically whenever he was communing with himself. He'd place his thumb, cocked back from his fist, against his chin and just think, think, think, and what he was thinking was not healthy for the rustlers.

Second, I want to go out to Lola Lane's ranch, if she still has it. I interviewed Miss Lane in New York once and she told me about her ranch, which formerly belonged to Edgar Rice Burroughs. A big tree stands in front of the main house and it is this tree that interests me. Miss Lane told me that one summer night Edgar Rice Burroughs couldn't get to sleep in the house because of the heat so he dragged a mattress into the yard, placed it beneath the tree, and lay down on it. He was lying there, still unable to get to sleep, staring up into the branches of the tree, when he saw something. It was Tarzan. When I heard about this I told Miss Lane I'd dearly love to try that tree. She said that I could spend a night at her ranch, she'd fix me up with a mattress, and I could stare up into the tree all night if I wanted to, and that anything I saw up there I could keep and write about. I have no idea of what I might see, but I do know that if Edgar Rice Burroughs could see Tarzan, I'll be able to see something.

My third minor ambition is to sit on Lana Turner's stool. It appears that Miss Turner was a high-school girl in Hollywood and one day she was sitting on a stool at a soda fountain when a big shot happened in and "discovered" her for the movies. Subsequently, I'm told, the proprietor of the soda fountain had a metal plate attached to the stool, saying: "This is the stool on which Lana Turner was sitting when she was discovered." I want to sit on that stool. It's an urge I can't explain. I can offer no reason why I want to sit on it, but I do, and I will if I can find it.

When I resolved not to interview any movie actresses during that last visit, I forgot about Gerta Rozan. Five years earlier in New York I had done an interview with Gerta at the time of her arrival in America from Vienna. Gerta came to America as a refugee, unable to talk our language but possessing a good reputation as an actress. Before long she was swallowed up by Hollywood and nobody heard of her until a press agent talked her into performing her famous strip-tease picketing act.

She had been given a minor role in an Albert Lewin-David Loew film. When the picture was completed, Gerta's bit part had been scissored out. So one of Hollywood's press agents set her to picketing the studio, marching up and down in front of the entrance and taking off one garment each day. Her threat was that she would keep on picketing until she had taken every stitch of her clothes off, but of course it never got that far. She is a lovely blonde and, if the capitalistic bosses had kept the dispute in a deadlock, the effect would have been devastating.

So Gerta, the strip picket, was the only actress I saw. She told me she was sad. She had been sad for a long time. Back in 1932, she explained, she was dining in a Berlin restaurant. At the next table was a puny political ward heeler who looked like Charlie Chaplin.

"I thought," said Gerta, "that he looked so funny, and I giggled at him, right in his face, and he scowled very bad at me. It would have been so easy for me. I could have picked up a big bottle champagne and hit him on top the head and killed him. I kick my pants I didn't do it. I kick my pants all the time."

Though Gerta was the only actress I really interviewed I got to see many other citizens of Never-Never Land. I got to talk to my favorite movie actress—Joan Crawford. I was taken out to Jack Benny's house one Monday morning to have breakfast and to be shown over the Beverly Hills mansion by the master himself. I visited in the home of Hedda Hopper, a gracious battleaxe. I saw the inside of the homes of two of Hollywood's most genial geniuses —Mark Sandrich and Norman Z. MacLeod. I had a swell afternoon at Irene Rich's little ranch, which is on top of a mountain. And I even saw Dorothy Lamour.

One evening Harry Flannery and I were sitting in the cocktail lounge at the Hotel Knickerbocker. We were debating whether we ought to go upstairs and abuse William Saroyan. I had called on Mr. Saroyan the evening before and found him sitting on a divan in his living room, punching at a portable typewriter. I went in and sat down and after a while, pretending that I didn't know he was busy revolutionizing the motion-picture industry, I asked him what he was doing in Hollywood. He stood up, pointed a finger at me for emphasis, and said:

"I'm revolutionizing the motion-picture industry."

He usually talks that way but underneath it he is a nice fellow and, for all I know, a genius.

The cocktail lounge where Flannery and I were sitting is a colorful institution. You don't often see the aristocrats of Hollywood around the Knickerbocker but, sooner or later, you'll see everyone else. On this particular evening the door opened and in came Dorothy Lamour. She appeared to be in a hurry. She swished around a pillar and grabbed the lady who reads horoscopes at the Knickerbocker. They ducked into a corner and put their heads together and I could see the horoscope reader's jaw wagging at a furious pace. After about fifteen minutes Miss Lamour scampered out of the place. I went over and talked to the seeress, trying to find out what was troubling Dottie. She wouldn't talk beyond saying:

"Miss Lamour is a regular customer of mine. Sir, I cannot tell you the nature of the things that I have just told her. That is locked forever in my breast."

Miss Lamour works at Paramount and Paramount is the only studio where I know my way around. It is a lovely place for aimless wandering. You might run into anybody in the little studio streets. You might, for example, encounter Robert Benchley, wearing a large white button on his lapel. The button carries a cabalistic inscription: "W T F H A Y D O H I C?" You ask Mr. Benchley the meaning of this inscription and he tells you:

"What the hell are you doing out here in California?"

If you happen to get on the set where Miss Lamour is working in a jungle scene, you might run into Muk, the chimpanzee, during the trying period when Muk is getting his bottom lacquered. Muk's rear end is bare of foliage and gleams a fiery red in its natural state. Thus his backside could very easily dominate any scene in a technicolor picture unless something were done to dim its luster. His keeper has the job of neutralizing Muk's behind. Muk doesn't like it, as who would? Yet at frequent intervals he is compelled to bend over while the keeper smears him with black shoe polish. It is said that this rite is performed by order of the Hayes office, but I don't believe it. I prefer to believe that the actors and actresses involved in Muk's pictures have demanded the paint job. If Muk were permitted to appear *au naturel* (look at me talk French!) his anatomical sunburst could easily capture an Academy Award for scene-stealing. It could even steal a scene from Dorothy Lamour.

The best Hollywood stories are those involving technical triumphs or technical mistakes. The men who work out the industry's technological problems are the real geniuses of Hollywood. Allyn Joslyn, the actor, has a collection of technological yarns and he tells them masterfully. My favorite among them is the story of the sunrise.

At one of the big studios a director was finishing a picture—a "B" product. As he neared the end of the job the director—a fellow with Art in his soul—decided his picture was more important than anybody thought. He discovered that his picture actually carried A Message.

Having reached this conclusion, he announced that he was going to film a brief epilogue. He wanted to crystallize The Message through this epilogue and he wanted it to be impressive. He would have the hero and the heroine standing against a beautiful setting, and they would talk to each other, and their talk would constitute a summarization of The Message. It would be nice. Maybe even terrific.

His mind made up, the director decided on the background for his epilogue. He would have the boy and the girl standing on a rocky promontory and, back of them as they talked, the great sun would rise slowly out of the sea. Oh, it would be lovely!

Such a shot as this is not actually made at the seashore. The sunrise at sea is photographed separately, then thrown on a screen in the studio. The actors stand in front of this screen and do their talking and the whole thing is photographed, and it comes out looking quite authentic.

So our director called in a camera crew and ordered his sunrise. He told the men to go down to the beach before dawn and get him a first-class sunrise.

The following morning they came back to the studio and said they hadn't been able to get it. They pointed out that the sun does not rise off the coast of California. The director was nettled at having been a dope, but he covered his embarrassment and said:

"Listen, you guys. You shoulda been able to figure it out. Go back to the beach this evening and get me a beautiful sunset. Then we'll simply reverse the film, run it through backwards, and we'll have our beautiful sunrise."

The next day they were ready with their sunset picture. The film was reversed and thrown on the studio screen. The boy and the girl took their places on the hand-wrought rocky promontory, directly in front of the screen. They talked—talked The Message of the epilogue.

Even the workmen on the set stopped to watch, for it was a beautiful scene that was being shot. The boy and the girl surged along with their impassioned colloquy and as they talked, behind them the rim of a huge sun peeped over the waves. On went the talk, and slowly and beautifully the sun came up from the majestic sea.

Then someone let out a yell. Something was wrong. A mistake had been made.

It was all very lovely, except for one thing. In the picture of the beautiful sunrise all the sea gulls were flying backward and the waves were going away from the shore.

One other little story involving a technical problem comes from Charlie Einfeld. This one involves a director who needed a couple of animals for a forthcoming sequence. The director got the name of an animal dealer and sat down to write him a letter. At the very beginning he was stumped. He wasn't sure about the plural of mongoose. He tried it this way first:

> Dear sir:
> Please send me two mongooses . . .

That didn't look right, so he threw the sheet in the wastebasket and started over again, this way:

> Dear sir:
> Please send me two mongeese . . .

That seemed even worse than the first try. The director sat and studied a bit, then got it figured out. On a fresh sheet of paper he wrote:

> Dear sir:
> Please send me a mongoose. By the way, while you're at it, send me another one.

*   *   *

It can be no news to the civilized world that Hollywood reeks with treachery and backbiting and malicious gossip and hatred. At almost any social gathering you'll find people who hate each other like Devil Anse Hatfield hated the McCoys. Hollywood's a feudin' town.

One of the most interesting feuds to be met with on the Paramount lot involves my friend Rufus Blair. For several years he has not been on speaking terms with a certain agent—a hulking fellow. He and Rufus Blair despise each other—all because of a goose.

Some years back, on a sunny afternoon, Rufus was having his shoes shined. The shoeshine man at Paramount had his chair outdoors, placed against a wall of one of the buildings. It was a matter of common knowledge that the shoeshine man, a colored gentleman, was the goosiest human being west of the Mississippi.

Even a mere gesture, the slightest threat of a goose in which no contact was actually made, was sufficient to give him the shrieks.

On this sunny day Rufus was in the high chair and the man was at work on his shoes. Sitting there in the sun, Rufus found himself getting drowsy and pretty soon he was slumped in the chair, sound asleep. The man was busy on his shoes, wielding the heavy wooden-backed brushes, swinging them back and forth in a rhythmic beat. Now the villain appears on the scene—the afore-mentioned agent. This man is not renowned for intellect and, to use Douglas Gilbert's phrase, possesses a magnificent grasp of the obvious. A goose, to him, represents the ultimate in humor.

The agent came down the street and spied the shoeshine man at work with the brushes. Creeping up behind the Negro, he managed to get within goosing distance without making his presence known. Then with tender and loving care he administered a masterpiece—a goose that had finesse to it; not too forceful, not too delicate, just precisely right.

That Negro screamed and went straight up in the air. When he came down, he landed squarely on top of the sleeping Blair. His wooden brushes were still going, by some sort of goose-induced reflex—still swinging back and forth and knocking against the sides of Rufus Blair's head.

Rufus says his awakening was the worst experience of his entire life. He came out of his pleasant doze with a colored gentleman in his lap and a pair of wooden brushes cracking against his noggin. He fought his way clear of the shoeshine man and the chair and found the agent standing there, convulsed with laughter.

"What a thing to do!" screamed Rufus, and flung himself at the malefactor with both fists flying. There was no great damage done because the thing was broken up before it had fairly begun. But to this day Rufus and the agent—to whom Rufus refers bitterly as The Gooser—pass each other without speaking, glowering as though murder inhabited their hearts.

That's one Hollywood feud. There are several thousand others. The Big People of the industry like to talk about how Harmony reigns in their sun-baked empire, where Intelligence sits on the throne and all men are Brothers. They know better.

One of the most intelligent men in the town, B. G. DeSylva, production chief at Paramount, has indirectly confessed the extent of

the trust he places in the people around him. He was attending a
luncheon with executives from several other studios. The talk got
around to baseball. An executive from a rival studio remarked to
Mr. DeSylva that he would like to get up a baseball team at his
plant and challenge a team chosen from among Paramount em-
ployees.

"No," said Buddy DeSylva. "We'd better not try it. I can't think
of eighteen men in all Hollywood that I could trust if they had
baseball bats in their hands."

Grab Bag

BY

BENNETT CERF

F RANK CASE, amiable Boniface of the Algonquin Hotel, tells the story of the day the late DeWolf Hopper protested to him that nowhere in New York could he find his favorite dessert, brown betty, on the menu. "I'd have it here for you," Case said, "if I thought there would be a reasonable demand for it." "You put it on your menu tomorrow night," proposed Hopper, "and I'll see to it personally that the demand develops." The next night brown betty was duly added to the Algonquin bill of fare, and Hopper, much gratified, made a personal tour of every table in the dining room. "I am DeWolf Hopper," he announced to the surprised patrons, "and I personally urge you to sample the brown betty this evening. It's delicious!" Hopper then repaired to his own table, toyed with a beefsteak, and summoned his waiter. "Now," he said, rubbing his hands in anticipation, "I'll have a double order of brown betty." "I'm very sorry, sir," said the waiter. "It's all gone."

* * *

Do you remember the New England hurricane of 1938?

A commuter who lived in Stamford had always wanted to own a barometer. Two days before the big blow he finally bought one at Abercrombie and Fitch. He tacked it up on his wall, read it, and exploded with anger. There was no phone in his house, so he walked a mile to the nearest drugstore and called up Abercrombie. "Fine barometer you sold me," he snorted. "I put it up in my Stamford house and what do you think it registers? *Hurricane!*"

"Return it," soothed the clerk. "We'll replace it with a perfect one."

313

He went back to fetch the barometer, but by the time he got there, his house had been blown away.

*   *   *

Two old friends who had not seen each other in twenty years rediscovered each other recently. "Great to see you, Joe," boomed one of them. "I suppose you are a married man with children by this time." "No," said the other, "I am afraid I never took the plunge." "Joe, you must be crazy," said the first one. "I guess you just don't realize what it means to be married. Take me, for instance. I come home every night from a hard day at the office to a beautiful, warm, comfortable apartment. My wife is waiting to hand me my slippers and the evening paper. Then she runs out to the kitchen, cooks me a luscious dinner. She tops that with my favorite liqueur, plants me in my easy chair by the fire, and hands me my pipe. Then she washes the dishes. Finally, she comes and snuggles down by my side and starts to talk. She talks, and talks, and talks, and talks. *I wish she'd drop dead.*"

*   *   *

Newman Levy, author of *Opera Guyed,* has a thirteen-year-old daughter who spends endless blissful hours at the movies. "How did you enjoy the picture this afternoon?" he asked her one Saturday. "It was simply awful," she replied. "I could hardly sit through it the second time."

*   *   *

Deaf people have a little publication called *The Volta Review.* One story that this little magazine made famous concerned three deaf gentlemen aboard a train bound for London. "What station is this?" inquired the first gent at a stop. "Wembley," answered the guard. "Heavens," said the second gent, "I thought it was Thursday!" "So am I," exclaimed the third. "Let's all have a drink!"

*   *   *

The urbane and witty Frank Crowninshield really surpassed himself on the day that he introduced Amelia Earhart to the members of the Dutch Treat Club.

"Gentlemen," he began, "I mean to tell you a little story about Eliza, a God-fearing and worthy colored girl who died and ascended straight to the Pearly Gates. 'You're in Heaven now, Eliza,' Saint

Peter told her, 'and you're an angel in good standing. Just go over to that lot next door and pick yourself out a becoming pair of wings.' 'Wings,' echoed Eliza. 'Lordy me, Mr. Peter, I don't know nothin' 'bout flyin'!' 'You'll learn, you'll learn,' Saint Peter assured her.

"So Eliza picked out a beautiful pair of gossamer wings and made a few tentative flights. She was pretty bad at first, and had a nasty tumble or two, but gradually she caught the knack of the thing, and finally was doing side-slips, Immelmann turns, and the most complicated maneuvers with scarcely any effort whatever. She was so pleased with her progress that she decided to show off a little bit before God.

"God and His Son were on Their thrones, enjoying an after-luncheon nap, when Eliza came zooming into view. God awakened and watched her with mounting astonishment. Finally He shook His sleeping Son. 'Jesus Christ,' He exclaimed, 'can that girl fly!' . . . Gentlemen, Amelia Earhart!"

*   *   *

Another memorable incident at the Dutch Treat Club centred in the appearance of Gertrude Lawrence, who was starring at the time in the very successful *Susan and God*.

Miss Lawrence expressed girlish embarrassment at finding herself the only female in a gathering of some three hundred handsome gentlemen. "Instead of making a silly speech," she suggested, "how would you like it if I raffled off two seats in the fourth row centre for Saturday night's performance of *Susan and God?*" The crowd roared its approval. "O.K.," said Miss Lawrence. "Every one of you has a green hat-check. I'll call out a number at random. The man whose hat-check number corresponds with it gets the ducats." Followed the business of three hundred gentlemen fishing in their jeans for their hat-checks.

"Ready?" asked Miss Lawrence. "The number I pick is 171."

"That's mine," said a happy voice from the back of the room. It belonged to Mr. John Golden, owner and producer of *Susan and God*. Miss Lawrence and Mr. Golden escaped from the room before the stunned audience could translate its mute rage into positive action.

*   *   *

Clarence Budington Kelland presided the day that Nicholas

Murray Butler, Columbia University prexy, was the guest of the Dutch Treat. "For years," said Kelland, gazing fondly at Dr. Butler, "organizations have been besieging this retiring gentleman to address them—with remarkable success."

*   *   *

Harry Hansen climbed into a taxicab, told the driver where he wanted to go, and added, "Please don't go down Third Avenue. I don't like those El pillars."

"Yessir," said the driver—and went right down Third Avenue. "Didn't you hear me?" screamed Hansen. "I said not to go weaving in and out around those El pillars. It drives me crazy."

The driver stopped his cab and looked at Hansen reproachfully. "Listen, Buddy," he remarked. "What do you suppose it does to *me?*"

*   *   *

The twelve-year-old daughter of a publisher of the *New York Times* volunteered to help her mother pass cocktails at an informal reception whipped up for a visiting General. Everything progressed beautifully until the horrified mother heard her daughter say to the General's wife, "May I serve you your eighth martini?"

*   *   *

Kid Stuff: A famous composer was questioning his ten-year-old son about his history lesson in school that day. "Was it interesting?" he asked. "I'll say!" declared the boy. "We heard all about Nebacadenza!"

*   *   *

And Leonard Lyons' young hopeful watched his mother try on a new dress. "You sure are beautiful," he assured her. "You look just like Abraham Lincoln!"

*   *   *

A Navy J.G., home on leave, took his little daughter on a shopping tour. In a crowded department-store elevator, a stout party gave the J.G. an outraged look, and smacked him squarely in the face. The J.G. compressed his lips, and said nothing. As they emerged on the ground floor, his daughter said, "I hated that woman too, papa. She stepped on my foot, so I pinched her right on the heinie!"

*   *   *

Paul Whiteman, the famous band leader, never could see why some people thought he was fat—even when he tipped the scales at something in the neighborhood of 250. He likes to tell the story of the *really* stout party who made a million dollars without budging from his comfortable couch. A visitor found him one day wearing a bathrobe with enormous checks, and a number sewed on to each check. "What's the idea of those numbers?" he inquired. "Watch me," said the Croesus. He summoned his butler, yawned, and ordered, "Jeeves, scratch Number 23!"

*   *   *

In my book, Fredric March's kid story still is tops. He found himself alone with a little seven-year-old one evening and, to pass the time before its parents entered the room, inquired, "What do you want to be when you grow up, sonny?" The boy looked him straight in the eye and replied firmly, "A sex pervert."

*   *   *

Olin Clark reports the story of a mother who lost her young daughter in the week-end confusion at Penn Station. After a frantic search, she finally located her in the midst of a group of nuns. Both the little girl and the nuns seemed to be having a very good time. "I hope my daughter hasn't been giving you too much trouble," exclaimed the relieved parent. "On the contrary," chuckled the Mother Superior. "Your little girl seems to have the notion that we are penguins."

*   *   *

When Bob Gilham, Paramount's publicity chief, vacationed in the Blue Ridge country a few summers ago, he noticed one old native who sat rocking on his porch day after day, a shotgun across his knees, staring intently into the hills. Uncle Eph was his name, they told Bob. One day he asked the old man what he was gunning for. "Sly old fox in them hills sneaks down ter steal my chickens, an' I'm aimin' ter dispose of him," said Uncle Eph grimly.

A week later Bob went by the cabin, and noticed that Uncle Eph had put away his gun, and was rocking happily with a look on his face that indicated he was at peace with the entire world. "I'll bet you got the fox!" said Bob. "Yep," said Uncle Eph. "Are you absolutely sure you bagged him?" said Bob. " 'Course I'm sure," said

Uncle Eph. "I been lookin' for him steady from the minute I killed him up there, and by cracky, I only seen him once since!"

Later, Bob remarked to Uncle Eph, "I bet you've seen plenty of changes here in your day." "Sure have," agreed the old man, "and I bin against every single one of them!"

*   *   *

Dialogue overheard on a cannibal island: "Who is that lady I seen you with last night?" "That wasn't no lady. That was my dinner."

*   *   *

When one famous explorer went on his Antarctic expeditions, report had it that the personnel invariably included the ugliest old crone he could sign up. "She's my yardstick," he explained. "When she starts looking good to me—I know it's time to start for home."

*   *   *

Willie Howard once appeared in a sketch which showed him and a few companions freezing and starving on an Antarctic ice floe. He turned on the radio just in time to hear an announcer describing a Thanksgiving dinner back home. "We'll start with a plate of hot, luscious soup," said the announcer. "With noodles?" groaned Howard. "Yes," said the voice on the radio—"with noodles."

*   *   *

"Jimmie" Walker, once mayor of New York, tells the story of the drunk who climbed into a taxi and demanded, "Drive me eighteen times around Central Park." The cab had gotten about as far as 86th Street when he banged on the window and cried, "Fashter, you idiot! I'm in a hurry!"

He probably was a brother of the gent who boarded a cab on 42nd Street, and pointing to the revolving electrical news sign on the Times Building, commanded, "Just follow that sign."

*   *   *

Hamish Hamilton, prominent English publisher, overheard two young ladies who were dining together at Lyons (the English equivalent of Child's). One of the ladies asked, "Is your boy friend a freethinker?" The other replied, "Bless me, 'e 'ardly ever thinks of hanything else."

*   *   *

There is a bone-dry town in Oklahoma where an honest-to-good-ness rattlesnake bite is the only way to get a shot of whiskey. One native came home angry and thirsty and told his wife, "It's about time this burg had more'n one rattler. I stood in line for three hours today and by the time it was my turn the rattler was so tired he wouldn't bite nobody any more."

* * *

You have read a lot about the knights of King Arthur who fared forth on coal-black chargers to rescue beautiful maidens from dragons' clutches, but did you ever know that one of them was mounted on a St. Bernard dog? His name was Sir Marmaduke, and he and the St. Bernard performed many a deed of derring-do. One evening, however, they were caught in a torrential thunder-storm, and sought shelter at a nearby tavern. "Reservation?" asked the room clerk. "No," admitted Sir Marmaduke. "Sorry," said the clerk, "no room without a reservation." It was at this moment that he discovered that Marmaduke was sitting astride his faithful St. Bernard. "Hold on," said the clerk. "We'll have to find *something* for you. I wouldn't put out a knight on a dog like this."

* * *

Barney Greengrass, who sells sturgeon to the White House, is reported to have waited on a customer who ordered a single raisin and one pinch of sugar. "What are you making, Mrs. Geddes?" he inquired. "A cookie?"

* * *

Earl Wilson tells about a well-known Broadway comedian, in his cups as usual, who careened into the 46th Street Automat, changed two dollar bills into nickels, and began inserting them in the pie slots. He had made a neat pile of four slices of apple pie, three of lemon, and five of peach, and was slipping a nickel into his first coconut pie slot when the manager collared him. "What the hell are you doing with our pies?" he cried. "Cut it out!" "Whaaat?" exclaimed the Broadwayite. "Quit now when my luck's running so good?"

* * *

Maybe that's how George Price got the notion for his cartoon of the flabbergasted Automat customer who had deposited a single nickel, and found an assortment of sandwiches, cakes, hard-boiled eggs, and crullers flying into his face. "Congratulations, sir," beamed an attendant. "You've hit the jackpot."

*　　*　　*

The *American Weekly* reports two strange accidents that occurred in New Jersey last year. Nine elephants were plodding peacefully toward the Newark fair grounds when a small boy urged his insignificant puppy to "sic 'em." The pup yapped shrilly at the heels of the leading elephant, and all nine pachyderms thereupon stampeded, scattering traffic and destruction until they were finally rounded up by six radio cops, two emergency squads, and a flock of motorcycle police.

A few blocks away a Mrs. Fitzgerald refused admission to a bedraggled and bleeding figure at the door, then discovered it was her husband Michael who had fallen off the third-floor sleeping porch.

*　　*　　*

That brings to mind the story of the battered figure at the Hotel Astor who demanded the key to Room 614.

"Room 614 is occupied by a Mr. James Collins," said the clerk at the desk.

"I know it," rasped the applicant. "I'm James Collins. I just fell out of the window."

*　　*　　*

Mable Jullup, relates Dorothy Sims, was a lady with taste. She bought a lovely vase at an auction and put it on her table. It was Ming, and it made the Grand Rapids furniture look very cheap. She was sad, so she sold the Grand Rapids and bought "period." That made her whole house look cheap. So she sold the house and took an exclusive apartment in town. But the apartment was so exclusive it made Mr. Jullup look cheap. Naturally she got a divorce, and married a Mr. Preston Potter. But here she was stymied. Mr. Preston Potter made her look cheap.

*　　*　　*

The Prize for Paralyzing Puns this year falls into the lap of the perpetrator of the following horror:

Waitress: Hawaii, mister? You must be Hungary?

Gent: Yes, Siam. And I can't Rumania long either. Venice lunch ready?

Waitress: I'll Russia table. What'll you Havre? Aix?

Gent: Whatever's ready. But can't Jamaica cook step on the gas?

Waitress: Odessa laugh! But Alaska.

Gent: Don't do me favors. Just put a Cuba sugar in my Java.

Waitress: Don't you be Sicily, big boy. Sweden it yourself. I'm only here to Serbia.

Gent: Denmark my check and call the Bosphorus. I hope he'll Kenya. I don't Bolivia know who I am!

Waitress: Canada noise! I don't Caribbean. You sure Ararat!

Gent: Samoa your wisecracks? What's got India? D'you think this arguing Alps business? Be Nice! Matter of fact, I gotta Smolensk for ya!

Waitress: Attu! Don't Kiev me that Boulogne! Alamein do! Spain in the neck. Pay your check and scram, Abyssinia!

FINNISH

*   *   *

An old drunkard from the Panhandle saw so many pink elephants and purple snakes that he hired a hall and put up a sign. "25c to See the Zoo." A couple of customers resented the fact that they saw nothing but four bare walls, and swore out a complaint. The sheriff took the warrant and set out to make the arrest. The old boy hauled his jug out from under his counter, the sheriff took three snifters—and paid him $600 for a half interest in his show.

*   *   *

Meyer Levin tells this story about a little eight-year-old girl in a Pennsylvania orphan asylum. She was a gangly, painfully unattractive child, with annoying mannerisms and secretive ways that set her apart from the others. She was shunned by the children and actively disliked by the teachers. The head of the institution longed only for a legitimate excuse to pack her off to a reform school, or get her out of the place some other way.

One afternoon it looked as though her opportunity had arrived. The girl who was the child's very unwilling roommate reported that she was conducting a clandestine correspondence with somebody outside the grounds. "I've seen her write these notes every day for a week now," she reported. "Just a little while ago she took one of them and hid it in a tree near the brick wall."

The head of the asylum and her assistant could scarcely conceal their elation. "We'll soon get to the bottom of this," they agreed. "Show us where she left the note."

Sure enough, they found the note in the branches of the tree. The headmistress pounced on it. Then she hung her head and passed it silently to her assistant.

It read: "To whoever finds this: I love you."

The Last Day

BY

ROBERT BENCHLEY

W HEN, during the long winter evenings, you sit around the snap-shot album and recall the merry, merry times you had on your vacation, there is one day which your memory mercifully overlooks. It is the day you packed up and left the summer resort to go home.

This Ultimate Day really begins the night before, when you sit up until one o'clock trying to get things into the trunks and bags. This is when you discover the well-known fact that summer air swells articles to twice or three times their original size; so that the sneakers which in June fitted in between the phonograph and the book (which you have never opened), in Septembr are found to re-quire a whole tray for themselves and even then one of them will probably have to be carried in the hand.

Along about midnight, the discouraging process begins to get on your nerves and you snap at your wife and she snaps at you every time it is found that something won't fit in the suitcase. As you have both gradually dispensed with the more attractive articles of cloth-ing under stress of the heat and the excitement, these little word passages taken on the sordid nature of a squabble in an East Side tenement, and all that is needed is for one of the children to wake up and start whimpering. This it does.

It is finally decided that there is no sense in trying to finish the job that night. General nervousness, combined with a specific fear of oversleeping, results in a troubled tossing of perhaps three hours in bed, and ushers in the dawn of the last day on just about as irrita-ble and bleary-eyed a little family as you will find outside an institution.

The trouble starts right away with the process of getting dressed in traveling clothes which haven't been worn since the trip up.

Junior's shoulders are still tender, and he decides that it will be impossible for him to wear his starched blouse. One of Philip's good shoes, finding that there has been no call for it during the summer, has become hurt and has disappeared; so Philip has to wear a pair of Daddy's old bathing shoes which had been thrown away. (After everything has been locked and taken out of the room, the good shoe is found in the closet and left for dead.)

You, yourself, aren't any too successful in reverting to city clothes. Several weeks of soft collars and rubber-soled shoes have softened you to a point where the old "Deroy-14½" feels like a napkin-ring around your neck, and your natty brogans are so heavy that you lose your balance and topple over forward if you step out suddenly. The whole effect of your civilian costume when surveyed in a mirror is that of a Maine guide all dressed up for an outing "up to Bangor."

Incidentally, it shapes up as one of the hottest days of the season —or any other season.

"Oh, look how funny Daddy looks in his straw hat!"

"I never realized before, Fred, how much too high the crown is for the length of your face. Are you sure it's your hat?"

"It's my hat, all right," is the proper reply, "but maybe the face belongs to somebody else."

This silences them for a while, but on and off during the day a lot of good-natured fun is had in calling the attention of outsiders to the spectacle presented by Daddy in his "store" clothes.

Once everyone is dressed, there must be an excursion to take one last look at the ocean, or lake, or whatever particular prank of Nature it may have been which has served as an inducement to you to leave the city. This must be done before breakfast. So down to the beach you go, getting your shoes full of sand, and wait while Sister, in a sentimental attempt to feel the water for the last time, has tripped and fallen in, soaking herself to the garters. There being no dry clothes left out, she has to go in the kitchen and stand in front of the stove until at least one side of her is dry.

Breakfast bears no resemblance to any other meal eaten in the place. There is a poorly suppressed feeling that you must hurry, coupled with the stiff collar and tight clothes, which makes it practically impossible to get any food down past the upper chest.

Then follows one of the worst features of the worst of all vacation days—the goodbyes. It isn't that you hate to part company with these people. They too, as they stand there in their summer clothes, seem to have undergone some process whereby you see them as they really are and not as they seemed when you were all together up to your necks in water or worrying a tennis ball back and forth over a net. And you may be sure that you, in your town clothes, seem doubly unattractive to them.

Here is Mrs. Tremble, who lives in Montclair, N. J., in the winter. That really is a terrible hat of hers, now that you get a good look at it. "Well, goodbye, Mrs. Tremble. Be sure to look us up if you ever get out our way. We are right in the telephone book, and we'll have a regular get-together meeting. . . . Goodbye, Marian. Think of us tonight in the hot city, and be sure to let us know when you are going through . . . Well, so long, Mr. Prothero; look out for those girls up at the post office. Don't let any of them marry you . . . Well, we're off, Mrs. Rostetter. Yes, we're leaving today. On the 10-45. We have to be back for Junior's school. It begins on the 11th. *Good*bye!"

It is then found that there is about an hour to wait before the machine comes to take you to the station; so all these goodbyes have been wasted and have to be gone through with again.

In the meantime, Mother decides that she must run over to the Bide-a-Wee cottage and say goodbye to the Sisbys. The children feel that they are about due for another last look at the ocean. And Daddy remembers that he hasn't been able to shut the big suitcase yet. So the family disperses in various directions and each unit gets lost. Mother, rushing out from the Sisbys' in a panic thinking that she hears the automobile, is unable to find the others. Little Mildred, having taken it upon herself to look out for the other children while they are gazing on the ocean, has felt it incumbent on her to spank Philip for trying to build one last tunnel in the sand, resulting in a bitter physical encounter in which Philip easily batters his sister into a state of hysteria. Daddy, having wilted his collar and put his knee through his straw hat in an attempt to jam the suitcase together, finds that the thing can't be done and takes out the box of sea-shells that Junior had planned to take home for his cabinet, and hides them under the bed.

The suitcase at last having been squeezed shut and placed with the rest of the bags in the hall, the maid comes running up with five damp bathing suits which she has found hanging on the line and wants to know if they belong here. Daddy looks cautiously down the hall and whispers: "No!"

At last the automobile arrives and stands honking by the roadside. "Come, Junior, quick, put your coat on! . . . Have you got the bag with the thermos? . . . Hurry, Philip! . . . Where's Sister? . . . Come, Sister! . . . Well, it's too late now. You'll have to wait till we get on the train . . . Goodbye, Mrs. Tremble . . . Be sure to look us up . . . Goodbye, everybody! . . . Here, Junior! Put that down! You can't take that with you. No, no! That belongs to that other little boy . . . *Junior!* . . . Goodbye, Marian! . . . Goodbye, Mrs. McNerdle! . . . Philip, say goodbye to Mrs. McNerdle, she's been so good to you, don't you remember? . . . Goodbye, Mrs. McNerdle, that's right. . . . *Goodbye!*"

And with that the automobile starts, the friends on the porch wave and call out indistinguishable pleasantries, Junior begins to cry, and it is found that Ed has no hat.

The trip home in the heat and cinders is enlivened by longing reminiscences: "Well, it's eleven o'clock. I suppose they're all getting into their bathing suits now. How'd you like to jump into that old ocean right this minute, eh?" (As a matter of fact, the speaker has probably not been induced to go into "that old ocean" more than three times during the whole summer.)

The fact that they reach home too late to get a regular dinner and have to go to bed hungry, and the more poignant impressions in the process of opening a house which has been closed all summer, have all been treated of before in an article called "The Entrance Into the Tomb." And so we will leave our buoyant little family, their vacation ended, all ready to jump into the swing of their work, refreshed, invigorated, and clear-eyed.

The Lure of the Limerick

BY

LOUIS UNTERMEYER

LIMERICKS MAY BE divided into three categories: the simple, the intricate, and the unprintable. The last, though transmitted verbally, are by no means the least popular, and hundreds of them have weathered the long years by word of mouth. But it is, perforce, with the other two that we are concerned.

It may surprise you to know that the most popular English verse form is the limerick, which has been and still is being composed by all kinds of people, from the most erudite writers to the humblest schoolboy scribbling on the flyleaf of his textbook, or the busy housewife who snatches a moment to sit down and enter a soap contest. Sonnets, heroic couplets, triolets, and the other complicated but intriguing French forms, ballads, blank verse, and free verse all fall short of the popularity of the limerick with the writing public. Frowned on by academic purists, belittled by hyperliterary poets, often ignored by anthologists, and adored by the public, the limerick has been used—and abused—ever since that odd ornithologist and landscape painter, Edward Lear, set the fashion with such irresponsible lines as:

> There was an old man who said, "Hush!
> I perceive a young bird in the bush."
> When they said, "Is it small?"
> He replied, "Not at all.
> It is four times as big as the bush!"

The origins of the form are dim; the name itself is a mystery. Even the encyclopedias are puzzled. The favorite theory is that the limerick derived its name from a song about the Irish town, each stanza of which ended, "Will you come up to Limerick?" But although sev-

eral examples of the form existed before 1830, it was not until
Edward Lear wrote his verses composed of moonshine and magic
that the limerick acquired a name and fame. Almost immediately
after publication of Lear's *Book of Nonsense* the brisk little stanza
caught the imagination of writers. It was imitated, varied, burlesqued. Countless newspaper competitions were instituted; people
who never had written poetry, or had not bothered to read it, supplied countless missing last lines, until today more than a million
limericks have come into existence.

What sort of people have succumbed to the lure of the limerick?
All sorts. Practically everyone has tried his hand at the construction
of these mocking verses, some of them political in purpose, some
critical, but most merely madcap. Great poets have vied with multi-
tudes of the unknown to sharpen the point of their five-line absur-
dities. Rudyard Kipling wrote:

> There once was a boy in Quebec
> Who was buried in snow to his neck.
>   When asked, "Are you friz?"
>   He replied, "Yes, I is.
> But we don't call this cold in Quebec."

Robert Louis Stevenson extended the geographic range—most
limericks insist on taking place in a definite locality—and added this
stanza, which cannot be found in *A Child's Garden of Verses*:

> There was an old man of the Cape,
> Who made himself garments of crêpe.
>   When asked, "Do they tear?"
>   He replied, "Here and there;
> But they're perfectly splendid for shape."

Oliver Wendell Holmes, that irrepressible punster, took a person
rather than a place for his subject, and the result was one of the
most often quoted of all limericks:

> The Reverend Henry Ward Beecher
> Called a hen a most elegant creature.
>   The hen, pleased with that,
>   Laid an egg in his hat—
> And thus did the hen reward Beecher.

Langford Reed, compiler of *The Complete Limerick Book,* also favors puns. Returning to place names for his rhyme, Reed created a limerick that has been collected continually (and misquoted) without credit:

> An indolent vicar of Bray
> His roses allowed to decay.
>   His wife, more alert,
>   Bought a powerful squirt
> And said to her spouse, "Let us spray."

Another that has gone round the world usually is credited to that famous author Anonymous. Every true fancier of limericks (limeratomist?) knows it was written by a witty Englishman, Cosmo Monkhouse:

> There was a young lady of Niger,
> Who smiled as she rode on a tiger.
>   They returned from the ride
>   With the lady inside—
> And the smile on the face of the tiger!

So great is the appeal that when people cannot make up limericks, they appropriate them. Woodrow Wilson was so fond of a particular modest limerick that he was thought to have written it. Even Langford Reed credited the President with the authorship of the following self-deprecating stanza, actually written by a forgotten poet named Anthony Euwer:

> As a beauty I'm not a great star;
> Others are handsomer far;
>   But my face—I don't mind it,
>   Because I'm behind it;
> It's the folks out in front that I jar!

Perhaps the simplest, and still the most famous of all limericks are those of Edward Lear, who immortalized, if he did not invent, the form. Written more than a hundred years ago to entertain the grandchildren of his patron, the Earl of Derby, they are models of direct and superb nonsense. The Lear formula was simplicity itself: a five-line stanza with the third and fourth lines one foot shorter than the other three. Built on two rhymes, Lear's limericks usually repeat one of the rhyme words in the concluding line. For example, these well-known stanzas:

> There was an old man with a beard,
> Who said, "It is just as I feared.
>   Two owls and a hen,
>   Four larks and a wren,
> Have *all* built their nests in my beard!"

*   *   *

> There was a young lady whose chin
> Resembled the point of a pin:
>   So she had it made sharp
>   And purchased a harp,
> And played several tunes with her chin.

*   *   *

> There was an old man in a tree,
> Who was horribly bored by a bee.
>   When they said, "Does it buzz?"
>   He replied, "Yes, it does!
> It's a regular brute of a bee."

Anybody could do it. Everybody did. But the formula lacked something; the repetitions began to cloy; the unvaried last rhyme came with wearisome regularity.

In one of his more wicked moments, W. S. Gilbert (without the aid of Sullivan) burlesqued Lear's limericks, especially the one about the man who was "bored" by a bee. Gilbert wrote a limerick that didn't have *any* rhymes at all! To wit:

> There was an old man of St. Bees.
> Who was stung in the arm by a Wasp.
>   When asked, "Does it hurt?"
>   He replied, "No, it doesn't;
> I'm so glad that it wasn't a Hornet."

But most of the limerick-makers were not so radical. They wanted to preserve the sound as well as the sense; yet they were not satisfied with Lear's model. They soon found what was missing: a last line

that would come like a climax, a surprise, a comic whiplash. So they
began fashioning new, sprightly variations on the old pattern. They
designed intricate and seemingly impossible situations—and then
brought them to a blithely nonchalant conclusion. They rollicked
in ridiculous rhymes. They turned Lear's little limerick inside out,
upside down, and helter-skelter. Here are a few of the more famous
of this new type:

There was a young man who was bitten
By twenty-two cats and a kitten.
    Cried he, "It is clear
    My end is quite near.
No matter! I'll die like a Briton!"

*   *   *

There once was a pious young priest,
Who lived almost wholly on yeast;
    "For," he said, "it is plain
    We must all rise again,
And I want to get started at least."

*   *   *

There was an old man from Peru,
Who dreamt he was eating his shoe.
    He awoke in the night
    In a terrible fright—
And found it was perfectly true!

*   *   *

A collegiate damsel named Breeze,
Weighed down by B. A.'s and Litt. D.'s,
    Collapsed from the strain.
    Alas, it was plain
She was killing herself by degrees.

*   *   *

There was a young lady named Banker,
Who slept while her ship lay at anchor.
    She awoke in dismay
    When she heard the mate say,
"Hi! Hoist up the top-sheet and spanker!"

*   *   *

There's a notable family named Stein:
There's Gertrude, there's Ep, and there's Ein.
    Gert's prose is the bunk;
    Ep's sculpture is junk;
And no one can understand Ein!

      *   *   *

There was a young wife from Antigua,
Who remarked to her spouse, "What a pigua!"
    He retorted, "My queen,
    Is it manners you mean?
Or do you refer to my figua?"

      *   *   *

A daring young lady of Guam
Observed, "The Pacific's so calm
    I'll swim out for a lark."
    She met a large shark. . . .
Let us now sing the Ninetieth Psalm.

      *   *   *

The bottle of perfume that Willie sent
Was highly displeasing to Millicent;
    Her thanks were so cold
    They quarreled, I'm told,
Through that silly scent Willie sent Millicent.

The last example suggested a new variation: limericks that were
tricks of pronunciation and spelling, triumphs of double meaning
and the ultimate twist. The late Carolyn Wells excelled in such
accomplished word-scrambling and tongue-twisting as:

A canner exceedingly canny
One morning remarked to his granny:
    "A canner can can
    Anything that he can,
But a canner can't can a can, can he?"

      *   *   *

There was a young fellow named Tate
Who dined with his girl at 8:08
    But I'd hate to relate
    What that fellow named Tate
And his tête-à-tête ate at 8:08.

      *   *   *

A certain young chap named Bill Beebee
Was in love with a lady named Phoebe.
    "But," said he, "I must see
    What the clerical fee
Be before Phoebe be Phoebe B. Beebee."

The inconsistencies in English pronunciation were seized upon
and exploited to the point of confusion. The limerick became more
and more freakish. Here are several samples of the more perverse and
precious puzzlers of this kind:

A girl who weighed many an oz.
Used language I dare not pronoz.
    For a fellow unkind
    Pulled her chair out behind
Just to see (so he said) if she'd boz.

*   *   *

An unpopular youth of Cologne
With a pain in his stomach did mogne.
    He heaved a great sigh
    And said, "I would digh,
But the loss would be only my ogne."

*   *   *

There was a young lady from Woosester
Who ussessed to crow like a roosester.
    She ussessed to climb
    Seven trees at a time—
But her sisister ussessed to boosester.

*   *   *

She frowned and called him Mr.
Because in sport he kr.
    And so in spite
    That very nite
This Mr. kr. sr.

But later tendencies indicate a departure from tricks and a return to the simple and straightforward norm. Recently the Mark
Twain Society instituted a nationwide contest for the best limerick

on its patron saint, and more than three thousand candidates were submitted. The prize (awarded to Mrs. W. S. Burgess of Fullerton, Nebraska) was an orthodox limerick, completely traditional, even to the final old-fashioned pun:

> Mark Twain was a mop-headed male,
> Whose narratives sparkle like ale;
> And this Prince of the Grin
> Who once fathered Huck Finn
> Can still hold the world by the tale!

In an effort to establish a difference in humor between American and British readers, H. J. Eysenck, the noted psychologist, reported his conclusions in *Character and Personality*. Among a group of limericks, the Americans chose this as the funniest:

> There was a young man of Laconia,
> Whose mother-in-law had pneumonia.
> He hoped for the worst—
> And after March first
> They buried her 'neath a begonia.

The British preferred the following:

> There was a young girl of Asturias,
> Whose temper was frantic and furious.
> She used to throw eggs
> At her grandmother's legs—
> A habit unpleasant, but curious.

Such choices may not be conclusive. But they prove that, though tastes change and temperaments differ, the limerick is still a test of humor, a favorite medium for millions, and an international lure.

The Demon Host

Dear God, why can't the man relax?
Must he continue thus to tax
His helpless guests' mentalities
With energetic games like these?

A party used to be for fun,
But now a docile guest must run
From bridge to bagatelle to chess,
Her arches flat with weariness.

And when I've worked hard all day long,
I can't help thinking he is wrong
Who drives me, in the name of pleasure,
To labor through my hours of leisure.

—*Margaret Fishback*

Lines to Long Island and Westchester

If anyone else says he slept in a bed
Under two blankets, a sheet and a spread,
While into his room galloped breeze after breeze,
Until he was just about ready to freeze,
I think I shall give way to violence and
Take hold of him then with my hot little hand
And lock him up tight in my hot little flat
Until he has learned to stop talking like that.

—*Margaret Fishback*

Song of the Open Road

I think that I shall never see
A billboard lovely as a tree.
Indeed, unless the billboards fall
I'll never see a tree at all.

—*Ogden Nash*

Song to Be Sung by the Fathers of
Six-Month-Old Female Children

My heart leaps up when I behold
A rainbow in the sky;
Contrariwise, my blood runs cold
When little boys go by.
For little boys as little boys,
No special hate I carry,
But now and then they grow to men,
And when they do, they marry.
No matter how they tarry,
Eventually they marry.
And, swine among the pearls,
They marry little girls.

Oh, somewhere, somewhere, an infant plays,
With parents whò feed and clothe him.
Their lips are sticky with pride and praise,
But I have begun to loathe him.
Yes, I loathe with a loathing shameless
This child who to me is nameless.
This bachelor child in his carriage
Gives never a thought to marriage,
But a person can hardly say knife
Before he will hunt him a wife.

I never see an infant (male),
A-sleeping in the sun,
Without I turn a trifle pale
And think, is he the one?

Oh, first he'll want to crop his curls,
And then he'll want a pony,
And then he'll think of pretty girls
And holy matrimony.
He'll put away his pony,
And sigh for matrimony.
A cat without a mouse
Is he without a spouse.

Oh, somewhere he bubbles bubbles of milk,
And quietly sucks his thumbs.
His cheeks are roses painted on silk,
And his teeth are tucked in his gums.
But alas, the teeth will begin to grow,
And the bubbles will cease to bubble;
Given a score of years or so,
The roses will turn to stubble.
He'll sell a bond, or he'll write a book,
And his eyes will get that acquisitive look,
And raging and ravenous for the kill,
He'll boldly ask for the hand of Jill.
This infant whose middle
Is diapered still
Will want to marry
My daughter Jill.

Oh sweet be his slumber and moist his middle!
My dreams, I fear, are infanticiddle.
A fig for embryo Lohengrins!
I'll open all of his safety pins,
I'll pepper his powder, and salt his bottle,
And give him readings from Aristotle.
Sand for his spinach I'll gladly bring,
And Tabasco sauce for his teething ring,
And an elegant, elegant alligator
To play with in his perambulator.
Then perhaps he'll struggle through fire and water
To marry somebody else's daughter.

—*Ogden Nash*

I Want New York

I think those people are utterly unreliable
Who say they'd be happy on a desert island with a copy of the
     Biable
And "Hamlet" (by Shakespeare) and "Don Quixote" (by Cervantes)
And poems by Homer and Virgil and perhaps a thing or two of
     Dante's.
And furthermore, I have a feeling that if they were marooned till
     the millennium's dawn,
Very few of us would notice that they were gone.
Perhaps they don't like my opinions any better than I like theirs,
But who cares?
If I were going to be marooned and could take only one thing along,
I'd be perfectly happy if I could take the thing which is the subject
     of this song.
I don't mean anything that was brought either by the postman or
     the stork.
I mean the City of New York.
For New York is a wonder city, a veritable fairyland
With many sights not to be seen in Massachusetts or Maryland.
It is situated on the island of Manhattan,
Which I prefer to such islands as Welfare or Staten.
And it is far superior
To the cities of the interior.
What if it has a heterogeneous populace?
That is one of the privileges of being a metropulace,
And heterogeneous people don't go round bothering each other,
And you can be reasonably sure that everything you do won't get
     right back to your dear old mother.
In New York beautiful girls can become more beautiful by going
     to Elizabeth Arden
And getting stuff put on their faces and waiting for it to harden,
And poor girls with nothing to their names but a letter or two can
     get rich and joyous
From a brief trip to their lawyers.
And anybody with a relative of whose will he is the beneficiary
Can do pretty well in the judiciary.
So I can say with impunity
That New York is a city of opportunity.
It also has many fine theatres and hotels,

And a lot of taxis, buses, subways, and "L"s;
And anybody can find somewhere in it his favorite diversion,
Whether he be Argentine, Scandinavian, or Persian.
Best of all, if you don't show up at the office or at a tea nobody will
     bother their head.
They will just think you are dead.
That's why I really think New York is exquisite.
It isn't all right just for a visit,
But by God's grace
I'd live in it and like it even better if they gave me the place.

—Ogden Nash

A Father Does His Best

Said I to Lord & Taylor:
  "Hot are the summer skies,
    And my son Joe would like to go
    In a big straw hat in the year-old size.
    Have you got such a thing, for summer skies,
    A nice straw hat in the year-old size?"
Said Lord & Taylor: "No."

Said I to Saks Fifth Avenue:
  "The sunshine hurts Joe's eyes;
    He used to nap in a small white cap,
    But a big straw hat in the year-old size
    Would keep the sunshine out of his eyes.
    Have you got such a thing in the year-old size?"
Said Saks Fifth Avenue: "No."

Said I to Best & Company:
  "I think it might be wise
    When noons are red to cover Joe's head
    With a big straw hat in the year-old size.
    Can you sell me one, if you think it's wise,
    A big straw hat in the year-old size?"
Said Best & Company: "No."

Said I to the infant's mother:
  "It comes as a great surprise
    That our son Joe may never go
    In a big straw hat in the year-old size.

We had no trouble with his other supplies,
His Pyrex bottles, his spoon for eating,
His year-old pot and his year-old sheeting,
His feeding bib of heavy material
To catch the spray from the flying cereal,
Rompers to match the color of his eyes
In the year-old size;
These things were bought with the greatest ease,
The stores were willing and able to please,
His bands and his year-old shirts all fit,
His crew-neck sweater and his Arnold-Knit,
I bought him a bear and a rubber cat,
Yet now, when he needs a big straw hat,
I don't know where to go.
Doesn't it come as a great surprise
That there's no straw hat in the year-old size
To keep the sun from the little lad's eyes?"
Said the infant's mother: "No."

                                                    —E. B. White

Love Song

My own dear love, he is strong and bold
    And he cares not what comes after.
His words ring sweet as a chime of gold,
    And his eyes are lit with laughter.
He is jubilant as a flag unfurled—
    Oh, a girl, she'd not forget him.
My own dear love, he is all my world—
    And I wish I'd never met him.

My love, he's mad, and my love, he's fleet,
    And a wild young wood-thing bore him!
The ways are fair to his roaming feet,
    And the skies are sunlit for him.
As sharply sweet to my heart he seems
    As the fragrance of acacia.
My own dear love, he is all my dreams—
    And I wish he were in Asia.

My love runs by like a day in June,
  And he makes no friends of sorrows.
He'll tread his galloping rigadoon
  In the pathway of the morrows.
He'll live his days where the sunbeams start,
  Nor could storm or wind uproot him.
My own dear love, he is all my heart—
  And I wish somebody'd shoot him.

         —*Dorothy Parker*

One Perfect Rose

A single flow'r he sent me, since we met.
  All tenderly his messenger he chose;
Deep-hearted, pure, with scented dew still wet—
  One perfect rose.

I knew the language of the floweret;
  "My fragile leaves," it said, "his heart enclose."
Love long has taken for his amulet
  One perfect rose.

Why is it no one ever sent me yet
  One perfect limousine, do you suppose?
Ah no, it's always just my luck to get
  One perfect rose.

         —*Dorothy Parker*

The Searched Soul

When I consider, pro and con,
What things my love is built upon—
A curly mouth; a sinewed wrist;
A questioning brow; a pretty twist
Of words as old and tried as sin;
A pointed ear; a cloven chin;
Long, tapered limbs; and slanted eyes
Not cold nor kind nor darkly wise—

When so I ponder, here apart,
What shallow boons suffice my heart,
What dust-bound trivia capture me,
I marvel at my normalcy.

—*Dorothy Parker*

The Walrus and the Carpenter

The sun was shining on the sea,
    Shining with all his might:
He did his very best to make
    The billows smooth and bright—
And this was odd, because it was
    The middle of the night.

The moon was shining sulkily,
    Because she thought the sun
Had got no business to be there
    After the day was done—
"It's very rude of him," she said,
    "To come and spoil the fun!"

The sea was wet as wet could be,
    The sands were dry as dry.
You could not see a cloud, because
    No cloud was in the sky:
No birds were flying overhead—
    There were no birds to fly.

The Walrus and the Carpenter
    Were walking close at hand:
They wept like anything to see
    Such quantities of sand:
"If this were only cleared away,"
    They said, "it would be grand!"

"If seven maids with seven mops
    Swept it for half a year,
Do you suppose," the Walrus said,
    "That they could get it clear?"
"I doubt it," said the Carpenter,
    And shed a bitter tear.

"O oysters, come and walk with us!"
   The Walrus did beseech.
"A pleasant walk, a pleasant talk,
   Along the briny beach:
We cannot do with more than four,
   To give a hand to each."

The eldest Oyster looked at him,
   But never a word he said:
The eldest Oyster winked his eye,
   And shook his heavy head—
Meaning to say he did not choose
   To leave the oyster-bed.

But four young Oysters hurried up,
   All eager for the treat:
Their coats were brushed, their faces washed,
   Their shoes were clean and neat—
And this was odd, because, you know,
   They hadn't any feet.

Four other Oysters followed them,
   And yet another four;
And thick and fast they came at last,
   And more, and more, and more—
All hopping through the frothy waves,
   And scrambling to the shore.

The Walrus and the Carpenter
   Walked on a mile or so,
And then they rested on a rock
   Conveniently low:
And all the little Oysters stood
   And waited in a row.

"The time has come," the Walrus said,
   "To talk of many things:
Of shoes—and ships—and sealing wax—
   Of cabbages—and kings—
And why the sea is boiling hot—
   And whether pigs have wings."

"But wait a bit," the Oysters cried,
  "Before we have our chat;
For some of us are out of breath,
  And all of us are fat!"
"No hurry!" said the Carpenter.
  They thanked him much for that.

"A loaf of bread," the Walrus said,
  "Is what we chiefly need:
Pepper and vinegar besides
  Are very good indeed—
Now, if you're ready, Oysters dear,
  We can begin to feed."

"But not on us!" the Oysters cried,
  Turning a little blue.
"After such kindness, that would be
  A dismal thing to do!"
"The night is fine," the Walrus said.
  "Do you admire the view?

"It was so kind of you to come!
  And you are very nice!"
The Carpenter said nothing but
  "Cut us another slice.
I wish you were not quite so deaf—
  I've had to ask you twice!"

"It seems a shame," the Walrus said,
  "To play them such a trick.
After we've brought them out so far,
  And made them trot so quick!"
The Carpenter said nothing but
  "The butter's spread too thick!"

"I weep for you," the Walrus said:
  "I deeply sympathize."
With sobs and tears he sorted out
  Those of the largest size,
Holding his pocket-handkerchief
  Before his streaming eyes.

"O Oysters," said the Carpenter,
   "You've had a pleasant run!
Shall we be trotting home again?"
   But answer came there none—
And this was scarcely odd, because
   They'd eaten every one.

                          —*Lewis Carroll*

Lovely Lady

Lovely lady, who does so
All my waking haunt,
Tell me, tell me, do you know
What the hell you want?

Lady, to whose feet I'd bring
The world, if I could win it,
Are you sure of anything
For a single minute?

You whose eyes can kindle flame
Only Death could smother,
Tell me, please, does any dame
Differ from another?

Was the apple applesauce
Eve ate in the garden?
Aren't you all a total loss?
No? I beg your pardon!

                    —*Samuel Hoffenstein*

A Policeman's Lot

When a felon's not engaged in his employment,
   Or maturing his felonious little plans,
His capacity for innocent enjoyment
   Is just as great as any honest man's.

Our feelings we with difficulty smother
  When constabulary duty's to be done;
Ah, take one consideration with another,
  A policeman's lot is not a happy one.

When the enterprising burglar's not a-burgling,
  When the cut-throat isn't occupied in crime,
He loves to hear the little brook a-gurgling,
  And listen to the merry village chime.
When the coster's finished jumping on his mother,
  He loves to lie a-basking in the sun;
Ah, take one consideration with another,
  A policeman's lot is not a happy one.

                                          —*W. S. Gilbert*

The Yarn of the "Nancy Bell"

'Twas on the shores that round our coast
  From Deal to Ramsgate span,
That I found alone on a piece of stone
  An elderly naval man.

His hair was weedy, his beard was long,
  And weedy and long was he,
And I heard this wight on the shore recite,
  In a singular minor key:

"Oh, I am a cook and the captain bold,
  And the mate of the *Nancy* brig,
And a bo'sun tight, and a midshipmite,
  And the crew of the captain's gig."

And he shook his fists and he tore his hair,
  Till I really felt afraid,
For I couldn't help thinking the man had been drinking,
  And so I simply said:

"Oh, elderly man, it's little I know
  Of the duties of men of the sea,
And I'll eat my hand if I understand
  How you can possibly be

"At once a cook, and a captain bold,
   And the mate of the *Nancy* brig,
And a bo'sun tight, and a midshipmite,
   And the crew of the captain's gig."

Then he gave a hitch to his trousers, which
   Is a trick all seamen larn,
And having got rid of a thumping quid,
   He spun this painful yarn:

" 'Twas in the good ship *Nancy Bell*
   That we sailed to the Indian Sea,
And there on a reef we come to grief,
   Which has often occurred to me.

"And pretty nigh all the crew was drowned
   (There was seventy-seven o' soul),
And only ten of the *Nancy's* men
   Said 'Here!' to the muster-roll.

"There was me and the cook and the captain bold,
   And the mate of the *Nancy* brig,
And the bo'sun tight, and a midshipmite,
   And the crew of the captain's gig.

"For a month we'd neither wittles nor drink,
   Till a-hungry we did feel,
So we drawed a lot, and accordin' shot
   The captain for our meal.

"The next lot fell to the *Nancy's* mate,
   And a delicate dish he made;
Then our appetite with the midshipmite
   We seven survivors stayed.

"And then we murdered the bo'sun tight,
   And he much resembled pig;
Then we wittled free, did the cook and me,
   On the crew of the captain's gig.

Then only the cook and me was left,
   And the delicate question, 'Which
Of us two goes to the kettle?' arose,
   And we argued it out as sich.

"For I loved that cook as a brother, I did,
  And the cook he worshipped me;
But we'd both be blowed if we'd either be stowed
  In the other chap's hold, you see.

" 'I'll be eat if you dines off me,' says Tom.
  'Yes, that,' says I, 'you'll be,—
I'm boiled if I die, my friend,' quoth I.
  And 'Exactly so,' quoth he.

"Says he, 'Dear James, to murder me
  Were a foolish thing to do,
For don't you see that you can't cook *me*,
  While I can—and—will—cook *you!*'

"So he boils the water, and takes the salt
  And the pepper in portions true
(Which he never forgot), and some chopped shalot,
  And some sage and parsley too.

" 'Come here,' says he, with a proper pride,
  Which his smiling features tell,
' 'Twill soothing be if I let you see
  How extremely nice you'll smell.'

"And he stirred it round and round and round,
  And he sniffed at the foaming froth;
When I ups with his heels, and smothers his squeals
  In the scum of the boiling broth.

"And I eat that cook in a week or less,
  And—as I eating be
The last of his chops, why, I almost drops,
  For a vessel in sight I see.

"And I never larf, and I never smile,
  And I never lark nor play,
But sit and croak, and a single joke
  I have—which is to say:

"Oh, I am a cook and a captain bold,
  And the mate of the *Nancy* brig,
And a bo'sun tight, and a midshipmite,
  And the crew of the captain's gig!"

                                        —*W. S. Gilbert*

On the Vanity of Earthly Greatness

The tusks that clashed in mighty brawls
Of mastodons, are billiard balls.

The sword of Charlemagne the Just
Is ferric oxide, known as rust.

The grizzly bear whose potent hug
Was feared by all, is now a rug.

Great Caesar's bust is on the shelf,
And I don't feel so well myself!

—Arthur Guiterman

Mad Dogs and Englishmen

In tropical climes there are certain times of day
When all the citizens retire
To tear their clothes off and perspire.
It's one of those rules that the greatest fools obey,
Because the sun is much too sultry
And one must avoid its ultry—violet ray.
Papalaka papalaka papalaka boo,
Papalaka papalaka papalaka boo,
Digariga digariga digariga doo,
Digariga digariga digariga doo.
The natives grieve when the white men leave their huts,
Because they're obviously definitely Nuts!

Mad dogs and Englishmen
Go out in the midday sun.
The Japanese don't care to,
The Chinese wouldn't dare to,
Hindoos and Argentines sleep firmly from twelve to one.
But Englishmen detest a—Siesta.
In the Philippines there are lovely screens
To protect you from the glare.
In the Malay States there are hats like plates

Which the Britishers won't wear.
At twelve noon the natives swoon
And no further work is done,
But mad dogs and Englishmen
Go out in the midday sun.

It's such a surprise for the Eastern eyes to see,
That tho' the English are effete,
They're quite impervious to heat.
When the white man rides every native hides in glee
Because the simple creatures hope he
Will impale his solar topee—on a tree.
Bolyboly bolyboly bolyboly baa,
Bolyboly bolyboly bolyboly baa,
Habaninny habaninny habaninny haa,
Habaninny habaninny habaninny haa,
It seems such a shame when the English claim the earth
That they give rise to such hilarity and mirth.

Mad dogs and Englishmen
Go out in the midday sun.
The toughest Burmese bandit
Can never understand it.
In Rangoon the heat of noon
Is just what the natives shun.
They put their Scotch or Rye down—and lie down.
In a jungle town where the sun beats down
To the rage of man and beast,
The English garb of the English Sahib
Merely gets a bit more creased.
In Bangkok at twelve o'clock
They foam at the mouth and run,
But mad dogs and Englishmen
Go out in the midday sun.

Mad dogs and Englishmen
Go out in the midday sun.
The smallest Malay rabbit
Deplores this stupid habit.
In Hong Kong they strike a gong
And fire off a noonday gun
To reprimand each inmate—who's in late.
In the mangrove swamps where the python romps

There is peace from twelve till two.
Even caribous lie around and snooze,
For there's nothing else to do.
In Bengal, to move at all
Is seldom if ever done,
But mad dogs and Englishmen
Go out in the midday sun.

—Noel Coward

Elegy from a Country Dooryard

When blizzards around us rejoice
    And week-enders think up excuses,
How kind seems the alien voice,
    How sweet, hospitality's uses.
But once in the summertime's clutch
    With lilies and lawns to affirm it,
I often reflect there is much
    To be said for the lot of the hermit.
For scarcely on porches and pickets
    The paint of the season is dry
But hitherward, swarming like crickets,
    The Visitors hie.

They hie here, they fly here,
    The tide never ceases.
And as they draw nigh here
    They open valises.
By steamer, by clipper,
    By train they arrive here.
Youth, granny and nipper,
    They walk or they drive here
To share in our rations
    Or stay for a night
And some are relations
    (Though some we invite).

They haste for a glimpse of our acres
    En route to conventions they stop in.
Or lustily bound for the breakers
    They feel it their duty to drop in.
As gaily as amorous larks
    They bring us their brides when they marry.

They pause on their way to the Parks.
　Returning from mountains they tarry.
We never sit down to our pottage,
　We never go calm to our rest,
But lo! at the door of our cottage,
　The knock of the Guest.

Oh, look to the plumbing
　And bring down the cots.
The Campbells are coming
　And so are the Potts.
The cook's given notice,
　The car's on vacation,
But dear cousin Otis
　Just phoned from the station.
It's dear Otis, is it?
　Well, tell him, the elf,
I've gone on a visit
　To someone myself.

—Phyllis McGinley

Ode to the End of Summer

Summer, adieu.
　　　　Adieu, gregarious season.
Goodbye, 'revoir, farewell.
Now day comes late; now chillier blows the breeze on
Forsaken beach and boarded-up hotel.
Now wild geese fly together in thin lines
And Tourist Homes take down their lettered signs.

It fades—this green, this lavish interval,
This time of flowers and fruits,
Of melon ripe along the orchard wall,
Of sun and sails and wrinkled linen suits;
Time when the world seems rather plus than minus
And pollen tickles the allergic sinus.

Now fugitives to farm and shore and highland
Cancel their brief escape.
The Ferris wheel is quiet at Coney Island
And quaintness trades no longer on the Cape;

While meek-eyed parents hasten down the ramps
To greet their offspring, terrible from camps.

Turn up the steam. The year is growing older.
The maple boughs are red.
Summer, farewell. Farewell the sunburnt shoulder,
Farewell the peasant kerchief on the head.
Farewell the thunderstorm, complete with lightning,
And the white shoe that ever needeth whitening.

Farewell, vacation friendships, sweet but tenuous.
Ditto to slacks and shorts.
Farewell, O strange compulsion to be strenuous
Which sends us forth to death on tennis courts.
Farewell, Mosquito, horror of our nights;
Clambakes, iced tea, and transatlantic flights.

The zinnia withers, mortal as the tulip.
Now from the dripping glass
I'll sip no more the amateur mint julep
Nor dine al fresco on the alien grass;
Nor scale the height nor breast the truculent billow
Nor lay my head on any weekend pillow.

Unstintingly I yield myself to Autumn
And Equinoctial sloth.
I hide my swim suit in the bureau's bottom
Nor fear the fury of the after-moth.
Forswearing porch and pool and beetled garden,
My heart shall rest, my arteries shall harden.

Welcome, kind Fall, and every month with "r" in
Whereto my mind is bent.
Come, sedentary season that I star in,
O fire-lit Winter of my deep content!
Amid the snow, the sleet, the blizzard's raw gust,
I shall be cozier than I was in August.

Safe from the picnic sleeps the unlittered dell.
The last Good Humor sounds its final bell,
And all is silence.

Summer, farewell, farewell.
—Phyllis McGinley

3

TRAVEL, EXPLORATION, AND NATURE

From a Train Window

BY

THOMAS WOLFE

IT WAS a little before midnight when the youth entered the smoking room of the pullman where, despite the lateness of the hour, several men still sat. At just this moment the train had entered the State of Virginia although, of course, none of the men who sat there talking knew this.

It is true that some of them might have known had their interest and attention been directed toward this geographic fact, had they been looking for it. Just at this moment, indeed, as the train, scarcely slackening its speed, was running through the last of the Catawba towns, one of the men glanced up suddenly from the conversation in which he and the others were earnestly engaged, which was exclusively concerned with the fascinating, ever mounting prices of their property and the tempting profits undoubtedly to be derived from real estate speculation in their native town.. He had looked up quickly, casually, and absently, with that staggering indifference of prosperous men who have been so far, so often, on such splendid trains, that a trip across the continent at night toward the terrific city is no longer a grand adventure of their lives, but just a thing of custom, need, and even weariness, and who, therefore, rarely look out windows any more:

"What is this?" he said quickly. "Oh, Maysville, probably. Yes, I guess this must be Maysville," and had then returned vigorously from his brief inspection of the continent of night, a few lights, and a little town, to the enticing topic which had for several hours absorbed the interests of the group.

Nor was there any good reason why this traveller who had glanced so swiftly and indifferently from the window of the train should feel any greater interest than he showed. Certainly the briefest and most

357

casual inspection would have convinced the observer that, in Bae-
deker's celebrated phrase, there was "little here that need detain
the tourist." What the man saw in the few seconds of his observation was the quiet, dusty and sparsely lighted street of a little town
in the upper South. The street was shaded by large trees and there
were some level lawns, more trees, and some white frame houses
with spacious porches, gables, occasionally the wooden magnificence
of Georgian columns.

On everything—trees, houses, foliage, yards, and street there was
a curious loneliness of departure and October, an attentive almost
mournful waiting. And yet this dark and dusty street of the tall trees
left a haunting, curiously pleasant feeling of strangeness and familiarity. One viewed it with a queer sudden ache in the heart, a feeling of friendship and farewell, and this feeling was probably in-
tensified by the swift and powerful movement of the train which
seemed to slide past the town almost noiselessly, its wheels turning
without friction, sound, or vibrance on the pressed steel ribbons
of the rails, giving to a traveller, and particularly to a youth who
was going into the secret North for the first time, a feeling of
illimitable and exultant power, evoking for him the huge mystery
of the night and darkness, and the image of ten thousand lonely
little towns like this across the continent.

Then the train slides by the darkened vacant-looking little station
and for a moment one has a glimpse of the town's chief square and
business centre. And as he sees it he is filled again with the same
feeling of loneliness, instant familiarity, and departure. The square
is one of those anomalous, shabby-ornate, inept, and pitifully pre-
tentious places that one finds in little towns like these. But once
seen, if only for this fraction of a moment, from the windows of a
train, the memory of it will haunt one forever after.

And this haunting and lonely memory is due probably to the
combination of two things: the ghastly imitation of swarming life
and metropolitan gaiety in the scene, and the almost total absence of life itself. The impression one gets, in fact, from that
brief vision is one of frozen cataleptic silence in a world from which
all life has recently been extinguished by some appalling catastrophe. The lights burn, the electric signs wink and flash, the place
is still horribly intact in all its bleak prognathous newness, but all
the people are dead, gone, vanished. The place is a tomb of frozen

silence, as terrifying in its empty bleakness as those advertising
backdrops one saw formerly in theatres, where the splendid buildings, stores, and shops of a great street are painted in the richest
and most flattering colors, and where there is no sign of life whatever.

So was it here, save that here the illusion of the dead world gained
a hideous physical reality by its stark, staring, nakedly concrete
dimensions.

All this the boy had seen, or rather sensed, in the wink of an eye,
a moment's vision of a dusty little street, a fleeting glimpse of a
silent little square, a few hard lights, and then the darkness of the
earth again—these half-splintered glimpses were all the boy could
really see in the eye-wink that it took the train to pass the town.
And yet, all these fragmentary things belonged so completely to
all the life of little towns which he had known, that it was not as if
he had seen only a few splintered images, but rather as if the whole
nocturnal picture of the town was instantly whole and living in
his mind.

Beyond the station, parked in a line against the curb is a row of
empty motor cars, and he knows instantly that they have been left
there by the patrons of the little moving-picture theatre which ex-
plodes out of the cataleptic silence of the left-hand side of the
square into a blaze of hard white and flaming posters which seem to
cover the entire façade. Even here, no movement of life is visible,
but one who has lived and known towns like these feels for the first
time an emotion of warmth and life as he looks at the gaudy, blazing bill-beplastered silence of that front.

For suddenly he seems to see the bluish blaze of carbon light that
comes from the small slit-like vent-hole cut into the wall and can
hear again—one of the loneliest and most haunting of all sounds—
the rapid shuttering sound of the projection camera late at night, a
sound lonely, hurried, unforgettable, coming out into those cataleptic squares of silence in the little towns—as if the operator is
fairly racing through the last performance of the night like a weary
and exhausted creature whose stale, over-driven life can find no joy
in what is giving so much joy to others, and who is pressing desperately ahead toward the merciful rewards of food, sleep, and oblivion
which are already almost in his grasp.

And as he remembers this, he also suddenly sees and knows the people in the theatre, and in that instant greets them, feels his lonely kinship with them, with the whole family of the earth, and says farewell. Small, dark, lonely, silent, thirsty, and insatiate, the people of the little town are gathered there in that one small cell of radiance, warmth, and joy. There for a little space they are united by the magic spell the theatre casts upon them. They are all dark and silent leaning forward like a single mind and congeries of life, and yet they are all separate too.

Yes, lonely, silent, for a moment beautiful, he knows the people of the town are there, lifting the small white petals of their faces, thirsty and insatiate, to that magic screen: now they laugh exult- antly as their hero triumphs, weep quietly as the mother dies, the little boys cheer wildly as the rascal gets his due—they are all there in darkness, under immense immortal skies of time, small nameless creatures in a lost town on the mighty continent, and for an instant we have seen them, known them, said farewell.

Around the four sides of the square at even intervals, the new standards of the five-bulbed lamps cast down implacably upon those cataleptic pavements the cataleptic silence of their hard white light. And this, he knows, is called "the Great White Way," of which the town is proud. Somehow the ghastly, lifeless silence of that little square is imaged nowhere else so cruelly as in the harsh, white si- lence of these lights. For they evoke terribly, as nothing else can do, the ghastly vacancy of light without life. And poignantly, pitifully, and unutterably their harsh, white silence evokes the moth-like hunger of the American for hard, brilliant, blazing incandescence.

It is as if there may be in his soul the horror of the ancient dark- ness, the terror of the old immortal silences, which will not down and must be heard. It is as if he feels again the ancient fear of— what? Of the wilderness, the wet and lidless eye of shame and desola- tion feeding always on unhoused and naked sides. It is as if he fears the brutal revelation of his loss and loneliness, the furious, irreme- diable confusion of his huge unrest, his desperate and unceasing flight from the immense and timeless skies that bend above him, the huge, doorless and unmeasured vacancies of distance, on which he lives, on which, as helpless as a leaf upon a hurricane, he is driven on forever, and on which he cannot pause, which he cannot fence, wall, conquer, make his own.

Then the train, running always with its smooth, powerful, almost noiseless movement, has left the station and the square behind it. The last outposts of the town appear and vanish in patterns of small, lonely light, and there is nothing but huge and secret night before us, the lonely, everlasting earth, and presently Virginia.

And surely, now, there is little more to be seen. Surely, now, there is almost nothing that by day would be worthy of more than a glance from those great travellers who have ranged the earth, and known all its wild and stormy seas, and seen its rarest glories. And by night, now, there is nothing, nothing by night but darkness and a space we call Virginia through which the huge projectile of the train is hurtling onward in the dark.

Field and fold and gulch and hill and hollow, forest and stream and bridge and bank and cut, the huge earth, the rude earth, the wild, formless, infinitely various, most familiar, ever haunting earth, the grand and casual earth that is so brown, so harsh, so dusty, so familiar, the strange and homely earth wrought in our blood, our brain, our heart, the earth that can never be forgotten or described, is flowing by us, by us, by us in the night.

What is it that we know so well and cannot speak? What is it that we want to say and cannot tell? What is it that keeps swelling in our hearts its grand and solemn music, that is aching in our throats, that is pulsing like a strange wild grape through all the conduits of our blood, that maddens us with its exultant and intolerable joy and that leaves us tongueless, wordless, maddened by our fury to the end?

We do not know. All that we know is that we lack a tongue that could reveal, a language that could perfectly express the wild joy swelling to a music in our heart, the wild pain welling to a strong ache in our throat, the wild cry mounting to a madness in our brain, the thing, the word, the joy we know so well, and cannot speak! All that we know is that the little stations whip by in the night, the straggling little towns whip by with all that is casual, rude, familiar, ugly, and unutterable. All that we know is that the earth is flowing by us in the darkness, and that this is the way the world goes—with a field and a wood and a field! And of the huge and secret earth all we know is that we feel with all our life its texture with our foot upon it.

All that we know is that having everything we yet hold nothing, that feeling the wild song of this great earth upwelling in us we have no words to give it utterance. All that we know is that here the passionate enigma of our lives is so bitterly expressed, the furious hunger that so haunts and hurts Americans so desperately felt— that being rich, we all are yet so poor, that having an incalculable wealth we have no way of spending it, that feeling an illimitable power we yet have found no way of using it.

Therefore we hurtle onward in the dark across Virginia, we hurtle onward in the darkness down a million roads, we hurtle onward driven by our hunger down the blind and brutal tunnel of ten thousand furious and kaleidoscopic days, the victims of the cruel impulse of a million chance and fleeting moments, without a wall at which to thrust the shoulder of our strength, a roof to hide us in our nakedness, a place to build on, or a door.

Reflections on a Scientific Fishing Trip

BY

JOHN STEINBECK AND EDWARD F. RICKETTS

THE PATTERN of a book, or a day, of a trip, becomes a characteristic design. The factors in a trip by boat, the many-formed personality phases all shuffled together, changing a little to fit into the box and yet bringing their own lumps and corners, make the trip. And from all these factors your expedition has a character of its own, so that one may say of it, "That was a good, kind trip." Or, "That was a mean one." The character of the whole becomes defined and definite. We ran from collecting station to new collecting station, and when the night came and the anchor was dropped, a quiet came over the boat and the trip slept. And then we talked and speculated, talked and drank beer. And our discussions ranged from the loveliness of remembered women to the complexities of relationships in every other field. It is very easy to grow tired at collecting; the period of a low tide is about all men can endure. At first the rocks are bright and every moving animal makes his mark on the attention. The picture is wide and colored and beautiful. But after an hour and a half the attention centers weary, the colors fade, and the field is likely to narrow to an individual animal. Here one may observe his own world narrowed down until interest and, with it, observation, flicker and go out. And what if with age this weariness become permanent and observation dim out and not recover? Can this be what happens to so many men of science? Enthusiasm, interest, sharpness, dulled with a weariness until finally they retire into easy didacticism? With this weariness, this stultification of the attention centers, perhaps there comes the pained and sad memory of what the old excitement was like, and regret might turn to envy of the men who still have it. Then out of the shell of didacticism, such a used-up man might attack the unwearied, and he would have in his hands proper weapons of attack. It does seem certain that to a wearied man an error in a mass of correct data wipes out all the correctness and is a focus for attack; whereas the unwearied man, in his energy and receptivity, might consider the little dross of error a by-product of his effort. These two may balance and produce a purer thing than either in the end. These two may be the stresses which hold up the structure, but it is a sad thing to see the interest in interested men thin out and weaken and die. We have known so many professors who once carried their listeners high on their single enthusiasm, and have seen these same men finally settle back comfortably into lectures prepared years before and never vary them again. Perhaps this is the same narrowing we observe in relation to ourselves and the tide pool—a man looking at reality brings his own limitations to the world. If he has strength and energy of mind the tide pool stretches both ways, digs back to electrons and leaps space into the universe and fights out of the moment into non-conceptual time. Then ecology has a synonym which is ALL.

It is strange how the time sense changes with different peoples. The Indians who sat on the rail of the Western Flyer had a different time sense—"time-world" would be the better term—from ours. And we think we can never get into them unless we can invade that time-world, for this expanding time seems to trail an expanding universe, or perhaps to lead it. One considers the durations indicated in geology, in paleontology, and, thinking out of our time-world with its duration between time-stone and time-stone, says, "What an incredible interval!" Then, when one struggles to build some picture of astro-physical time, he is faced with a light-year, a thought-deranging duration unless the relativity of all things intervenes and time expands and contracts, matching itself relatively to the pulsings of a relative universe.

It is amazing how the strictures of the old teleologies infect our observation, causal thinking warped by hope. It was said earlier that hope is a diagnostic human trait, and this simple cortex symptom seems to be a prime factor in our inspection of our universe. For hope implies a change from a present bad condition to a future better one. The slave hopes for freedom, the weary man for rest, the hungry for food. And the feeders of hope, economic and religious, have from these simple strivings of dissatisfaction managed to create a world picture which is very hard to escape. Man grows toward perfection; animals grow toward man; bad grows toward good; and down toward up, until our little mechanism, hope, achieved in ourselves probably to cushion the shock of thought, manages to warp our whole world. Probably when our species developed the trick of memory and with it the counterbalancing projection called "the future," this shock-absorber, hope, had to be included in the series, else the species would have destroyed itself in despair. For if ever any man were deeply and unconsciously sure that his future would be no better than his past, he might deeply wish to cease to live. And out of this therapeutic poultice we build our iron teleologies and twist the tide pools and the stars into the pattern. To most men the most hateful statement possible is, "A thing is because it is." Even those who have managed to drop the leading-strings of a Sunday-school deity are still led by the unconscious teleology of their developed track. And in saying that hope cushions the shock of experience, that one trait balances the directionalism of another, a teleology is implied, unless one know or feel or think that we are here, and that without this balance, hope, our species in its blind mutation might have joined many, many others in extinction. Dr. Torsten Gislén, in his fine paper on fossil echinoderms called "Evolutional Series toward Death and Renewal," has shown that as often as not, in his studied group at least, mutations have had destructive, rather than survival value. Extending this thesis, it is interesting to think of the mutations of our own species. It is said and thought there has been none in historical times. We wonder, though, where in man a mutation might take place. Man is the only animal whose interest and whose drive are outside himself. Other animals may dig holes to live in; may weave nests or take possession of hollow trees. Some species, like bees or spiders, even create complicated homes, but they do it with the fluids and processes of their own bodies. They make little impression on the world. But the world is furrowed and cut, torn and blasted by man. Its flora has been swept away and changed; its mountains torn down by man; its flat lands littered by the debris of his living. And these changes have been wrought, not because any inherent technical ability has demanded them, but because his desire has created that technical ability. Physiological man does not require this paraphernalia to exist, but the whole man does. He is the only animal who lives outside of himself, whose drive is in external things—property, houses, money, concepts of power. He lives in his cities and his factories, in his business and job and art. But having projected himself into these external complexities, he is them. His house, his automobile are a part of him and a large part of him. This is beautifully demonstrated by a thing doctors know—that when a man loses his possessions a very common result is sexual impotence. If then the projection, the preoccupation of man, lies in external things so that even his subjectivity is a mirror of houses and cars and grain elevators, the place to look for his mutation would be in the direction of his drive, or in other words in the external things he deals with. And here we can indeed readily find evidence of mutation. The industrial revolution would then be indeed a true mutation, and the present tendency toward collectivism, whether attributed to Marx or Hitler or Henry Ford, might be as definite a mutation of the species as the lengthening neck of the evolving giraffe. For it must be that mutations take place in the direction of a species drive or preoccupation. If then this tendency toward collectivization is mutation there is no reason to suppose it is for the better. It is a rule in paleontology that ornamentation and complication precede extinction. And our mutation, of which the assembly line, the collective farm, the mechanized army, and the mass production of food are evidences or even symptoms, might well correspond to the thickening armor of the great reptiles—a tendency that can end only in extinction. If this should happen to be true, nothing stemming from thought can interfere with it or bend it. Conscious thought seems to have little effect on the action or direction of our species. There is a war now which no one wants to fight, in which no one can see a gain—a zombie war of sleep-walkers which nevertheless goes on out of all control of intelligence. Some time ago a Congress of honest men refused an appropriation of several hundreds of millions of dollars to feed our people. They said, and meant it, that the economic structure of the country would collapse under the pressure of such expenditure. And now the same men, just as honestly, are devoting many billions to the manufacture, transportation, and detonation of explosives to protect the people they would not feed. And it must go on. Perhaps it is all a part of the process of mutation and perhaps the mutation will see us done for. We have made our mark on the world, but we have really done nothing that the trees and creeping plants, ice and erosion, cannot remove in a fairly short time. And it is strange and sad and again symptomatic that most people, reading this speculation which is only speculation, will feel that it is a treason to our species so to speculate. For in spite of overwhelming evidence to the contrary, the trait of hope still controls the future, and man, not a species, but a triumphant race, will approach perfection, and, finally, tearing himself free, will march up the stars and take his place where, because of his power and virtue, he belongs: on the right hand of the $^{T}\sqrt{-1}$. From which majestic seat he will direct with pure intelligence the ordering of the universe. And perhaps when that occurs—when our species progresses toward extinction or marches into the forehead of God—there will be certain degenerate groups left behind, say, the Indians of Lower California, in the shadows of the rocks or sitting motionless in the dugout canoes. They may remain to sun themselves, to eat and starve and sleep and reproduce. Now they have many legends as hazy and magical as the mirage. Perhaps then they will have another concerning a great and god-like race that flew away in four-motored bombers to the accompaniment of exploding bombs, the voice of God calling them home.

Summit of the World: The Fight for Everest

BY

JAMES R. ULLMAN

IN THE EARLY afternoon of June 8, 1924, a man stood on a crag in the freezing sub-stratosphere, 26,000 feet above the sea, raised his eyes and stared. On a ridge high overhead he saw two human figures, black and tiny against the sky. Less than 800 feet above them was the snow-plumed summit of the highest mountain on earth.—A minute, two minutes the watcher gazed, while the climbers crept upward. Then clouds swept in upon the mountain-top, blotting them from view.

They were never seen again.

So ended the most splendid and tragic of many attempts to conquer Everest, king of mountains. To this day no one knows whether George Leigh-Mallory and Andrew Irvine reached the top before death overtook them. No one, probably, will ever know. One thing is certain: no man has ever reached the summit and returned to tell the tale.

The story of Mount Everest begins in 1852, when a clerk in the office of the Indian Trigonometrical Survey looked up excitedly from a page of figures and cried to his superior, "Sir, I have discovered the highest mountain in the world!" A careful checking of his calculations proved him right. The remote Himalayan summit listed prosaically on the charts as "Peak XV" was found to be 29,002 feet high—almost a thousand feet higher than its closest rival. Later observers corrected its altitude to 29,141 feet and named it for Sir George Everest, first Surveyor-General of India. But its supremacy remained, and remains today, unchallenged.

What began as an exercise in higher mathematics was to become, as years passed, one of the great adventures of the human spirit.

For a half century after its discovery Everest was a mountain of mystery. Tibet and Nepal, on whose frontiers it rises, were both rigorously closed to outsiders, and, far from climbing it, men of the West were unable even to approach it or learn anything about it. All they knew were the tantalizing figures of the Trigonometrical Survey. All they could see was a remote pinnacle of rock and ice, one of thousands in the great sea of peaks to the north of the Indian plain. The mountain itself—its structure and appearance, its surroundings and approaches—was as unknown as if it stood upon another planet.

Then, in the late 1890's, as we have seen, the full tide of mountaineering interest and activity turned toward the Himalayas. Soon a thin trickle of pioneers began to penetrate into the great passes and gorges where no white man had ever been before; adventurous spirits crossed the frontiers into forbidden Tibet and Nepal, disguised as Hindu or Mohammedan traders; men like Freshfield, Kellas and Longstaff turned their attention from the Sikkim and Garhwal foothills to the greater peaks that lay beyond. Slowly the net closed in about the remote, secret place where rose the highest mountain in the world. Mountaineers had heard the siren call of the mysterious and the unknown, and all the obstacles of man and nature were not going to stop them in their quest.

A lone traveler might slip into Tibet without official sanction; not so a large expedition equipped to tackle Everest. The permission of the Tibetan government was essential, and for long years this permission was not forthcoming. At last, in 1913, it appeared that the way was clear, and an exploring party was about to be organized by Freshfield; but the project was ended before it began by the outbreak of the First World War. It was not until seven years later that men were again able to turn their eyes and thoughts to the greatest mountain.

Early in 1920 the Royal Geographical Society of London and the British Alpine Club joined forces to form the Mount Everest Committee and after prolonged negotiations secured permission for an all-English party to approach and, if possible, ascend the mountain. Preparations were immediately begun on an elaborate scale. It was planned to send out two expeditions, a year apart, the first to explore and reconnoitre, the second to climb. As it eventually turned out, there was a third, and it was this final attack that was to end, a scant few hundred feet from triumph in mystery and tragedy.

But to begin at the beginning:

The 1921 reconnaissance expedition to Everest was composed of the flower of English mountaineers and explorers. The leader was Colonel C. K. Howard-Bury, who had traveled widely in Tibet and knew that mysterious land as well as any white man living. Next in command were Dr. Kellas, and A. F. R. Wollaston, who had won fame on Ruwenzori and many another far-flung mountain range. Others were Harold Raeburn, a veteran Himalayan climber, Dr. A. M. Heron, a geologist, and Major Morshead and Captain Wheeler, army surveyors who had known and traveled among the great Asiatic peaks for years. To these mature and experienced hands were added two younger men with brilliant, if briefer, mountaineering records: G. H. Bullock, of the Consular Service, and George Leigh-Mallory, master at Charterhouse College, Cambridge.

It was Mallory who was to become the foremost of the "Everesters" and the most famous mountaineer of his day. He was the only man to participate in all three of the great expeditions between 1921 and 1924, and although never the official leader (he was only thirty-eight when he died), his marvellous climbing accomplishments and his flaming spirit made him the outstanding figure in every one of them. Everest became *his* mountain, as completely as the Matterhorn, sixty years before, had been Whymper's. His climbing companions, to a man, believed that if any one of them was to achieve conquest of the highest summit on earth Mallory would be the one, and many of them, in later days, clung staunchly to the belief that he attained his goal before death overtook him in the clouds.

There was nothing of the conventional athlete about Mallory. Slight and slim, with a round boyish face, he was anything but the popular conception of a rugged outdoor man. Again like Whymper, climbing was to him not exercise or amusement, but passionate devotion, and, like all great mountaineers, less a physical than a spiritual adventure. His explanation of why men climb remains today the simplest, and at the same time perhaps the most profound, that has ever been given.

"But *why?*" a friend asked him as he set out for a renewed assault on Everest. "Why do you try to climb this mountain?"

Mallory's answer consisted of four words:

"Because it is there."

"There," however, was a remote, unknown corner of the earth, and it required an arduous journey of many weeks before the Everesters of the 1921 reconnoitering party came even within sight of their goal. Beginning at Darjeeling in the middle of May their march carried them first through the steaming tropical jungles of Sikkim, then up through great mountain passes onto the desolate, windswept wilderness of the Tibetan plateau. In a straight line the distance from Darjeeling to Everest is only a hundred miles, but they had to journey more than three hundred, threading their way among the great peaks and gorges of the eastern Himalayas.

These were days of endless toil and hardship, and they took their toll in sudden and tragic fashion. Dr. Kellas, whose health was no longer robust, strained his heart while crossing the high passes and died in the Tibetan village of Kampa Dzong. Soon after, Raeburn became seriously ill and had to return to India, with Wollaston accompanying him. These two were not able to rejoin the expedition until the middle of the summer. Everest had begun to claim her victims even before they had had so much as a glimpse of her.

The others struggled on, saddened but resolute. There were only six white men now, at the head of a vast cavalcade of Sherpa porters, Tibetan guides and helpers, ponies, donkeys, bullocks and yaks. Day after day they pushed northward and westward across as savage country as exists anywhere on the earth's surface—through sand-storms and raging, glacial torrents, across vast boulder-strewn plains and passes 20,000 feet above the sea. At night they camped under the stars or enjoyed the primitive hospitality of Buddhist mon-asteries and village headmen. Their passports from the Tibetan au-thorities in Lhassa assured them kindly and courteous treatment, but the announcement of the purpose of their journey elicited only a dubious shaking of heads and a solemn turning of prayer wheels. To these devout and superstitious orientals, Everest was more than a mountain. Chomolungma, they called it—Goddess-Mother-of-the-World. It was sacrilege, they believed, for mere mortals even to ap-proach it.

At last, late in June, the expedition arrived at the great Rongbuk Monastery, where an isolated colony of priests and hermits dwelt, some twenty miles due north of Everest. And from here, at last, they saw their mountain head on, in its titanic majesty— the first white men ever to have a close-up view of the summit of the world. "We paused," wrote Mallory, "in sheer astonishment. The sight of it banished every thought; we asked no questions and made no comment, but simply looked. . . . At the end of the valley and above the glacier Everest rises, not so much a peak as a prodigious mountain-mass. There is no complication for the eye. The highest of the world's mountains, it seems, has to make but a single gesture of magnificence to be the lord of all, vast in unchallenged and isolated supremacy. To the discerning eye other mountains are visible, giants between 23,000 and 26,000 feet high. Not one of their slenderer heads even reaches their chief's shoulder; beside Everest they escape notice—such is the pre-eminence of the greatest."

The explorers set themselves at once to their tasks, reconnoitering, surveying, studying the colossal rock-and-ice mass that towered before them and probing the possible routes to its summit. They were already at an altitude of 18,000 feet—far higher than the highest summit in the Alps or Rockies—and the slightest exertion set their lungs to heaving and their hearts to pounding. The world around them was a trackless wilderness of peaks, ridges and glaciers, and wind and snow roared down from the heights with hurricane fury. And still there remained two vertical miles of mountain soaring above them into the sky.

Working slowly around its base Mallory and Bullock discovered that Everest was constructed as an almost perfect pyramid, with three great faces and three main ridges sweeping downward from the summit like vast buttresses. The faces were all built up in tiers of precipices which no man could even dream of scaling, and the south and northwest ridges, miles in length and flanked by vertical ice-walls, appeared almost equally hopeless. In addition, the whole southern half of the mountain lay in Nepal and was therefore politically closed to them.

Only on the northeast did Mallory detect any possibilities whatever. Here, bordering the ten-thousand-foot precipice of the north face, a jagged arête descended from a great rocky shoulder near the summit to a high snow saddle on the east of the Rongbuk Glacier. The angle of the arête was steep, but not so steep that experienced mountaineers could not ascend it, and from the shoulder upward the main east ridge and the wedge-like summit pyramid seemed to present no insuperable obstacles. The first great question mark was whether a way could be found to reach the saddle.

A way was found, but the finding required two long months of planning and toil. The saddle—or North Col, as it came to be known—rose from the Rongbuk Glacier as an almost perpendicular ice-wall 4000 feet high, and even the dauntless Mallory realized that it could never be scaled from that side. His only hope was that the far, or eastern, side might prove more feasible. The next and greatest job was to get there.

The Rongbuk Glacier was a narrow avenue of ice walled in by tremendous mountains in which no break appeared to exist. Actually there was a break, and if Mallory had found it he would have been able to reach the far side of the col in a day or two. But it was so tiny and obscure a passage that he missed it. The result was a circuitous journey of more than a hundred miles, back across the plateaus and passes which they had traversed before, and then south and west again toward the base of Everest.

This last stage of their journey took them through a mountain wonderland such as no man had ever been privileged to look upon before. The Kama and Kharta valleys, up which they pushed, were great gashes in the earth, so deep at their lower ends that their floors were covered with lush, tropical vegetation, so lofty at their apexes that the explorers found themselves struggling in snow up their armpits. At their head loomed the mighty upper slopes of Everest, flanked by the pinnacles of Makalu, Chomolönzo and Lhotse, themselves among the highest summits in the world.

At last, after innumerable delays and hardships, the climbers reached the apex of the Kharta Valley—a wild, blizzard-racked pass known as the Lhakpa La, 22,000 feet above the sea. From here they could see the long-sought eastern approach to the North Col, and it was indeed as Mallory had hoped: the great saddle of snow and ice rose on this side to a height of only 1500 feet above the glacier floor, as against 4000 feet on the Rongbuk side. It appeared not impossible to scale. A cheer went up from the lips of the frozen, exhausted men, for they knew they had found the key to the mountain.

By this time it was late August and the brief Himalayan summer was almost over. The work of the expedition, however, would not be done until they had reached the col, and so the three strongest climbers, Mallory, Bullock and Wheeler, pushed on over the Lhakpa La, down its far side and across the glacier below. On their way they made a second important discovery: that there was, after all, a passage from the Rongbuk Glacier to the eastern side of the col. It was of course too late now for it to be of any help to them that year, but the narrow defile was used by all subsequent Everest expeditions.

Once found, the eastern wall of the North Col did not prove a particularly formidable obstacle—at least not in 1921. The outer surface of the wall was composed of frozen avalanche snow, and up it the three climbers hacked their way, slanting carefully to right and left to avoid the gaping blue abysses with which it was scarred. At noon on the twenty-fourth of August they stood upon the top, at an altitude of 23,000 feet—higher than any mountain-top in the world outside of the Himalayas.

The pinnacle of Everest, however, was still 6000 feet above them and two and a half miles away. Scanning the northeast ridge, the shoulder and the summit pyramid, they saw that Mallory's earlier surmise had been right: the upper mountain slanted upward in a fairly easy gradient of rock and snow, seeming to present neither difficulty nor great danger. The temptation was strong to venture still higher, but they were almost done in from their exertions as it was and realized they could not hope to match their strength against the wild wind and blizzards of the exposed heights. After taking as complete observations as they could they descended from the col, rejoined their companions on the Lhakpa La and began the long return journey to India.

The members of the 1921 expedition had never once actually set foot on Everest itself; their highest point on the North Col was where subsequent expeditions would begin their real work. Yet, except for the untimely death of Dr. Kellas, the venture had been a complete and distinguished success. The trail to the mountain had been blazed, the weakness in its armor found. Everyone was agreed that, as far as actual climbing problems were concerned, the greatest mountain *might* be climbed. That "might" was all the Everesters needed. No sooner had the reconnaissance party returned to England than preparations for the real assault began.

On May 1, 1922, the first Mount Everest climbing expedition pitched its base camp within sight of the great lamasery near the snout of the Rongbuk Glacier. It was composed of thirteen Englishmen, sixty hillmen from Nepal and northern India, a hundred-odd Tibetan helpers and more than three hundred pack animals—a veritable army in miniature. Remote and isolated Tibet had not witnessed such a sight in the thousands of years of its history.

In the preceding year the purpose had been to explore, reconnoitre and learn. Now, however, all else was to be subordinated to one great purpose: to reach the top of Everest. To this end, the personnel of the party had been almost completely changed, with only Mallory and Morshead remaining from the original group. The new leader was Brigadier-General Charles G. Bruce, a veteran of the British army in India and a far-ranging Himalayan explorer over a period of many years. Colonel E. T. Strutt, another noted mountaineer, was second in command, and Dr. T. E. Longstaff, although now too old for the highest climbing, was on hand to lend the benefit of his wide experience. The others included Lieutenant-Colonel E. F. Norton, Dr. T. Howard Somervell and Dr. Wakefield; Captains Geoffrey Bruce, George Finch and C. G. Morris; C. G. Crawford, of the India Civil Service; and, as official photographer, Captain John Noel. Of these, Norton, Somervell and Finch were climbers in the prime of their careers and were expected, together with Mallory, to make the final bid for the summit.

As we have repeatedly seen, the climbing of a great mountain is far more than a matter of putting one foot in front of the other and moving uphill. Indeed, in the case of a giant like Everest, climbing in itself may be said to be of merely secondary importance. Two-thirds of the 1922 expedition's battles had to be fought before a single man set foot on the mountain proper.

First, there was the all-important problem of weather. No man, to be sure, could hope to prophesy the day-by-day variations of calm and storm in those wild Himalayan uplands, but the observations of the previous year had convinced everyone concerned that Everest was climbable, if at all, only during a very brief period of the year. Until early May the whole region was locked in savage, blizzard-driven winter; after the middle of June the eastern Himalayas received the full brunt of the Indian monsoon and remained through the summer a death-trap of snow and sleet and rotten, melting ice. A period of only some six weeks intervened in which the climbers might hope for reasonably clear skies, a minimum of wind and at least a fighting chance for success. It was therefore not accident, but careful planning, that brought the 1922 expedition to the skirts of Everest on May first. Their next great task was to get onto the mountain itself as quickly as possible. The race with the monsoon was on.

For two long weeks climbers and porters crept back and forth along the vast northern glaciers, transporting food, supplies and equipment. Mallory, in an analysis of the problems of Everest, had likened a climbing expedition to a ladder, in which the higher rungs were useless unless the rungs below were dependable and strong. It was these lower rungs which now had to be fashioned— a chain of camps, not more than an easy day's march apart, extending as high as human strength could take them. Camp I was pitched between the Rongbuk and East Rongbuk Glaciers, in the narrow defile which Mallory had missed the previous year. Camp II was established halfway up the East Rongbuk Glacier, and Camp III near its head, close by the eastern wall of the North Col. The older and less acclimatized members of the party were left behind to staff and maintain communication between these lower stations, while the stronger climbers and porters proceeded to the establishment of Camp IV on top of the col.

This in itself was a feat more difficult than the ascent to the summit of a lesser mountain. Mallory and Somervell led the way, chopping countless steps in the glaring ice-cliffs, edging their way around bottomless, dark crevasses and snow-masses as vast as toppled buildings. The porters followed, straining on the ropes, scarcely more than creeping under their heavy loads. On their return to civilization the Everesters were unanimous in declaring that without these sturdy Sherpas from the hill country of northern India their assault on the mountain would have bogged down before it even began. Unlike the Tibetans, who refused even to set foot on Chomolungma, the haunted mountain, these men climbed doggedly and cheerfully to heights where no men had ever stood before and in 1924 achieved the almost incredible feat of carrying packs and establishing a camp at an altitude of more than 27,000 feet. "Tigers," the Englishmen called them, and they richly deserved the name.

With a huddle of tiny green tents established on the col, the assault on Everest proper was at last at hand. Mallory, Somervell, Norton and Morshead were selected for the first attempt, and at dawn on May twentieth, accompanied by a group of the strongest porters, they set out for the unknown, untrodden heights. The cold was almost unendurable; the wild west wind roared down upon them like an invisible avalanche; and their goal was still a mile above them, remote and tantalizing in the sky. But their hopes and hearts were high. "No end," wrote Mallory, "was visible or even conceivable to this kingdom of adventure!"

Hour after hour the climbers toiled up the northeast ridge. The going underfoot was not technically difficult, but constant care was necessary to guard against a slip on the steep, ice-coated slabs. The wind tore at them relentlessly, and, worse yet, as they ascended it grew more difficult to breathe. Later expeditions were to learn an important lesson from their ordeal and allow themselves more time for acclimatization before storming the almost oxygen-less heights.

They had hoped to pitch their highest camp close under the northeast shoulder, but at 25,000 feet cold and exhaustion forced a halt. Sending their faithful "tigers" down to Camp IV they pitched their two tiny tents in as sheltered a spot as they could find and crawled into their sleeping bags. All night they lay there, while the wind howled and the mercury in their thermometers dropped to seven degrees above zero.

At first daylight they were moving upward again through thick mist and gusts of windblown snow. After an hour's climbing Morshead reached the limit of his endurance and had to turn back, but Mallory, Somervell and Norton still struggled on. Their progress consisted of fifteen or twenty minutes' slow, painful climbing, a long rest, another period of climbing, another rest. Before long their hands and feet grew numb and their mouths hung wide open, gasping for air. Even their minds and senses, they reported later, were affected by oxygen starvation: ambition, judgment and will disappeared, and they moved forward mechanically, like men in a trance.

By mid-afternoon they had reached a height of 27,000 feet. They had ascended two-thirds of the vertical distance between the North Col and the summit and were a full 2400 feet higher than any man had ever stood before. Physically they could have gone even

farther, but to have done so at that late hour, without food or shelter, would have been suicidal. Too exhausted to feel disappointment, or any other emotion, they turned their backs on their goal
and began the descent.

As it was they were lucky to return to their companions alive.
At Camp V they found Morshead so crippled by frostbite that he
had almost to be carried down to the col. Then, crossing a steep
snow-slope lower down, one of them slipped, and the four were
carried to the very brink of the precipitous north face before Mallory succeeded in jamming his ax into the snow and holding the
rope fast. As a crowning misfortune, night overtook them before
they reached the col, and it was past midnight when at last they
groped their way into their tents.

The same day that the first attempt ended in heroic failure, the
second was launched. The climbers now were Finch, Geoffrey Bruce
and Tejber Bura, a Gurkha corporal who had proved himself a first-
class mountaineer. Captain Noel ascended with them to the North
Col camp, where he remained in reserve, and twelve porters set up
a fifth camp for them at 25,500 feet—a full 500 feet higher than
where Mallory and his companions had bivouacked a few nights
before. This headstart for the final dash, added to the advantage
that they were supplied with tanks of oxygen to aid their breathing,
gave the second party high hopes of success.

They were hopes, however, that were to be quickly shattered. No
sooner had Finch, Bruce and Tejbir crawled into their tent for the
night than a blizzard swooped down upon the mountain. For more
than twenty-four hours the wind shrieked, the snow drove down in
an almost solid mass, and the climbers struggled desperately with
ripping canvas and breaking guy-ropes. It was little less than a
miracle that men, tent and all were not blown bodily off the mountain into the mile-deep gulfs below.

After two nights and a day the weather at last cleared, and the
climbers made their delayed start in a still, frozen dawn. At 26,000
feet Tejbir collapsed and had to return to the tent, Finch and
Bruce continuing. The oxygen which they carried spared them the
tortures which their predecessors had endured, but this advantage
was more than nullified by the thirty pounds of tank and apparatus
which each carried on his back. Worse than this, Bruce's apparatus
was almost the cause of his death, for without warning, at an alti-

tude of about 26,500 feet, something went wrong with it and the flow of oxygen stopped. Accustomed by then to artificial breathing, Bruce would have been able to live for only a few minutes without it. Finch, however, quickly connected Bruce's mouthpiece to his own tank, and between them they were able to make the necessary repairs.

Hoping to escape the full brunt of the wind, they left the northeast ridge a few hundred feet below the shoulder and headed diagonally upward across the smooth slabs and powdered snow of Everest's north face. They made remarkable progress and by midday had gained a point only half a mile from the summit and a scant 1900 feet below it. But here they reached the end of their tether. Their bodies and brains were numb; their limbs were ceasing to function and their eyes to focus; each additional foot upward would probably be a foot that they could never return. They turned back defeated, like their companions before them, but in defeat they had set a new world's climbing record of 27,235 feet.

One more attempt the expedition of 1922 was to make. It was doomed to be the most short-lived and disastrous one that has ever been made against the king of mountains.

The dreaded monsoon came early that year, and already in the first days of June dark banks of clouds appeared above the mountains to the south and the snow fell in billowing drifts on the upper slopes of Everest. A final thrust, if it were to be made at all, must be made quickly.

The main base, at which the whole expedition now gathered, resembled a field hospital more than a mountaineers' camp; of the high climbers only Mallory and Somervell were fit for further work. Resolved on a last try, however, they again pushed up the glaciers and, with Crawford, Wakefield and a squad of porters helping, resumed the laborious task of packing supplies up to the North Col. A night of sub-zero temperature had apparently solidified the fresh snow on the great wall, and they had reason to believe the going would be comparatively easy.

Starting early one morning from Camp III, Mallory, Somervell, Crawford and fourteen heavily loaded porters began the ascent. The Englishmen were on one rope, cutting steps and leading the way; three roped groups of porters followed. All went well until they had reached a point some 600 feet below the summit of the col.

Then suddenly they were startled by a deep rumbling sound beneath them. An instant later there was a dull, ominous explosion, and the rampart of snow and ice to which they clung seemed to shudder along its entire face. An ocean of soft, billowing snow poured down upon them, knocked them from their feet and swept them away.

By miraculous good fortune, Mallory, Somervell and Crawford were not in the direct path of the avalanche. Caught by its flank, they were carried down a distance of some fifty feet; but by striking out like swimmers they were at last able to struggle to the surface and gain a secure foothold. Not so the unfortunate porters. Struck by the full force of the snowslide, they were catapulted down the steep slope to the lip of a sheer ice-wall below. A moment before there had been a gaping crevasse beneath the wall; now it was filled by the avalanche. Hurtling over the brink, the porters plunged into the soft, hissing sea of snow, disappearing from sight one by one as thousands of more tons poured down after them.

Grim and heroic work was carried out on the ice-wall that day. Hour after hour the climbers floundered through the great drifts, burrowing, straining at ropes, expending their last reserve of strength to find and rescue the buried porters. One or two they found almost uninjured. A few more, who at first appeared dead from suffocation, they were able to revive. But seven were beyond help. To this day their bodies lie entombed in the snow and ice beneath the North Col, tragic victims of the wrath of the greatest mountain.

So the 1922 attack on Everest ended, not only in defeat but in disaster. Any further attempt on the peak that year was unthinkable, and it was a silent, saddened band of mountaineers who, a few days later, began the long trek across Tibet toward India and home. Behind them the summit of the greatest mountain loomed white and lonely in the sky, its snow-plume streaming in the wild west wind.

The curtain drops for two years on Chomolungma, Goddess-Mother-of-the-World. No expedition was sent out in 1923, but the struggle was by no means at an end. The Mount Everest Committee continued with its work—planning, financing, organizing—and in late March of 1924 a third expedition set out from Darjeeling on the high, wild trail to the heart of the Himalayas. Before it returned it was destined to write the most famous chapter in the history of mountaineering.

Several of the old Everesters were back again in harness: the indefatigable Mallory. of course; Somervell, Norton and Geoffrey Bruce; Noel with his cameras. General Bruce had again been appointed leader, but early in the march through Tibet he was stricken with malaria and had to return to India while Norton carried on as first-in-command. New recruits included N. E. Odell, the geologist, who twelve years later was to reach the top of Nanda Devi; E. O. Shebbeare, of the Indian Forest Service, as transport officer; Major R. W. G. Hingston as physician; Beetham and Hazard, both experienced mountaineers, and Andrew Irvine, young and powerful Oxford oarsman. In addition to these were the usual retinue of native porters and helpers, among them many of the veteran "tigers" from the 1922 attempt. Almost three hundred men, all told, were in the party when at the end of April it set up its base camp beside the great moraines of the now familiar Rongbuk Glacier.

The preliminary moves of the campaign were carried out according to the same plan as before—but more methodically and rapidly. The first three advance camps were established a day's march apart on the glaciers, and within two weeks the advance guard was ready to tackle the North Col. The whole organization was functioning like an oiled machine; there were no accidents or illness, and the weather was fine. According to their schedule they would be on the northeast ridge by the middle of May and have almost a full month for climbing before the arrival of the monsoon. Even the most sceptical among them, staring eagerly at the heights above, could not but believe that Everest at last was theirs.

This time, however, misfortune struck even before they reached the mountain.

Scarcely had Camp III been set up below the col than a blizzard swept down from the north, wrecking everything in its path, turning camps and communication lines into a shambles. The porters, many of them caught unprepared and without adequate clothing or shelter, suffered terribly from exposure and exhaustion. Two of them died. The climbers, who were supposed to be conserving their energies for the great effort higher up, wore themselves out in their efforts to save men and supplies. Two weeks after the vanguard had left the base camp, full of strength and optimism, they were back again where they started, frostbitten, battered and fagged out.

A major blow had been dealt their chances for success, but the Everesters pulled in their belts and went at it again. The porters' drooping spirits were raised by a blessing from the Holy Lama of the Rongbuk Monastery, and a few days later a second assault was begun. At the beginning all went well, and the three glacier camps were re-established and provisioned in short order. But trouble began again on the great ice-wall beneath the North Col. The storms and avalanches of two years had transformed the thousand-foot face into a wild slanting chaos of cliffs and chasms. No vestige of their former route remained.

Then followed days of killing labor. Thousands of steps had to be chopped in the ice and snow. An almost perpendicular chimney, a hundred feet high, had to be negotiated. Ladders and ropes had to be installed so that the porters could come up with their loads. There were many narrow escapes from disaster, notably on one occasion when Mallory, descending the wall alone, plunged through a snow-bridge into a gaping hole beneath. Luckily his ice-ax jammed against the sides of the crevasse after he had fallen only ten feet, for below him was only blue-black space. As it was, his companions were all too far away to hear his shouts for help and he was barely able to claw his way upward to the surface snow and safety.

At last, however, the route up the wall was completed. The body of climbers retired to Camp III, at its foot, for a much-needed rest, leaving Hazard and twelve porters in the newly established camp on the col. During the night the mercury fell to twenty-four below zero and at dawn a heavy snowfall began; but Geoffrey Bruce and Odell nevertheless decided to ascend to the col. They did not get far. Halfway up they encountered Hazard and eight of the porters coming down. They were near collapse after the night of frightful cold and wind on the exposed col. Worse yet, four of the porters were still up above, having absolutely refused to budge downward over the treacherous fresh snow of the chimney.

A sombre council of war ensued at Camp III. Snow and wind were now driving down the mountain in wild blasts, and it was obvious that the marooned men could not survive for long. All plans had to be set aside and every effort devoted to getting them down.

What followed constitutes one of the most remarkable and courageous rescues in mountaineering annals. Mallory, Norton and Somervell, the three outstanding climbers of the expedition, fought their way up the ice-wall and came out at last upon a steep snow-slope a short distance below the top and immediately above a gaping crevasse. At the top of the slope the porters huddled, half-dead from exposure, but afraid to move. The snow between them and the rescuing party was loose and powdery, liable to crumble away at any moment.

At this point Somervell insisted on taking the lead. Roping up, he crept toward the porters along the upper lip of the crevasse, while Mallory and Norton payed out behind him. But the rope's two hundred feet were not enough, when he had reached its end he was still ten yards short of the men. There was nothing for it but that they must risk the unbridged stretch on their own. After long persuasion two of them began edging across. And made it. Somervell passed them along the rope to Mallory and Norton. Then the other two started over, but at their first step the snow gave way and they began sliding toward the abyss below. Only a patch of solid snow saved them. They brought up at the very edge of the crevasse, gasping, shaken, unable to move an inch.

Now Somervell called into action all his superb talents as a mountaineer. He jammed his ice-ax into the snow and, untying the rope from his waist, passed it around the ax and strained it to its fullest length. Then he lowered himself down the slope until he was clinging to its last strands with one hand. With the other he reached out and, while the snow shuddered ominously underfoot, seized each porter in turn by the scruff of the neck and hauled him up to safety. Within a few hours climbers and porters were back in Camp III, all of them still alive, but little more.

After this harrowing experience a few days' rest at lower altitudes was absolutely necessary, and for the second time in two weeks the Everesters found themselves driven back to the base camp. Their situation could scarcely have been more discouraging. They had planned to be on the northeast ridge by the middle of May, and now it was already June and no man had yet set foot on the mountain proper. In another ten days, at most, the monsoon would blow in and all hopes of success would be gone. They must strike hard and strike fast, or go down again to defeat.

The next week witnessed climbing such as the world had never seen before.

The plan called for an assault in continuous waves, each climbing party consisting of two men, each attempt to begin the day after the preceding one. The base of operations was to be Camp IV on the North Col. Camp V was to be set up on the ridge, near the site of the 1922 bivouac, and a sixth camp higher yet—as near to the summit as the porters could possibly take it. The climbers believed that the establishment of Camp VI was the key to the ascent; the experiences of the previous expedition had convinced them that the top could be reached only if the final "dash" were reduced to not more than 2000 feet. In the first fine weather they had experienced in weeks the band of determined men struggled back up the glaciers.

Mallory and Geoffrey Bruce were chosen for the first attack. With Odell, Irvine and nine porters they reached the North Col safely, spent the night there, and the next morning struck out up the ridge, accompanied by eight of the "tigers." Odell, Irvine and one helper remained on the col in support. The climbers made good progress the first day and set up their tents at 25,300 feet—a mere 200 feet lower than the highest camp of 1922. A night of zero cold and shrieking wind, however, was too much for the porters, and the next morning no amount of persuasion would induce them to go higher. Seething with frustration, Mallory and Bruce were forced to descend with them.

Meanwhile the second team of Norton and Somervell, had started up from the col, according to plan. They passed the first party on its way down, reached Camp V and spent the night there. In the morning their porters, too, refused at first to go on, but after four solid hours of urging three of them at last agreed to make a try. The work they subsequently did that day has seldom been matched anywhere for endurance, courage and loyalty. Step by gasping step they struggled upward with their packs—freezing, leaden-footed, choking for air—until at last Camp VI was pitched at the amazing altitude of 26,800 feet. Their task completed, they then descended to the North Col, to be hailed as heroes by all below: Lhakpa Chede, Napoo Yishay and Semchumbi, greatest of all "tigers."

That night Norton and Somervell slept in a single tiny tent,

higher than men had ever slept before. Their hearts now were
pounding with more than the mere physical strain of their exertions: the long dreamed-of summit loomed in the darkness only
2300 feet above them; victory was at last within their reach. Carefully, for the hundredth time, they reviewed their plans for the
final day. There were two opinions in the expedition as to the best
route to be followed. Mallory and some of the others were in favor
of ascending straight to the northeast shoulder and then following the crest of the main east ridge to the base of the summit
pyramid. Norton and Somervell, however, believed that by keeping a few hundred feet below the ridge they would not only find
easier climbing, but also escape the full fury of the west wind; and
it was this route that they now determined to take.

Dawn of the next day broke clear and still. By full sunrise they
were on their way, creeping upward and to the west over steeply
tilted, snow-powdered slabs. As they had hoped, they were protected
from the wind, but the cold was bitter and both men coughed and
gasped in the thin, freezing air. They could take only a dozen
steps in succession before pausing to rest. While moving, they were
forced to take from four to ten breaths for each single step. Yet
they kept going for five hours: to 27,000 feet—27,500—28,000—

At noon Somervell succumbed. His throat was a throbbing knot
of pain and it was only by the most violent effort that he was able
to breathe at all. Another few minutes of the ordeal would have
been the end of him. Sinking down on a small ledge in a paroxysm
of coughing, he gestured to his companion to go on alone.

With the last ounce of his strength Norton tried. An hour's
climbing brought him to a great couloir, or gully, which cuts the
upper slopes of Everest between the summit pyramid and the
precipices of the north face below. The couloir was filled with soft,
loose snow, and a slip would have meant a 10,000-foot plunge to
the Rongbuk Glacier. Norton crossed it safely, but, clinging feebly
to the ledges on the far side, he knew that the game was up. His
head and heart were pounding as if any moment they might literally
explode. In addition, he had begun to see double, and his leaden
feet would no longer move where his will directed them. In his
clouded consciousness he was just able to realize that to climb
farther would be to die.

For a few moments Norton stood motionless. He was at an altitude of 28,126 feet—higher than any man had ever stood before; so high that the greatest mountain range on earth, spreading endlessly to the horizon, seemed flattened out beneath him. Only a few yards above him began the culminating pyramid of Everest. To his aching eyes it seemed to present an easy slope—a mere thousand feet of almost snow-free slanting rock beckoning him upward to the shining goal. If only his body possessed the strength of his will; if only he were more than human—

Somehow Norton and Somervell got down the terrible slopes of Everest. By nine-thirty that night they were back in the North Col camp in the ministering hands of their companions, safe, but more dead than alive. Somervell was a seriously sick man. Norton was suffering the tortures of snow-blindness and did not regain his sight for several days. Both had given all they had. That it was not enough is surely no reflection on two of the most determined and courageous mountaineers who ever lived.

Norton and Somervell's assault was the next-to-last in the adventure of 1924. One more was to come—and, with it, mystery and tragedy.

Bitterly chagrined at the failure of his first effort, Mallory was determined to have one last fling before the monsoon struck. Everest was *his* mountain, more than any other man's. He had pioneered the way to it and blazed the trail to its heights; his flaming spirit had been the principal driving force behind each assault; the conquest of the summit was the great dream of his life. His companions, watching him now, realized that he was preparing for his mightiest effort.

Mallory moved with characteristic speed. With young Andrew Irvine as partner he started upward from the col the day after Norton and Somervell had descended. They spent the first night at Camp V and the second at Camp VI, at 26,800 feet. Unlike Norton and Somervell, they planned to use oxygen on the final dash and to follow the crest of the northeast ridge instead of traversing the north face to the couloir. The ridge appeared to present more formidable climbing difficulties than the lower route, particularly near the base of the summit pyramid where it buckled upward in two great rock-towers which the Everesters called the First and Second Steps. Mallory, however, was all for the frontal attack and

had frequently expressed the belief that the steps could be surmounted. The last "tigers" descending that night from the highest
camp to the col brought word that both climbers were in good condition and full of hope for success.

One man only was to have another glimpse of Mallory and Irvine.

On the morning of June eighth—the day set for the assault on the
summit—Odell, the geologist, who had spent the night alone at
Camp V, set out for Camp VI with a rucksack of food. The day
was as warm and windless as any the expedition had experienced,
but a thin gray mist clung to the upper reaches of the mountain,
and Odell could see little of what lay above him. Presently, however, he scaled the top of a small crag at about 26,000 feet, and,
standing there, he stopped and stared. For a moment the mist
cleared. The whole summit ridge and final pyramid of Everest were
unveiled, and high above him, on the very crest of the ridge, he
saw two tiny figures outlined against the sky. They appeared to
be at the base of one of the great steps, not more than seven or
eight hundred feet below the final pinnacle. As Odell watched,
the figures moved slowly upward. Then, as suddenly as it had
parted, the mist closed in again, and they were gone.

The feats of endurance that Odell performed during the next
forty-eight hours are unsurpassed by those of any mountaineer.
That same day he went to Camp VI with his load of provisions, and
then even higher, watching and waiting. But the mountain-top remained veiled in mist and there was no sign of the climbers returning. As night came on, he descended all the way to the col,
only to start off again the following dawn. Camp V was empty. He
spent a solitary night there in sub-zero cold and the next morning
ascended again to Camp VI. It was empty too. With sinking heart
he struggled upward for another thousand feet, searching and shouting, to the very limit of human endurance. The only answering
sound was the deep moaning of the wind. The great peak above
him loomed bleakly in the sky, wrapped in the loneliness and
desolation of the ages. All hope was gone. Odell descended to the
highest camp and signalled the tidings of tragedy to the watchers
far below.

So ended the second attempt on Everest—and, with it, the lives
of two brave men. The bodies of George Mallory and Andrew

Irvine lie somewhere in the vast wilderness of rock and ice that guards the summit of the world. Where and how death overtook them no one knows. And whether victory came before the end no one knows either. Our last glimpse of them is through Odell's eyes —two tiny specks against the sky, fighting upward.

The rest is mystery.

The Headlong Wave

BY

HENRY BESTON

I

I AM GOING to try my hand at something that I do not recall ever having encountered either in a periodical or in a book, namely, a chapter on the ways, the forms, and the sounds of ocean near a beach. Friends are forever asking me about the surf on the great beach and if I am not sometimes troubled or haunted by its sound. To this I reply that I have grown unconscious of the roar, and though it sounds all day long in my waking ears, and all night long in my sleeping ones, my ears seldom send on the long tumult to the mind. I hear the roar the instant I wake in the morning and return to consciousness, I listen to it a while consciously, and then accept and forget it; I hear it during the day only when I stop again to listen, or when some change in the nature of the sound breaks through my acceptance of it to my curiosity.

They say here that great waves reach this coast in threes. Three great waves, then an indeterminate run of lesser rhythms, then three great waves again. On Celtic coasts it is the seventh wave that is seen coming like a king out of the grey, cold sea. The Cape tradition, however, is no half-real, half-mystical fancy, but the truth itself. Great waves do indeed approach this beach by threes. Again and again have I watched three giants roll in one after the other out of the Atlantic, cross the outer bar, break, form again, and follow each other in to fulfillment and destruction on this solitary beach. Coast guard crews are all well aware of this triple rhythm and take advantage of the lull that follows the last wave to launch their boats.

It is true that there are single giants as well. I have been roused by them in the night. Waked by their tremendous and unexpected

crash, I have sometimes heard the last of the heavy overspill, sometimes only the loud, withdrawing roar. After the roar came a briefest
pause, and after the pause the return of ocean to the night's long
cadences. Such solitary titans, flinging their green tons down upon a
quiet world, shake beach and dune. Late one September night, as I
sat reading, the very father of all waves must have flung himself
down before the house, for the quiet of the night was suddenly over-
turned by a gigantic, tumbling crash and an earthquake rumbling;
the beach trembled beneath the avalanche, the dune shook, and my
house so shook in its dune that the flame of a lamp quivered and
pictures jarred on the wall.

The three great elemental sounds in nature are the sound of rain,
the sound of wind in a primeval wood, and the sound of outer ocean
on a beach. I have heard them all, and of the three elemental voices,
that of ocean is the most awesome, beautiful, and varied. For it is a
mistake to talk of the monotone of ocean or of the monotonous
nature of its sound. The sea has many voices. Listen to the surf,
really lend it your ears, and you will hear in it a world of sounds:
hollow boomings and heavy roarings, great watery tumblings and
tramplings, long hissing seethes, sharp rifle-shot reports, splashes,
whispers, the grinding undertone of stones, and sometimes vocal
sounds that might be the half-heard talk of people in the sea. And
not only is the great sound varied in the manner of its making, it is
also constantly changing its tempo, its pitch, its accent, and its
rhythm, being now loud and thundering, now almost placid, now
furious, now grave and solemn-slow, now a simple measure, now a
rhythm monstrous with a sense of purpose and elemental will.
Every mood of the wind, every change in the day's weather, every
phase of the tide—all these have subtle sea musics all their own.
Surf of the ebb, for instance, is one music, surf of the flood another,
the change in the two musics being most clearly marked during the
first hour of a rising tide. With the renewal of the tidal energy, the
sound of the surf grows louder, the fury of battle returns to it as it
turns again on the land, and beat and sound change with the renewal of the war.

Sound of surf in these autumnal dunes—the continuousness of it,
sound of endless charging, endless incoming and gathering, endless
fulfilment and dissolution, endless fecundity, and endless death. I
have been trying to study out the mechanics of that mighty reso-

nance. The dominant note is the great spilling crash made by each arriving wave. It may be hollow and booming, it may be heavy and churning, it may be a tumbling roar. The second fundamental sound is the wild seething cataract roar of the wave's dissolution and the rush of its foaming waters up the beach—this second sound *diminuendo*. The third fundamental sound is the endless dissolving hiss of the inmost slides of foam. The first two sounds reach the ear as a unisonance—the booming impact of the tons of water and the wild roar of the up-rush blending—and this mingled sound dissolves into the foam-bubble hissing of the third. Above the tumult, like birds, fly wisps of watery noise, splashes and counter splashes, whispers, seething, slaps, and chucklings. An overtone sound of other breakers, mingled with a general rumbling, fills earth and sea and air.

Here do I pause to warn my reader that although I have recounted the history of a breaker—an ideal breaker—the surf process must be understood as mingled and continuous, waves hurrying after waves, interrupting waves, washing back on waves, overwhelming waves. Moreover, I have described the sound of a high surf in fair weather. A storm surf is mechanically the same thing, but it grinds, and this same long, sepulchral grinding—sound of utter terror to all mariners—is a development of the second fundamental sound; it is the cry of the breaker water roaring its way ashore and dragging at the sand. A strange underbody of sound when heard through the high, wild screaming of a gale.

Breaking waves that have to run up a steep tilt of the beach are often followed by a dragging, grinding sound—the note of the baffled water running downhill again to the sea. It is loudest when the tide is low and breakers are rolling beach stones up and down a slope of the lower beach.

I am, perhaps, most conscious of the sound of surf just after I have gone to bed. Even here I read myself to drowsiness, and, reading, I hear the cadenced trampling roar filling all the dark. So close is the Fo'castle to the ocean's edge that the rhythm of sound I hear oftenest in fair weather is not so much a general tumult as an endless arrival, overspill, and dissolution of separate great seas. Through the dark, mathematic square of the screened half window, I listen to the rushes and the bursts, the tramplings, and the long, intermingled thunderings, never wearying of the sonorous and universal sound.

Away from the beach, the various sounds of the surf melt into one great thundering symphonic roar. Autumnal nights in Eastham village are full of this ocean sound. The "summer people" have gone, the village rests and prepares for winter, lamps shine from kitchen windows, and from across the moors, the great levels of the marsh, and the bulwark of the dunes resounds the long wintry roaring of the sea. Listen to it a while, and it will seem but one remote and formidable sound; listen still longer and you will discern in it a symphony of breaker thunderings, an endless, distant, elemental cannonade. There is beauty in it, and ancient terror. I heard it last as I walked through the village on a starry October night; there was no wind, the leafless trees were still, all the village was abed, and the whole sombre world was awesome with the sound.

2

The seas are the heart's blood of the earth. Plucked up and kneaded by the sun and the moon, the tides are systole and diastole of earth's veins.

The rhythm of waves beats in the sea like a pulse in living flesh. It is pure force, forever embodying itself in a succession of watery shapes which vanish on its passing.

I stand on my dune top watching a great wave coursing in from sea, and know that I am watching an illusion, that the distant water has not left its place in ocean to advance upon me, but only a force shaped in water, a bodiless pulse beat, a vibration.

Consider the marvel of what we see. Somewhere in ocean, perhaps a thousand miles and more from this beach, the pulse beat of earth liberates a vibration, an ocean wave. Is the original force circular, I wonder, and do ocean waves ring out from the creative beat as they do on a quiet surface broken by a stone? Are there, perhaps, ocean circles so great and so intricate that they are unperceived? Once created, the wave or the arc of a wave begins its journey through the sea. Countless vibrations precede it, countless vibrations follow after. It approaches the continent, swings into the coast line, courses ashore, breaks, dissolves, is gone. The innermost waters it last inhabited flow back in marbly foam to become a body to another beat, and to be again flung down. So it goes night and day, and will go till the secret heart of earth strikes out its last slow beat and the last wave dissolves upon the last forsaken shore.

As I stand on my dune top, however, I do not think of the illusion and the beat of earth, for I watch the waves with my outer rather than my inner eye. After all, the illusion is set off by an extraordinary, an almost miraculous thing—the embodiment of the wave beat in an almost constant shape. We see a wave a quarter of a mile off, then a few hundred yards nearer in, then just offshore; we seem to have been watching the same travelling mass of water—there has been no appreciable change in mass or in shape—yet all the while the original beat has taken on a flowing series of liquid bodies, bodies so alike, so much the same, that our eye will individualize them and follow them in—the third wave, we say, or the second wave behind the great wave. How strange it is that this beat of earth, this mysterious undulation of the seas, moving through and among the other forces stirring the waters close off the continent, should thus keep its constancy of form and mass, and how odd a blend of illusion and reality it all is! On the whole, the outer eye has the best of it.

Blowing all day long, a northwest wind yesterday swept the sky clear of every tatter and wisp of cloud. Clear it still is, though the wind has shifted to the east. The sky this afternoon is a harmony of universal blue, bordered with a surf rim of snowiest blue-white. Far out at sea, in the northeast and near the horizon, is a pool of the loveliest blue I have ever seen here—a light blue, a petal blue, blue of the emperor's gown in a Chinese fairy tale. If you would see waves at their best, come on such a day, when the ocean reflects a lovely sky, and the wind is light and onshore; plan to arrive in the afternoon so that you will have the sun facing the breakers. Come early, for the glints on the waves are most beautiful and interesting when the light is oblique and high. And come with a rising tide.

The surf is high, and on the far side of it, a wave greater than its fellows is shouldering out of the blue, glinting immensity of sea.

Friends tell me that there are certain tropic beaches where waves miles long break all at once in one cannonading crash: a little of this, I imagine, would be magnificent; a constancy of it, unbearable. The surf here is broken; it approaches the beach in long intercurrent parallels, some a few hundred feet long, some an eighth of a

mile long, some, and the longest, attaining the quarter-mile length
and perhaps just over. Thus, at all times and instants of the day,
along the five miles of beach visible from the Fo'castle deck, waves
are to be seen breaking, coursing in to break, seething up and sliding back.

But to return to the blue wave rolling in out of the blue spacious-
ness of sea. On the other side of the world, just opposite the Cape,
lies the ancient Spanish province of Galicia, and the town of Ponte-
vedra and St. James Compostella, renowned of pilgrims. (When I
was there they offered me a silver cockle shell, but I would have
none of it, and got myself a sea shell from some Galician fisherfolk.)
Somewhere between this Spanish land and Cape Cod the pulse of
earth has engendered this wave and sent it coursing westward
through the seas. Far off the coast, the spray of its passing has, perhaps, risen on the windward bow of some rusty freighter and fallen
in rainbow drops upon her plates; the great liners have felt it course
beneath their keels.

A continent rises in the west, and the pulse beat approaches this
bulwark of Cape Cod. Two thirds of a mile out, the wave is still a
sea vibration, a billow. Slice it across, and its outline will be that
of a slightly flattened semicircle; the pulse is shaped in a long, advancing mound. I watch it approach the beach. Closer and closer in,
it is rising with the rise of the beach and the shoaling of the water;
closer still, it is changing from a mound to a pyramid, a pyramid
which swiftly distorts, the seaward side lengthening, the landward
side incurving—the wave is now a breaker. Along the ridge of blue
forms a rippling crest of clear, bright water; a little spray flies off.
Under the racing foam churned up by the dissolution of other
breakers the beach now catches at the last shape of sea inhabited by
the pulse—the wave is *tripped* by the shoaling sand—the giant stum-
bles, crashes, and is pushed over and ahead by the sloping line of
force behind. The fall of a breaker is never the work of gravity
alone.

It is the last line of the wave that has captured the decorative
imagination of the world—the long seaward slope, the curling crest,
the incurved volute ahead.

Toppling over and hurled ahead, the wave crashes, its mass of
glinting blue falling down in a confusion of seething, splendid

white, the tumbling water rebounding from the sand to a height almost always a little above that of the original crest. Out of the wild, crumbling confusion born of the dissolution of the force and the last great shape, foamy fountains spurt, and ringlets of spray. The mass of water, still all furiously a-churn and seething white, now rushes for the rim of the beach as it might for an inconceivable cataract. Within thirty-five feet the water shoals from two feet to dry land. The edge of the rush thins, and the last impulse disappears in inches-deep slides of foam which reflect the sky in one last moment of energy and beauty and then vanish all at once into the sands.

Another thundering, and the water that has escaped and withdrawn is gathered up and swept forward again by another breaking wave. Night and day, age after age, so works the sea, with infinite variation obeying an unalterable rhythm moving through an intricacy of chance and law.

I can watch a fine surf for hours, taking pleasure in all its wild plays and variations. I like to stand on my beach, watching a long wave start breaking in many places, and see the curling water run north and south from the several beginnings, and collide in furious white pyramids built of the opposing energies. Splendid fountains often delight the eye. A towering and deep-bellied wave, toppling, encloses in its volute a quantity of air, and a few seconds after the spill this prisoned and compressed vapour bursts up through the boiling rush in feathery, foamy jets and geyser plumes. I have seen fountains here, on a September day, twenty and twenty-five and even thirty feet high. Sometimes a curious thing happens. Instead of escaping vertically, the rolled-up air escapes horizontally, and the breaker suddenly blows, as from a dragon's mouth, a great lateral puff of steamy spray. On sunny days, the toppling crest is often mirrored in the glassy volute as the wave is breaking. One lovely autumn afternoon, I saw a beautiful white gull sailing along the volute of a breaker accompanied by his reflection in the wave.

I add one curious effect of the wind. When the wind is directly offshore or well offshore, the waves approach fighting it; when the wind is offshore but so little off that its angle with the coast line is oblique—say an angle never greater than twenty-two degrees and never less than about twelve—the waves that approach the coast do not give battle, but run in with their long axis parallel to the wind.

Sitting in the Fo'castle, I can often tell the exact quarter of an off-shore wind simply by looking at this oblique alignment of the waves.

The long miles of beach are never more beautiful than when waves are rolling in fighting a strong breeze. Then do the breakers actually seem to charge the coast. As they approach, the wind meets them in a shock of war, the chargers rear but go on, and the wind blows back their manes. North and south, I watch them coursing in, the manes of white, sun-brilliant spray streaming behind them for thirty and even forty feet. Sea horses do men call such waves on every coast of the world. If you would see them at their best, come to this beach on a bright October day when a northwest wind is billowing off to sea across the moors.

3

I will close with a few paragraphs about heavy surf.

It is best to be seen, I think, when the wind is not too high. A gale blows up a surf, but it also flattens out the incoming rollers, making monstrous, foamy travelling mounds of them much like those visible from a ship at sea. Not until the wind has dropped do the breakers gather form. The finest surf I have ever seen here—it was a Northern recoil of the great Florida hurricane—broke on three pleasant and almost windless autumn days. The storm itself had passed us, but our seas had been stirred to their deeps. Returning to the Cape at night from a trip to town, I heard the roar of the ocean in Orleans, and on arriving at Nauset, found the beach flooded to the dunes, and covered with a churn of surf and moonlight. Dragging a heavy suitcase and clad in my go-to-town clothes, I had an evil time getting to the Fo'castle over the dune tops and along the flooded marsh.

Many forces mingle in the surf of a storm—the great earth rhythm of the waves, the violence of wind, the struggle of water to obey its own elemental law. Out of the storm at sea come the giants and, being giants, trip far out, spilling first on the outer bar. Shoreward then they rush, breaking all the way. Touching the beach, they tumble in a roar lost in a general noise of storm. Trampled by the wind and everlastingly moved and lifted up and flung down by the incoming seas, the water offshore becomes a furious glassiness of marbly foam; wild, rushing sheets of seethe fifty feet wide border it; the water streams with sand.

Under all this move furious tidal currents, the longshore undertow of outer Cape Cod. Shore currents here move in a southerly direction; old wreckage and driftwood is forever being carried down here from the north. Coast guard friends often look at a box or stick I have retrieved, and say, "Saw that two weeks ago up by the light."

After an easterly, I find things on the beach which have been blown down from the Gulf of Maine—young, uprooted spruce trees, lobster buoys from Matinicus, and, after one storm, a great strewing of empty sea-urchin shells. Another easterly washed up a strewing of curious wooden pebbles shaped by the sea out of the ancient submerged forests which lie just off the present coast. They were brownblack, shaped like beach stones, and as smooth as such stones.

The last creature I found in the surf was a huge horseshoe crab, the only one I have ever chanced to find on the outside. Poor *Limulus polyphemus!* The surf having turned him upside down, he had as usual doubled up, and the surf had then filled with sand the angle of his doubling. When I discovered him, he was being bullied by a foam slide, and altogether in a desperate way. So I picked him up, rinsed the sand out of his waving gills, held him up all dripping by the tail, and flung him as far as I could to seaward of the breakers. A tiny splash, and I had seen the last of him, a moment more, and the surf had filled the hollow in which he had lain.

Autumnal easterlies and November tides having scoured from the beach its summer deeps of sand, the high seasonal tides now run clear across to the very foot of the dunes. Under this daily overflow of cold, the last of the tide-rim hoppers and foragers vanish from the beach. An icy wind blusters; I hear a dry tinkle of sand against my western wall; December nears, and winter closes in upon the coast.

Odyssey of the Eel

BY

RACHEL L. CARSON

T HERE IS a pond that lies under a hill, where the threading roots
of many trees—mountain ash, hickory, chestnut, oak, and hemlock—hold the rains in a deep sponge of humus. The pond is fed by
two streams that carry the runoff of higher ground to the west, coming down over rocky beds grooved in the hill. Cattails, bur reeds,
spike rushes, and pickerel weeds stand rooted in the soft mud
around its shores and, on the side under the hill, wade out halfway
into its waters. Willows grow in the wet ground along the eastern
shore of the pond, where the overflow seeps down a grass-lined spill-
way, seeking its passage to the sea.

The smooth surface of the pond is often ringed by spreading
ripples made when shiners, dace, or other minnows push against the
tough sheet between air and water, and the film is dimpled, too, by
the hurrying feet of small water insects that live among the reeds
and rushes. The pond is called Bittern Pond, because never a spring
passes without a few of these shy herons nesting in its bordering
reeds, and the strange, pumping cries of the birds that stand and
sway in the cattails, hidden in the blend of lights and shadows, are
thought by some who hear them to be the voice of an unseen spirit
of the pond.

From Bittern Pond to the sea is two hundred miles as a fish swims.
Thirty miles of the way is by narrow hill streams, seventy miles by
a sluggish river crawling over the coastal plain, and a hundred miles
through the brackish water of a shallow bay where the sea came in,
millions of years ago, and drowned the estuary of a river.

Every spring a number of small creatures come up the grassy spill-
way and enter Bittern Pond, having made the two-hundred-mile
journey from the sea. They are curiously formed, like pieces of slen-

398

der glass rods shorter than a man's finger. They are young eels, or elvers, that were born in the deep sea. Some of the eels go higher into the hills, but a few remain in the pond, where they live on crayfish and water beetles, and catch frogs and small fishes and grow to adulthood.

Now it was autumn and the end of the year. From the moon's quarter to its half, rains had fallen, and all the hill streams ran in flood. The water of the two feeder streams of the pond was deep and swift and jostled the rocks of the stream beds as it hurried to the sea. The pond was deeply stirred by the inrush of water, which swept through its weed forests and swirled through its crayfish holes and crept up six inches on the trunks of its bordering willows.

The wind had sprung up at dusk. At first it had been a gentle breeze, stroking the surface of the pond to velvet smoothness. At midnight it had grown to a half gale that set all the rushes to swaying wildly and rattled the dead seed heads of the weeds and plowed deep furrows in the surface waters of the pond. The wind roared down from the hills, over forests of oak and beech and hickory and pine. It blew toward the east, toward the sea two hundred miles away.

Anguilla, the eel, nosed into the swift water that raced toward the overflow from the pond. With her keen senses she savored strange tastes and smells in the water. They were the bitter tastes and smells of dead and rainsoaked autumn leaves, the tastes of forest moss and lichen and root-held humus. Such was the water that hurried past the eel, on its way to the sea.

Anguilla had entered Bittern Pond as a finger-long elver ten years before. She had lived in the pond through its summers and autumns and winters and springs, hiding in its weed beds by day and prowling through its waters by night, for like all eels she was a lover of darkness. She knew every crayfish burrow that ran in honeycombing furrows through the mudbank under the hill. She knew her way among the swaying, rubbery stems of spatterdock, where frogs sat on the thick leaves; and she knew where to find the spring peepers clinging to grass blades, bubbling shrilly, where in spring the pond overflowed its grassy northern shore. She could find the banks where the water rats ran and squeaked in play or tusseled in anger, so that sometimes they fell with a splash into the water—easy prey for a lurking eel. She knew the soft mud beds deep in the bottom of the

pond, where in winter she could lie buried, secure against the cold—
for like all eels she was a lover of warmth.

Now it was autumn again, and the water was chilling to the cold
rains shed off the hard backbones of the hills. A strange restiveness
was growing in Anguilla the eel. For the first time in her adult life,
the food hunger was forgotten. In its place was a strange, new hunger, formless and ill-defined. Its dimly perceived object was a place
of warmth and darkness—darker than the blackest night over Bittern Pond. She had known such a place once—in the dim beginnings
of life, before memory began. She could not know that the way to it
lay beyond the pond outlet over which she had clambered ten years
before. But many times at night, as the wind and the rain tore at
the surface film of the pond, Anguilla was drawn irresistibly toward
the outlet over which the water was spilling on its journey to the
sea. When the cocks were crowing in the farmyard over the hill,
saluting the third hour of the new day, Anguilla slipped into the
channel spilling down to the stream below and followed the moving
water.

Even in flood, the hill stream was shallow, and its voice was the
noisy voice of a young stream, full of gurglings and tricklings and
the sound of water striking stone and of stone rubbing against stone.
Anguilla followed the stream, feeling her way by the changing pressure of the swift water currents. She was a creature of night and
darkness, and so the black water path neither confused nor frightened her.

In five miles the stream dropped a hundred feet over a rough and
boulder-strewn bed. At the end of the fifth mile it slipped between
two hills, following along a deep gap made by another and larger
stream years before. The hills were clothed with oak and beech and
hickory, and the stream ran under their interlacing branches.

At daybreak Anguilla came to a bright, shallow riffle where the
stream chattered sharply over gravel and small rubble. The water
moved with a sudden acceleration, raining swiftly toward the brink
of a ten-foot fall where it spilled over a sheer rock face into a basin
below. The rush of water carried Anguilla with it, down the steep,
thin slant of white water and into the pool. The basin was deep and
still and cool, having been rounded out of the rock by centuries of
falling water. Dark water mosses grew on its sides and stoneworts
were rooted in its silt, thriving on the lime which they took from

the stones and incorporated in their round, brittle stems. Anguilla hid among the stoneworts of the pool, seeking a shelter from light and sun, for now the bright shallows of the stream repelled her.

Before she had lain in the pool for an hour another eel came over the falls and sought the darkness of the deep leaf beds. The second eel had come from higher up in the hills, and her body was lacerated in many places from the rocks of the thin upland streams she had descended. The newcomer was a larger and more powerful eel than Anguilla, for she had spent two more years in fresh water before coming to maturity.

Anguilla, who had been the largest eel in Bittern Pond for more than a year, dived down through the stoneworts at sight of the strange eel. Her passage swayed the stiff, limy stems of the chara and disturbed three water boatmen that were clinging to the chara stems, each holding its position by the grip of a jointed leg, set with rows of bristles. The insects were browsing on the film of desmids and diatoms that coated the stems of the stoneworts. The boatmen were clothed in glistening blankets of air which they had carried down with them when they dived through the surface film, and when the passing of the eel dislodged them from their quiet anchorage they rose like air bubbles, for they were lighter than water.

An insect with a body like a fragment of twig supported by six jointed legs was walking over the floating leaves and skating on the surface of the water, on which it moved as on strong silk. Its feet depressed the film into six dimples, but did not break it, so light was its body. The insect's name meant "a marsh treader," for its kind often lived in the deep sphagnum moss of bogs. The marsh treader was foraging, watching for creatures like mosquito larvae or small crustaceans to move up to the surface from the pool below. When one of the water boatmen suddenly broke through the film at the feet of the marsh treader, the twiglike insect speared it with the sharp stilettos projecting beyond its mouth and sucked the little body dry.

When Anguilla felt the strange eel pushing into the thick mat of dead leaves on the floor of the pool, she moved back into the dark recess behind the waterfall. Above her the steep face of the rock was green with the soft fronds of mosses that grew where their leaves escaped the flow of water, yet were always wet with fine spray from the falls. In spring the midges came there to lay their eggs, spinning them in thin white skeins on the wet rocks. Later when the eggs hatched and the gauzy-winged insects began to emerge from the falls in swarms, they were watched for by bright-eyed little birds who sat on overhanging branches and darted open-mouthed into the clouds of midges. Now the midges were gone, but other small animals lived in the green, water-soaked thickets of the moss. They were the larvae of beetles and soldier flies and crane flies. They were smooth-bodied creatures, lacking the grappling hooks and suckers and the flattened, stream-molded bodies that enabled their relatives to live in the swift currents draining to the brink of the falls overhead or a dozen feet away where the pool spilled its water into the stream bed. Although they lived only a few inches from the veil of water that dropped sheer to the pool, they knew nothing of swift water and its dangers; their peaceful world was of water seeping slow through green forests of moss.

The beginning of the great leaf fall had come with the rains of the past fortnight. Throughout the day, from the roof of the forest to its floor, there was a continuous downdrift of leaves. The leaves fell so silently that the rustle of their settling to the ground was no louder than the thin scratching of the feet of mice and moles moving through their passages in the leaf mold.

All day flights of broad-winged hawks passed down along the ridges of the hills, going south. They moved with scarcely a beat of their outspread wings, for they were riding on the updrafts of air made as the west wind struck the hills and leaped upward to pass over them. The hawks were fall migrants from Canada that had followed down along the Appalachians for the sake of the air currents that made the flight easier.

At dusk, as the owls began to hoot in the woods, Anguilla left the pool and traveled downstream alone. Soon the stream flowed through rolling farm country. Twice during the night it dropped over small milldams that were white in the thin moonlight. In the stretch below the second dam, Anguilla lay for a time under an overhanging bank, where the swift currents were undercutting the heavy, grassy turf. The sharp hiss of the water over the slanting boards of the dam had frightened her. As she lay under the bank the eel that had rested with her in the pool of the waterfall came over the milldam and passed on downstream. Anguilla followed, letting the current take her bumping and jolting over the shallow riffles and gliding swiftly through the deeper stretches. Often she was aware of dark forms moving in the water near her. They were other eels, come from many of the upland feeder creeks of the main stream. Like Anguilla, the other long, slender fishes yielded to the hurrying water and let the currents speed their passage. All of the migrants were roe eels, for only the females ascend far into the fresh-water streams, beyond all reminders of the sea.

The eels were almost the only creatures that were moving in the stream that night. Once, in a copse of beech, the stream made a sharp bend and scoured out a deeper bed. As Anguilla swam into this rounded basin, several frogs dived down from the soft mud bank where they had been sitting half out of water and hid on the bottom close to the bole of a fallen tree. The frogs had been startled by the approach of a furred animal that left prints like those of human feet in the soft mud and whose small black mask and black-ringed tail showed in the faint moonlight. The raccoon lived in a hole high up in one of the beeches near by and often caught frogs and crayfish in the stream. He was not disconcerted by the series of splashes that greeted his approach, for he knew where the foolish frogs would hide. He walked out on the fallen tree and lay down flat on its trunk. He took a firm grip on its bark with the claws of his hind feet and left forepaw. The right paw he dipped into the water, reaching down as far as he could and exploring with busy, sensitive fingers the leaves and mud under the trunk. The frogs tried to burrow deeper into the litter of leaves and sticks and other stream debris. The patient fingers felt into every hole and crevice, pushed away leaves and probed the mud. Soon the coon felt a small, firm body beneath his fingers—felt the sudden movement as the frog tried to escape. The coon's grip tightened and he drew the frog quickly up onto the log. There he killed it, washed it carefully by dipping it into the stream, and ate it. As he was finishing his meal, three small black masks moved into a patch of moonlight at the edge of the stream. They belonged to the coon's mate and their two cubs, who had come down the tree to prowl for their night's food.

From force of habit, the eel thrust her snout inquisitively into the leaf litter under the log, adding to the terror of the frogs, but she did not molest them as she would have done in the pond, for hunger was forgotten in the stronger instinct that made her a part of the moving stream. When Anguilla slipped into the central current of water that swept past the end of the log, the two young coons and their mother had walked out onto the trunk and four black-masked faces were peering into the water, preparing to fish the pool for frogs.

By morning the stream had broadened and deepened. Now it fell silent and mirrored an open woods of sycamore, oak, and dogwood. Passing through the woods, it carried a freight of brightly colored leaves—bright-red, crackling leaves from the oaks, mottled green and yellow leaves from the sycamores, dull-red, leathery leaves from the dogwoods. In the great wind the dogwoods had lost their leaves, but they held their scarlet berries. Yesterday robins had gathered in flocks in the dogwoods, eating the berries; today the robins were gone south and in their place flurries of starlings swept from tree to tree, chattering and rattling and whistling to one another as they stripped the branches of berries. The starlings were in bright new fall plumage, with every breast feather spear-tipped with white.

Anguilla came to a shallow pool formed when an oak had been uprooted in a great autumn storm ten years before and had fallen across the stream. Oak dam and pool were new in the stream since Anguilla had ascended it as an elver in the spring of that year. Now a great mat of weeds, silt, sticks, dead branches, and other debris was packed around the massive trunk, plastering all the crevices, so that the water was backed up into a pool two feet deep. During the period of the full moon the eels lay in the oak-dam pool, fearing to travel in the moon-white water of the stream almost as much as they feared the sunlight.

In the mud of the pool were many burrowing, wormlike larvae— the young of lamprey eels. They were not true eels, but fishlike creatures whose skeleton was gristle instead of bone, with round, tooth-studded mouths that were always open because there were no jaws. Some of the young lampreys had hatched from eggs spawned in the pool as much as four years before and had spent most of their life buried in the mud flats of the shallow stream, blind and toothless. These older larvae, grown nearly twice the length of a man's finger, had this fall been transformed into the adult shape, and for the first time they had eyes to see the water world in which they lived. Now, like the true eels, they felt in the gentle flow of water to the sea something that urged them to follow, to descend to salt water for an interval of sea life. There they would prey semiparasitically on cod, haddock, mackerel, salmon, and many other fishes and in time would return to the river, like their parents, to spawn and die. A few of the young lampreys slipped away over the log dam every day, and on a cloudy night, when rain had fallen and white mist lay in the stream valley, the eels followed. ·

The next night the eels came to a place where the stream diverged around an island grown thickly with willows. The eels followed the south channel around the island, where there were broad mud flats. The island had been formed over centuries of time as the stream had dropped part of its silt load before it joined the main river. Grass seeds had taken root; seeds of trees had been brought by the water and by birds; willow shoots had sprung from broken twigs and branches carried down in flood waters; an island had been born.

The water of the main river was gray with approaching day when the eels entered it. The river channel was twelve feet deep and its water was turbid because of the impouring of many tributary streams swollen with autumn rains. The eels did not fear the gloomy channel water by day as they had feared the bright shallows of the hill streams, and so this day they did not rest but pushed on downstream. There were many other eels in the river—migrants from other tributaries. With the increase in their numbers the excitement of the eels grew, and as the days passed they rested less often, pressing on downstream with fevered haste.

As the river widened and deepened, a strange taste came into the water. It was a slightly bitter taste, and at certain hours of the day and night it grew stronger in the water that the eels drew into their mouths and passed over their gills. With the bitter taste came unfamiliar movements of the water—a period of pressure against the down flow of the river currents followed by slow release and then swift acceleration of the current. Now groups of slender posts stood at intervals in the river, marking out funnel shapes from which straight rows of posts ran slanting toward the shore. Blackened netting, coated with slimy algae, was run from post to post and showed several feet above the water. Gulls were often sitting on the pound nets, waiting for men to come and fish the nets so that they could pick up any fish that might be thrown away or lost. The posts were coated with barnacles and with small oysters, for now there was enough salt in the water for these shellfish to grow.

Sometimes the sandspits of the river were dotted with small shore birds standing at rest or probing at the water's edge for snails, small shrimps, worms, or other food. The shore birds were of the sea's edge, and their presence in numbers hinted of the nearness of the sea.

The strange, bitter taste grew in the water and the pulse of the tides beat stronger. On one of the ebb tides a group of small eels— none more than two feet long—came out of a brackish-water marsh and joined the migrants from the hill streams. They were males, who had never ascended the rivers but had remained within the zone of tides and brackish water.

In all of the migrants striking changes in appearance were taking place. Gradually the river garb of olive brown was changing to a glistening black, with underparts of silver. These were the colors worn only by mature eels about to undertake a far sea journey. Their bodies were firm and rounded with fat—stored energy that would be needed before the journey's end. Already in many of the migrants the snouts were becoming higher and more compressed, as though from some sharpening of the sense of smell. Their eyes were enlarged to twice their normal size, perhaps in preparation for a descent along darkening sea lanes.

Where the river broadened out to its estuary, it flowed past a high clay cliff on its southern bank. Buried in the cliff were thousands of teeth of ancient sharks, vertebrae of whales, and shells of mollusks that had been dead when the first eels had come in from the sea, eons ago. The teeth, bones, and shells were relics of the time when a warm sea had overlain all the coastal plain and the hard remains of its creatures had settled down into its bottom oozes. Buried millions of years in darkness, they were washed out of the clay by every storm to lie exposed, warmed by sunshine and bathed by rain.

The eels spent a week descending the bay, hurrying through water of increasing saltiness. The currents moved with a rhythm that was of neither river nor sea, being governed by eddies at the mouths of the many rivers that emptied into the bay and by holes in the muddy bottom thirty or forty feet beneath. The ebb tides ran stronger than the floods, because the strong outflow of the rivers resisted the press of water from the sea.

At last Anguilla neared the mouth of the bay. With her were thousands of eels, come down, like the water that brought them, from all the hills and uplands of thousands of square miles, from every stream and river that drained away to the sea by the bay. The eels followed a deep channel that hugged the eastern shore of the bay and came to where the land passed into a great salt marsh. Beyond the marsh, and between it and the sea, was a vast shallow arm of the bay, studded with islands of green marsh grass. The eels gathered in the marsh, waiting for the moment when they should pass to the sea.

The next night a strong southeast wind blew in from the sea, and when the tide began to rise the wind was behind the water, pushing it into the bay and out into the marshes. That night the bitterness of brine was tasted by fish, birds, crabs, shellfish, and all the other water creatures of the marsh. The eels lay deep under water, savoring the salt that grew stronger hour by hour as the wind-driven wall of sea water advanced into the bay. The salt was of the sea. The eels were ready for the sea—for the deep sea and all it held for them. Their years of river life were ended.

The wind was stronger than the forces of moon and sun, and, when the tide turned an hour after midnight, the salt water continued to pile up in the marsh, being blown upstream in a deep surface layer while the underlying water ebbed to the sea.

Soon after the tide turn, the seaward movement of the eels began. In the large and strange rhythms of a great water which each had known in the beginning of life, but each had long since forgotten, the eels at first moved hesitantly in the ebbing tide. The water carried them through an inlet between two islands. It took them under a fleet of oyster boats riding at anchor, waiting for daybreak. When morning came, the eels would be far away. It carried them past leaning spar buoys that marked the inlet channel and past several whistle and bell buoys anchored on shoals of sand or rock. The tide took them close under the lee shore of the larger island, from which a lighthouse flashed a long beam of light toward the sea.

From a sandy spit of the island came the cries of shore birds that were feeding in darkness on the ebb tide. Cry of shore bird and crash of surf were the sounds of the edge of land—the edge of the sea.

The eels struggled through the line of breakers, where foam seething over black water caught the gleam of the lighthouse beacon and frothed whitely. Once beyond the wind-driven breakers they found the sea gentler, and as they followed out over the shelving sand they sank into deep water, unrocked by violence of wind and wave.

As long as the tide ebbed, eels were leaving the marshes and running out to sea. Thousands passed the lighthouse that night, on the first lap of a far sea journey—all the silver eels, in fact, that the marsh contained. And as they passed through the surf and out to sea, so also they passed from human sight and almost from human knowledge.

The record of the eels' journey to their spawning place is hidden in the deep sea. No one can trace the path of the eels that left the salt marsh at the mouth of the bay on that November night when wind and tide brought them the feeling of warm ocean water—how they passed from the bay to the deep Atlantic basin that lies south of Bermuda and east of Florida half a thousand miles. Nor is there a clearer record of the journey of those other eel hordes that in autumn passed to the sea from almost every river and stream of the whole Atlantic Coast from Greenland to Central America.

No one knows how the eels traveled to their common destination. Probably they shunned the pale-green surface waters, chilled by wintry winds and bright as the hill streams they had feared to descend by day. Perhaps they traveled instead at mid-depths or followed the contours of the gently sloping continental shelf, descending the drowned valleys of their native rivers that had cut channels across the coastal plain in sunshine millions of years ago. But somehow they came to the continent's edge, where the muddy slopes of the sea's wall fell away steeply, and so they passed to the deepest abyss of the Atlantic. There the young were to be born of the darkness of the deep sea and the old eels were to die and become sea again.

In early February billions of specks of protoplasm floated in darkness, suspended far below the surface of the sea. They were the newly hatched larvae—the only testament that remained of the parent eels. The young eels first knew life in the transition zone between the surface sea and the abyss. A thousand feet of water lay above them, straining out the rays of the sun. Only the longest and strongest of the rays filtered down to the level where the eels drifted in the sea—a cold and sterile residue of blue and ultraviolet, shorn of all its warmth of reds and yellows and greens. For a twentieth part of the day the blackness was displaced by a strange light of a vivid and unearthly blue that came stealing down from above. But only the straight, long rays of the sun when it passed the zenith had power to dispel the blackness, and the deep sea's hour of dawn light was merged in its hour of twilight. Quickly the blue light faded away, and the eels lived again in the long night that was only less black than the abyss, where the night had no end.

At first the young eels knew little of the strange world into which they had come, but lived passively in its waters. They sought no food, sustaining their flattened, leaf-shaped bodies on the residue of embryonic tissue, and so they were the foes of none of their neighbors. They drifted without effort, buoyed by their leafy form and by the balance between the density of their own tissues and that of the sea water. Their small bodies were colorless as crystal. Even the blood that ran in its channels, pumped by hearts of infinitesimal size, was unpigmented; only the eyes, small as black pinpricks, showed color. By their transparency the young eels were better fitted to live in this twilight zone of the sea, where safety from hungry foragers was to be found only in blending with the surroundings.

Billions of young eels—billions of pairs of black, pinprick eyes peering into the strange sea world that overlay the abyss. Before the eyes of the eels, clouds of copepods vibrated in their ceaseless dance of life, their crystal bodies catching the light like dust motes when the blue gleam came down from above. Clear bells pulsated in the water, fragile jellyfish adjusted to life where five hundred pounds of water pressed on every square inch of surface. Fleeing before the descending light, shoals of pteropods, or winged snails, swept down from above before the eyes of the watching eels, their forms glistening with reflected light like a rain of strangely shaped hailstones— daggers and spirals and cones of glassy clearness. Shrimps loomed up—pale ghosts in the dim light. Sometimes the shrimps were pursued by pale fishes, round of mouth and flabby of flesh, with rows of light organs set like jewels on their gray flanks. Then the shrimps often expelled jets of luminous fluid that turned to a fiery cloud to blind and confuse their enemies. Most of the fishes seen by the eels wore silver armor, for silver is the prevailing color or badge of those waters that lie at the end of the sun's rays. Such were the small dragonfish, long and slender of form, with fangs glistening in their opened mouths as they roamed through the water in an endless pursuit of prey. Strangest of all were the fishes, half as long as a man's finger and clothed in a leathery skin, that shone with turquoise and amethyst lights and gleamed like quicksilver over their flanks. Their bodies were thin from side to side and tapered to sharp edges. When enemies looked down from above, they saw nothing, for the backs of the hatchetfish were a bluish black that was invisible in the black sea. When sea hunters looked up from below, they were confused and could not distinguish their prey with certainty, for the mirror-like flanks of the hatchetfish reflected the blueness of the water and their outlines were lost in a shimmer of light.

The young eels lived in one layer or tier of a whole series of horizontal communities that lay one below the other, from the nereid worms that spun their strands of silk from frond to frond of the brown sargassum weed floating on the surface to the sea spiders and prawns that crawled precariously over the deep and yielding oozes of the floor of the abyss.

Above the eels was the sunlight world where plants grew, and small fishes shone green and azure in the sun, and blue and crystal jellyfish moved at the surface.

Then came the twilight zone where fishes were opalescent or silver, and red prawns shed eggs of a bright orange color, and round-mouthed fishes were pale, and the first light organs twinkled in the gloom.

Then came the first black layer, where none wore silvery sheen or opalescent luster, but all were as drab as the water in which they lived, wearing monotones of reds and browns and blacks whereby they might fade into the surrounding obscurity and defer the moment of death in the jaws of an enemy. Here the red prawns shed deep-red eggs, and the round-mouthed fishes were black, and many creatures wore luminous torches or a multitude of small lights arranged in rows or patterns that they might recognize friend or enemy.

Below them lay the abyss, the primeval bed of the sea, the deepest of all the Atlantic. The abyss is a place where change comes slow, where the passing of the years has no meaning, nor the swift succession of the seasons. The sun has no power in those depths, and so their blackness is a blackness without end, or beginning, or degree. The wind is unknown there. No pull of moon and sun can move that weight of inert water to surge and lapse in the rhythm of the tides. No beating of tropical sun on the surface miles above can lessen the bleak iciness of those abyssal waters that varies little through summer or winter, through the years that melt into centuries, and the centuries into ages of geologic time.

Down beneath mile after mile of water—more than four miles in all—lay the sea bottom, covered with a soft, deep ooze that had been accumulating there through eons upon eons of time. These greatest depths of the Atlantic are carpeted with red clay, a pumicelike deposit hurled out of the earth from time to time by submarine volcanoes. Mingled with the pumice are spherules of iron and nickel that had their origin on some far-off sun and once rushed millions of miles through interstellar space, to perish in the earth's atmosphere and find their grave in the deep sea. Far up on the sides of the great bowl of the Atlantic the bottom oozes are thick with the skeletal remains of minute sea creatures of the surface waters—the shells of starry Foraminifera and the limy remains of algae and corals, the flintlike skeletons of Radiolaria and the frustules of diatoms. But long before such delicate structures reach this deepest bed of the abyss, they are dissolved and made one with the sea. Almost the only organic remains that have not passed into solution before they reach these cold and silent deeps are the ear bones of whales and the teeth of sharks. Here in the red clay, in the darkness and stillness, lies all that remains of ancient races of sharks that lived, perhaps, before there were whales in the sea; before the giant ferns flourished on the earth or ever the coal measures were laid down. All of the living flesh of these sharks was returned to the sea millions of years before, to be used over and over again in the fashioning of other creatures, but here and there a tooth still lies in the red-clay ooze of the deep sea, coated with a deposit of iron from a distant sun.

The abyss south of Bermuda is a meeting place for the eels of the western and eastern Atlantic. There are other great deeps in the ocean between Europe and America—chasms sunk between the mountain ranges of the sea's floor—but only this one is both deep enough and warm enough to provide the conditions which the eels need for the act of spawning. So once a year the mature eels of Europe set out across the ocean on a journey of three to four thousand miles; and once a year the mature eels of eastern America go out as though to meet them. In the westernmost part of the drifting sea of sargassum weed some of them meet and intermingle—those that travel farthest west from Europe and farthest east from America. So in the central part of the vast spawning grounds of the eels, the eggs and young of two species float side by side in the water. They are so alike in appearance that only by counting with infinite care the vertebrae that make up their backbones and the plates of muscle that flank their spines can they be distinguished. Yet some, toward the end of their period of larval life, seek the coast of America and others the coast of Europe, and none ever stray to the wrong continent.

As the months of the year passed, one by one, the young eels grew, lengthening and broadening. As they grew and the tissues of their bodies changed in density, they drifted into light. Upward passage through space in the sea was like passage through time in the Arctic world in spring, with the hours of sunlight increasing day by day. Little by little the blue haze of midday lengthened and the long night grew shorter. Soon the eels came to the level where the first green rays, filtering down from above, warmed the blue light. So they passed into the zone of vegetation and found their first food.

The plants that received enough energy for their life processes from the sea-strained residue of sunlight were microscopic, floating spheres. On the cells of ancient brown algae the young eels first nourished their glass-clear bodies—plants of a race that had lived for untold millions of years before the first eel, or the first back-boned animal of any kind, moved in the earth's seas. Through all the intervening eons of time, while group after group of living things had risen up and died away, these lime-bearing algae had continued to live in the sea, forming their small protective shields of lime that were unchanged in shape and form from those of their earliest ancestors.

Not only the eels browsed on the algae. In this blue-green zone, the sea was clouded with copepods and other plankton foraging on the drifting plants, and dotted with the swarms of shrimplike animals that fed on the copepods, and lit by the twinkling silver flashes of small fishes that pursued the shrimps. The young eels themselves were preyed upon by hungry crustaceans, squids, jellyfish, and biting worms, and by many fishes who roved open-mouthed through the water, straining food through mouth and gill raker.

By midsummer the young eels were an inch long. They were the shape of willow leaves—a perfect shape for drifters in the currents. Now they had risen to the surface layers of the sea, where the black dots of their eyes could be seen by enemies in the bright-green water. They felt the lift and roll of waves; they knew the dazzling brightness of the midday sun in the pure waters of the open ocean. Sometimes they moved in the midst of floating forests of sargassum weed, perhaps taking shelter beneath the nests of flying fishes or, in the open spaces, hiding in the shadow of the blue sail or float of a Portuguese man-of-war.

In these surface waters were moving currents, and where the currents flowed the young eels were carried. All alike were swept into the moving vortex of the north Atlantic drift—the young of the eels from Europe and the young of the eels from America. Their caravans flowed through the sea like a great river, fed from the waters south of Bermuda and composed of young eels in numbers beyond enumeration. In at least a part of this living river, the two kinds or species of eels traveled side by side, but now they could be distinguished with ease, for the young of the American eels were nearly twice as large as their companions.

The ocean currents swept in their great circle, moving from south through west and north. Summer drew to its end. All the sea's crops had been sown and harvested, one by one—the spring crop of diatoms, the swarms of plankton animals that grew and multiplied on the abundant plants, the young of myriad fishes that fed on the plankton herds. Now the lull of autumn was upon the sea.

The young eels were far from their first home. Gradually the caravan began to diverge into two columns, one swinging to the west, one to the east. Before this time there must have been some subtle change in the responses of the faster-growing group of eels—something that led them more and more to the west of the broad river of moving surface water. As the time approached for them to lose the leaflike form of the larva and become rounded and sinuous like their parents, the impulse to seek fresher, shallowing waters grew. Now they found the latent power of unused muscles, and against the urging of wind and current they moved shoreward. Under the blind but powerful drive of instinct, every activity of their small and glassy bodies was directed unconsciously toward the attainment of a goal unknown in their own experience—something stamped so deeply upon the memory of their race that each of them turned without hesitation toward the coast from which their parents had come.

A few eastern-Atlantic eels still drifted in the midst of the west-ern-Atlantic larvae, but none among them felt the impulse to leave the deep sea. All their body processes of growth and development were geared to a slower rate. Not for two more years would they be ready for the change to the eel-like form and the transition to fresh water. So they drifted passively in the currents.

To the east, midway across the Atlantic, was another little band of leaflike travelers—eels spawned a year before. Farther to the east, in the latitude of the coastal banks of Europe, was still another host of drifting eel larvae, these yet a year older and grown to their full length. And that very season a fourth group of young eels had reached the end of their stupendous journey and was entering the bays and inlets and ascending the rivers of Europe.

For the American eels the journey was shorter. By midwinter their hordes were moving in across the continental shelf, approaching the coast. Although the sea was chilled by the icy winds that moved over it, and by the remoteness of the sun, the migrating eels remained in the surface waters, no longer needing the tropical warmth of the sea in which they had been born.

As the young moved shoreward, there passed beneath them an-other host of eels, another generation come to maturity and clothed in the black and silver splendor of eels returning to their first home. They must have passed without recognition—these two generations of eels—one on the threshold of a new life; the other about to lose itself in the darkness of the deep sea.

The water grew shallower beneath them as they neared the shore. The young eels took on their new form, in which they would ascend the rivers. Their leafy bodies became more compact by a shrinkage in length as well as in depth, so that the flattened leaf became a thickened cylinder. The large teeth of larval life were shed, and the heads became more rounded. A scattering of small pigment-carrying cells appeared along the backbone, but for the most part the young eels were still as transparent as glass. In this stage they were called "glass eels," or elvers.

Now they waited in the gray March sea, creatures of the deep sea, ready to invade the land. They waited off the sloughs and bayous and the wild-rice fields of the Gulf Coast, off the South Atlantic in-lets, ready to run into the sounds and green marshes that edged the river estuaries. They waited off the ice-choked northern rivers that came down with a surge and a rush of spring floods and thrust long arms of fresh water into the sea, so that the eels tasted the strange water taste and moved in excitement toward it. By the hundreds of thousands they waited off the mouth of the bay from which, little more than a year before, Anguilla and her companions had set out for the deep sea, blindly obeying a racial purpose which was now fulfilled in the return of the young.

The eels were nearing a point of land marked by the slim white shaft of a lighthouse. The sea ducks could see it—the piebald old-squaw ducks—when they circled high above the sea on their return every afternoon from inshore feeding grounds, coming down at dusk to the dark water with a great rush and a roar of wings. The whistling swans saw it, too, painted by the sunrise on the green sea beneath them as their flocks swept northward in the spring migration. The leader swans blew a triple note at the sight, for the point of land marked the nearness of the first stop on the swans' long flight from the Carolina Sounds to the great barrens of the Arctic.

The tides were running high with the fullness of the moon. On the ebb tides the taste of fresh water came strongly to the fish that lay at sea, off the mouth of the bay, for all the rivers were in flood.

In the moon's light the young eels saw the water fill with many fish, large and full-bellied and silvery of scale. The fish were shad returned from their feeding grounds in the sea, waiting for the ice to come out of the bay that they might ascend its rivers to spawn. Schools of croakers lay on the bottom, and the roll of their drums vibrated in the water. The croakers, with sea trout and spots, had moved in from their offshore wintering place, seeking the feeding grounds of the bay. Other fish came up into the tide flow and lay with heads to the currents, waiting to snap up the small sea animals that the swiftly moving water had dislodged, but these were bass who were of the sea and would not ascend the rivers.

As the moon waned and the surge of the tides grew less, the elvers pressed forward toward the mouth of the bay. Soon a night would come, after most of the snow had melted and run as water to the sea, when the moon's light and the tide's press would be feeble and a warm rain would fall, mist-laden and bittersweet with the scent of opening buds. Then the elvers would pour into the bay and, traveling up its shores, would find its rivers.

Some would linger in the river estuaries, brackish with the taste of the sea. These were the young male eels, who were repelled by the strangeness of fresh water. But the females would press on, swimming up against the currents of the rivers. They would move swiftly and by night as their mothers had come down the rivers. Their columns, miles in length, would wind up along the shallows of river and stream, each elver pressing close to the tail of the next before it, the whole like a serpent of monstrous length. No hardship and no obstacle would deter them. They would be preyed upon by hungry fishes—trout, bass, pickerel, and even by older eels; by rats hunting the edge of the water; and by gulls, herons, kingfishers, crows, grebes, and loons. They would swarm up waterfalls and clamber over moss-grown rocks, wet with spray; they would squirm up the spillways of dams. Some would go on for hundreds of miles—creatures of the deep sea spreading over all the land where the sea itself had lain many times before.

And as the eels lay offshore in the March sea, waiting for the time when they should enter the waters of the land, the sea, too, lay restless, awaiting the time when once more it should encroach upon the coastal plain, and creep up the sides of the foothills, and lap at the bases of the mountain ranges. As the waiting of the eels off the mouth of the bay was only an interlude in a long life filled with constant change, so the relation of sea and coast and mountain ranges was that of a moment in geologic time. For once more the mountains would be worn away by the endless erosion of water and carried in silt to the sea, and once more all the coast would be water again, and the places of its cities and towns would belong to the sea.

The Deer Mouse

BY

SALLY CARRIGHAR

THE DEER MOUSE was trapped by a sound. Startled as she sped about on the floor of the night, she had run beneath the edge of a stone. There now she hid in her fur, nose on her chest, feet all covered. But her ears' wide membranes stood high with alarm, twitching as though attached to the sound by threads.

She heard a whisper of something coming. Something was sweeping on thin wings between the needles of the trees; something was streaming across the hillside grasses, brushing the brittle husks of the seeds. Feet were stealing, seeking through the dry stalks, and leaping over the Mouse's stone.

Sometimes the sound sighed down. Then the Mouse would dare to turn around, trying to fit deeper into the crack between the stone and the ground. She wanted the walls of the nook to press her all over, but, however she crouched, one of her sides had no touch of shelter on it. That side yearned with a sense of lack, with a sort of skin-hunger, quite apart from its feeling of cold.

At other times the sound snapped. Then the Deer Mouse dropped flat, ready to dodge a hunter's pounce. She did not know that the enemy was less substantial, even, than she—that it was the wind, tossing twigs and rustling the grasses. Most of her experience was in matters as small as seeds and flies, the voices of mice, and the look of her clean white forepaw with it tiny claws, like pearl slivers. What could she understand of a battle of winds above a canyon?

The Deer Mouse wished to return to her mother's nest, an earthy cavern among the roots of a manzanita bush. The nest-ball of grass and feathers was as soft as the arching belly of a mother mouse, and behind it the roots were strong, like a mother's bones that would

417

hold off any enemy. The Deer Mouse had grown beyond the need for cuddling, but she longed for the proof on her skin of sheltering walls. Not tonight alone, but for several days, she had been obsessed with the loveliness of crannies shaped to cover a mouse.

Shortly before midnight she could have run back to the nest quite safely, for there were signs that the real dangers had drawn away. The owls were down in the hollow, as their hooting told, but in tones too low to sound in ears of deer mice. The bears had gone up the draw and were not yet due to return. Now the coral king snake would be too cold to forage. The swirling wind carried no warning of wildcat or shrew. But the swish in the grass had more meaning for a mouse.

Finally the sound shifted farther off. The Deer Mouse left the stone and raced to the manzanita, each bound as light as if she were a woolly aster released from the wind's pressure. She entered the nest and crept upon the furry heap that was her mother and sister. Now her back and sides were pushed against the dome of fibres, giving her such solid, real assurance of being hidden that she quickly relaxed in sleepy peace.

Her vibrissae were brushed by a fourth mouse groping in. He was the brother, who had left the family several days before. The wind had brought him home. Its uneasy sounds had meant for him, too, that predators were swarming through the forest, and made him long for the security he associated with his mother's nest. But while he was fitting himself among the other mice, the earth jarred. A powerful weight had struck beside the bush. It was a great horned owl, who had seen the brother slip into the dead leaves over the roots.

The leaves were swept away and claws scraped into the soil. Then the nest jolted as the roots were pulled apart. The whole pile of mice was a-tremble with frantic little heartbeats. All the mice were ready to leap as soon as the nest was torn—that was now!

The Deer Mouse alighted beneath a pine tree and darted into the fallen needles. Around her was a fanning out of quick patters. That shriek must have meant that the owl caught one mouse, perhaps the sister, always slower, more cautious, abnormally afraid of predators. The Deer Mouse's nose was pushed into the soil, but her great black eyes looked up through the needles. Against the brightness of moon-silvered clouds she saw the owl rise and sweep away.

The needles were no firm shelter. Now the Mouse was bounding down to a log in the crease of a gully. She crept under the log's curve and waited until her panting ceased. Then she found a split in the wood where she could hide. It was a tight refuge, but after such a fright she could endure being crowded by the touch of walls. The middle of the night had come, a heavy time when deer mice liked to sleep. She let her fears fall away and closed her eyes.

Moonlight woke her. It had entered even her cramped little niche. The Mouse slipped out and down the dark side of the log. She was hungry, but the log was surrounded with glittering granite gravel. The very sight of it made her back up tighter against the wood. Not even a tuft of grass grew near, for the log lay in a cradle of sand. But its shadow extended beyond the sand. The Mouse prowled out and found a spot where the soil smelled tempting. Her forepaws whirled into it, scooping it towards her so fast that she was continually astride a mound, which her hind feet kicked back. Now her claws struck an acorn, split by its swelling germ. She hooked her sharp front teeth into it, gave it a mighty pull, and it came free. She ran back to the log, then, with the acorn in her mouth. There she ate it, morsel by morsel—delicious nut, succulent with new life. The Chickaree had buried it. His stores, cached around the gully, had furnished the deer mice with many a meal. They watched even his cones, and when one dried enough to open they reached between the scales with their tiny paws, drew out the seeds and carried them to their own hoard in a pine stump.

Feeling untidy now, the Mouse licked her forepaws and scrubbed the pink tip of her nose. Taking each hind foot in her forepaws, she turned it and washed it. With the hind feet she smoothed her shoulders, and she washed her sides and back. Even her striped furry tail she cleaned. A quick shake then, and all her pretty coat, white below, oak-leaf brown above, was smooth. She seemed hardly at all like a house mouse, more like a toy doe, and so similar in color that it was clear why human beings had named her a deer mouse.

She had slept, she had eaten, and she was groomed. With these needs out of the way, she became a quiet mouse, facing a great emergency, for she was homeless. As she crouched in the shadow of the log, some delicacy of pose, or soft wildness in her eyes, gave her the unreal look of fawns. She was a small, brief union of breath, pulse, and grace, yet the apparent nothingness of her, the hint that she soon would vanish, if she had not already, actually was her strength.

All mice were so hunted that some kinds had become erratic, but deer mice learned to bound ahead of the strain of attack. They lived with a lightness that served very well for poise. Always—their way was—be ready to drop the game or gnawing or nest-building, and disappear, noiseless as a blown thistle. Dig to the sprout with airy speed, before a falling leaf may warn of claws on the bough above, before the breeze flies ahead of an enemy bringing his scent. However close come the beak or teeth, then, never hoard the fright. Don't let even death be important, since it is so familiar. Try to escape if there is a chance, but if there is not, give up life quickly.

Yet the Deer Mouse was more than a fluff of a little being. She, as well as any bear or coyote, must have her established place at Beetle Rock. Among the boulders, brush, and trees must be one cranny recognized as hers. The wrecking of her mother's nest had made it necessary to find her own niche and her own life, but she was ready, anyway, to cease the play of a young mouse and become a grown one. Before her brother left, he had raced with her on the boughs of the manzanita, and she had loved that swift motion as fawns love to bound down a slope, or chickarees to leap from tree to tree. Afterwards she sometimes had run through the bush alone, whirling herself exquisitely half out of her senses, but now a different interest had stirred in her, an impulse that soft speed would not quiet.

Oh, where, now, was a cranny into which she might fit—some hole sweet and snug, with firm walls, a secret entrance, so placed that winds would not blow, nor moisture drain, into it? Lowland deer mice dug burrows, and in some other places they made nests in trees, but the Beetle Rock deer mice searched for their nooks instead of building them. The Mouse would begin at the log.

She found a knothole and started into it, eager and pleased until she discovered a scent of other mice. She turned down towards the ground. A strip of bark, loosened by beetles, hung away from the wood. The Mouse crept under and felt the space, its size and shape, not with her paws or nose but with her vibrissae, the whiskers of various lengths which she moved like fingers over an object to give her information about it. Around this pocket went the spray of her tactile hairs, quivering into every crack. At the far end she turned.

The wood and bark touched her all over, as she liked, yet some instinct warned her that this could not be a permanent home.

Now she looked up the moon-spangled gully. Almost irresistible was her wish to return to the thicket above. The shadow of a cloud fell upon the gravel, and gave her the chance to go.

Back in the manzanita thicket, the Mouse slipped under the dead leaves beneath. As she pattered along, ears flattened and vibrissae down her sides, she was hidden from any searching eye, although the leaves kept whispering:

"She is *here.*"

She was making her way towards one of the root-crowns, but when she reached it she found that a family of juncos lived at the center of that bush. The Mouse crept close to their cup of woven grasses, so softly that the mother bird continued to sleep. She climbed up on the rim of the nest. Most of the junco's feathers were the color of a night shadow, but the sides of her tail gleamed white, and so did her ivory beak. The Mouse touched her tactile hairs over the wings and tail, outspread to cover four nestlings. She was sniffing, too, scenting the birds' light breaths, and their flesh, delicate with the sweetness of seed-food. Once more she felt over the strong walls of the birds' home, over the mother, and the nestlings' down at the edges of her wings. Then the Mouse dropped again into the brittle, rustling leaves.

At an opening in the brush she came to a mound of the leaves, pawed together by a deer. She scrambled through them, but they all flew; nothing here was strong enough to support a nest. The next manzanita bush had been home. The Mouse sped past. A short way beyond, she came to a braid of scents left by the Weasel and her five kits when the pack of little hunters crossed the thicket. The Mouse dodged away towards the open ground under the trees.

Her home-range extended on one side as far as a spring, and on the other to the foot of an open slope. In the space between grew three pines and an ancient fir. The Mouse knew the exposed part of the trees only as circular trunks and a vague overhead thicket; trees, to her, were underground things. She had her own view, too, of the earth's surface. That was not the smooth mat of needles it looked to a human eye. Chains of small shelters led almost everywhere.

Here was this tumbleweed, only a tuft of dry twigs but a mouse could hide under it. One leap from there and she reached a fallen branch. The tiny foliage of staghorn lichen covered it. Beneath the lichen she ran to the other end, her feet spinning like the feet of a house mouse. A bound, then, to a piece of bark, and from that to a root of the fir—she must let this search for her nook take her wherever it would. Most animals looked in particular kinds of places for their home-sites, but a deer mouse's cranny was accidental, an earth pocket washed out by the rain, a stump just enough decayed, a log fallen aslant a rock.

The cloud passed; moonlight slid out upon the forest floor. Now the Mouse must go underground, down into other animals' burrows, hoping to find an abandoned one. Deer mice often did appropriate such homes, whose owners had disappeared, having suddenly, unexpectedly, no more use for the patiently dug tunnel, the nest chamber, and the storeroom filled with seeds.

She would begin with the burrows of the meadow mice, who lived in the grass near the spring. She crept into the stems, moving over a web of runners and dry fallen stalks. In it was the ground-litter of this tiny wilderness—petals of the grass flowers, seed husks, skeletons of dead insects, and living insects, sleeping or numb with cold. When she found these, the Deer Mouse stopped to nibble them up, while the wavy currents of the grass stirred above her, the sound in the moist green blades as harmless as the song of gnats.

Before she had gone far she reached one of the meadow mice's surface roads, which led to all parts of the grass patch, in a curving network, regular as a cobweb but more graceful. Underfoot was a smooth pavement, kept clear by the industrious owners. The Deer Mouse passed two at work on the roads, chewing off new shoots which might be food in some places but here were troublesome weeds. She went into each sidepath, and soon found one that ended at a burrow entrance.

Down she sped into the clean little tube, just mouse-width, now straight, now curving to pass a root, a path all dark but impossible to lose. With the smell of the soil was mixed the meadow-mouse odor, grass juice crushed into fur, and musk, and here an extra odor, that of milk. The Deer Mouse followed a branch tunnel to a nest chamber. There she found five new-born young. They cried to her with appealing squeaks; perhaps they thought her their mother. She felt all over the little mice, then returned to the main burrow.

She saw mice eating, carrying nest fibres, and sleeping, for meadow mice worked either night or day. At the opening of each tunnel she sniffed the mouse scent and everywhere found it fresh; there was no vacant home for her in the grass patch. She was not anxious, anyway, to live where a road through the stems might lead snakes or weasels direct to one's nest.

Each time she had left a burrow, she had shaken the dirt out of her fur. Now she washed all over. When she felt clean she was ready for a new exploration.

She bounded to a break in the matted fir needles, but it led to no cave, only to the emerging stalk of a snow plant. She crouched there briefly, above the roots of the tree. She knew that a crook of its largest root was sheltering a chipmunk family, parents and young, whose burrow was the cleanest of all the underground neighborhood. It had even a separate space for empty seed husks. Twice while the owners slept, the Mouse had prowled through their home, one to envy but never likely to be hers. Chance hardly would remove seven chipmunks at one time.

Meshing into the roots of the fir, too, was an underground village of digger squirrels, a labyrinth of hiding places, nests for families and single squirrels, and places for the stores of seeds packed in dry sand. Sometimes the squirrels deserted old nests, but the Deer Mouse would not investigate now. Morning was too near. The waking squirrels would not be friendly to mice.

Among these tunnels were others that the Mouse did not know. Her last search took her into one. The entrance was a well-concealed hole between stones. Beyond the Mouse crept down and down, much lower into the earth than she had been before. Finally the tunnel turned and wound beneath the tree's root-platform.

Strange and remote was the smell here, of very old soil, powdered fibres of ancient plants, and the dust of rocks. Even the roots above the tunnel smelled of the past, for the tree's food and drink came now from newer roots, pushed out into fresher humus. The Mouse knew the odor of the occupant; she had smelled it behind the lively heels of the golden-mantled squirrels. The air in the burrow was very cold, but the Mouse, delicate though she was, could hold away the chill. In fact, when the winter snows would fall, her little white feet would be running over the frosty white crystals, while the owner of this home, much larger than she, would have retreated into sleep.

The Mouse reached the nest chamber, where the squirrel lay sleeping, coiled in his fur. From here several tunnels radiated to a passageway that half circled the nest—a whole web of roads for escape. The Mouse went into a tunnel beyond and abruptly found herself in the open air. She had come out at the foot of the fir trunk, through an emergency exit disguised in the bark.

Now daylight was lifting the night away. The ground had a yellow-gray cast on it, too bright for safety. The Mouse would spend the day behind the loose bark on the gully log, not a trustworthy niche, but the best she knew. She started towards it. But why did this strange deer mouse lie on the needles, warm, alive, yet surely not sleeping? The Mouse found the hole in its skin, smelling of the poison transferred with a shrew's bite. And here came the shrew, smaller than the Mouse but with venom for her, too, in its pointed snout. The Mouse escaped the death-sleep; practice in racing had made her feet faster than the shrew's. Soon she had curled up between the bark and the log, her panting already becoming lighter, and her round eyes narrower, now but gleaming black lines, and now lost in fur.

A few times she roused, but only briefly, until late morning. Then a strange sound reached in and loosened her sleep. The wind had shifted and was driving the sand in gusts, like minute, sharp rain, against the bark. Soon real rain was dropping in coarse thuds on the log. All damp things smelled strongly of their dampness.

The Mouse pushed back against the walls of the niche. The rain was becoming a roar. A sudden thunderclap startled her to a blank. Her ears had not begun to rise again, nor her forepaws to relax, when a stream of cold water began to flow over her tail.

She climbed higher in the nook, and the water rose. She crept along to the end of the bark. A turbulent brook now entirely circled the log. The Mouse did what she must—plunged into it and spun over the top. Soon the current whirled her against a branch. She raced back upon it to the gully-side, then bounded in pelting rain up through the thicket, to the trunk of the fir and the burrow exit of the golden-mantled squirrel. In his tunnel she shook herself vigorously, made herself as flat as a turtle, and pushed into the soft soil of the wall. Here her own heat would make her dry. She fell asleep.

After the Deer Mouse woke, she slipped out into the tunnel and, perched on the sloping floor, washed and groomed her fur. No place more practical than this cranny could be found for a deer mouse's nest. But of course she could not stay; a golden-mantled squirrel would not allow his exit to be revealed by the path to a nest of mice. The squirrel already had smelled her there. She heard him coming up to drive her away, so she slipped out into the daylight.

Now sunshine fell in most places where the rain had fallen, making the earth steamy. The Deer Mouse crouched between the fir trunk and a fallen cone. Her eyes were flicking over the ground, trying to find a better shelter, when the Coyote came prowling from under the thicket. He walked towards the fir.

His scent was almost as tangible as the pierce of sharp teeth. How keen was his hunting; he was not living lightly; for him this instant might have been the storm's peak, so intense were his nerves. His nose was at the ground and his feet moved forward compactly. He was following a scent trail, perhaps of the Mouse herself.

Of course he would find her here. She had no chance to escape— yet she must make that last, desperate leap. But when the instant came that she would have jumped, the bit of buff shadow lay instead a trifle lower between the cone and the fir trunk. The Mouse had slipped into a faint, perhaps thus saving her life, for if she had sprung from her refuge the Coyote certainly would have seen her.

When her speck of consciousness drifted back, the Coyote was gone and the Mule Deer Buck had come under the tree. He stood looking across the gully, apparently also aware of the Coyote, for his feet shifted in a strained way and his head was high, his ears pointing stiffly forward. What a great, powerful creature he was—yet he shared with the Deer Mouse a fear of their common enemy.

With the Deer there, the Mouse felt more safe. He would not harm her. When he relaxed, she ran out from her hiding place and examined branches and tufts of lichen torn down by the storm. One might be large enough to give her a refuge. But while she searched, another deer came, a doe in so nervous a temper that soon the Buck's hoofs and the doe's were stomping wildly. The Mouse must leave.

As the Grouse fluttered down from one of the fir boughs, the Mouse looked up. At once she raced for the trunk. In a hole up in the tree she had seen the face of a flying squirrel, a gentle creature that she had met at night on the ground. Now the Mouse reached the hole and stopped, clinging to the bark. The squirrel turned its mellow eyes upon her. The Mouse crept over the rim of the hole and down into the nest cavity. At the bottom lay four young flying squirrels, piled together as the Mouse had slept with her family. She pushed between the fur of one and the bed of shredded cedar bark.

During the afternoon the screams of a red-tailed hawk woke the innocent creatures in the tree. There was a brief, startled stir as each tried to creep in deeper, and then they lay still. When the fearful cries came no more, the squirrels moved slightly, easing their tension, and the Deer Mouse slipped farther into her furry refuge.

The next time she opened her eyes she backed out of the squirrel's coat. Now she was sharply awake. The hole at the top of the nest cavity shone but faintly. She ran up. The night's darkness had drawn to the western horizon, but the star-brightened sky cast a soft light into the trees bordering Beetle Rock.

On a branch outside the hole the flying squirrel crouched, ready to glide to the ground. Looking like a furry leaf, with her legs and their connecting membranes spread, the squirrel dropped into an air current that took her lightly to the ground. The Deer Mouse ran down the trunk of the tree. Families of deer mice sometimes shared the nests of flying squirrels, but the Mouse still preferred to find her own niche. Besides, she had no family.

Perhaps tonight she would explore the slope above her home-range. The air was so still that no stalk or leaf stirred against another. She nibbled through the bases of several lupines so they would fall, and then ate the succulent tips. When her hunger was satisfied, she made herself dainty and neat, and bounded off into the grasses.

Near the top of the slope the grasses thinned, finally coming to an end. The Mouse continued on among the trees. Ahead she saw the speeding, white, upcurved tail of another deer mouse. He led towards something that was new to her—a cabin, a nook of human beings. He ran into its open door and the Deer Mouse went in, too.

The human creatures were not there. But upon everything lay their scent, the scent of predators but not of animals that preyed upon mice. The Deer Mouse did not belong to the unclean species of mice who lived in the dark corners of human homes, but she felt no terror here, only her natural wariness in a strange place. The other deer mouse had climbed at once to a shelf and was gnawing a box, apparently familiar with the cabin and not frightened. The Deer Mouse began to explore.

Everywhere she found corners, and they gave her confidence. Few were completely covered, but they were nooks that she could back into and feel the shelter-touch. The room itself had corners and there were others around the shelves, luggage, books, and many more objects, mysterious to a mouse. She liked the fact that nothing moved. Since hunters must always move to catch prey, mice's eyes were alarmed by most motions, even of leaves. Here all was pleasantly still.

The Mouse smelled and touched many curious things. While she was examining a cold metal flashlight, she seemed suddenly overwhelmed by all the strangeness and sat up, clenching a small forepaw against her breast and quivering her ears to find the other mouse. His gnawing had ceased. The Deer Mouse raced down the table-leg and towards the door, but discovered her companion eating at a pile of oats which had poured from his hole in the box and onto the floor. She stopped and tasted the oats. Delicious! Now she sat beside the other mouse, rapidly nibbling pawfuls of the new food.

Outside, sounds approached—a man and woman talking, walking towards the cabin. They entered and shut the door. The Deer Mouse zigzagged across the floor, hunting one of the room's crannies. Dimly she saw her companion's tail slipping behind a dustpan. She glided along the edge of the wall and joined him.

Now the darkness was destroyed, not gradually as when the dawn comes, but instantaneously. The man exclaimed over the spilled oats, came striding towards the mice, and lifted the dustpan away. Silent as shadows the mice moved behind an ax. The man swept up the oats and threw them into the stove, hitting the dustpan on the iron with a noise so sharp that both mice winced.

The people's voices were tremendous, and might have been frightening, but curiously were not. For all their loudness, they had no angry tones, as animals' growls did. The Mouse could hear only the higher tones, and therefore caught more of the woman's voice than the man's. Both people were getting undressed, and the mice watched. After the human beings had taken off their shoes and part of their clothes they sat on the beds, across the room from each other, still talking.

As abruptly as the light had come on, it went out. There was a creaking of springs, shrill in the Mouse's ears, when the people got into their beds. Their voices continued. The other mouse returned to the food shelves as soon as the room was dark, and the Deer Mouse followed. Now he was gnawing a new hole in the box of oats, for the man had turned the other hole to the top. The Deer Mouse helped with the gnawing. The man said:

"Do you hear something?"

Then both people were silent, and the mice, too, kept quiet. When the voices began again the mice chewed once more at the box. Soon the oats were spilling onto the shelf and the mice were eating them.

Finally the people talked no longer. First one, then the other, breathed more deeply and slowly. For the male mouse this was a sign that he could make more noise. He began to gnaw at a crack under the door. He was a little knot of energy, now flat, his mouth turned straight up as he chewed at the bottom of the door, now huddled against the crack so that nothing of him showed but his furry haunches, and now a mound that pivoted from side to side while his hind feet kept a steady grip on the floor. While he worked, he held his tail straight out, its tip upturned with eagerness. But occasionally he became tired or bored, and pattered around the cabin.

A large splinter came away and the male mouse slid out. The Deer Mouse followed. She leapt from the sill to the ground airily and ran to the base of a tree, where she crouched. The other mouse came out of a burrow hole under a stone, and bounded towards her.

Lightly she sped away from him, back down the slope and into the grasses, dodging among the stems in a bewildering way. She seemed to be trying to lose the fine small rustle that followed, yet she never ran so fast that she quite escaped. Soon she was in her home-range, leading over familiar ways.

This was like racing with her brother, only somehow more amusing. The Deer Mouse dipped under a root, up and over another root, a gasp of a little run. A pause, then as soon as the pursuing patter came close, she rippled across the gravel to the log. She slipped to the log's other end. Finally she led to one of the manzanita bushes.

Back and forth on the gnarled stalks the Mouse flew, as if she had snapped the threads of gravity. Even the lift of a bird's wing hadn't a freer motion. The other mouse raced well, too. Sometimes he would leap from behind her onto the branch above or below, and skim ahead. Then, unexpectedly, he left her, ran down the main stalk and crouched at the base of the bush, a secret place only visible from the branches above. The Deer Mouse could see him there. And he could see her, the gleaming white fur under all of her body, streaming along the boughs.

The male mouse beat on the bush with her forepaw, a spray of patters, a pause, then another quick knocking. The Deer Mouse crouched motionless and listened. The drumming was repeated. She came in along the branch. Once more he drummed. She hesitated— then sped down. With a soft brightness she drew up to the mouse. Playfully she began to nibble his ankle.

The Dance of the Sprouting Corn

BY

D. H. LAWRENCE

PALE, DRY, baked earth, that blows into dust of fine sand. Low hills of baked pale earth, sinking heavily, and speckled sparsely with dark dots of cedar bushes. A river on the plain of drought, just a cleft of dark, reddish-brown water, almost a flood. And over all, the blue, uneasy, alkaline sky.

A pale, uneven, parched world, where a motorcar rocks and lurches and churns in sand. A world pallid with dryness, inhuman with a faint taste of alkali. Like driving in the bed of a great sea that dried up unthinkable ages ago, and now is drier than any other dryness, yet still reminiscent of the bottom of the sea, sandhills sinking, and straight, cracked mesas, like cracks in the dry-mud bottom of the sea.

So, the mud church standing discreetly outside, just outside the pueblo, not to see too much. And on its façade of mud, under the timbered mud-eaves, two speckled horses rampant, painted by the Indians, a red piebald and a black one.

Swish! Over the logs of the ditch-bridge, where brown water is flowing full. There below is the pueblo, dried mud like mudpie houses, all squatting in a jumble, prepared to crumble into dust and be invisible, dust to dust returning, earth to earth.

That they don't crumble is the mystery. That these little squarish mud-heaps endure for centuries after centuries, while Greek marble tumbles asunder, and cathedrals totter, is the wonder. But then, the naked human hand with a bit of new soft mud is quicker than time, and defies the centuries.

Roughly the low, square, mud-pie houses make a wide street where all is naked earth save a doorway or a window with a pale-

430

blue sash. At the end of the street, turn again into a parallel wide, dry street.. And there, in the dry, oblong aridity, there tosses a small forest that is alive; and thud—thud—thud goes the drum, and the deep sound of men singing is like the deep soughing of the wind, in the depths of a wood.

You realize that you had heard the drum from the distance, also the deep, distant roar and boom of the singing, but that you had not heeded, as you don't heed the wind.

It all tosses like young, agile trees in a wind. This is the dance of the sprouting corn, and everybody holds a little, beating branch of green pine. Thud—thud—thud—thud—thud! goes the drum, heavily the men hop and hop and hop, sway, sway, sway, sway go the little branches of green pine. It tosses like a little forest, and the deep sound of men's singing is like the booming and tearing of a wind deep inside a forest. They are dancing the Spring Corn Dance.

This is the Wednesday after Easter, after Christ Risen and the corn germinated. They dance on Monday and on Tuesday. Wednesday is the third and last dance of this green resurrection.

You realize the long lines of dancers, and a solid cluster of men singing near the drum. You realize the intermittent black-and-white fantasy of the hopping Koshare, the jesters, the Delight-Makers. You become aware of the ripple of bells on the knee-garters of the dancers, a continual pulsing ripple of little bells; and of the sudden wild, whooping yells from near the drum. Then you become aware of the seed-like shudder of the gourd-rattles, as the dance changes, and the swaying of the tufts of green pine-twigs stuck behind the arms of all the dancing men, in the broad green arm-bands.

Gradually comes through to you the black, stable solidity of the dancing women, who poise like solid shadow, one woman behind each rippling, leaping male. The long, silky black hair of the women, streaming down their backs, and the equally long, streaming, gleaming hair of the males, loose over broad, naked, orange-brown shoulders.

Then the faces, the impassive, rather fat, golden-brown faces of the women, with eyes cast down, crowned above with the green tableta, like a flat tiara. Something strange and noble about the impassive, barefoot women in the short black cassocks, as they subtly tread the dance, scarcely moving, and yet edging rhythmically along, swaying from each hand the green spray of pine-twig out—out—out

—out, to the thud of the drum, immediately behind the leaping fox-skins of the men dancers. And all the emerald-green, painted tab-letas, the flat wooden tiaras shaped like a castle gateway, rise steady and noble from the soft, slightly bowed heads of the women, held by a band under the chin. All the tabletas down the line, emerald green, almost steady, while the bright black heads of the men leap softly up and down, between.

Bit by bit you take it in. You cannot get a whole impression, save of some sort of wood tossing, a little forest of trees in motion, with gleaming black hair and gold-ruddy breasts that somehow do not destroy the illusion of forest.

When you look at the women, you forget the men. The bare-armed, bare-legged, barefoot women with streaming hair and lofty green tiaras, impassive, downward-looking faces, twigs swaying out-wards from subtle, rhythmic wrists; women clad in the black, pre-historic short gown fastened over one shoulder, leaving the other shoulder bare, and showing at the arm-place a bit of pink or white undershirt; belted also round the waist with a woven woollen sash, scarlet and green on the hand-woven black cassock. The noble, slightly submissive bending of the tiara-ed head. The subtle meas-ure of the bare, breathing, bird-like feet, that are flat, and seem to cleave to earth softly, and softly lift away. The continuous outward swaying of the pine-sprays.

But when you look at the men, you forget the women. The men are naked to the waist, and ruddy-golden, and in the rhythmic, hop-ping leap of the dance their breasts shake downwards, as the strong, heavy body comes down, down, down, down, in the downward plunge of the dance. The black hair streams loose and living down their backs, the black brows are level, the black eyes look out un-changing from under the silky lashes. They are handsome, and ab-sorbed with a deep rhythmic absorption, which still leaves them awake and aware. Down, down, down they drop, on the heavy, ceaseless leap of the dance, and the great necklaces of shell-cores spring on the naked breasts, the neck-shell flaps up and down, the short white kilt of woven stuff, with the heavy woollen embroidery, green and red and black, opens and shuts slightly to the strong lift-ing of the knees: the heavy whitish cords that hang from the kilt-band at the side sway and coil forever down the side of the right leg, down to the ankle, the bells on the red-woven garters under the knees ripple without end, and the feet, in buckskin boots furred round the ankle with a beautiful band of skunk fur, black with a white tip, come down with a lovely, heavy, soft precision, first one, then the other, dropping always plumb to earth. Slightly bending forward, a black gourd rattle in the right hand, a small green bough in the left, the dancer dances the eternal drooping leap, that brings his life down, down, down, down from the mind, down from the broad, beautiful, shaking breast, down to the powerful pivot of the knees, then to the ankles, and plunges deep from the ball of the foot into the earth, towards the earth's red centre, where these men belong, as is signified by the red earth with which they are smeared.

And meanwhile, the shell-cores from the Pacific sway up and down, ceaselessly, on their breasts.

Mindless, without effort, under the hot sun, unceasing, yet never perspiring nor even breathing heavily, they dance on and on. Mindless, yet still listening, observing. They hear the deep, surging singing of the bunch of old men, like a great wind soughing. They hear the cries and yells of the man waving his bough by the drum. They catch the word of the song, and at a moment, shudder the black rattles, wheel, and the line breaks, women from men, they thread across to a new formation. And as the men wheel round, their black hair gleams and shakes, and the long fox-skin sways like a tail.

And always, when they form into line again, it is a beautiful long straight line, flexible as life, but straight as rain.

The men round the drum are old, or elderly. They are all in a bunch, and they wear day dress, loose cotton drawers, pink or white cotton shirt, hair tied up behind with the red cords, and banded round the head with a strip of pink rag, or white rag, or blue. There they are, solid like a cluster of bees, their black heads with the pink rag circles all close together, swaying their pine-twigs with rhythmic, windswept hands, dancing slightly, mostly on the right foot, ceaselessly, and singing, their black bright eyes absorbed, their dark lips pushed out, while the deep strong sound rushes like wind, and the unknown words form themselves in the dark.

Suddenly the solitary man pounding the drum swings his drum round, and begins to pound on the other end, on a higher note, pang—pang—pang! instead of the previous brumm! brumm! brumm! of the bass note. The watchful man next the drummer yells and waves lightly, dancing on bird-feet. The Koshare make strange, eloquent gestures to the sky.

And again the gleaming bronze-and-dark men dancing in the rows shudder their rattles, break the rhythm, change into a queer, beautiful two-step, the long lines suddenly curl into rings, four rings of dancers, the leaping, gleaming-seeming men between the solid, subtle, submissive blackness of the women who are crowned with emerald-green tiaras, all going subtly round in rings. Then slowly they change again, and form a star. Then again, unmingling, they come back into rows.

And all the while, all the while the naked Koshare are threading about. Of bronze-and-dark men-dancers there are some forty-two, each with a dark, crowned woman attending him like a shadow. The old men, the bunch of singers in shirts and tied-up black hair, are about sixty in number, or sixty-four. The Koshare are about twenty-four.

They are slim and naked, daubed with black-and-white earth, their hair daubed white and gathered upwards to a great knot on top of the head, whence springs a tuft of corn-husks, dry corn-leaves. Though they wear nothing but a little black square cloth, front and back, at their middle, they do not seem naked, for some are white with black spots, like a leopard, and some have broad black lines or zigzags on their smeared bodies, and all their faces are blackened with triangles or lines till they look like weird masks. Meanwhile their hair, gathered straight up and daubed white and sticking up from the top of the head with corn-husks, completes the fantasy. They are anything but natural. Like blackened ghosts of a dead corn-cob, tufted at the top.

And all the time, running like queer spotted dogs, they weave nakedly through the unheeding dance, comical, weird, dancing the dance-step naked and fine, prancing through the lines, up and down the lines, and making fine gestures with their flexible hands, calling something up from the earth, and dancing forward all the time. Suddenly as they catch a word from the singers, name of a star, of a wind, a name for the sun, for a cloud, their hands soar up and gather in the air, soar down with a slow motion. And again, as they catch a word that means earth, earth deeps, water within the earth, or red-earth-quickening, the hands flutter softly down, and draw up the water, draw up the earth-quickening, earth to sky, sky to

earth, influences above to influences below, to meet in the germ-
quick of corn, where life is.

And as they dance, the Koshare watch the dancing men. And if a
fox-skin is coming loose at the belt, they fasten it as the man dances,
or they stoop and tie another man's shoe. For the dancer must not
hesitate to the end.

And then, after some forty minutes, the drum stops. Slowly the
dancers file into one line, woman behind man, and move away,
threading towards their kiva, with no sound but the tinkle of knee-
bells in the silence.

But at the same moment the thud of an unseen drum, from beyond, the soughing of deep song approaching from the unseen. It is
the other half, the other half of the tribe coming to continue the
dance. They appear round the kiva—one Koshare and one dancer
leading the rows, the old men all abreast, singing already in a great
strong burst.

So, from ten o'clock in the morning till about four in the afternoon, first one-half then the other. Till at last, as the day wanes,
the two halves meet, and the two singings like two great winds
surge one past the other, and the thicket of the dance becomes a
real forest. It is the close of the third day.

Afterwards, the men and women crowd on the roofs of the two
low round towers, the kivas, while the Koshare run round jesting
and miming, and taking big offerings from the women, loaves of
bread and cakes of blue-maize meal. Women come carrying the big
baskets of bread and guayava, on two hands, an offering.

And the mystery of germination, not procreation, but *putting
forth*, resurrection, life springing within the seed, is accomplished.
The sky has its fire, its waters, its stars, its wandering electricity,
its winds, its fingers of cold. The earth has its reddened body, its invisible hot heart, its inner waters and many juices and unaccounta-
ble stuffs. Between them all, the little seed: and also man, like a
seed that is busy and aware. And from the heights and from the
depths man, the caller, calls: man, the knower, brings down the
influences and brings up the influences, with his knowledge: man,
so vulnerable, so subject, and yet even in his vulnerability and
subjection, a master, commands the invisible influences and is
obeyed. Commands in that song, in that rhythmic energy of dance,
in that still-submissive mockery of the Koshare. And he accom-

plishes his end, as master. He partakes in the springing of the corn, in the rising and budding and earing of the corn. And when he eats his bread, at last, he recovers all he once sent forth, and partakes again of the energies he called to the corn, from out of the wide universe.

Beduin Hospitality

BY

T. E. LAWRENCE

THE CHIEFS of the Fitenna waited on us, and said that they were honoured to feast us twice a day, forenoon and sunset, so long as we remained with them; and they meant what they said. Howeitat hospitality was unlimited—no three-day niggardliness for them of the nominal desert law—and importunate, and left us no honourable escape from the entirety of the nomad's dream of well-being.

Each morning, between eight and ten, a little group of blood mares under an assortment of imperfect saddlery would come to our camping place, and on them Nasir, Nesib, Zeki and I would mount, and with perhaps a dozen of our men on foot would move solemnly across the valley by the sandy paths between the bushes. Our horses were led by our servants, since it would be immodest to ride free or fast. So eventually we would reach the tent which was to be our feast-hall for that time; each family claiming us in turn, and bitterly offended if Zaal, the adjudicator, preferred one out of just order.

As we arrived, the dogs would rush out at us, and be driven off by onlookers—always a crowd had collected round the chosen tent— and we stepped in under the ropes to its guest half, made very large for the occasion and carefully dressed with its wall-curtain on the sunny side to give us the shade. The bashful host would murmur and vanish again out of sight. The tribal rugs, lurid red things from Beyrout, were ready for us, arranged down the partition curtain, along the back wall and across the dropped end, so that we sat down on three sides of an open dusty space. We might be fifty men in all.

The host would reappear, standing by the pole; our local fellow-

437

guests, el Dheilan, Zaal and other sheikhs, reluctantly let themselves
be placed on the rugs between us, sharing our elbow-room on the
packsaddles, padded with folded felt rugs, over which we leaned.
The front of the tent was cleared, and the dogs were frequently
chased away by excited children, who ran across the empty space
pulling yet smaller children after them. Their clothes were less as
their years were less, and their pot-bodies rounder. The smallest
infants of all, out of their fly-black eyes, would stare at the company,
gravely balanced on spread legs, stark naked, sucking their thumbs
and pushing out expectant bellies towards us.

Then would follow an awkward pause, which our friends would
try to cover, by showing us on its perch the household hawk (when
possible a sea-bird taken young on the Red Sea coast) or their
watch-cockerel, or their greyhound. Once a tame ibex was dragged
in for our admiration: another time an oryx. When these interests
were exhausted they would try and find small talk to distract us
from the household noises, and from noticing the urgent whispered
cookery-directions wafted through the dividing curtain with a
powerful smell of boiled fat and drifts of tasty meat-smoke.

After a silence the host or a deputy would come forward and
whisper, 'Black or white?' an invitation for us to choose coffee or tea.
Nasir would always answer 'Black,' and the slave would be beckoned forward with the beaked coffee-pot in one hand, and three or
four clinking cups of white ware in the other. He would dash a few
drops of coffee into the uppermost cup, and proffer it to Nasir; then
pour the second for me, and the third for Nesib; and pause while
we turned the cups about in our hands, and sucked them carefully,
to get appreciatively from them the last richest drop.

As soon as they were empty his hand was stretched to clap them
noisily one above the other, and toss them out with a lesser flourish
for the next guest in order, and so on round the assembly till all had
drunk. Then back to Nasir again. This second cup would be tastier than the first, partly because the pot was yielding deeper from
the brew, partly because of the heel-taps of so many previous drinkers present in the cups; whilst the third and fourth rounds, if the
serving of the meat delayed so long, would be of surprising flavour.

However, at last, two men came staggering through the thrilled
crowd, carrying the rice and meat on a tinned copper tray or shallow bath, five feet across, set like a great brazier on a foot. In the

tribe there was only this one food-bowl of the size, and an incised inscription ran round it in florid Arabic characters: 'To the glory of God, and in trust of mercy at the last, the property of His poor suppliant, Auda abu Tayi.' It was borrowed by the host who was to entertain us for the time; and, since my urgent brain and body made me wakeful, from my blankets in the first light I would see the dish going across the country, and by marking down its goal would know where we were to feed that day.

The bowl was now brim-full, ringed round its edge by white rice in an embankment a foot wide and six inches deep, filled with legs and ribs of mutton till they toppled over. It needed two or three victims to make in the centre a dressed pyramid of meat such as honour prescribed. The centre-pieces were the boiled, upturned heads, propped on their severed stumps of neck, so that the ears, brown like old leaves, flapped out on the rice surface. The jaws gaped emptily upward, pulled open to show the hollow throat with the tongue, still pink, clinging to the lower teeth; and the long incisors whitely crowned the pile, very prominent above the nostrils' pricking hair and the lips which sneered away blackly from them.

This load was set down on the soil of the cleared space between us, where it steamed hotly, while a procession of minor helpers bore small cauldrons and copper vats in which the cooking had been done. From them, with much-bruised bowls of enamelled iron, they ladled out over the main dish all the inside and outside of the sheep; little bits of yellow intestine, the white tail-cushion of fat, brown muscles and meat and bristly skin, all swimming in the liquid butter and grease of the seething. The bystanders watched anxiously, muttering satisfactions when a very juicy scrap plopped out.

The fat was scalding. Every now and then a man would drop his baler with an exclamation, and plunge his burnt fingers, not reluctantly, in his mouth to cool them: but they persevered till at last their scooping rang loudly on the bottoms of the pots; and, with a gesture of triumph, they fished out the intact livers from their hiding place in the gravy and topped the yawning jaws with them.

Two raised each smaller cauldron and tilted it, letting the liquid splash down upon the meat till the rice-crater was full, and the loose grains at the edge swam in the abundance: and yet they poured, till, amid cries of astonishment from us, it was running

over, and a little pool congealing in the dust. That was the final
touch of splendour, and the host called us to come and eat.

We feigned a deafness, as manners demanded: at last we heard
him, and looked surprised at one another, each urging his fellow
to move first; till Nasir rose coyly, and after him we all came forward to sink on one knee round the tray, wedging in and cuddling
up till the twenty-two for whom there was barely space were grouped
around the food. We turned back our right sleeves to the elbow,
and, taking lead from Nasir with a low 'In the name of God the
merciful, the loving-kind,' we dipped together.

The first dip, for me, at least, was always cautious, since the liquid
fat was so hot that my unaccustomed fingers could seldom bear it:
and so I would toy with an exposed and cooling lump of meat till
others' excavations had drained my rice-segment. We would knead
between the fingers (not soiling the palm), neat balls of rice and fat
and liver and meat cemented by gentle pressure, and project them
by leverage of the thumb from the crooked fore-finger into the
mouth. With the right trick and the right construction the little
lump held together and came clean off the hand; but when surplus
butter and odd fragments clung, cooling, to the fingers, they had to
be licked carefully to make the next effort slip easier away.

As the meat pile wore down (nobody really cared about rice:
flesh was the luxury) one of the chief Howeitat eating with us
would draw his dagger, silver hilted, set with turquoise, a signed
masterpiece of Mohammed ibn Zari, of Jauf, (the most famous
sword-smith of my time was ibn Bani, a craftsman of the Ibn Rashid
dynasty of Hail. He rode once on foray with the Shammar against
the Rualla, and was captured. When Nuri recognized him, he shut
up with him in prison ibn Zari, his own sword-smith, swearing they
should not come out till their work was indistinguishable. So ibn
Zari improved greatly in the skill of his craft, while remaining in
design the better artist.) and would cut criss-cross from the larger
bones long diamonds of meat easily torn up between the fingers; for
it was necessarily boiled very tender, since all had to be disposed
of with the right hand which alone was honourable.

Our host stood by the circle, encouraging the appetite with pious
ejaculations. At top speed we twisted, tore, cut and stuffed: never
speaking, since conversation would insult a meal's quality; though
it was proper to smile thanks when an intimate guest passed a select

fragment, or when Mohammed el Dheilan gravely handed over a huge barren bone with a blessing. On such occasions I would return the compliment with some hideous impossible lump of guts, a flippancy which rejoiced the Howeitat, but which the gracious, aristocratic Nasir saw with disapproval.

At length some of us were nearly filled, and began to play and pick; glancing sideways at the rest till they too grew slow, and at last ceased eating, elbow on knee, the hand hanging down from the wrist over the tray edge to drip, while the fat, butter and scattered grains of rice cooled into a stiff white grease which gummed the fingers together. When all had stopped, Nasir meaningly cleared his throat, and we rose up together in haste with an explosive 'God requite it you, O host,' to group ourselves outside among the tent-ropes while the next twenty guests inherited our leaving.

Those of us who were nice would go to the end of the tent where the flap of the roof-cloth, beyond the last poles, drooped down as an end curtain; and on this clan handkerchief (whose coarse goat-hair mesh was pliant and glossy with much use) would scrape the thickest of the fat from the hands. Then we would make back to our seats, and re-take them sighingly; while the slaves, leaving aside their portion, the skulls of the sheep, would come round our rank with a wooden bowl of water, and a coffee-cup as a dipper, to splash over our fingers, while we rubbed them with the tribal soap-cake.

Meantime the second and third sittings by the dish were having their turn, and then there would be one more cup of coffee, or a glass of syrup-like tea; and at last the horses would be brought and we would slip out to them, and mount, with a quiet blessing to the hosts as we passed by. When our backs were turned the children would run in disorder upon the ravaged dish, tear our gnawed bones from one another, and escape into the open with valuable fragments to be devoured in security behind some distant bush: while the watchdogs of all the camp prowled round snapping, and the master of the tent fed the choicest offal to his grey-hound.

On Being the Right Size

BY

J. B. S. HALDANE

THE MOST obvious differences between different animals are differences of size, but for some reason the zoologists have paid
singularly little attention to them. In a large textbook of zoology
before me I find no indication that the eagle is larger than the
sparrow, or the hippopotamus bigger than the hare, though some
grudging admissions are made in the case of the mouse and the
whale. But yet it is easy to show that a hare could not be as large as
a hippopotamus, or a whale as small as a herring. For every type of
animal there is a most convenient size, and a large change in size
inevitably carries with it a change of form.

Let us take the most obvious of possible cases, and consider a
giant man sixty feet high—about the height of Giant Pope and
Giant Pagan in the illustrated *Pilgrim's Progress* of my childhood.
These monsters were not only ten times as high as Christian, but
ten times as wide and ten times as thick, so that their total weight
was a thousand times his, or about eighty to ninety tons. Unfortunately the cross sections of their bones were only a hundred times
those of Christian, so that every square inch of giant bone had to
support ten times the weight borne by a square inch of human bone.
As the human thigh-bone breaks under about ten times the human
weight, Pope and Pagan would have broken their thighs every time
they took a step. This was doubtless why they were sitting down in
the picture I remember. But it lessens one's respect for Christian
and Jack the Giant Killer.

To turn to zoology, suppose that a gazelle, a graceful little creature with long thin legs, is to become large, it will break its bones
unless it does one of two things. It may make its legs short and thick,
like the rhinoceros, so that every pound of weight has still about the

same area of bone to support it. Or it can compress its body and stretch out its legs obliquely to gain stability, like the giraffe. I mention these two beasts because they happen to belong to the same order as the gazelle, and both are quite successful mechanically, being remarkably fast runners.

Gravity, a mere nuisance to Christian, was a terror to Pope, Pagan, and Despair. To the mouse and any smaller animal it presents practically no dangers. You can drop a mouse down a thousand-yard mine shaft; and, on arriving at the bottom, it gets a slight shock and walks away, provided that the ground is fairly soft. A rat is killed, a man is broken, a horse splashes. For the resistance presented to movement by the air is proportional to the surface of the moving object. Divide an animal's length, breadth, and height each by ten; its weight is reduced to a thousandth but its surface only to a hundredth. So the resistance to falling in the case of the small animal is relatively ten times greater than the driving force.

An insect, therefore, is not afraid of gravity; it can fall without danger, and can cling to the ceiling with remarkably little trouble. It can go in for elegant and fantastic forms of support like that of the daddy-longlegs. But there is a force which is as formidable to an insect as gravitation to a mammal. This is surface tension. A man coming out of a bath carries with him a film of water of about one-fiftieth of an inch in thickness. This weighs roughly a pound. A wet mouse has to carry about its own weight of water. A wet fly has to lift many times its own weight and, as everyone knows, a fly once wetted by water or any other liquid is in a very serious position indeed. An insect going for a drink is in as great danger as a man leaning out over a precipice in search of food. If it once falls into the grip of the surface tension of the water—that is to say, gets wet—it is likely to remain so until it drowns. A few insects, such as water-beetles, contrive to be unwettable; the majority keep well away from their drink by means of a long proboscis.

Of course tall land animals have other difficulties. They have to pump their blood to greater heights than a man, and therefore, require a larger blood pressure and tougher blood-vessels. A great many men die from burst arteries, especially in the brain, and this danger is presumably still greater for an elephant or a giraffe. But animals of all kinds find difficulties in size for the following reason. A typical small animal, say a microscopic worm or rotifer, has a smooth skin through which all the oxygen it requires can soak in, a straight gut with sufficient surface to absorb its food, and a single kidney. Increase its dimensions tenfold in every direction, and its weight is increased a thousand times, so that if it is to use its muscles as efficiently as its miniature counterpart, it will need a thousand times as much food and oxygen per day and will excrete a thousand times as much of waste products.

Now if its shape is unaltered its surface will be increased only a hundredfold, and ten times as much oxygen must enter per minute through each square millimetre of skin, ten times as much food through each square millimetre of intestine. When a limit is reached to their absorptive powers their surface has to be increased by some special device. For example, a part of the skin may be drawn out into tufts to make gills or pushed in to make lungs, thus increasing the oxygen-absorbing surface in proportion to the animal's bulk. A man, for example, has a hundred square yards of lung. Similarly, the gut, instead of being smooth and straight, becomes coiled and develops a velvety surface, and other organs increase in complication. The higher animals are not larger than the lower because they are more complicated. They are more complicated because they are larger. Just the same is true of plants. The simplest plants, such as the green algae growing in stagnant water or on the bark of trees, are mere round cells. The higher plants increase their surface by putting out leaves and roots. Comparative anatomy is largely the story of the struggle to increase surface in proportion to volume.

Some of the methods of increasing the surface are useful up to a point, but not capable of a very wide adaptation. For example, while vertebrates carry the oxygen from the gills or lungs all over the body in the blood, insects take air directly to every part of their body by tiny blind tubes called tracheae which open to the surface at many different points. Now, although by their breathing movements they can renew the air in the outer part of the tracheal system, the oxygen has to penetrate the finer branches by means of diffusion. Gases can diffuse easily through very small distances, not many times larger than the average length travelled by a gas molecule between collisions with other molecules. But when such vast journeys—from the point of view of a molecule—as a quarter of an inch have to be made, a process becomes slow. So the portions of an insect's body more than a quarter of an inch from the air would always be short of oxygen. In consequence hardly any insects are much more than half an inch thick. Land crabs are built on the same general plan as insects, but are much clumsier. Yet like ourselves they carry oxygen around in their blood, and are therefore able to grow far larger than any insects. If the insects had hit on a plan for driving air through their tissues instead of letting it soak in, they might well have become as large as lobsters, though other considerations would have prevented them from becoming as large as man.

Exactly the same difficulties attach to flying. It is an elementary principle of aeronautics that the minimum speed needed to keep an aeroplane of a given shape in the air varies as the square root of its length. If its linear dimensions are increased four times, it must fly twice as fast. Now the power needed for the minimum speed increases more rapidly than the weight of the machine. So the larger aeroplane, which weighs sixty-four times as much as the smaller, needs one hundred and twenty-eight times its horsepower to keep up. Applying the same principles to the birds, we find that the limit to their size is soon reached. An angel whose muscles developed no more power weight for weight than those of an eagle or a pigeon would require a breast projecting for about four feet to house the muscles engaged in working its wings, while to economize in weight, its legs would have to be reduced to mere stilts. Actually a large bird such as an eagle or kite does not keep in the air mainly by moving its wings. It is generally to be seen soaring, that is to say balanced on a rising column of air. And even soaring becomes more and more difficult with increasing size. Were this not the case eagles might be as large as tigers and as formidable to man as hostile aeroplanes.

But it is time that we pass to some of the advantages of size. One of the most obvious is that it enables one to keep warm. All warm-blooded animals at rest lose the same amount of heat from a unit area of skin, for which purpose they need a food-supply proportional to their surface and not to their weight. Five thousand mice weigh as much as a man. Their combined surface and food or oxygen consumption are about seventeen times a man's. In fact a mouse eats about one quarter its own weight of food every day, which is mainly used in keeping it warm. For the same reason small animals cannot live in cold countries. In the arctic regions there are no reptiles or amphibians, and no small mammals. The smallest mammal in Spitzbergen is the fox. The small birds fly away in winter, while the insects die, though their eggs can survive six months or more of frost. The most successful mammals are bears, seals, and walruses.

Similarly, the eye is a rather inefficient organ until it reaches a large size. The back of the human eye on which an image of the outside world is thrown, and which corresponds to the film of a camera, is composed of a mosaic of 'rods and cones' whose diameter is little more than a length of an average light wave. Each eye has about a half a million, and for two objects to be distinguishable their images must fall on separate rods or cones. It is obvious that with fewer but larger rods and cones we should see less distinctly. If they were twice as broad two points would have to be twice as far apart before we could distinguish them at a given distance. But if their size were diminished and their number increased we should see no better. For it is impossible to form a definite image smaller than a wave-length of light. Hence a mouse's eye is not a small-scale model of a human eye. Its rods and cones are not much smaller than ours, and therefore there are far fewer of them. A mouse could not distinguish one human face from another six feet away. In order that they should be of any use at all the eyes of small animals have to be much larger in proportion to their bodies than our own. Large animals on the other hand only require relatively small eyes, and those of the whale and elephant are little larger than our own.

For rather more recondite reasons the same general principle holds true of the brain. If we compare the brain-weights of a set of very similar animals such as the cat, cheetah, leopard, and tiger, we find that as we quadruple the body-weight the brain-weight is only doubled. The larger animal with proportionately larger bones can economize on brain, eyes, and certain other organs.

Such are a very few of the considerations which show that for every type of animal there is an optimum size. Yet although Galileo demonstrated the contrary more than three hundred years ago, people still believe that if a flea were as large as a man it could jump a thousand feet into the air. As a matter of fact the height to which an animal can jump is more nearly independent of its size than proportional to it. A flea can jump about two feet, a man about five. To jump a given height, if we neglect the resistance of the air, requires an expenditure of energy proportional to the jumper's weight. But if the jumping muscles form a constant fraction of the animal's body, the energy developed per ounce of muscle is independent of the size, provided it can be developed quickly enough in the small animal. As a matter of fact an insect's muscles, although they can contract more quickly than our own, appear to be less efficient; as otherwise a flea or grasshopper could rise six feet into the air.

4
MYSTERY, FANTASY, AND MURDER

The Machine Stops

BY

E. M. FORSTER

Part I

THE AIR-SHIP

IMAGINE, if you can, a small room, hexagonal in shape, like the cell of a bee. It is lighted neither by window nor by lamp, yet it is filled with a soft radiance. There are no apertures for ventilation, yet the air is fresh. There are no musical instruments, and yet, at the moment that my meditation opens, this room is throbbing with melodious sounds. An arm-chair is in the centre, by its side a reading-desk—that is all the furniture. And in the arm-chair there sits a swaddled lump of flesh—a woman, about five feet high, with a face as white as a fungus. It is to her that the little room belongs.

An electric bell rang.

The woman touched a switch and the music was silent.

"I suppose I must see who it is," she thought, and set her chair in motion. The chair, like the music, was worked by machinery, and it rolled her to the other side of the room, where the bell still rang importunately.

"Who is it?" she called. Her voice was irritable, for she had been interrupted often since the music began. She knew several thousand people; in certain directions human intercourse had advanced enormously.

But when she listened into the receiver, her white face wrinkled into smiles, and she said:

"Very well. Let us talk, I will isolate myself. I do not expect anything important will happen for the next five minutes—for I can give you fully five minutes, Kuno. Then I must deliver my lecture on 'Music during the Australian Period.' "

She touched the isolation knob, so that no one else could speak to her. Then she touched the lighting apparatus, and the little room was plunged into darkness.

"Be quick!" she called, her irritation returning. "Be quick, Kuno; here I am in the dark wasting my time."

But it was fully fifteen seconds before the round plate that she held in her hands began to glow. A faint blue light shot across it, darkening to purple, and presently she could see the image of her son, who lived on the other side of the earth, and he could see her.

"Kuno, how slow you are."

He smiled gravely.

"I really believe you enjoy dawdling."

"I have called you before, mother, but you were always busy or isolated. I have something particular to say."

"What is it, dearest boy? Be quick. Why could you not send it by pneumatic post?"

"Because I prefer saying such a thing. I want——"

"Well?"

"I want you to come and see me."

Vashti watched his face in the blue plate.

"But I can see you!" she exclaimed. "What more do you want?"

"I want to see you not through the Machine," said Kuno. "I want to speak to you not through the wearisome Machine."

"Oh, hush!" said his mother, vaguely shocked. "You mustn't say anything against the Machine."

"Why not?"

"One mustn't."

"You talk as if a god had made the Machine," cried the other. "I believe that you pray to it when you are unhappy. Men made it, do not forget that. Great men, but men. The Machine is much, but it is not everything. I see something like you in this plate, but I do not see you. I hear something like you through this telephone, but I do not hear you. That is why I want you to come. Come and stop with me. Pay me a visit, so that we can meet face to face, and talk about the hopes that are in my mind."

She replied that she could scarcely spare the time for a visit.

"The air-ship barely takes two days to fly between me and you."

"I dislike air-ships."

"Why?"

"I dislike seeing the horrible brown earth, and the sea, and the stars when it is dark. I get no ideas in an air-ship."

"I do not get them anywhere else."

"What kind of ideas can the air give you?"

He paused for an instant.

"Do you not know four big stars that form an oblong, and three stars close together in the middle of the oblong, and hanging from these stars, three other stars?"

"No, I do not. I dislike the stars. But did they give you an idea? How interesting; tell me."

"I had an idea that they were like a man."

"I do not understand."

"The four big stars are the man's shoulders and his knees. The three stars in the middle are like the belts that men wore once, and the three stars hanging are like a sword."

"A sword?"

"Men carried swords about with them, to kill animals and other men."

"It does not strike me as a very good idea, but it is certainly original. When did it come to you first?"

"In the air-ship——" He broke off, and she fancied that he looked sad. She could not be sure, for the Machine did not transmit *nuances* of expression. It only gave a general idea of people—an idea that was good enough for all practical purposes, Vashti thought. The imponderable bloom, declared by a discredited philosophy to be the actual essence of intercourse, was rightly ignored by the Machine, just as the imponderable bloom of the grape was ignored by the manufacturers of artificial fruit. Something "good enough" had long since been accepted by our race.

"The truth is," he continued, "that I want to see these stars again. They are curious stars. I want to see them not from the air-ship, but from the surface of the earth, as our ancestors did, thousands of years ago. I want to visit the surface of the earth."

She was shocked again.

"Mother, you must come, if only to explain to me what is the harm of visiting the surface of the earth."

"No harm," she replied, controlling herself. "But no advantage.

The surface of the earth is only dust and mud, no life remains on it, and you would need a respirator, or the cold of the outer air would kill you. One dies immediately in the outer air."

"I know; of course I shall take all precautions."

"And besides——"

"Well?"

She considered, and chose her words with care. Her son had a queer temper, and she wished to dissuade him from the expedition. "It is contrary to the spirit of the age," she asserted.

"Do you mean by that, contrary to the Machine?"

"In a sense, but——"

His image in the blue plate faded.

"Kuno!"

He had isolated himself.

For a moment Vashti felt lonely.

Then she generated the light, and the sight of her room, flooded with radiance and studded with electric buttons, revived her. There were buttons and switches everywhere—buttons to call for food, for music, for clothing. There was the hot-bath button, by pressure of which a basin of (imitation) marble rose out of the floor, filled to the brim with a warm deodorised liquid. There was the cold-bath button. There was the button that produced literature. And there were of course the buttons by which she communicated with her friends. The room, though it contained nothing, was in touch with all that she cared for in the world.

Vashti's next move was to turn off the isolation-switch, and all the accumulations of the last three minutes burst upon her. The room was filled with the noise of bells, and speaking-tubes. What was the new food like? Could she recommend it? Had she had any ideas lately? Might one tell her one's own ideas? Would she make an engagement to visit the public nurseries at an early date?—say this day month.

To most of these questions she replied with irritation—a growing quality in that accelerated age. She said that the new food was horrible. That she could not visit the public nurseries through press of engagements. That she had no ideas of her own but had just been told one—that four stars and three in the middle were like a man: she doubted there was much in it. Then she switched off her correspondents, for it was time to deliver her lecture on Australian music.

The clumsy system of public gatherings had been long since abandoned; neither Vashti nor her audience stirred from their rooms. Seated in her arm-chair she spoke, while they in their arm-chairs heard her, fairly well, and saw her, fairly well. She opened with a humorous account of music in the pre-Mongolian epoch, and went on to describe the great outburst of song that followed the Chinese conquest. Remote and primæval as were the methods of I-San-So and the Brisbane school, she yet felt (she said) that study of them might repay the musician of today: they had freshness; they had, above all, ideas.

Her lecture, which lasted ten minutes, was well received, and at its conclusion she and many of her audience listened to a lecture on the sea; there were ideas to be got from the sea; the speaker had donned a respirator and visited it lately. Then she fed, talked to many friends, had a bath, talked again, and summoned her bed.

The bed was not to her liking. It was too large, and she had a feeling for a small bed. Complaint was useless, for beds were of the same dimension all over the world, and to have had an alternative size would have involved vast alterations in the Machine. Vashti isolated herself—it was necessary, for neither day nor night existed under the ground—and reviewed all that had happened since she had summoned the bed last. Ideas? Scarcely any. Events—was Kuno's invitation an event?

By her side, on the little reading-desk, was a survival from the ages of litter—one book. This was the Book of the Machine. In it were instructions against every possible contingency. If she was hot or cold or dyspeptic or at loss for a word, she went to the book, and it told her which button to press. The Central Committee published it. In accordance with a growing habit, it was richly bound.

Sitting up in the bed, she took it reverently in her hands. She glanced round the glowing room as if some one might be watching her. Then, half ashamed, half joyful, she murmured "O Machine! O Machine!" and raised the volume to her lips. Thrice she kissed it, thrice inclined her head, thrice she felt the delirium of acquiescence. Her ritual performed, she turned to page 1367, which gave the times of the departure of the air-ships from the island in the southern hemisphere, under whose soil she lived, to the island in the northern hemisphere, whereunder lived her son.

She thought, "I have not the time."

She made the room dark and slept; she awoke and made the room light; she ate and exchanged ideas with her friends, and listened to music and attended lectures; she made the room dark and slept. Above her, beneath her, and around her, the Machine hummed eternally; she did not notice the noise, for she had been born with it in her ears. The earth, carrying her, hummed as it sped through silence, turning her now to the invisible sun, now to the invisible stars. She awoke and made the room light.

"Kuno!"

"I will not talk to you," he answered, "until you come."

"Have you been on the surface of the earth since we spoke last?"

His image faded.

Again she consulted the Book. She became very nervous and lay back in her chair palpitating. Think of her as without teeth or hair. Presently she directed the chair to the wall, and pressed an unfamiliar button. The wall swung apart slowly. Through the opening she saw a tunnel that curved slightly, so that its goal was not visible. Should she go to see her son, here was the beginning of the journey.

Of course she knew all about the communication-system. There was nothing mysterious in it. She would summon a car and it would fly with her down the tunnel until it reached the lift that communicated with the air-ship station: the system had been in use for many, many years, long before the universal establishment of the Machine. And of course she had studied the civilisation that had immediately preceded her own—the civilisation that had mistaken the functions of the system, and had used it for bringing people to things, instead of for bringing things to people. Those funny old days, when men went for change of air instead of changing the air in their rooms! And yet—she was frightened of the tunnel: she had not seen it since her last child was born. It curved—but not quite as she remembered; it was brilliant—but not quite as brilliant as a lecturer had suggested. Vashti was seized with the terrors of direct experience. She shrank back into the room, and the wall closed up again.

"Kuno," she said, "I cannot come to see you. I am not well."

Immediately an enormous apparatus fell on to her out of the ceiling, a thermometer was automatically inserted between her lips, a stethoscope was automatically laid upon her heart. She lay powerless. Cool pads soothed her forehead. Kuno had telegraphed to her doctor.

So the human passions still blundered up and down in the Machine. Vashti drank the medicine that the doctor projected into her mouth, and the machinery retired into the ceiling. The voice of Kuno was heard asking how she felt.

"Better." Then with irritation: "But why do you not come to me instead?"

"Because I cannot leave this place."

"Why?"

"Because, any moment, something tremendous may happen."

"Have you been on the surface of the earth yet?"

"Not yet."

"Then what is it?"

"I will not tell you through the Machine."

She resumed her life.

But she thought of Kuno as a baby, his birth, his removal to the public nurseries, her one visit to him there, his visits to her—visits which stopped when the Machine had assigned him a room on the other side of the earth. "Parents, duties of," said the Book of the Machine, "cease at the moment of birth. P. 422327483." True, but there was something special about Kuno—indeed there had been something special about all her children—and, after all, she must brave the journey if he desired it. And "something tremendous might happen." What did that mean? The nonsense of a youthful man, no doubt, but she must go. Again she pressed the unfamiliar button, again the wall swung back, and she saw the tunnel that curved out of sight. Clasping the Book, she rose, tottered on to the platform, and summoned the car. Her room closed behind her: the journey to the northern hemisphere had begun.

Of course it was perfectly easy. The car approached and in it she found arm-chairs exactly like her own. When she signalled, it stopped, and she tottered into the lift. One other passenger was in the lift, the first fellow creature she had seen face to face for months. Few travelled in these days, for, thanks to the advance of science, the earth was exactly alike all over. Rapid intercourse, from which the previous civilisation had hoped so much, had ended by defeating itself. What was the good of going to Pekin when it was just like Shrewsbury? Why return to Shrewsbury when it would be just like

Pekin? Men seldom moved their bodies; all unrest was concentrated in the soul.

The air-ship service was a relic from the former age. It was kept up, because it was easier to keep it up than to stop it or to diminish it, but it now far exceeded the wants of the population. Vessel after vessel would rise from the vomitories of Rye or of Christchurch (I use the antique names), would sail into the crowded sky, and would draw up at the wharves of the south—empty. So nicely adjusted was the system, so independent of meteorology, that the sky, whether calm or cloudy, resembled a vast kaleidoscope whereon the same patterns periodically recurred. The ship on which Vashti sailed started now at sunset, now at dawn. But always, as it passed above Rheims, it would neighbour the ship that served between Helsingfors and the Brazils, and, every third time it surmounted the Alps, the fleet of Palermo would cross its track behind. Night and day, wind and storm, tide and earthquake, impeded man no longer. He had harnessed Leviathan. All the old literature, with its praise of Nature, and its fear of Nature, rang false as the prattle of a child.

Yet as Vashti saw the vast flank of the ship, stained with exposure to the outer air, her horror of direct experience returned. It was not quite like the air-ship in the cinematophoto. For one thing it smelt —not strongly or unpleasantly, but it did smell, and with her eyes shut she should have known that a new thing was close to her. Then she had to walk to it from the lift, had to submit to glances from the other passengers. The man in front dropped his Book—no great matter, but it disquieted them all. In the rooms, if the Book was dropped, the floor raised it mechanically, but the gangway to the air-ship was not so prepared, and the sacred volume lay motionless. They stopped—the thing was unforeseen—and the man, instead of picking up his property, felt the muscles of his arm to see how they had failed him. Then some one actually said with direct utterance: "We shall be late"—and they trooped on board, Vashti treading on the pages as she did so.

Inside, her anxiety increased. The arrangements were old-fashioned and rough. There was even a female attendant, to whom she would have to announce her wants during the voyage. Of course a revolving platform ran the length of the boat, but she was expected to walk from it to her cabin. Some cabins were better than others, and she did not get the best. She thought the attendant had been un-

fair, and spasms of rage shook her. The glass valves had closed, she
could not go back. She saw, at the end of the vestibule, the lift in
which she had ascended going quietly up and down, empty. Beneath
those corridors of shining tiles were rooms, tier below tier, reaching
far into the earth, and in each room there sat a human being, eating, or sleeping, or producing ideas. And buried deep in the hive
was her own room. Vashti was afraid.

"O Machine! O Machine!" she murmured, and caressed her Book,
and was comforted.

Then the sides of the vestibule seemed to melt together, as do the
passages that we see in dreams, the lift vanished, the Book that had
been dropped slid to the left and vanished, polished tiles rushed by
like a stream of water, there was a slight jar, and the air-ship, issuing from its tunnel, soared above the waters of a tropical ocean.

It was night. For a moment she saw the coast of Sumatra edged by
the phosphorescence of waves, and crowned by lighthouses, still
sending forth their disregarded beams. These also vanished, and
only the stars distracted her. They were not motionless, but swayed
to and fro above her head, thronging out of one skylight into another, as if the universe and not the air-ship was careening. And, as
often happens on clear nights, they seemed now to be in perspec-
tive, now on a plane; now piled tier beyond tier into the infinite
heavens, now concealing infinity, a roof limiting for ever the visions
of men. In either case they seemed intolerable. "Are we to travel in
the dark?" called the passengers angrily, and the attendant, who had
been careless, generated the light, and pulled down the blinds of
pliable metal. When the air-ships had been built, the desire to look
direct at things still lingered in the world. Hence the extraordinary
number of skylights and windows, and the proportionate discomfort to those who were civilised and refined. Even in Vashti's cabin
one star peeped through a flaw in the blind, and after a few hours'
uneasy slumber, she was disturbed by an unfamiliar glow, which
was the dawn.

Quick as the ship had sped westwards, the earth had rolled east-
wards quicker still, and had dragged back Vashti and her companions towards the sun. Science could prolong the night, but only for
a little, and those high hopes of neutralising the earth's diurnal
revolution had passed, together with hopes that were possibly higher.
To "keep pace with the sun," or even to outstrip it, had been the

aim of the civilization preceding this. Racing aeroplanes had been built for the purpose, capable of enormous speed, and steered by the greatest intellects of the epoch. Round the globe they went, round and round, westward, westward, round and round, amidst humanity's applause. In vain. The globe went eastward quicker still, horrible accidents occurred, and the Committee of the Machine, at the time rising into prominence, declared the pursuit illegal, unmechanical, and punishable by Homelessness.

Of Homelessness more will be said later.

Doubtless the Committee was right. Yet the attempt to "defeat the sun" aroused the last common interest that our race experienced about the heavenly bodies, or indeed about anything. It was the last time that men were compacted by thinking of a power outside the world. The sun had conquered, yet it was the end of his spiritual dominion. Dawn, midday, twilight, the zodiacal path, touched neither men's lives nor their hearts, and science retreated into the ground, to concentrate herself upon problems that she was certain of solving.

So when Vashti found her cabin invaded by a rosy finger of light, she was annoyed, and tried to adjust the blind. But the blind flew up altogether, and she saw through the skylight small pink clouds, swaying against a background of blue, and as the sun crept higher, its radiance entered direct, brimming down the wall, like a golden sea. It rose and fell with the air-ship's motion, just as waves rise and fall, but it advanced steadily, as a tide advances. Unless she was careful, it would strike her face. A spasm of horror shook her and she rang for the attendant. The attendant too was horrified, but she could do nothing; it was not her place to mend the blind. She could only suggest that the lady should change her cabin, which she accordingly prepared to do.

People were almost exactly alike all over the world, but the attendant of the air-ship, perhaps owing to her exceptional duties, had grown a little out of the common. She had often to address passengers with direct speech, and this had given her a certain roughness and originality of manner. When Vashti swerved away from the sunbeams with a cry, she behaved barbarically—she put out her hand to steady her.

"How dare you!" exclaimed the passenger. "You forget yourself!"

The woman was confused, and apologized for not having let her fall. People never touched one another. The custom had become obsolete, owing to the Machine.

"Where are we now?" asked Vashti haughtily.

"We are over Asia," said the attendant, anxious to be polite.

"Asia?"

"You must excuse my common way of speaking. I have got into the habit of calling places over which I pass by their unmechanical names."

"Oh, I remember Asia. The Mongols came from it."

"Beneath us, in the open air, stood a city that was once called Simla."

"Have you ever heard of the Mongols and of the Brisbane school?"

"No."

"Brisbane also stood in the open air."

"Those mountains to the right—let me show you them." She pushed back a metal blind. The main chain of the Himalayas was revealed. "They were once called the Roof of the World, those mountains."

"What a foolish name!"

"You must remember that, before the dawn of civilisation, they seemed to be an impenetrable wall that touched the stars. It was supposed that no one but the gods could exist above their summits. How we have advanced, thanks to the Machine!"

"How we have advanced, thanks to the Machine!" said Vashti.

"How we have advanced, thanks to the Machine!" echoed the passenger who had dropped his Book the night before, and who was standing in the passage.

"And that white stuff in the cracks?—what is it?"

"I have forgotten its name."

"Cover the window, please. These mountains give me no ideas."

The northern aspect of the Himalayas was in deep shadow: on the India slope the sun had just prevailed. The forests had been destroyed during the literature epoch for the purpose of making newspaper-pulp, but the snows were awakening to their morning glory, and clouds still hung on the breasts of Kinchinjunga. In the plain were seen the ruins of cities, with diminished rivers creeping by their walls, and by the sides of these were sometimes the signs of vomitories, marking the cities of today. Over the whole prospect air-ships rushed, crossing and intercrossing with incredible *aplomb*, and rising nonchalantly when they desired to escape the perturbations of the lower atmosphere and to traverse the Roof of the World.

"We have indeed advanced, thanks to the Machine," repeated the attendant, and hid the Himalayas behind a metal blind.

The day dragged wearily forward. The passengers sat each in his cabin, avoiding one another with an almost physical repulsion and longing to be once more under the surface of the earth. There were eight or ten of them, mostly young males, sent out from the public nurseries to inhabit the rooms of those who had died in various parts of the earth. The man who had dropped his Book was on the homeward journey. He had been sent to Sumatra for the purpose of propagating the race. Vashti alone was travelling by her private will.

At midday she took a second glance at the earth. The air-ship was crossing another range of mountains, but she could see little, owing to clouds. Masses of black rock hovered below her, and merged indistinctly into grey. Their shapes were fantastic; one of them resembled a prostrate man.

"No ideas here," murmured Vashti, and hid the Caucasus behind a metal blind.

In the evening she looked again. They were crossing a golden sea, in which lay many small islands and one peninsula.

She repeated, "No ideas here," and hid Greece behind a metal blind.

Part II

THE MENDING APPARATUS

By a vestibule, by a lift, by a tubular railway, by a platform, by a sliding door—by reversing all the steps of her departure did Vashti arrive at her son's room, which exactly resembled her own. She might well declare that the visit was superfluous. The buttons, the knobs, the reading-desk with the Book, the temperature, the atmosphere, the illumination—all were exactly the same. And if Kuno himself, flesh of her flesh, stood close beside her at last, what profit was there in that? She was too well-bred to shake him by the hand.

Averting her eyes, she spoke as follows:

"Here I am. I have had the most terrible journey and greatly retarded the development of my soul. It is not worth it, Kuno, it is not worth it. My time is too precious. The sunlight almost touched me, and I have met with the rudest people. I can only stop a few minutes. Say what you want to say, and then I must return."

"I have been threatened with Homelessness," said Kuno.

She looked at him now.

"I have been threatened with Homelessness, and I could not tell you such a thing through the Machine."

Homelessness means death. The victim is exposed to the air, which kills him.

"I have been outside since I spoke to you last. The tremendous thing has happened, and they have discovered me."

"But why shouldn't you go outside!" she exclaimed. "It is perfectly legal, perfectly mechanical, to visit the surface of the earth. I have lately been to a lecture on the sea; there is no objection to that; one simply summons a respirator and gets an Egression-permit. It is not the kind of thing that spiritually-minded people do, and I begged you not to do it, but there is no legal objection to it."

"I did not get an Egression-permit."

"Then how did you get out?"

"I found out a way of my own."

The phrase conveyed no meaning to her, and he had to repeat it.

"A way of your own?" she whispered. "But that would be wrong."

"Why?"

The question shocked her beyond measure.

"You are beginning to worship the Machine," he said coldly. "You think it irreligious of me to have found out a way of my own. It was just what the Committee thought, when they threatened me with Homelessness."

At this she grew angry. "I worship nothing!" she cried. "I am most advanced. I don't think you irreligious, for there is no such thing as religion left. All the fear and the superstition that existed once have been destroyed by the Machine. I only meant that to find out a way of your own was—— Besides, there is no new way out."

"So it is always supposed."

"Except through the vomitories, for which one must have an Egression-permit, it is impossible to get out. The Book says so."

"Well, the Book's wrong, for I have been out on my feet."

For Kuno was possessed of a certain physical strength.

By these days it was a demerit to be muscular. Each infant was examined at birth, and all who promised undue strength were de-·stroyed. Humanitarians may protest, but it would have been no true kindness to let an athlete live; he would never have been happy in that state of life to which the Machine had called him; he would have yearned for trees to climb, rivers to bathe in, meadows and hills against which he might measure his body. Man must be adapted to his surroundings, must he not? In the dawn of the world our weakly must be exposed on Mount Taygetus, in its twilight our strong will suffer euthanasia, that the Machine may progress, that the Machine may progress, that the Machine may progress eternally.

"You know that we have lost the sense of space. We say 'space is annihilated,' but we have annihilated not space, but the sense thereof. We have lost a part of ourselves. I determined to recover it, and I began by walking up and down the platform of the railway outside my room. Up and down, until I was tired, and so did recapture the meaning of 'Near' and 'Far.' 'Near' is a place to which I can get quickly *on my feet,* not a place to which the train or the air-ship will take me quickly. 'Far' is a place to which I cannot get quickly on my feet; the vomitory is 'far,' though I could be there in thirty-eight seconds by summoning the train. Man is the measure. That was my first lesson. Man's feet are the measure for distance, his hands are the measure for ownership, his body is the measure for all that is lovable and desirable and strong. Then I went further: it was then that I called to you for the first time, and you would not come.

"This city, as you know, is built deep beneath the surface of the earth, with only the vomitories protruding. Having paced the platform outside my own room, I took the lift to the next platform and paced that also, and so with each in turn, until I came to the topmost, above which begins the earth. All the platforms were exactly alike, and all that I gained by visiting them was to develop my sense of space and my muscles. I think I should have been content with this—it is not a little thing—but as I walked and brooded, it occurred to me that our cities had been built in the days when men still breathed the outer air, and that there had been ventilation shafts for the workmen. I could think of nothing but these ventilation shafts. Had they been destroyed by all the food-tubes and medicine-tubes and music-tubes that the Machine has evolved lately? Or did traces of them remain? One thing was certain. If I came upon them anywhere, it would be in the railway-tunnels of the topmost story. Everywhere else, all space was accounted for.

"I am telling my story quickly, but don't think that I was not a coward or that your answers never depressed me. It is not the proper thing, it is not mechanical, it is not decent to walk along a railway-tunnel. I did not fear that I might tread upon a live rail and be killed. I feared something far more intangible—doing what was not contemplated by the Machine. Then I said to myself, 'Man is the measure,' and I went, and after many visits I found an opening.

"The tunnels, of course, were lighted. Everything is light, artificial light; darkness is the exception. So when I saw a black gap in the tiles, I knew that it was an exception, and rejoiced. I put in my arm—I could put in no more at first—and waved it round and round in ecstasy. I loosed another tile, and put in my head, and shouted into the darkness: 'I am coming, I shall do it yet,' and my voice reverberated down endless passages. I seemed to hear the spirits of those dead workmen who had returned each evening to the starlight and to their wives, and all the generations who had lived in the open air called back to me, 'You will do it yet, you are coming.'"

He paused, and, absurd as he was, his last words moved her. For Kuno had lately asked to be a father, and his request had been refused by the Committee. His was not a type that the Machine desired to hand on.

"Then a train passed. It brushed by me, but I thrust my head and arms into the hole. I had done enough for one day, so I crawled back to the platform, went down in the lift, and summoned my bed. Ah, what dreams! And again I called you, and again you refused."

She shook her head and said:

"Don't. Don't talk of these terrible things. You make me miserable. You are throwing civilisation away."

"But I had got back the sense of space and a man cannot rest then. I determined to get in at the hole and climb the shaft. And so I exercised my arms. Day after day I went through ridiculous movements, until my flesh ached, and I could hang by my hands and hold the pillow of my bed outstretched for many minutes. Then I summoned a respirator, and started.

"It was easy at first. The mortar had somehow rotted, and I soon pushed some more tiles in, and clambered after them into the darkness, and the spirits of the dead comforted me. I don't know what I mean by that. I just say what I felt. I felt, for the first time, that a protest had been lodged against corruption, and that even as the dead were comforting me, so I was comforting the unborn. I felt that humanity existed, and that it existed without clothes. How can I possibly explain this? It was naked, humanity seemed naked, and all these tubes and buttons and machineries neither came into the world with us, nor will they follow us out, nor do they matter supremely while we are here. Had I been strong, I would have torn off every garment I had, and gone out in the outer air unswaddled. But this is not for me, nor perhaps for my generation. I climbed with my respirator and my hygienic clothes and my dietetic tabloids! Better thus than not at all.

"There was a ladder, made of some primæval metal. The light from the railway fell upon its lowest rungs, and I saw that it led straight upwards out of the rubble at the bottom of the shaft. Perhaps our ancestors ran up and down it a dozen times daily, in their building. As I climbed, the rough edges cut through my gloves so that my hands bled. The light helped me for a little, and then came darkness and, worse still, silence which pierced my ears like a sword. The Machine hums! Did you know that? Its hum penetrates our blood, and may even guide our thoughts. Who knows! I was getting beyond its power. Then I thought: 'This silence means that I am doing wrong.' But I heard voices in the silence, and again they strengthened me." He laughed. "I had need of them. The next moment I cracked my head against something."

She sighed.

"I had reached one of those pneumatic stoppers that defend us from the outer air. You may have noticed them on the air-ship. Pitch dark, my feet on the rungs of an invisible ladder, my hands cut; I cannot explain how I lived through this part, but the voices still comforted me, and I felt for fastenings. The stopper, I suppose, was about eight feet across. I passed my hand over it as far as I could reach. It was perfectly smooth. I felt it almost to the centre. Not quite to the centre, for my arm was too short. Then the voice said: 'Jump. It is worth it. There may be a handle in the centre, and you may catch hold of it and so come to us your own way. And if there is no handle, so that you may fall and are dashed to pieces—it is still worth it: you will still come to us your own way.' So I jumped. There was a handle, and——"

He paused. Tears gathered in his mother's eyes. She knew that he was fated. If he did not die today he would die tomorrow. There was not room for such a person in the world. And with her pity disgust mingled. She was ashamed at having borne such a son, she who had always been so respectable and so full of ideas. Was he really the little boy to whom she had taught the use of his stops and buttons, and to whom she had given his first lessons in the Book? The very hair that disfigured his lip showed that he was reverting to some savage type. On atavism the Machine can have no mercy.

"There was a handle, and I did catch it. I hung tranced over the darkness and heard the hum of these workings as the last whisper in a dying dream. All the things I had cared about and all the people I had spoken to through tubes appeared infinitely little. Meanwhile the handle revolved. My weight had set something in motion and I span slowly, and then——

"I cannot describe it. I was lying with my face to the sunshine. Blood poured from my nose and ears and I heard a tremendous roaring. The stopper, with me clinging to it, had simply been blown out of the earth, and the air that we make down here was escaping through the vent into the air above. It burst up like a fountain. I crawled back to it—for the upper air hurts—and, as it were, I took great sips from the edge. My respirator had flown goodness knows where, my clothes were torn. I just lay with my lips close to the hole, and I sipped until the bleeding stopped. You can imagine nothing so curious. This hollow in the grass—I will speak of it in a minute, —the sun shining into it, not brilliantly but through marbled clouds,—the peace, the nonchalance, the sense of space, and, brushing my cheek, the roaring fountain of our artificial air! Soon I spied my respirator, bobbing up and down in the current high above my head, and higher still were many air-ships. But no one ever looks out of air-ships, and in my case they could not have picked me up. There I was, stranded. The sun shone a little way down the shaft, and revealed the topmost rung of the ladder, but it was hopeless trying to reach it. I should either have been tossed up again by the escape, or else have fallen in, and died. I could only lie on the grass, sipping and sipping, and from time to time glancing around me.

"I knew that I was in Wessex, for I had taken care to go to a lecture on the subject before starting. Wessex lies above the room in which we are talking now. It was once an important state. Its kings held all the southern coast from the Andredswald to Cornwall, while the Wansdyke protected them on the north, running over the high ground. The lecturer was only concerned with the rise of Wessex, so I do not know how long it remained an international power, nor would the knowledge have assisted me. To tell the truth I could do nothing but laugh, during this part. There was I, with a pneumatic stopper by my side and a respirator bobbing over my head, imprisoned, all three of us, in a grass-grown hollow that was edged with fern."

Then he grew grave again.

"Lucky for me that it was a hollow. For the air began to fall back into it and to fill it as water fills a bowl. I could crawl about. Presently I stood. I breathed a mixture, in which the air that hurts predominated whenever I tried to climb the sides. This was not so bad. I had not lost my tabloids and remained ridiculously cheerful, and as for the Machine, I forgot about it altogether. My one aim now was to get to the top, where the ferns were, and to view whatever objects lay beyond.

"I rushed the slope. The new air was still too bitter for me and I came rolling back, after a momentary vision of something grey. The sun grew very feeble, and I remembered that he was in Scorpio—I had been to a lecture on that too. If the sun is in Scorpio and you are in Wessex, it means that you must be as quick as you can, or it will get too dark. (This is the first bit of useful information I have ever got from a lecture, and I expect it will be the last.) It made me try frantically to breathe the new air, and to advance as far as I dared out of my pond. The hollow filled so slowly. At times I thought that the fountain played with less vigour. My respirator seemed to dance nearer the earth; the roar was decreasing."

He broke off.

"I don't think this is interesting you. The rest will interest you even less. There are no ideas in it, and I wish that I had not troubled you to come. We are too different, mother."

She told him to continue.

"It was evening before I climbed the bank. The sun had very nearly slipped out of the sky by this time, and I could not get a good view. You, who have just crossed the Roof of the World, will not want to hear an account of the little hills that I saw—low colourless hills. But to me they were living and the turf that covered them was a skin, under which their muscles rippled, and I felt that those hills had called with incalculable force to men in the past, and that men had loved them. Now they sleep—perhaps for ever. They commune with humanity in dreams. Happy the man, happy the woman, who awakes the hills of Wessex. For though they sleep, they will never die."

His voice rose passionately.

"Cannot you see, cannot all your lecturers see, that it is we who are dying, and that down here the only thing that really lives is the Machine? We created the Machine, to do our will, but we cannot make it do our will now. It has robbed us of the sense of space and of the sense of touch, it has blurred every human relation and narrowed down love to a carnal act, it has paralysed our bodies and our wills, and now it compels us to worship it. The Machine develops—but not on our lines. The Machine proceeds—but not to our goal. We only exist as the blood corpuscles that course through its arteries, and if it could work without us, it would let us die. Oh, I have no remedy—or, at least, only one—to tell men again and again that I have seen the hills of Wessex as Ælfrid saw them when he overthrew the Danes.

"So the sun set. I forgot to mention that a belt of mist lay between my hill and other hills, and that it was the colour of pearl."

He broke off for the second time.

"Go on," said his mother wearily.

He shook his head.

"Go on. Nothing that you say can distress me now. I am hardened."

"I had meant to tell you the rest, but I cannot: I know that I cannot: good-bye."

Vashti stood irresolute. All her nerves were tingling with his blasphemies. But she was also inquisitive.

"This is unfair," she complained. "You have called me across the world to hear your story, and hear it I will. Tell me—as briefly as possible, for this is a disastrous waste of time—tell me how you returned to civilisation."

"Oh—that!" he said, starting. "You would like to hear about

civilisation. Certainly. Had I got to where my respirator fell down?"

"No—but I understand everything now. You put on your respirator, and managed to walk along the surface of the earth to a vomitory, and there your conduct was reported to the Central Committee."

"By no means."

He passed his hand over his forehead, as if dispelling some strong impression. Then, resuming his narrative, he warmed to it again.

"My respirator fell about sunset. I had mentioned that the fountain seemed feebler, had I not?"

"Yes."

"About sunset, it let the respirator fall. As I said, I had entirely forgotten about the Machine, and I paid no great attention at the time, being occupied with other things. I had my pool of air, into which I could dip when the outer keenness became intolerable, and which would possibly remain for days, provided that no wind sprang up to disperse it. Not until it was too late, did I realize what the stoppage of the escape implied. You see—the gap in the tunnel had been mended; the Mending Apparatus; the Mending Apparatus, was after me.

"One other warning I had, but I neglected it. The sky at night was clearer than it had been in the day, and the moon, which was about half the sky behind the sun, shone into the dell at moments quite brightly. I was in my usual place—on the boundary between the two atmospheres—when I thought I saw something dark move across the bottom of the dell, and vanish into the shaft. In my folly, I ran down. I bent over and listened, and I thought I heard a faint scraping noise in the depths.

"At this—but it was too late—I took alarm. I determined to put on my respirator and to walk right out of the dell. But my respirator had gone. I knew exactly where it had fallen—between the stopper and the aperture—and I could even feel the mark that it had made in the turf. It had gone, and I realized that something evil was at work, and I had better escape to the outer air, and, if I must die, die running towards the cloud that had been the colour of a pearl. I never started. Out of the shaft—it is too horrible. A worm, a long white worm, had crawled out of the shaft and was gliding over the moonlit grass.

"I screamed. I did everything that I should not have done, I

stamped upon the creature instead of flying from it, and it at once
curled round the ankle. Then we fought. The worm let me run all
over the dell, but edged up my leg as I ran. 'Help!' I cried. (That
part is too awful. It belongs to the part that you will never know.)
'Help!' I cried. (Why cannot we suffer in silence?) 'Help!' I cried.
Then my feet were wound together, I fell, I was dragged away from
the dear ferns and the living hills, and past the great metal stopper
(I can tell you this part), and I thought it might save me again if I
caught hold of the handle. It also was enwrapped, it also. Oh, the
whole dell was full of the things. They were searching it in all directions, they were denuding it, and the white snouts of others peeped
out of the hole, ready if needed. Everything that could be moved
they brought—brushwood, bundles of fern, everything, and down
we all went intertwined into hell. The last things that I saw, ere
the stopper closed after us, were certain stars, and I felt that a man
of my sort lived in the sky. For I did fight, I fought till the very
end, and it was only my head hitting against the ladder that quieted
me. I woke up in this room. The worms had vanished. I was surrounded by artificial air, artificial light, artificial peace, and my
friends were calling to me down speaking-tubes to know whether I
had come across any new ideas lately."

Here his story ended. Discussion of it was impossible, and Vashti
turned to go.

"It will end in Homelessness," she said quietly.

"I wish it would," retorted Kuno.

"The Machine has been most merciful."

"I prefer the mercy of God."

"By that superstitious phrase, do you mean that you could live in
the outer air?"

"Yes."

"Have you ever seen, round the vomitories, the bones of those
who were extruded after the Great Rebellion?"

"Yes."

"They were left where they perished for our edification. A few
crawled away, but they perished, too—who can doubt it? And so
with the Homeless of our own day. The surface of the earth sup-
ports life no longer."

"Indeed."

"Ferns and a little grass may survive, but all higher forms have
perished. Has any air-ship detected them?"

"No."

"Then why this obstinacy?"

"Because I have seen them," he exploded.

"Seen *what?*"

"Because I have seen her in the twilight—because she came to my
help when I called—because she, too, was entangled by the worms,
and, luckier than I, was killed by one of them piercing her throat." ·

He was mad. Vashti departed, nor, in the troubles that followed,
did she ever see his face again.

Part III

THE HOMELESS

During the years that followed Kuno's escapade, two important
developments took place in the Machine. On the surface they were
revolutionary, but in either case men's minds had been prepared
beforehand, and they did but express tendencies that were latent
already.

The first of these was the abolition of respirators.

Advanced thinkers, like Vashti, had always held it foolish to visit
the surface of the earth. Air-ships might be necessary, but what was
the good of going out for mere curiosity and crawling along for a
mile or two in a terrestrial motor? The habit was vulgar and perhaps faintly improper: it was unproductive of ideas, and had no
connection with the habits that really mattered. So respirators were
abolished, and with them, of course, the terrestial motors, and except for a few lecturers, who complained that they were debarred
access to their subject-matter, the development was accepted quietly.
Those who still wanted to know what the earth was like had after
all only to listen to some gramophone, or to look into some cine-
matophote. And even the lecturers acquiesced when they found that
a lecture on the sea was none the less stimulating when compiled
out of other lectures that had already been delivered on the same
subject. "Beware of first-hand ideas!" exclaimed one of the most
advanced of them. "First-hand ideas do not really exist. They are
but the physical impressions produced by love and fear, and on this

gross foundation who could erect a philosophy? Let your ideas be
second-hand, and if possible tenth-hand, for then they will be far
removed from that disturbing element—direct observation. Do not
learn anything about this subject of mine—the French Revolution.
Learn instead what I think that Enicharmon thought Urizen
thought Gutch thought Ho-Yung thought Chi-Bo-Sing thought
Lafcadio Hearn thought Carlyle thought Mirabeau said about the
French Revolution. Through the medium of these eight great
minds, the blood that was shed at Paris and the windows that were
broken at Versailles will be clarified to an idea which you may
employ most profitably in your daily lives. But be sure that the
intermediates are many and varied, for in history one authority
exists to counteract another. Urizen must counteract the scepticism
of Ho-Yung and Enicharmon, I must myself counteract the impetu-
osity of Gutch. You who listen to me are in a better position to
judge about the French Revolution than I am. Your descendants
will be even in a better position than you, for they will learn what
you think I think, and yet another intermediate will be added to
the chain. And in time"—his voice rose—"there will come a generation that has got beyond facts, beyond impressions, a generation
absolutely colourless, a generation

'seraphically free
From taint of personality,'

which will see the French Revolution not as it happened, nor as
they would like it to have happened, but as it would have happened, had it taken place in the days of the Machine."

Tremendous applause greeted this lecture, which did but voice a
feeling already latent in the minds of men—a feeling that terrestrial
facts must be ignored, and that the abolition of respirators was a
positive gain. It was even suggested that air-ships should be abolished too. This was not done, because air-ships had somehow worked
themselves into the Machine's system. But year by year they were
used less, and mentioned less by thoughtful men.

The second great development was the re-establishment of religion.

This, too, had been voiced in the celebrated lecture. No one could
mistake the reverent tone in which the peroration had concluded,

and it awakened a responsive echo in the heart of each. Those who had long worshipped silently, now began to talk. They described the strange feeling of peace that came over them when they handled the Book of the Machine, the pleasure that it was to repeat certain numerals out of it, however little meaning those numerals conveyed to the outward ear, the ecstasy of touching a button, however unimportant, or of ringing an electric bell, however superfluously.

"The Machine," they exclaimed, "feeds us and clothes us and houses us; through it we speak to one another, through it we see one another, in it we have our being. The Machine is the friend of ideas and the enemy of superstition: the Machine is omnipotent, eternal; blessed is the Machine." And before long this allocution was printed on the first page of the Book, and in subsequent editions the ritual swelled into a complicated system of praise and prayer. The word "religion" was sedulously avoided, and in theory the Machine was still the creation and the implement of man. But in practice all, save a few retrogrades, worshipped it as divine. Nor was it worshipped in unity. One believer would be chiefly impressed by the blue optic plates, through which he saw other believers; another by the mending apparatus, which sinful Kuno had compared to worms; another by the lifts, another by the Book. And each would pray to this or to that, and ask it to intercede for him with the Machine as a whole. Persecution—that also was present. It did not break out, for reasons that will be set forward shortly. But it was latent, and all who did not accept the minimum known as "undenominational Mechanism" lived in danger of Homelessness, which means death, as we know.

To attribute these two great developments to the Central Committee, is to take a very narrow view of civilisation. The Central Committee announced the developments, it is true, but they were no more the cause of them than were the kings of the imperialistic period the cause of war. Rather did they yield to some invincible pressure, which came no one knew whither, and which, when gratified, was succeeded by some new pressure equally invincible. To such a state of affairs it is convenient to give the name of progress. No one confessed the Machine was out of hand. Year by year it was served with increased efficiency and decreased intelligence. The better a man knew his own duties upon it, the less he understood the duties of his neighbour, and in all the world there was not one who understood the monster as a whole. Those master brains had perished. They had left full directions, it is true, and their successors had each of them mastered a portion of those directions. But Humanity, in its desire for comfort, had over-reached itself. It had exploited the riches of nature too far. Quietly and complacently, it was sinking into decadence, and progress had come to mean the progress of the Machine.

As for Vashti, her life went peacefully forward until the final disaster. She made her room dark and slept; she awoke and made the room light. She lectured and attended lectures. She exchanged ideas with her innumerable friends and believed she was growing more spiritual. At times a friend was granted Euthanasia, and left his or her room for the homelessness that is beyond all human conception. Vashti did not much mind. After an unsuccessful lecture, she would sometimes ask for Euthanasia herself. But the death-rate was not permitted to exceed the birth-rate, and the Machine had hitherto refused it to her.

The troubles began quietly, long before she was conscious of them.

One day she was astonished at receiving a message from her son. They never communicated, having nothing in common, and she had only heard indirectly that he was still alive, and had been transferred from the northern hemisphere, where he had behaved so mischievously, to the southern—indeed, to a room not far from her own.

"Does he want me to visit him?" she thought. "Never again, never. And I have not the time."

No, it was madness of another kind.

He refused to visualize his face upon the blue plate, and speaking out of the darkness with solemnity said:

"The Machine stops."

"What do you say?"

"The Machine is stopping, I know it, I know the signs."

She burst into a peal of laughter. He heard her and was angry, and they spoke no more.

"Can you imagine anything more absurd?" she cried to a friend. "A man who was my son believes that the Machine is stopping. It would be impious if it was not mad."

"The Machine is stopping?" her friend replied. "What does that mean? The phrase conveys nothing to me."

"Nor to me."

"He does not refer, I suppose, to the trouble there has been lately with the music?"

"Oh no, of course not. Let us talk about music."

"Have you complained to the authorities?"

"Yes, and they say it wants mending, and referred me to the Committee of the Mending Apparatus. I complained of those curious gasping sighs that disfigure the symphonies of the Brisbane school. They sound like some one in pain. The Committee of the Mending Apparatus say that it shall be remedied shortly."

Obscurely worried, she resumed her life. For one thing, the defect in the music irritated her. For another thing, she could not forget Kuno's speech. If he had known that the music was out of repair—he could not know it, for he detested music—if he had known that it was wrong, "the Machine stops" was exactly the venomous sort of remark he would have made. Of course he had made it at a venture, but the coincidence annoyed her, and she spoke with some petulance to the Committee of the Mending Apparatus.

They replied, as before, that the defect would be set right shortly.

"Shortly! At once!" she retorted. "Why should I be worried by imperfect music? Things are always put right at once. If you do not mend it at once, I shall complain to the Central Committee."

"No personal complaints are received by the Central Committee," the Committee of the Mending Apparatus replied.

"Through whom am I to make my complaint, then?"

"Through us."

"I complain then."

"Your complaint shall be forwarded in its turn."

"Have others complained?"

This question was unmechanical, and the Committee of the Mending Apparatus refused to answer it.

"It is too bad!" she exclaimed to another of her friends. "There never was such an unfortunate woman as myself. I can never be sure of my music now. It gets worse and worse each time I summon it."

"I too have my troubles," the friend replied. "Sometimes my ideas are interrupted by a slight jarring noise."

"What is it?"

"I do not know whether it is inside my head, or inside the wall."

"Complain, in either case."

"I have complained, and my complaint will be forwarded in its turn to the Central Committee."

Time passed, and they resented the defects no longer. The defects had not been remedied, but the human tissues in that latter day had become so subservient, that they readily adapted themselves to every caprice of the Machine. The sigh at the crisis of the Brisbane symphony no longer irritated Vashti; she accepted it as part of the melody. The jarring noise, whether in the head or in the wall, was no longer resented by her friend. And so with the mouldy artificial fruit, so with the bath water that began to stink, so with the defective rhymes that the poetry machine had taken to emitting. All were bitterly complained of at first, and then acquiesced in and forgotten. Things went from bad to worse unchallenged.

It was otherwise with the failure of the sleeping apparatus. That was a more serious stoppage. There came a day when over the whole world—in Sumatra, in Wessex, in the innumerable cities of Courland and Brazil—the beds, when summoned by their tired owners, failed to appear. It may seem a ludicrous matter, but from it we may date the collapse of humanity. The Committee responsible for the failure was assailed by complainants, whom it referred, as usual, to the Committee of the Mending Apparatus, who in its turn assured them that their complaints would be forwarded to the Central Committee. But the discontent grew, for mankind was not yet sufficiently adaptable to do without sleeping.

"Some one is meddling with the Machine——" they began.

"Some one is trying to make himself king, to reintroduce the personal element."

"Punish that man with Homelessness."

"To the rescue! Avenge the Machine! Avenge the Machine!"

"War! Kill the man!"

But the Committee of the Mending Apparatus now came forward, and allayed the panic with well-chosen words. It confessed that the Mending Apparatus was itself in need of repair.

The effect of this frank confession was admirable.

"Of course," said a famous lecturer—he of the French Revolution, who gilded each new decay with splendour—"of course we shall not press our complaints now. The Mending Apparatus has treated us so well in the past that we all sympathize with it, and will wait patiently for its recovery. In its own good time it will resume its duties. Meanwhile let us do without our beds, our tabloids, our other little wants. Such, I feel sure, would be the wish of the Machine."

Thousands of miles away his audience applauded. The Machine still linked them. Under the seas, beneath the roots of the mountains, ran the wires through which they saw and heard, the enormous eyes and ears that were their heritage, and the hum of many workings clothed their thoughts in one garment of subserviency. Only the old and the sick remained ungrateful, for it was rumoured that Euthanasia, too, was out of order, and that pain had reappeared among men.

It became difficult to read. A blight entered the atmosphere and dulled its luminosity. At times Vashti could scarcely see across her room. The air, too, was foul. Loud were the complaints, impotent the remedies, heroic the tone of the lecturer as he cried: "Courage, courage! What matter so long as the Machine goes on? To it the darkness and the light are one." And though things improved again after a time, the old brilliancy was never recaptured, and humanity never recovered from its entrance into twilight. There was an hysterical talk of "measures," of "provisional dictatorship," and the inhabitants of Sumatra were asked to familiarize themselves with the workings of the central power station, the said power station being situated in France. But for the most part panic reigned, and men spent their strength praying to their Books, tangible proofs of the Machine's omnipotence. There were gradations of terror—at times came rumours of hope—the Mending Apparatus was almost mended—the enemies of the Machine had been got under—new "nerve-centres" were evolving which would do the work even more magnificently than before. But there came a day when, without the slightest warning, without any previous hint of feebleness, the entire communication-system broke down, all over the world, and the world, as they understood it, ended.

Vashti was lecturing at the time and her earlier remarks had been punctuated with applause. As she proceeded the audience became silent, and at the conclusion there was no sound. Somewhat displeased, she called to a friend who was a specialist in sympathy. No sound: doubtless the friend was sleeping. And so with the next friend whom she tried to summon, and so with the next, until she remembered Kuno's cryptic remark, "The Machine stops."

The phrase still conveyed nothing. If Eternity was stopping it would of course be set going shortly.

For example, there was still a little light and air—the atmosphere had improved a few hours previously. There was still the Book, and while there was the Book there was security.

Then she broke down, for with the cessation of activity came an unexpected terror—silence.

She had never known silence, and the coming of it nearly killed her—it did kill many thousands of people outright. Ever since her birth she had been surrounded by the steady hum. It was to the ear what artificial air was to the lungs, and agonizing pains shot across her head. And scarcely knowing what she did, she stumbled forward and pressed the unfamiliar button, the one that opened the door of her cell.

Now the door of the cell worked on a simple hinge of its own. It was not connected with the central power station, dying far away in France. It opened, rousing immoderate hopes in Vashti, for she thought that the Machine had been mended. It opened, and she saw the dim tunnel that curved far away towards freedom. One look, and then she shrank back. For the tunnel was full of people—she was almost the last in that city to have taken alarm.

People at any time repelled her, and these were nightmares from her worst dreams. People were crawling about, people were screaming, whimpering, gasping for breath, touching each other, vanishing in the dark, and ever and anon being pushed off the platform on to the live rail. Some were fighting round the electric bells, trying to summon trains which could not be summoned. Others were yelling for Euthanasia or for respirators, or blaspheming the Machine. Others stood at the doors of their cells fearing, like herself, either to stop in them or to leave them. And behind all the uproar was silence—the silence which is the voice of the earth and of the generations who have gone.

No—it was worse than solitude. She closed the door again and sat down to wait for the end. The disintegration went on, accompanied by horrible cracks and rumbling. The valves that restrained the Medical Apparatus must have been weakened, for it ruptured and hung hideously from the ceiling. The floor heaved and fell and flung her from her chair. A tube oozed towards her serpent fashion. And at last the final horror approached—light began to ebb, and she knew that civilisation's long day was closing.

She whirled round, praying to be saved from this, at any rate, kissing the Book, pressing button after button. The uproar outside was increasing, and even penetrated the wall. Slowly the brilliancy of her cell was dimmed, the reflections faded from her metal switches. Now she could not see the reading-stand, now not the Book, though she held it in her hand. Light followed the flight of sound, air was following light, and the original void returned to the cavern from which it had been so long excluded. Vashti continued to whirl, like the devotees of an earlier religion, screaming, praying, striking at the buttons with bleeding hands.

It was thus that she opened her prison and escaped—escaped in the spirit: at least so it seems to me, ere my meditation closes. That she escapes in the body—I cannot perceive that. She struck, by chance, the switch that released the door, and the rush of foul air on her skin, the loud throbbing whispers in her ears, told her that she was facing the tunnel again, and that tremendous platform on which she had seen men fighting. They were not fighting now. Only the whispers remained, and the little whimpering groans. They were dying by hundreds out in the dark.

She burst into tears.

Tears answered her.

They wept for humanity, those two, not for themselves. They could not bear that this should be the end. Ere silence was completed their hearts were opened, and they knew what had been important on the earth. Man, the flower of all flesh, the noblest of all creatures visible, man who had once made god in his image, and had mirrored his strength on the constellations, beautiful naked man was dying, strangled in the garments that he had woven. Century after century had he toiled, and here was his reward. Truly the garment had seemed heavenly at first, shot with the colours of culture, sewn with the threads of self-denial. And heavenly it had been so long as it was a garment and no more, so long as man could shed it at will and live by the essence that is his soul, and the essence, equally divine, that is his body. The sin against the body—it was for that they wept in chief; the centuries of wrong against the muscles

and the nerves, and those five portals by which we can alone appre-
hend—glozing it over with talk of evolution, until the body was
white pap, the home of ideas as colourless, last sloshy stirrings of a
spirit that had grasped the stars.

"Where are you?" she sobbed.

His voice in the darkness said, "Here."

"Is there any hope, Kuno?"

"None for us."

"Where are you?"

She crawled towards him over the bodies of the dead. His blood
spurted over her hands.

"Quicker," he gasped, "I am dying—but we touch, we talk, not
through the Machine."

He kissed her.

"We have come back to our own. We die, but we have recaptured
life, as it was in Wessex, when Ælfrid overthrew the Danes. We
know what they know outside, they who dwelt in the cloud that is
the colour of a pearl."

"But, Kuno, is it true? Are there still men on the surface of the
earth? Is this—this tunnel, this poisoned darkness—really not the
end?"

He replied:

"I have seen them, spoken to them, loved them. They are hiding
in the mist and the ferns until our civilisation stops. Today they are
the Homeless—tomorrow——"

"Oh, tomorrow—some fool will start the Machine again, tomorrow."

"Never," said Kuno, "never. Humanity has learnt its lesson."

As he spoke, the whole city was broken like a honeycomb. An air-
ship had sailed in through the vomitory into a ruined wharf. It
crashed downwards, exploding as it went, rending gallery after gallery with its wings of steel. For a moment they saw the nations of
the dead, and, before they joined them, scraps of the untainted sky.

Our Feathered Friends

BY

PHILIP MacDONALD

THE HOT, hard August sunshine poured its pale and blazing gold over the countryside. At the crest of the hill, which overlooked a county and a half, the tiny motor-car drawn up to the side of the dusty road which wound up the hill like a white riband looked not so much mechanical as insectile. It looked like a Brobdingnagian bee which, wings folded, had settled for a moment's sleep basking in the fierce sunshine.

Beside the car, seeming almost ludicrously out of proportion with it, stood a man and a woman. The sum of their ages could not have exceeded forty-five. The dress of the girl, which was silken and slight, would not, at all events upon her charming body, have done aught save grace a car as large and costly as this one was minute and cheap. But the clothes of the boy, despite his youth and erect comeliness, were somehow eloquent of Norwood, a careful and not unintelligent clerkliness pursued in the city of London, and a pseudo-charitable arrangement whereby the bee-like motor-car should be purchased, for many pounds more than its actual worth, in small but almost eternal slices.

The girl was hatless, and her clipped golden poll glittered in the sunrays. She looked, and was, cool, despite the great heat of the afternoon. The boy, in his tweed jacket, thick flannel trousers, and over-tight collar, at whose front blazed a tie which hoped to look like that of some famous school or college, was hot, and very hot. He pulled his hat from his dark head and mopped at his brow with a vivid handkerchief.

"Coo!" he said. "Hot enough for you, Vi?"

She wriggled slim, half-covered shoulders. "It's a treat!" she said.

She gazed about her with wide blue eyes; she looked down and round at the county-and-a-half. "Where's this, Jack?"

The boy continued to puff and mop. He said:

"Blessed if *I* know! . . . I lost me bearings after that big village place—what was it? . . ."

"Greyne, or some such," said the girl absently. Her gaze was now directed down the hillside to her right, where the emerald roof of a dense wood shone through the sun's gold. There was no breath of wind, even right up upon this hill, and the green of the leaves showed smooth and unbroken.

The boy put on his hat again. "Better be getting on, I s'pose. You've had that leg-stretch you were wanting."

"Ooh! Not *yet,* Jack. Don't let's yet!" She put the fingers of her left hand upon his sleeve. On the third of these fingers there sparkled a ring of doubtful brilliance. "Don't let's go on yet, Jack!" she said. She looked up into his face, her lips pouted in a way which was not the least of reasons for the flashing ring.

He slid an arm about the slim shoulders; he bent his head and kissed thoroughly the red mouth. "Just's *you* like, Vi. . . . But what you want to do?" He looked about him with curling lip. "Sit around up here on this dusty grass and frizzle?"

"Silly!" she said, pulling herself away from him. She pointed down to the green roof, "I want to go down there. . . . Into that wood. Jest to see what it's like. Haven't been in a real wood since the summer holidays before last, when Effie an' me went to Hastings. . . . Cummon! Bet it's lovely and cool down there. . . ."

This last sentence floated up to him, for already she was off the narrow road and beginning a slipping descent of the short rough grass of the hillside's first twenty feet.

He went sliding and stumbling after her. But he could not catch up with the light, fragile little figure in its absurdly enchanting wisp of blue silk. The soles of his thick shoes were of leather, and, growing polished by the brushing of the close, arid grass, were treacherous. Forty feet down, on the suddenly jutting and only gently sloping plateau where the wood began, he did come up with her: he ended a stumbling, sliding rush with an imperfect and involuntary somersault which landed him asprawl at her feet.

He sat up, shouting with laughter. With a shock of surprise greater than any of his short life, he felt a little foot kick sharply—

nearly savagely—at his arm, and heard a tensely whispered "SSH!"

He scrambled to his feet, to see that she was standing facing the trees, her shining golden head thrust forward, her whole body tense as that of a sprinter waiting for the pistol's crack. As, wonderingly, he shuffled to take his stand at her shoulder, she said:

"*Listen!* . . . Birds! . . . Jever hear the like? . . ." Her tone was a hushed yet clear whisper—like none he had ever heard her use before.

He said nothing. He stood scowling sulkily down at the grass beneath his feet and rubbing at the spot where her shoe had met his arm.

It seemed to him an hour before she turned. But turn at last she did. He still had his hand at the kicked arm, for all the world as if it really were causing him pain. From beneath his brows he watched her, covertly. He saw the odd rapt look leave the small face once more its pertly pretty self; saw the blue eyes suddenly widen with memory of what she had done. . . .

And then soft warm arms came about his neck and by their pressure pulled down his head so that, close pressed against him and standing upon tiptoe, she might smother his face with the kisses of contrition.

He said, in answer to the pleas for forgiveness with which the caresses were interspersed:

"Never known you do a thing like that before, Vi!"

"No," she said. "And you never won't again! Reely, Jack darling! . . . It . . . it . . ."—a cloud came over the blue eyes—"it . . . I don't rightly know what came over me. . . . I was listening to the birds. . . . I never heard the like . . . and . . . and I never heard you till you laughed . . . and I dunno *what* it was, but it seemed 's if I jest *had* to go on hearing what the birds were . . . 's if it was . . . was *wrong* to listen to anything else. . . . Oh, *I* dunno!"

The small face was troubled and the eyes desperate with the realization of explanation's impossibility. But the mouth pouted. The boy kissed it. He laughed and said:

"Funny kid, you!" He drew her arm through the crook of his and began to walk towards the first ranks of the trees. He put up his free hand and felt tenderly at the back of his neck. He said:

"Shan't be sorry for some shade. Neck's gettin' all sore."

They walked on, finding that the trees were strangely further away than they had seemed. They did not speak, but every now and then the slim, naked arm would squeeze the thick, clothed arm and have its pressure returned.

They had only some ten paces to go to reach the fringe of the wood when the girl halted. He turned his head to look down at her and found that once more she was tense in every muscle and thrusting the golden head forward as if the better to hear. He frowned; then smiled; then again bent his brows. He sensed that there was somewhere an oddness which he knew he would never understand, a feeling abhorrent to him, as, indeed, to most men. He found that he, too, was straining to listen.

He supposed it must be birds that he was listening for. And quite suddenly he laughed. For he had realized that he was listening for something which had been for the last few moments so incessantly in his ears that he had forgotten he was hearing it. He explained this to the girl. She seemed to listen to him with only half an ear, and for a moment he came near to losing his temper. But only for a moment. He was a good-natured boy, with sensitive instincts serving him well in place of realized tact.

He felt a little tugging at his arm and fell into step with her as she began to go forward again. He went on with his theme, ignoring her patently half-hearted attention.

"Like at a dance," he said. "You know, Vi—you never hear the noise of the people's feet on the floor unless you happen to listen for it, an' when you do listen for it an' hear that sort of *shishing*— then you know you've been hearing it all the time, see? That's what we were doing about the birds. . . ." He became suddenly conscious that, in order to make himself clearly heard above the chattering, twittering flood of bird-song, he was speaking in a tone at least twice as loud as the normal. He said:

"Coo! . . . You're right, Vi. *I* never heard anything like it!"

They were passing now through the ranks of the outer line of trees. To the boy, a little worried by the strangeness of his adored, and more than a little discomfited by the truly abnormal heat of the sun, it seemed that he passed from an inferno to a paradise at one step. No more did the sun beat implacably down upon the world. In here, under the roof of green which no ray pierced but only a gentle, pervading, filtered softness of light, there was a cool peacefulness which seemed to bathe him, instantly, in a placid bath of contentment.

But the girl shivered a little. She said:

"Oh! It's almost cold in here!"

He did not catch the words. The chirping and carolling which was going on all about and above them seemed to catch up and absorb the sound of her voice.

"Drat the birds!" he said. "What you say?"

He saw her lips move, but though he bent his head, did not catch a sound. There had come, from immediately above their heads, the furious squeaks and flutterings of a bird-quarrel.

"Drat the birds!" he said again.

They were quite deep in the wood now. Looking round, he could not see at all the sun-drenched grass plateau from which they had come. He felt a tugging at his arm. The girl was pointing to a gently sloping bed of thick moss which was like a carpet spread at the foot of an old and twisted tree.

They sauntered to this carpet and sat down upon it, the boy sprawling at his ease, the girl very straight of back, with her hands clasped tightly about her raised knees. Had he been looking at her, rather than at the pipe he was filling, he would have seen again that craning forward of her head.

He did not finish the filling of his pipe. The singing of the birds went on. It seemed to gather volume until the whole world was filled with its chaotic whistling. The boy found, now that he had once consciously listened for and to it, that he could not again make his ears unconscious of the sound; the sound which, with its seemingly momentarily increased volume, was now so plucking at the nerves within his head—indeed over his whole body—that he felt he could not sit much longer to endure it. He thrust pipe and pouch savagely back into his pocket and turned to say to the girl that the quicker they got away from this blinking twittering the better he'd be pleased.

But the words died upon his lips. For even as he turned he became aware of a diminution of the reedy babel. He saw, too, calmer now with the decrease of irritation, that the girl was still in rapt attention.

So he held his tongue. The singing of the birds grew less and lesser with each moment. He began to feel drowsy, and once caught

himself with a startled jerk from the edge of actual slumber. He
peered sideways at his companion and saw that still she sat rigid;
not by the breadth of a hair had she altered her first attentive pose.
He felt again for pipe and pouch.

His fingers idle in the jacket-pocket, he found himself listening
again. Only this time he listened because he wanted to listen. There
was now but one bird who sang. And the boy was curiously conscious, hearing these liquid notes alone and in the fullness of their
uninterrupted and almost unbearable beauty, that the reason for his
hatred of that full and somehow discordant chorus which a few
moments ago had nearly driven him from the trees and their lovely
shelter had been his inability to hear more than an isolated note or
two of this song whose existence then he had realized only subconsciously.

The full, deep notes ceased their rapid and incredible trilling,
cutting their sound off sharply, almost in the manner of an operatic
singer. There was, then, only silence in the wood. It lasted, for the
town-bred boy and girl caught suddenly in this placid whirlpool
of natural beauty, for moments which seemed strained and incalculable ages. And then into this pool of pregnant no-sound were
dropped, one by one, six exquisite jewels of sound, each pause
between these isolated lovelinesses being of twice the duration of
its predecessor.

After the last of these notes—deep and varying and crystal-pure,
yet misty with unimaginable beauties—the silence fell again; a
silence not pregnant, as the last, with the vibrant foreshadowings of
the magic to come, but a silence which had in it the utter and
miserable quietness of endings and nothingness.

The boy's arm went up and wrapped itself gently about slim,
barely covered shoulders. Two heads turned, and dark eyes looked
into blue. The blue were abrim with unshed tears. She whispered:

"It was *him* I was listening to all the while. I could hear *that* all
. . . all through the others. . . ."

A tear brimmed over and rolled down the pale cheek. The arm
about her shoulders tightened, and at last she relaxed. The little
body grew limp and lay against his strength.

"You lay quiet, darling," he said. His voice trembled a little. And
he spoke in the hushed voice of a man who knows himself in a holy
or enchanted place.

Then silence. Silence which weighed and pressed upon a man's soul. Silence which seemed a living deadness about them. From the boy's shoulder came a hushed, small voice which endeavoured to conceal its shaking. It said:

"I . . . I . . . felt all along . . . we shouldn't . . . shouldn't be here. . . . We didn't ought to 've come. . . ."

Despite its quietness there was something like panic in the voice.

He spoke reassuring words. To shake her from this queer, repressed hysteria, he said these words in a loud and virile tone. But this had only the effect of conveying to himself something of the odd disquiet which had possessed the girl.

"It's cold in here," she whispered suddenly. Her body pressed itself against him.

He laughed; an odd sound. He said hastily:

"Cold! You're talking out of the back of your neck, Vi."

"It is," she said. But her voice was more natural now. "We better be getting along, hadn't we?"

He nodded. "Think we had," he said. He stirred, as if to get to his feet. But a small hand suddenly gripped his arm, and her voice whispered:

"Look! *Look!*" It was her own voice again, so that, even while he started a little at her sudden clutch and the urgency of her tone, he felt a wave of relief and a sudden quietening of his own vague but discomfortable uneasiness.

His gaze followed the line of her pointing finger. He saw, upon the carpeting of rotten twigs and brown mouldering leaves, just at the point where this brown and the dark cool green of their moss-bank met, a small bird. It stood upon its slender sticks of legs and gazed up at them, over the plump bright-hued breast, with shining little eyes. Its head was cocked to one side.

"D'you know," said the girl's whisper, "that's the first one we've *seen?*"

The boy pondered for a moment. "Gosh!" he said at last. "So it is and all!"

They watched in silence. The bird hopped nearer.

"Isn't he *sweet,* Jack?" Her whisper was a delighted chuckle.

"Talk about tame!" said the boy softly. "Cunning little beggar!"

Her elbow nudged his ribs. She said, her lips barely moving:

"Keep still. If we don't move, I believe he'll come right up to us."

Almost on her words, the bird hopped nearer. Now he was actually upon the moss, and thus less than an inch from the toe of the girl's left shoe. His little pert head, which was of a shining green with a rather comically long beak of yellow, was still cocked to one side. His bright, small eyes still surveyed them with the unwinking stare of his kind.

The girl's fascinated eyes were upon the small creature. She saw nothing else. Not so the boy. There was a nudge, this time from his elbow.

"Look there!" he whispered, pointing. "And there!"

She took, reluctantly enough, her eyes from the small intruder by her foot. She gazed in the directions he had indicated. She gasped in wonder. She whispered:

"Why, they're *all* coming to see us!"

Everywhere between the boles of the close-growing trees were birds. Some stood singly, some in pairs, some in little clumps of four and more. Some seemed, even to urban eyes, patently of the same family as their first visitor, who still stood by the white shoe, staring up at the face of its owner. But there were many more families. There were very small birds, and birds of sparrow size but unsparrowlike plumage, and birds which were a little bigger than this, and birds which were twice and three times the size. But one and all faced the carpet of moss and stared with their shining eyes at the two humans who lay upon it.

"This," said the boy, "is the rummest start *I* ever . . ."

The girl's elbow nudged him to silence. He followed the nod of her head and, looking down, saw that the first visitor was now perched actually upon her instep. He seemed very much at his ease there. But he was no longer looking up at them with those bright little eyes. And his head was no longer cocked to one side: it was level, so that he appeared to be in contemplation of a silk-clad shin.

Something—perhaps it was a little whispering, pattering rustle among the rotting leaves of the wood's carpet—took the boy's fascinated eyes from this strange sight. He lifted them to see a stranger; a sight perhaps more fascinating, but with by no means the same fascination.

The birds were nearer. Much, much nearer. And their line was solid now; an unborn semicircle with bounding-line so wide-flung that he felt rather than saw its extent. One little corner of his brain

for an instant busied itself with wild essays at numerical computa-
tion, but reeled back defeated by the impossibility of the task. Even
as he stared, his face pale now, and his eyes wide with something
like terror, that semicircle drew yet nearer, each unit of it taking
four hops and four hops only. Now, its line unmarred, it was close
upon the edge of the moss.

But was it only a semicircle? A dread doubt of this flashed into
his mind.

One horrified glance across his shoulder told him that semicircle
it was not. Full circle it was.

Birds, birds, birds! Was it possible that the world itself should
hold such numbers of birds?

Eyes! Small, shining, myriad button-points of glittering eyes. All
fixed upon him . . . and—God!—upon *her*. . . .

In one wild glance he saw that as yet she had not seen. Still she
was in rapt, silent ecstasy over her one bird. And this now sat upon
the outspread palm of her hand. Close to her face she was holding
this hand. . . .

Through the pall of silence he could feel those countless eyes
upon him. Little eyes; bright, glittering eyes. . . .

His breath came in shuddering gasps. He tried to get himself in
hand; tried, until the sweat ran off him with the intensity of his
effort, to master his fear. To some extent he succeeded. He would
no longer sit idle while the circle . . . while the circle . . .

The silence was again ruffled upon its surface by a rustling patter.
. . . It was one hop this time. It brought the semicircle fronting him
so near that there were birds within an inch of his feet.

He leapt up. He waved his arms and kicked out and uttered one
shout which somehow cracked and was half-strangled in his throat.

Nothing happened. At the edge of the moss a small bird, crushed
by his kick, lay in a soft, small heap.

Not one of the birds moved. Still their eyes were upon him.

The girl sat like a statue in living stone. She had seen, and terror
held her. Her palm, the one bird still motionless upon it, still was
outspread near her face.

From high above them there dropped slowly into the black depths
of the silence one note of a sweetness ineffable. It lingered upon the
breathless air, dying slowly until it fused with the silence.

And then the girl screamed. Suddenly and dreadfully. The small green poll had darted forward. The yellow beak had struck and sunk. A scarlet runnel coursed down the tender cheek.

Above the lingering echo of that scream there came another of those single notes from on high.

The silence died then. There was a whirring which filled the air. That circle was no more.

There were two feathered mounds which screamed and ran and leapt, and at last lay and were silent.

By the Rude Bridge

BY

ALEXANDER WOOLLCOTT

L ET ME begin by admitting that through the years I have become a
more and more spasmodic newspaper reader. This may be due
to a conviction that by faithfully absorbing the imparted wisdom of
the two Walters (Lippmann and Winchell) I can learn all I really
care to know about what is going on in the world. But, occasionally,
through this failure of attention to the news columns, I lose the
final chapter of some tale that has really interested me.

These somber reflections were induced one day when a chance re-
màrk brought to mind the Bennett killing which enlivened Kansas
City some years ago, and with a start I realized that although it had
involved four shots heard round the world, I never did know what
happened afterwards. Wherefore I moved about among my neighbors, as might an inquiring reporter, only to find that, one and all,
they too had lost track of the case. Yet at the time there was probably not a literate household in Europe or the three Americas of
which the emotional seismograph had not recorded its tremors.

The Bennett killing, which occurred on the night of September
29, 1929, was usually spoken of, with approximate accuracy, as the
Bridge-Table Murder. The victim was a personable and prosperous
young salesman whose mission, as representative of the house of
Hudnut, was to add to the fragrance of life in the Middle West. He
had been married eleven years before to a Miss Myrtle Adkins,
originally from Arkansas, who first saw his photograph at the home
of a friend, announced at once that she intended to marry him, and
then, perhaps with this purpose still in mind, recognized and ac-
costed him a year later when she happened to encounter him on a
train. That was during the war when the good points of our per-

fume salesman's physique were enhanced by an officer's uniform. They were married in Memphis during the considerable agitation of November 11, 1918. The marriage was a happy one. At least, Senator Jim Reed, who represented Mrs. Bennett in the trying but inevitable legal formalities which ensued upon her bereavement, announced in court—between sobs—that they had always been more like sweethearts than man and wife.

On Mr. Bennett's last Sunday on earth, these wedded sweethearts spent the day playing a foursome at golf with their friends, Charles and Mayme Hofman, who had an apartment in the Park Manor on Ward Parkway, which is, I think, a shiny new part of the town that was just forlorn, uncropped meadowland in the days when the great Dr. Logan Clendening, the late Ralph Barton, and your correspondent were all sweet-faced tots together in dear old K.C. After dark and after an ice-box supper at the Bennetts', the men folk professed themselves too weary to dress for the movies, so the four settled down to a more slatternly evening of contract bridge. They played family against family at a tenth of a cent a side. With a pretty laugh, Mayme Hofman on the witness stand referred to such a game as playing for "fun stakes," though whether this was a repulsive little phrase of her own or one prevalent in the now devitalized society of a once rugged community, I do not know.

They played for some hours. At first the luck went against the Hofmans and the married sweethearts were as merry as grigs. Later the tide turned and the cross-table talk of the Bennetts became tinged with constructive criticism. Finally, just before midnight, the fatal hand was dealt by Bennett himself and he opened the bidding with one spade. Hofman hazarded two diamonds. Mrs. Bennett leaped to four spades. Discreet silence from Mrs. Hofman. Stunned silence from Bennett. Hofman doubled. That ended the bidding and the play began.

Mrs. Bennett put down her hand. At her trial it was the policy of the defense, for strategic reasons, to minimize the part the bridge game had played in the ensuing drama, but the jury could not be confused on this point and three of the jurors went so far as to learn bridge in the long leisure of the jury room. Nor could the mind of that stern realist, Mayme Hofman, be befogged. When summoned as a witness by Senator Reed, she knew she was really coming to the defense of Mrs. Bennett as a bridge player.

"Myrtle put down a good hand," she said stanchly, "it was a perfectly beautiful hand."

In any event, while she was dummy, Mrs. Bennett retired to the kitchen to prepare breakfast for her lord and master, who would be leaving at the crack of dawn for St. Joe. She came back to find he had been set two and to be greeted with the almost automatic charge that she had overbid. Thereupon she ventured to opine that he was, in her phrase, "a bum bridge player." His reply to that was a slap in the face, followed by several more of the same—whether three or four more, witnesses were uncertain. Then while he stormed about proclaiming his intention to leave for St. Joe at once and while Mr. Hofman prudently devoted the interval to totting up the score, Mrs. Bennett retired to the davenport to weep on the sympathetic bosom of Mayme Hofman, saying many things, through her tears, including one utterance which, in my opinion, should give the Bennett case a permanent place in the files of such fond annalists as William Roughead of Edinburgh and Edmund (Whatever became of the Lester?) Pearson of New York. Mrs. Bennett's sentiments were expressed as follows:

"No one but a cur would strike a woman in the presence of friends."

I have not as yet been able to learn whether the game was ever settled, but when Mr. Hofman had completed his work as accountant, he ventured to reproach the host for unseemly behavior, to which comment Bennett replied by a strong suggestion that it was time for the guests to go home. Mrs. Hofman—one can imagine her bridling a good deal and saying that she considered the source—had got into her wraps and Mr. Hofman was tidying up in the bathroom, when he saw his hostess advancing through the den, revolver in hand.

"My God, Myrtle," he cried. "What are you going to do?"

He soon learned.

There were four shots, with a brief interval after the second. The first went through the hastily closed bathroom door. The second was embedded in the lintel. The next two were embedded in Mr. Bennett, the fourth and fatal shot hitting him in the back.

The next day the story went round the world. In its first reverberations, I noticed, with interest, that after her visit to the mortuary chapel Mrs. Bennett objected plaintively to her husband's being buried without a pocket-handkerchief showing in his coat. To interested visitors, she would make cryptic remarks such as "Nobody knows but me and my God why I did it," thus leaving open to pleasant speculation the probable nature of her defense.

It would be difficult to explain to a puzzled Englishman, brought up as he is to think of America as a country of breathless speed, how seventeen months could be allowed to pass before Mrs. Bennett was called upon to stand trial. By that time I myself had lost track. Wherefore, when the aforesaid Clendening called at Wit's End one Sunday, I asked what, if anything, had ever happened in the Bennett case.

"Oh!" the good doctor replied, "she was acquitted. It seems it was just an unfortunate accident."

For corroborative detail I have since consulted the files of the *Kansas City Star*, one of the three or four newspapers left in this country of which the staff still preserves, like the guarded secret of some medieval guild, the lost art of reportorial writing. The *Star* accounts of the trial are in the finest tradition of our craft. I cannot hope in so small a space to reproduce the flavor of Senator Reed's more than adequate performance. It seems the dutiful Mrs. Bennett had merely gone for the revolver because her husband wanted to take it with him to St. Joe; that in stumbling over a misplaced chair in the den she fired the first two shots unintentionally and that her husband (pardonably misreading her kind intentions) had sought to disarm her. In the ensuing Apache dance of their struggle for the gun, it had gone off and wounded him fatally.

The defense was materially aided by the exclusion on technical grounds of crucial testimony which would have tended to indicate that at the time Mrs. Bennett had told a rather different story. It was also helped no little by the defendant herself who, in the course of the trial, is estimated to have shed more tears than Jane Cowl did in the entire season of *Common Clay*. Even the Senator was occasionally unmanned, breaking into sobs several times in the presence of the jury. "I just can't help it," he replied, when the calloused prosecutor urged him to bear up.

The Reed construction of the fatal night's events proved subsequently important to Mrs. Bennett, in whose favor her husband had once taken out a policy to cover the contingency of his death through accident. Some months after the acquittal a dazed insurance company paid her thirty thousand dollars.

It was Harpo Marx who, on hearing the doctor's hasty but spirited résumé of the case, suggested that I make use of it for one of my little articles. He even professed to have thought of a title for it. Skeptically I inquired what this might be and he answered, "Vulnerable."

FOOTNOTE: Protesting as I do against the short-weight reporting in the *Notable British Trials* series, it would ill become me to hoard for my private pleasure certain postscripts to the Bennett case which have recently drifted my way. It looked for a time as if we all might be vouchsafed the luxury of reading Myrtle's autobiography, but this great work has been indefinitely postponed. I understand she could not come to terms with the local journalist who was to do the actual writing. That ink-stained wretch demanded half the royalties. Mrs. Bennett felt this division would be inequitable, since, as she pointed out, she herself had done all the work.

Then it seems she has not allowed her bridge to grow rusty, even though she occasionally encounters an explicable difficulty in finding a partner. Recently she took on one unacquainted with her history. Having made an impulsive bid, he put his hand down with some diffidence. "Partner," he said, "I'm afraid you'll want to shoot me for this." Mrs. Bennett, says my informant, had the good taste to faint.

"Oh, Whistle, and I'll Come to You, My Lad"

BY

M. R. JAMES

"I SUPPOSE you will be getting away pretty soon, now Full term is over, Professor," said a person not in the story to the Professor of Ontography, soon after they had sat down next to each other at a feast in the hospital hall of St. James's College.

The Professor was young, neat, and precise in speech.

"Yes," he said; "my friends have been making me take up golf this term, and I mean to go to the East Coast—in point of fact to Burnstow—(I dare say you know it) for a week or ten days, to improve my game. I hope to get off to-morrow."

"Oh, Parkins," said his neighbour on the other side, "if you are going to Burnstow, I wish you would look at the site of the Templars' preceptory, and let me know if you think it would be any good to have a dig there in the summer."

It was, as you might suppose, a person of antiquarian pursuits who said this, but since he merely appears in this prologue there is no need to give his entitlements.

"Certainly," said Parkins, the Professor, "if you will describe to me whereabouts the site is, I will do my best to give you an idea of the lie of the land when I get back, or I could write to you about it, if you would tell me where you are likely to be."

"Don't trouble to do that, thanks. It's only that I'm thinking of taking my family in that direction in the Long, and it occurred to me that, as very few of the English preceptories have ever been properly planned, I might have an opportunity of doing something useful on off-days."

The Professor rather sniffed at the idea that planning out a preceptory could be described as useful. His neighbour continued:

"The site—I doubt if there is anything showing above ground—

must be down quite close to the beach now. The sea has encroached tremendously, as you know, all along that bit of coast. I should think, from the map, that it must be about three-quarters of a mile from the Globe Inn, at the north of the town. Where are you going to stay?"

"Well, *at* the Globe Inn, as a matter of fact," said Parkins; "I have engaged a room there. I couldn't get in anywhere else; most of the lodging-houses are shut up in winter, it seems; and, as it is, they tell me that the only room of any size I can have is really a double-bedded one, and that they haven't a corner in which to store the other bed, and so on. But I must have a fairly large room, for I am taking some books down, and mean to do a bit of work; and though I don't quite fancy having an empty bed—not to speak of two—in what I may call for the time being my study, I suppose I can manage to rough it for the short time I shall be there."

"Do you call having an extra bed in your room roughing it, Parkins?" said a bluff person opposite. "Look here, I shall come down and occupy it for a bit; it'll be company for you."

The Professor quivered, but managed to laugh in a courteous manner.

"By all means, Rogers; there's nothing I should like better. But I'm afraid you would find it rather dull; you don't play golf, do you?"

"No, thank Heaven!" said rude Mr. Rogers.

"Well, you see, when I'm not writing I shall most likely be out on the links, and that, as I say, would be rather dull for you, I'm afraid."

"Oh, I don't know! There's certain to be somebody I know in the place; but, of course, if you don't want me, speak the word, Parkins; I shan't be offended. Truth, as you always tell us, is never offensive."

Parkins was, indeed, scrupulously polite and strictly truthful. It is to be feared that Mr. Rogers sometimes practised upon his knowledge of these characteristics. In Parkins's breast there was a conflict now raging, which for a moment or two did not allow him to answer. That interval being over, he said:

"Well, if you want the exact truth, Rogers. I was considering whether the room I speak of would really be large enough to accommodate us both comfortably; and also whether (mind, I shouldn't have said this if you hadn't pressed me) you would not constitute something in the nature of a hindrance to my work."

Rogers laughed loudly.

"Well done, Parkins!" he said. "It's all right. I promise not to interrupt your work; don't you disturb yourself about that. No, I won't come if you don't want me; but I thought I should do so nicely to keep the ghosts off." Here he might have been seen to wink and to nudge his next neighbour. Parkins might also have been seen to become pink. "I beg pardon, Parkins," Rogers continued; "I oughtn't to have said that. I forgot you didn't like levity on these topics."

"Well," Parkins said, "as you have mentioned the matter, I freely own that I do *not* like careless talk about what you call ghosts. A man in my position," he went on, raising his voice a little, "cannot, I find, be too careful about appearing to sanction the current belief on such subjects. As you know, Rogers, or as you ought to know; for I think I have never concealed my views—"

"No, you certainly have not, old man," put in Rogers *sotto voce.*

"—I hold that any semblance, any appearance of concession to the view that such things might exist is equivalent to a renunciation of all that I hold most sacred. But I'm afraid I have not succeeded in securing your attention."

"Your *undivided* attention, was what Dr. Blimber actually *said*,"[1] Rogers interrupted, with every appearance of an earnest desire for accuracy. "But I beg your pardon, Parkins: I'm stopping you."

"No, not at all," said Parkins. "I don't remember Blimber; perhaps he was before my time. But I needn't go on. I'm sure you know what I mean."

"Yes, yes," said Rogers, rather hastily—"just so. We'll go into it fully at Burnstow, or somewhere."

In repeating the above dialogue I have tried to give the impression which it made on me, that Parkins was something of an old woman—rather henlike, perhaps, in his little ways; totally destitute, alas! of the sense of humour, but at the same time dauntless and sincere in his convictions, and a man deserving of the greatest respect. Whether or not the reader has gathered so much, that was the character which Parkins had.

On the following day Parkins did, as he had hoped, succeed in

[1] Mr. Rogers was wrong, *vide Dombey and Son,* chapter xii.

getting away from his college, and in arriving at Burnstow. He was made welcome at the Globe Inn, was safely installed in the large double-bedded room of which we have heard, and was able before retiring to rest to arrange his materials for work in apple-pie order upon a commodious table which occupied the outer end of the room, and was surrounded on three sides by windows looking out seaward: that is to say, the central window looked straight out to sea, and those on the left and right commanded prospects along the shore to the north and south respectively. On the south you saw the village of Burnstow. On the north no houses were to be seen, but only the beach and the low cliff backing it. Immediately in front was a strip—not considerable—of rough grass, dotted with old anchors, capstans, and so forth; then a broad path; then the beach. Whatever may have been the original distance between the Globe Inn and the sea, not more than sixty yards now separated them.

The rest of the population of the inn was, of course, a golfing one, and included a few elements that call for a special description. The most conspicuous figure was, perhaps, that of an *ancien militaire,* secretary of a London club, and possessed of a voice of incredible strength, and of views of a pronouncedly Protestant type. These were apt to find utterance after his attendance upon the ministrations of the Vicar, an estimable man with inclinations towards a picturesque ritual, which he gallantly kept down as far as he could out of deference to East Anglian tradition.

Professor Parkins, one of whose principal characteristics was pluck, spent the greater part of the day following his arrival at Burnstow in what he had called improving his game, in company with this Colonel Wilson: and during the afternoon—whether the process of improvement were to blame or not, I am not sure—the Colonel's demeanour assumed a colouring so lurid that even Parkins jibbed at the thought of walking home with him from the links. He determined, after a short and furtive look at that bristling moustache and those incarnadined features, that it would be wiser to allow the influences of tea and tobacco to do what they could with the Colonel before the dinner-hour should render a meeting inevitable.

"I might walk home to-night along the beach," he reflected—"yes, and take a look—there will be light enough for that—at the ruins of which Disney was talking. I don't exactly know where they are, by the way; but I expect I can hardly help stumbling on them."

This he accomplished, I may say, in the most literal sense, for in picking his way from the links to the shingle beach his foot caught, partly in a gorse-root and partly in a biggish stone, and over he went. When he got up and surveyed his surroundings, he found himself in a patch of somewhat broken ground covered with small depressions and mounds. These latter, when he came to examine them, proved to be simply masses of flints embedded in mortar and grown over with turf. He must, he quite rightly concluded, be on the site of the preceptory he had promised to look at. It seemed not unlikely to reward the spade of the explorer; enough of the foundations was probably left at no great depth to throw a good deal of light on the general plan. He remembered vaguely that the Templars, to whom this site had belonged, were in the habit of building round churches, and he thought a particular series of the humps or mounds near him did appear to be arranged in something of a circular form. Few people can resist the temptation to try a little amateur research in a department quite outside their own, if only for the satisfaction of showing how successful they would have been had they only taken it up seriously. Our Professor, however, if he felt something of this mean desire, was also truly anxious to oblige Mr. Disney. So he paced with care the circular area he had noticed, and wrote down its rough dimensions in his pocket-book. Then he proceeded to examine an oblong eminence which lay east of the centre of the circle, and seemed to his thinking likely to be the base of a platform or altar. At one end of it, the northern, a patch of the turf was gone—removed by some boy or other creature *feræ naturæ*. It might, he thought, be as well to probe the soil here for evidences of masonry, and he took out his knife and began scraping away the earth. And now followed another little discovery: a portion of soil fell inward as he scraped, and disclosed a small cavity. He lighted one match after another to help him to see of what nature the hole was, but the wind was too strong for them all. By tapping and scratching the sides with his knife, however, he was able to make out that it must be an artificial hole in masonry. It was rectangular, and the sides, top, and bottom, if not actually plastered, were smooth and regular. Of course it was empty. No! As he withdrew the knife he heard a metallic clink, and when he introduced his hand it met with a cylindrical object lying on the floor of the hole. Naturally enough, he picked it up, and when he brought it into the light, now fast fading, he could see that it, too, was of man's making—a metal tube about four inches long, and evidently of some considerable age.

By the time Parkins had made sure that there was nothing else in this odd receptacle, it was too late and too dark for him to think of undertaking any further search. What he had done had proved so unexpectedly interesting that he determined to sacrifice a little more of the daylight on the morrow to archæology. The object which he now had safe in his pocket was bound to be of some slight value at least, he felt sure.

Bleak and solemn was the view on which he took a last look before starting homeward. A faint yellow light in the west showed the links, on which a few figures moving towards the club-house were still visible, the squat martello tower, the lights of Aldsley village, the pale ribbon of sands intersected at intervals by black wooden groynes, the dim and murmuring sea. The wind was bitter from the north, but was at his back when he set out for the Globe. He quickly rattled and clashed through the shingle and gained the sand, upon which, but for the groynes which had to be got over every few yards, the going was both good and quiet. One last look behind, to measure the distance he had made since leaving the ruined Templars' church, showed him a prospect of company on his walk, in the shape of a rather indistinct personage, who seemed to be making great efforts to catch up with him, but made little, if any, progress. I mean that there was an appearance of running about his movements, but that the distance between him and Parkins did not seem materially to lessen. So, at least, Parkins thought, and decided that he almost certainly did not know him, and that it would be absurd to wait until he came up. For all that, company, he began to think, would really be very welcome on that lonely shore, if only you could choose your companion. In his unenlightened days he had read of meetings in such places which even now would hardly bear thinking of. He went on thinking of them, however, until he reached home, and particularly of one which catches most people's fancy at some time of their childhood. "Now I saw in my dream that Christian had gone but a very little way when he saw a foul fiend coming over the field to meet him." "What should I do now," he thought, "if I looked back and caught sight of a black figure sharply defined against the yellow sky, and saw that it had horns and wings? I wonder whether I should stand or run for it. Luckily, the gentleman behind is not of that kind, and he seems to be about as far off now as when I saw him first. Well, at this rate he won't get his dinner as soon as I shall; and, dear me! it's within a quarter of an hour of the time now. I must run!"

Parkins had, in fact, very little time for dressing. When he met the Colonel at dinner, Peace—or as much of her as that gentleman could manage—reigned once more in the military bosom; nor was she put to flight in the hours of bridge that followed dinner, for Parkins was a more than respectable player. When, therefore, he retired towards twelve o'clock, he felt that he had spent his evening in quite a satisfactory way, and that, even for so long as a fortnight or three weeks, life at the Globe would be supportable under similar conditions—"especially," thought he, "if I go on improving my game."

As he went along the passages he met the boots of the Globe, who stopped and said:

"Beg your pardon, sir, but as I was a-brushing your coat just now there was somethink fell out of the pocket. I put it on your chest of drawers, sir, in your room, sir—a piece of a pipe or somethink of that, sir. Thank you, sir. You'll find it on your chest of draws, sir— yes, sir. Good night, sir."

The speech served to remind Parkins of his little discovery of that afternoon. It was with some considerable curiosity that he turned it over by the light of his candles. It was of bronze, he now saw, and was shaped very much after the manner of the modern dog-whistle; in fact it was—yes, certainly it was—actually no more nor less than a whistle. He put it to his lips, but it was quite full of a fine, caked-up sand or earth, which would not yield to knocking, but must be loosened with a knife. Tidy as ever in his habits, Parkins cleared out the earth on to a piece of paper, and took the latter to the window to empty it out. The night was clear and bright, as he saw when he had opened the casement, and he stopped for an instant to look at the sea and note a belated wanderer stationed on the shore in front of the inn. Then he shut the window, a little surprised at the late hours people kept at Burnstow, and took his whistle to the light again. Why, surely there were marks on it, and

not merely marks, but letters! A very little rubbing rendered the
deeply-cut inscription quite legible, but the Professor had to confess, after some earnest thought, that the meaning of it was as obscure to him as the writing on the wall to Belshazzar. There were
legends both on the front and on the back of the whistle. The one
read thus:

FLA

FUR   BIS

FLE

The other:

卐   QUIS EST ISTE QUI UENIT   卐

"I ought to be able to make it out," he thought; "but I suppose I
am a little rusty in my Latin. When I come to think of it, I don't
believe I even know the word for a whistle. The long one does seem
simple enough. It ought to mean, 'Who is this who is coming?' Well,
the best way to find out is evidently to whistle for him."

He blew tentatively and stopped suddenly, startled and yet
pleased at the note he had elicited. It had a quality of infinite distance in it, and, soft as it was, he somehow felt it must be audible
for miles round. It was a sound, too, that seemed to have the power
(which many scents possess) of forming pictures in the brain. He saw
quite clearly for a moment a vision of a wide, dark expanse at night,
with a fresh wind blowing, and in the midst a lonely figure—how
employed, he could not tell. Perhaps he would have seen more had
not the picture been broken by the sudden surge of a gust of wind
against his casement, so sudden that it made him look up, just in
time to see the white glint of a sea-bird's wing somewhere outside
the dark panes.

The sound of the whistle had so fascinated him that he could not
help trying it once more, this time more boldly. The note was little,
if at all, louder than before, and repetition broke the illusion—no
picture followed, as he had half hoped it might. "But what is this?
Goodness! what force the wind can get up in a few minutes! What
a tremendous gust! There! I knew that window-fastening was no
use! Ah! I thought so—both candles out. It's enough to tear the room
to pieces."

The first thing was to get the window shut. While you might

count twenty Parkins was struggling with the small casement, and felt almost as if he were pushing back a sturdy burglar, so strong was the pressure. It slackened all at once, and the window banged to and latched itself. Now to relight the candles and see what damage, if any, had been done. No, nothing seemed amiss; no glass even was broken in the casement. But the noise had evidently roused at least one member of the household: the Colonel was to be heard stumping in his stockinged feet on the floor above, and growling.

Quickly as it had risen, the wind did not fall at once. On it went, moaning and rushing past the house, at times rising to a cry so desolate that, as Parkins disinterestedly said, it might have made fanciful people feel quite uncomfortable; even the unimaginative, he thought after a quarter of an hour, might be happier without it.

Whether it was the wind, or the excitement of golf, or of the researches in the preceptory that kept Parkins awake, he was not sure. Awake he remained, in any case, long enough to fancy (as I am afraid I often do myself under such conditions) that he was the victim of all manner of fatal disorders: he would lie counting the beats of his heart, convinced that it was going to stop work every moment, and would entertain grave suspicions of his lungs, brain, liver, etc.— suspicions which he was sure would be dispelled by the return of daylight, but which until then refused to be put aside. He found a little vicarious comfort in the idea that someone else was in the same boat. A near neighbour (in the darkness it was not easy to tell his direction) was tossing and rustling in his bed, too.

The next stage was that Parkins shut his eyes and determined to give sleep every chance. Here again over-excitement asserted itself in another form—that of making pictures. *Experto crede,* pictures do come to the closed eyes of one trying to sleep, and are often so little to his taste that he must open his eyes and disperse them.

Parkins's experience on this occasion was a very distressing one. He found that the picture which presented itself to him was continuous. When he opened his eyes, of course, it went; but when he shut them once more it framed itself afresh, and acted itself out again, neither quicker nor slower than before. What he saw was this:

A long stretch of shore—shingle edged by sand, and intersected at short intervals with black groynes running down to the water—a scene, in fact, so like that of his afternoon's walk that, in the absence of any landmark, it could not be distinguished therefrom. The light was obscure, conveying an impression of gathering storm, late winter evening, and slight cold rain. On this bleak stage at first no actor was visible. Then, in the distance, a bobbing black object appeared; a moment more, and it was a man running, jumping, clambering over the groynes, and every few seconds looking eagerly back. The nearer he came the more obvious it was that he was not only anxious, but even terribly frightened, though his face was not to be distinguished. He was, moreover, almost at the end of his strength. On he came; each successive obstacle seemed to cause him more difficulty than the last. "Will he get over this next one?" thought Parkins; "it seems a little higher than the others." Yes, half climbing, half throwing himself, he did get over, and fell all in a heap on the other side (the side nearest to the spectator). There, as if really unable to get up again, he remained crouching under the groyne, looking up in an attitude of painful anxiety.

So far no cause whatever for the fear of the runner had been shown; but now there began to be seen, far up the shore, a little flicker of something light-coloured moving to and fro with great swiftness and irregularity. Rapidly growing larger, it, too, declared itself as a figure in pale, fluttering draperies, ill-defined. There was something about its motion which made Parkins very unwilling to see it at close quarters. It would stop, raise arms, bow itself toward the sand, then run stooping across the beach to the water-edge and back again; and then, rising upright, once more continue its course forward at a speed that was startling and terrifying. The moment came when the pursuer was hovering about from left to right only a few yards beyond the groyne where the runner lay in hiding. After two or three ineffectual castings hither and thither it came to a stop, stood upright, with arms raised high, and then darted straight forward towards the groyne.

It was at this point that Parkins always failed in his resolution to keep his eyes shut. With many misgivings as to incipient failure of eyesight, overworked brain, excessive smoking, and so on, he finally resigned himself to light his candle, get out a book, and pass the night waking, rather than be tormented by this persistent panorama, which he saw clearly enough could only be a morbid reflection of his walk and his thoughts on that very day.

The scraping of match on box and the glare of light must have startled some creatures of the night—rats or what not—which he heard scurry across the floor from the side of his bed with much rustling. Dear, dear! the match is out! Fool that it is! But the second one burnt better, and a candle and book were duly procured, over which Parkins pored till sleep of a wholesome kind came upon him, and that in no long space. For about the first time in his orderly and prudent life he forgot to blow out the candle, and when he was called next morning at eight there was still a flicker in the socket and a sad mess of guttered grease on the top of the little table.

After breakfast he was in his room, putting the finishing touches to his golfing costume—fortune had again allotted the Colonel to him for a partner—when one of the maids came in.

"Oh, if you please," she said, "would you like any extra blankets on your bed, sir?"

"Ah! thank you," said Parkins. "Yes, I think I should like one. It seems likely to turn rather colder."

In a very short time the maid was back with the blanket.

"Which bed should I put it on, sir?" she asked.

"What? Why, that one—the one I slept in last night," he said, pointing to it.

"Oh yes! I beg your pardon, sir, but you seemed to have tried both of 'em; leastways, we had to make 'em both up this morning."

"Really? How very absurd!" said Parkins. "I certainly never touched the other, except to lay some things on it. Did it actually seem to have been slept in?"

"Oh yes, sir!" said the maid. "Why, all the things was crumpled and throwed about all ways, if you'll excuse me, sir—quite as if anyone 'adn't passed but a very poor night, sir."

"Dear me," said Parkins. "Well, I may have disordered it more than I thought when I unpacked my things. I'm very sorry to have given you the extra trouble, I'm sure. I expect a friend of mine soon, by the way—a gentleman from Cambridge—to come and occupy it for a night or two. That will be all right, I suppose, won't it?"

"Oh yes, to be sure, sir. Thank you, sir. It's no trouble, I'm sure," said the maid, and departed to giggle with her colleagues.

Parkins set forth, with a stern determination to improve his game.

I am glad to be able to report that he succeeded so far in this enterprise that the Colonel, who had been rather repining at the prospect of a second day's play in his company, became quite chatty as the morning advanced; and his voice boomed out over the flats, as certain also of our own minor poets have said, "like some great bourdon in a minster tower."

"Extraordinary wind, that, we had last night," he said. "In my old home we should have said someone had been whistling for it."

"Should you, indeed!" said Parkins. "Is there a superstition of that kind still current in your part of the country?"

"I don't know about superstition," said the Colonel. "They believe in it all over Denmark and Norway, as well as on the Yorkshire coast; and my experience is, mind you, that there's generally something at the bottom of what these country-folks hold to, and have held to for generations. But it's your drive" (or whatever it might have been: the golfing reader will have to imagine appropriate digressions at the proper intervals).

When conversation was resumed, Parkins said, with a slight hesitancy:

"Apropos of what you were saying just now, Colonel, I think I ought to tell you that my own views on such subjects are very strong. I am, in fact, a convinced disbeliever in what is called the 'supernatural.'"

"What!" said the Colonel, "do you mean to tell me you don't believe in second-sight, or ghosts, or anything of that kind?"

"In nothing whatever of that kind," returned Parkins firmly.

"Well," said the Colonel, "but it appears to me at that rate, sir, that you must be little better than a Sadducee."

Parkins was on the point of answering that, in his opinion, the Sadducees were the most sensible persons he had ever read of in the Old Testament; but, feeling some doubt as to whether much mention of them was to be found in that work, he preferred to laugh the accusation off.

"Perhaps I am," he said; "but— Here, give me my cleek, boy!— Excuse me one moment, Colonel." A short interval. "Now, as to whistling for the wind, let me give you my theory about it. The laws which govern winds are really not at all perfectly known—to fisherfolk and such, of course, not known at all. A man or woman of eccentric habits, perhaps, or a stranger, is seen repeatedly on the beach at some unusual hour, and is heard whistling. Soon afterwards a violent wind rises; a man who could read the sky perfectly or who possessed a barometer could have foretold that it would. The simple people of a fishing-village have no barometers, and only a few rough rules for prophesying weather. What more natural than that the eccentric personage I postulated should be regarded as having raised the wind, or that he or she should clutch eagerly at the reputation of being able to do so? Now, take last night's wind: as it happens, I myself was whistling. I blew a whistle twice, and the wind seemed to come absolutely in answer to my call. If anyone had seen me—"

The audience had been a little restive under this harangue, and Parkins had, I fear, fallen somewhat into the tone of a lecturer; but at the last sentence the Colonel stopped.

"Whistling, were you?" he said. "And what sort of whistle did you use? Play this stroke first." Interval.

"About that whistle you were asking, Colonel. It's rather a curious one. I have it in my— No; I see I've left it in my room. As a matter of fact, I found it yesterday."

And then Parkins narrated the manner of his discovery of the whistle, upon hearing which the Colonel grunted, and opined that, in Parkins's place, he should himself be careful about using a thing that had belonged to a set of Papists, of whom, speaking generally, it might be affirmed that you never knew what they might not have been up to. From this topic he diverged to the enormities of the Vicar, who had given notice on the previous Sunday that Friday would be the Feast of St. Thomas the Apostle, and that there would be service at eleven o'clock in the church. This and other similar proceedings constituted in the Colonel's view a strong presumption that the Vicar was a concealed Papist, if not a Jesuit; and Parkins, who could not very readily follow the Colonel in this region, did not disagree with him. In fact, they got on so well together in the morning that there was no talk on either side of their separating after lunch.

Both continued to play well during the afternoon, or, at least well enough to make them forget everything else until the light began to fail them. Not until then did Parkins remember that he had meant to do some more investigating at the preceptory; but it was of no great importance, he reflected. One day was as good as another; he might as well go home with the Colonel.

As they turned the corner of the house, the Colonel was almost knocked down by a boy who rushed into him at the very top of his speed, and then, instead of running away, remained hanging on to him and panting. The first words of the warrior were naturally those of reproof and objurgation, but he very quickly discerned that the boy was almost speechless with fright. Inquiries were useless at first. When the boy got his breath he began to howl, and still clung to the Colonel's legs. He was at last detached, but continued to howl.

"What in the world *is* the matter with you? What have you been up to? What have you seen?" said the two men.

"Ow, I seen it wive at me out of the winder," wailed the boy, "and I don't like it. I don't like it one bit."

"What window?" said the irritated Colonel. "Come, pull yourself together, my boy."

"The front winder it was, at the 'otel," said the boy.

At this point Parkins was in favour of sending the boy home, but the Colonel refused; he wanted to get to the bottom of it, he said; it was most dangerous to give a boy such a fright as this one had had, and if it turned out that people had been playing jokes, they should suffer for it in some way. And by a series of questions he made out this story: The boy had been playing about on the grass in front of the Globe with some others; then they had gone home to their teas, and he was just going, when he happened to look up at the front winder and see it a-wiving at him. *It* seemed to be a figure of some sort, in white as far as he knew—couldn't see its face; but it wived at him, and it warn't a right thing—not to say not a right person. Was there a light in the room? No, he didn't think to look if there was a light. Which was the window? Was it the top one or the second one? The seckind one it was—the big winder what got two little uns at the sides.

"Very well, my boy," said the Colonel, after a few more questions. "You run away home now. I expect it was some person trying to give you a start. Another time, like a brave English boy, you just throw a stone—well, no, not that exactly, but you go and speak to the waiter, or to Mr. Simpson, the landlord, and—yes—and say that I advised you to do so."

The boy's face expressed some of the doubt he felt as to the likelihood of Mr. Simpson's lending a favourable ear to his complaint, but the Colonel did not appear to perceive this, and went on:

"And here's a sixpence—no, I see it's a shilling—and you be off home, and don't think any more about it."

The youth hurried off with agitated thanks, and the Colonel and Parkins went round to the front of the Globe and reconnoitred. There was only one window answering to the description they had been hearing.

"Well, that's curious," said Parkins; "it's evidently my window the lad was talking about. Will you come up for a moment, Colonel Wilson? We ought to be able to see if anyone has been taking liberties in my room."

They were soon in the passage, and Parkins made as if to open the door. Then he stopped and felt in his pockets.

"This is more serious than I thought," was his next remark. "I remember now that before I started this morning I locked the door. It is locked now, and, what is more, here is the key." And he held it up. "Now," he went on, "if the servants are in the habit of going into one's room during the day when one is away, I can only say that—well, that I don't approve of it at all." Conscious of a somewhat weak climax, he busied himself in opening the door (which was indeed locked) and in lighting candles. "No," he said, "nothing seems disturbed."

"Except your bed," put in the Colonel.

"Excuse me, that isn't my bed," said Parkins. "I don't use that one. But it does look as if someone had been playing tricks with it."

It certainly did: the clothes were bundled up and twisted together in a most tortuous confusion. Parkins pondered.

"That must be it," he said at last: "I disordered the clothes last night in unpacking, and they haven't made it since. Perhaps they came in to make it, and that boy saw them through the window; and then they were called away and locked the door after them. Yes, I think that must be it."

"Well, ring and ask," said the Colonel, and this appealed to Parkins as practical.

The maid appeared, and, to make a long story short, deposed that she had made the bed in the morning when the gentleman was in the room, and hadn't been there since. No, she hadn't no other key. Mr. Simpson he kep' the keys; he'd be able to tell the gentleman if anyone had been up.

This was a puzzle. Investigation showed that nothing of value had been taken, and Parkins remembered the disposition of the small objects on tables and so forth well enough to be pretty sure that no

pranks had been played with them. Mr. and Mrs. Simpson furthermore agreed that neither of them had given the duplicate key of
the room to any person whatever during the day. Nor could Parkins,
fair-minded man as he was, detect anything in the demeanour of
master, mistress, or maid that indicated guilt. He was much more
inclined to think that the boy had been imposing on the Colonel.

The latter was unwontedly silent and pensive at dinner and
throughout the evening. When he bade good night to Parkins, he
murmured in a gruff undertone:

"You know where I am if you want me during the night."

"Why, yes, thank you, Colonel Wilson, I think I do; but there
isn't much prospect of my disturbing you, I hope. By the way," he
added, "did I show you that old whistle I spoke of? I think not.
Well, here it is."

The Colonel turned it over gingerly in the light of the candle.

"Can you make anything of the inscription?" asked Parkins, as he
took it back.

"No, not in this light. What do you mean to do with it?"

"Oh, well, when I get back to Cambridge I shall submit it to some
of the archæologists there, and see what they think of it, and very
likely, if they consider it worth having, I may present it to one of
the museums."

" 'M!" said the Colonel. "Well, you may be right. All I know is
that, if it were mine, I should chuck it straight into the sea. It's no
use talking, I'm well aware, but I expect that with you it's a case of
live and learn. I hope so, I'm sure, and I wish you a good night."

He turned away, leaving Parkins in act to speak at the bottom of
the stair, and soon each was in his own bedroom.

By some unfortunate accident, there were neither blinds nor curtains to the windows of the Professor's room. The previous night he
had thought little of this, but to-night there seemed every prospect
of a bright moon rising to shine directly on his bed, and probably
wake him later on. When he noticed this he was a good deal annoyed, but, with an ingenuity which I can only envy, he succeeded
in rigging up, with the help of a railway-rug, some safety-pins, and
a stick and umbrella, a screen which, if it only held together, would
completely keep the moonlight off his bed. And shortly afterwards
he was comfortably in that bed. When he had read a somewhat solid
work long enough to produce a decided wish for sleep, he cast a

drowsy glance round the room, blew out the candle, and fell back upon the pillow.

He must have slept soundly for an hour or more, when a sudden clatter shook him up in a most unwelcome manner. In a moment he realized what had happened: his carefully constructed screen had given way, and a very bright frosty moon was shining directly on his face. This was highly annoying. Could he possibly get up and reconstruct the screen? or could he manage to sleep if he did not?

For some minutes he lay and pondered over the possibilities; then he turned over sharply, and with all his eyes open lay breathlessly listening. There had been a movement, he was sure, in the empty bed on the opposite side of the room. To-morrow he would have it moved, for there must be rats or something playing about in it. It was quiet now. No! the commotion began again. There was a rustling and shaking: surely more than any rat could cause.

I can figure to myself something of the Professor's bewilderment and horror, for I have in a dream thirty years back seen the same thing happen; but the reader will hardly, perhaps, imagine how dreadful it was to him to see a figure suddenly sit up in what he had known was an empty bed. He was out of his own bed in one bound, and made a dash towards the window, where lay his only weapon, the stick with which he had propped his screen. This was, as it turned out, the worst thing he could have done, because the personage in the empty bed, with a sudden smooth motion, slipped from the bed and took up a position, with outspread arms, between the two beds, and in front of the door. Parkins watched it in a horrid perplexity. Somehow, the idea of getting past it and escaping through the door was intolerable to him; he could not have borne— he didn't know why—to touch it; and as for its touching him, he would sooner dash himself through the window than have that happen. It stood for the moment in a band of dark shadow, and he had not seen what its face was like. Now it began to move, in a stooping posture, and all at once the spectator realized, with some horror and some relief, that it must be blind, for it seemed to feel about it with its muffled arms in a groping and random fashion. Turning half away from him, it became suddenly conscious of the bed he had just left, and darted towards it, and bent over and felt the pillows in a way which made Parkins shudder as he had never in his life thought it possible. In a very few moments it seemed to know that the bed was empty, and then, moving forward into the area of light and facing the window, it showed for the first time what manner of thing it was.

Parkins, who very much dislikes being questioned about it, did once describe something of it in my hearing, and I gathered that what he chiefly remembers about it is a horrible, an intensely horrible, face *of crumpled linen*. What expression he read upon it he could not or would not tell, but that the fear of it went nigh to maddening him is certain.

But he was not at leisure to watch it for long. With formidable quickness it moved into the middle of the room, and, as it groped and waved, one corner of its draperies swept across Parkins's face. He could not—though he knew how perilous a sound was—he could not keep back a cry of disgust, and this gave the searcher an instant clue. It leapt towards him upon the instant, and the next moment he was half-way through the window backwards, uttering cry upon cry at the utmost pitch of his voice, and the linen face was thrust close into his own. At this, almost the last possible second, deliverance came, as you will have guessed: the Colonel burst the door open, and was just in time to see the dreadful group at the window. When he reached the figures only one was left. Parkins sank forward into the room in a faint, and before him on the floor lay a tumbled heap of bed-clothes.

Colonel Wilson asked no questions, but busied himself in keeping everyone else out of the room and in getting Parkins back to his bed; and himself, wrapped in a rug, occupied the other bed for the rest of the night. Early on the next day Rogers arrived, more welcome than he would have been a day before, and the three of them held a very long consultation in the Professor's room. At the end of it the Colonel left the hotel door carrying a small object between his finger and thumb, which he cast as far into the sea as a very brawny arm could send it. Later on the smoke of a burning ascended from the back premises of the Globe.

Exactly what explanation was patched up for the staff and visitors at the hotel I must confess I do not recollect. The Professor was somehow cleared of the ready suspicion of delirium tremens, and the hotel of the reputation of a troubled house.

There is not much question as to what would have happened to Parkins if the Colonel had not intervened when he did. He would either have fallen out of the window or else lost his wits. But it is not so evident what more the creature that came in answer to the whistle could have done than frighten. There seemed to be absolutely nothing material about it save the bed-clothes of which it had made itself a body. The Colonel, who remembered a not very dissimilar occurrence in India, was of opinion that if Parkins had closed with it it could really have done very little, and that its one power was that of frightening. The whole thing, he said, served to confirm his opinion of the Church of Rome.

There is really nothing more to tell, but, as you may imagine, the Professor's views on certain points are less clear cut than they used to be. His nerves, too, have suffered: he cannot even now see a surplice hanging on a door quite unmoved, and the spectacle of a scarecrow in a field late on a winter afternoon has cost him more than one sleepless night.

A Psychical Invasion

BY

ALGERNON BLACKWOOD

"AND WHAT is it makes you think I could be of use in this particular case?" asked Dr. John Silence, looking across somewhat sceptically at the Swedish lady in the chair facing him.

"Your sympathetic heart and your knowledge of occultism—"

"Oh, please—that dreadful word!" he interrupted, holding up a finger with a gesture of impatience.

"Well, then," she laughed, "your wonderful clairvoyant gift and your trained psychic knowledge of the processes by which a personality may be disintegrated and destroyed—these strange studies you've been experimenting with all these years—"

"If it's only a case of multiple personality I must really cry off," interrupted the doctor again hastily, a bored expression in his eyes as he stood up.

"It's not that; now please be serious, for I want your help," she said; "and if I choose my words poorly you must be patient with my ignorance. The case I know will interest you, and no one else could deal with it so well. In fact, no ordinary professional man could deal with it at all, for I know of no treatment or medicine that can restore a lost sense of humour!"

"You begin to interest me with your 'case'," he replied, and made himself comfortable to listen.

Mrs. Sivendson drew a sigh of contentment as she watched him go to the tube and heard him tell the servant he was not to be disturbed.

"I believe you have read my thoughts already," she said; "your intuitive knowledge of what goes on in other people's minds is positively uncanny."

Her friend shook his head and smiled as he drew his chair up to

516

a convenient position and prepared to listen attentively to what she had to say. He closed his eyes, as he always did when he wished to absorb the real meaning of a recital that might be inadequately expressed, for by this method he found it easier to set himself in tune with the living thoughts that lay behind the broken words.

By his friends John Silence was regarded as an eccentric, because he was rich by accident, and by choice—a doctor. That a man of independent means should devote his time to doctoring, chiefly doctoring folk who could not pay, passed their comprehension entirely. The native nobility of a soul whose first desire was to help those who could not help themselves, puzzled them. After that, it irritated them, and, greatly to his own satisfaction, they left him to his own devices.

Dr. Silence was a free-lance, though, among doctors, having neither consulting-room, book-keeper, nor professional manner. He took no fees, being at heart a genuine philanthropist, yet at the same time did no harm to his fellow-practitioners, because he only accepted unremunerative cases, and cases that interested him for some very special reason. He argued that the rich could pay, and the very poor could avail themselves of organised charity, but that a very large class of ill-paid, self-respecting workers, often followers of the arts, could not afford the price of a week's comforts merely to be told to travel. And it was these he desired to help: cases often requiring special and patient study—things no doctor can give for a guinea, and that no one would dream of expecting him to give.

But there was another side to his personality and practice, and one with which we are now more directly concerned; for the cases that especially appealed to him were of no ordinary kind, but rather of that intangible, elusive, and difficult nature best described as psychical afflictions; and, though he would have been the last person himself to approve of the title, it was beyond question that he was known more or less generally as the "Psychic Doctor."

In order to grapple with cases of this peculiar kind, he had submitted himself to a long and severe training, at once physical, mental, and spiritual. What precisely this training had been, or where undergone, no one seemed to know—for he never spoke of it, as, indeed, he betrayed no single other characteristic of the charlatan—but the fact that it had involved a total disappearance from the world for five years, and that after he returned and began his singular practice no one ever dreamed of applying to him the so easily acquired epithet of quack, spoke much for the seriousness of his strange quest and also for the genuineness of his attainments.

For the modern psychical researcher he felt the calm tolerance of the "man who knows." There was a trace of pity in his voice—contempt he never showed—when he spoke of their methods.

"This classification of results is uninspired work at best," he said once to me, when I had been his confidential assistant for some years. "It leads nowhere, and after a hundred years will lead nowhere. It is playing with the wrong end of a rather dangerous toy. Far better, it would be, to examine the causes, and then the results would so easily slip into place and explain themselves. For the sources are accessible, and open to all who have the courage to lead the life that alone makes practical investigation safe and possible."

And towards the question of clairvoyance, too, his attitude was significantly sane, for he knew how extremely rare the genuine power was, and that what is commonly called clairvoyance is nothing more than a keen power of visualising.

"It connotes a slightly increased sensibility, nothing more," he would say. "The true clairvoyant deplores his power, recognising that it adds a new horror to life, and is in the nature of an affliction. And you will find this always to be the real test."

Thus it was that John Silence, this singularly developed doctor, was able to select his cases with a clear knowledge of the difference between mere hysterical delusion and the kind of psychical affliction that claimed his special powers. It was never necessary for him to resort to the cheap mysteries of divination; for, as I have heard him observe, after the solution of some peculiarly intricate problem:

"Systems of divination, from geomancy down to reading by tea-leaves, are merely so many methods of obscuring the outer vision, in order that the inner vision may become open. Once the method is mastered, no system is necessary at all."

And the words were significant of the methods of this remarkable man, the keynote of whose power lay, perhaps, more than anything else, in the knowledge, first, that thought can act at a distance, and, secondly, that thought is dynamic and can accomplish material results.

"Learn how to *think*," he would have expressed it, "and you have learned to tap power at its source."

To look at—he was now past forty—he was sparely built, with speaking brown eyes in which shone the light of knowledge and self-confidence, while at the same time they made one think of that wondrous gentleness seen most often in the eyes of animals. A close beard concealed the mouth without disguising the grim determination of lips and jaw, and the face somehow conveyed an impression of transparency, almost of light, so delicately were the features refined away. On the fine forehead was that indefinable touch of peace that comes from identifying the mind with what is permanent in the soul, and letting the impermanent slip by without power to wound or distress; while from his manner—so gentle, quiet, sympathetic—few could have guessed the strength of purpose that burned within like a great flame.

"I think I should describe it as a psychical case," continued the Swedish lady, obviously trying to explain herself very intelligently, "and just the kind you like. I mean a case where the cause is hidden deep down in some spiritual distress, and——"

"But the symptoms first, please, my dear Svenska," he interrupted, with a strangely compelling seriousness of manner, "and your deductions afterwards."

She turned round sharply on the edge of her chair and looked him in the face, lowering her voice to prevent her emotion betraying itself too obviously.

"In my opinion there's only one symptom," she half whispered, as though telling something disagreeable—"fear—simply fear."

"Physical fear?"

"I think not; though how can I say? I think it's a horror in the psychical region. It's no ordinary delusion; the man is quite sane; but he lives in mortal terror of something——"

"I don't know what you mean by his 'psychical region'," said the doctor, with a smile; "though I suppose you wish me to understand that his spiritual, and not his mental, processes are affected. Anyhow, try and tell me briefly and pointedly what you know about the man, his symptoms, his need for help, *my* peculiar help, that is, and all that seems vital in the case. I promise to listen devotedly."

"I am trying," she continued earnestly, "but must do so in my own words and trust to your intelligence to disentangle as I go along. He is a young author, and lives in a tiny house off Putney Heath somewhere. He writes humorous stories—quite a genre of his own: Pender—you must have heard his name—Felix Pender? Oh, the man had a great gift, and married on the strength of it; his future seemed assured. I say 'had', for quite suddenly his talent utterly failed him. Worse, it became transformed into its opposite. He can no longer write a line in the old way that was bringing him success——"

Dr. Silence opened his eyes for a second and looked at her.

"He still writes, then? The force has not gone?" he asked briefly, and then closed his eyes again to listen.

"He works like a fury," she went on, "but produces nothing"—she hesitated a moment—"nothing that he can use or sell. His earnings have practically ceased, and he makes a precarious living by book-reviewing and odd jobs—very odd, some of them. Yet, I am certain his talent has not really deserted him finally, but is merely——"

Again Mrs. Sivendson hesitated for the appropriate word.

"In abeyance," he suggested, without opening his eyes.

"Obliterated," she went on, after a moment to weigh the word, "merely obliterated by something else——"

"By some*one* else?"

"I wish I knew. All I can say is that he is haunted, and temporarily his sense of humour is shrouded—gone—replaced by something dreadful that writes other things. Unless something competent is done, he will simply starve to death. Yet he is afraid to go to a doctor for fear of being pronounced insane; and, anyhow, a man can hardly ask a doctor to take a guinea to restore a vanished sense of humour, can he?"

"Has he tried anyone at all——?"

"Not doctors yet. He tried some clergymen and religious people; but they *know* so little and have so little intelligent sympathy. And most of them are so busy balancing on their own little pedestals——"

John Silence stopped her tirade with a gesture.

"And how is it that you know so much about him?" he asked gently.

"I know Mrs. Pender well—I knew her before she married him——"

"And is she a cause, perhaps?"

"Not in the least. She is devoted; a woman very well educated, though without being really intelligent, and with so little sense of humour herself that she always laughs at the wrong places. But she has nothing to do with the cause of his distress; and, indeed, has chiefly guessed it from observing him, rather than from what little he has told her. And he, you know, is a really lovable fellow, hard-working, patient—altogether worth saving."

Dr. Silence opened his eyes and went over to ring for tea. He did not know very much more about the case of the humorist than when he first sat down to listen; but he realised that no amount of words from his Swedish friend would help to reveal the real facts. A personal interview with the author himself could alone do that.

"All humorists are worth saving," he said with a smile, as she poured out the tea. "We can't afford to lose a single one in these strenuous days. I will go and see your friend at the first opportunity."

She thanked him elaborately, effusively, with many words, and he, with much difficulty, kept the conversation thenceforward strictly to the teapot.

And, as a result of this conversation, and a little more he had gathered by means best known to himself and his secretary, he was whizzing in his motor-car one afternoon a few days later up Putney Hill to have his first interview with Felix Pender, the humourous writer who was the victim of some mysterious malady in his "psychical region" that had obliterated his sense of the comic and threatened to wreck his life and destroy his talent. And his desire to help was probably of equal strength with his desire to know and to investigate.

The motor stopped with a deep purring sound, as though a great black panther lay concealed within its hood, and the doctor—the "psychic doctor," as he was sometimes called—stepped out through the gathering fog, and walked across the tiny garden that held a blackened fir tree and a stunted laurel shrubbery. The house was very small, and it was some time before anyone answered the bell. Then, suddenly, a light appeared in the hall, and he saw a pretty little woman standing on the top step begging him to come in. She was dressed in grey, and the gaslight fell on a mass of deliberately brushed light hair. Stuffed, dusty birds, and a shabby array of African spears, hung on the wall behind her. A hat-rack, with a bronze plate full of very large cards, led his eye swiftly to a dark staircase beyond. Mrs. Pender had round eyes like a child's, and she greeted him with an effusiveness that barely concealed her emotion, yet strove to appear naturally cordial. Evidently she had been looking out for his arrival, and had outrun the servant girl. She was a little breathless.

"I hope you've not been kept waiting—I think it's *most* good of you to come——" she began, and then stopped sharp when she saw his face in the gaslight. There was something in Dr. Silence's look that did not encourage mere talk. He was in earnest now, if ever man was.

"Good evening, Mrs. Pender," he said, with a quiet smile that won confidence, yet deprecated unnecessary words, "the fog delayed me a little. I am glad to see you."

They went into a dingy sitting-room at the back of the house, neatly furnished but depressing. Books stood in a row upon the mantelpiece. The fire had evidently just been lit. It smoked in great puffs into the room.

"Mrs. Sivendson said she thought you might be able to come," ventured the little woman again, looking up engagingly into his face and betraying anxiety and eagerness in every gesture. "But I hardly dared to believe it. I think it is really too good of you. My husband's case is so peculiar that—well, you know, I am quite sure any *ordinary* doctor would say at once the asylum——"

"Isn't he in, then?" asked Dr. Silence gently.

"In the asylum?" she gasped. "Oh dear, no—not yet!"

"In the house, I meant," he laughed.

She gave a great sigh.

"He'll be back any minute now," she replied, obviously relieved to see him laugh; "but the fact is, we didn't expect you so early—I mean, my husband hardly thought you would come at all."

"I am always delighted to come—when I am really wanted, and can be of help," he said quickly; "and, perhaps, it's all for the best that your husband is out, for now that we are alone you can tell me something about his difficulties. So far, you know, I have heard very little."

Her voice trembled as she thanked him, and when he came and took a chair close beside her she actually had difficulty in finding words with which to begin.

"In the first place," she began timidly, and then continuing with a nervous incoherent rush of words, "he will be simply delighted

that you've really come, because he said you were the only person
he would consent to see at all—the only doctor, I mean. But, of
course, he doesn't know how frightened I am, or how much I have
noticed. He pretends with me that it's just a nervous breakdown,
and I'm sure he doesn't realise all the odd things I've noticed him
doing. But the main thing, I suppose——"

"Yes, the main thing, Mrs. Pender," he said encouragingly, noticing her hesitation.

"——is that he thinks we are not alone in the house. That's the
chief thing."

"Tell me more facts—just facts."

"It began last summer when I came back from Ireland; he had
been here alone for six weeks, and I thought him looking tired and
queer—ragged and scattered about the face, if you know what I
mean, and his manner worn out. He said he had been writing hard,
but his inspiration had somehow failed him, and he was dissatis-
fied with his work. His sense of humour was leaving him, or changing into something else, he said. There was something in the house,
he declared, that"—she emphasised the words—"prevented his feeling funny."

"Something in the house that prevented his feeling funny," repeated the doctor. "Ah, now we're getting to the heart of it!"

"Yes," she resumed vaguely; "that's what he kept saying."

"And what was it he *did* that you thought strange?" he asked
sympathetically. "Be brief, or he may be here before you finish."

"Very small things, but significant it seemed to me. He changed
his workroom from the library, as we call it, to the smoking-room.
He said all his characters became wrong and terrible in the library;
they altered, so that he felt like writing tragedies—vile, debased
tragedies, the tragedies of broken souls. But now he says the same
of the smoking-room, and he's gone back to the library."

"Ah!"

"You see, there's so little I can tell you," she went on, with increasing speed and countless gestures. "I mean it's only very small
things he does and says that are queer. What frightens me is that
he assumes there is someone else in the house all the time—someone
I never see. He does not actually say so, but on the stairs I've seen
him standing aside to let someone pass; I've seen him open a door

to let someone in or out; and often in our bedroom he puts chairs
about as though for someone else to sit in. Oh—oh yes, and once or
twice," she cried—"once or twice——"

She paused and looked about her with a startled air.

"Yes?"

"Once or twice," she resumed hurriedly, as though she heard a
sound that alarmed her, "I've heard him running—coming in and
out of the rooms breathless as if something were after him——"

The door opened while she was still speaking, cutting her words
off in the middle, and a man came into the room. He was dark and
clean-shaven, sallow rather, with the eyes of imagination, and dark
hair growing scantily about the temples. He was dressed in a shabby
tweed suit, and wore an untidy flannel collar at the neck. The dominant expression of his face was startled—hunted; an expression that
might any moment leap into the dreadful stare of terror and announce a total loss of self-control.

The moment he saw his visitor a smile spread over his worn
features, and he advanced to shake hands.

"I hoped you would come; Mrs. Sivendson said you might be able
to find time," he said simply. His voice was thin and reedy. "I am
very glad to see you, Dr. Silence. It is 'Doctor', is it not?"

"Well, I am entitled to the description," laughed the other, "but
I rarely get it. You know, I do not practise as a regular thing; that
is, I only take cases that specially interest me, or——"

He did not finish the sentence, for the men exchanged a glance
of sympathy that rendered it unnecessary.

"I have heard of your great kindness."

"It's my hobby," said the other quickly, "and my privilege."

"I trust you will still think so when you have heard what I have
to tell you," continued the author, a little wearily. He led the way
across the hall into the little smoking-room where they could talk
freely and undisturbed.

In the smoking-room, the door shut and privacy about them,
Pender's attitude changed somewhat, and his manner became very
grave. The doctor sat opposite, where he could watch his face. Already, he saw, it looked more haggard. Evidently it cost him much
to refer to his trouble at all.

"What I have is, in my belief, a profound spiritual affliction," he
began quite bluntly, looking straight into the other's eyes.

"I saw that at once," Dr. Silence said.

"Yes, you saw that, of course; my atmosphere must convey that much to anyone with psychic perceptions. Besides which, I feel sure from all I've heard, that you are really a soul-doctor, are you not, more than a healer merely of the body?"

"You think of me too highly," returned the other; "though I prefer cases, as you know, in which the spirit is disturbed first, the body afterwards."

"I understand, yes. Well, I have experienced a curious disturbance in—*not* in my physical region primarily. I mean my nerves are all right, and my body is all right. I have no delusions exactly, but my spirit is tortured by a calamitous fear which first came upon me in a strange manner."

John Silence leaned forward a moment and took the speaker's hand and held it in his own for a few brief seconds, closing his eyes as he did so. He was not feeling his pulse, or doing any of the things that doctors ordinarily do; he was merely absorbing into himself the main note of the man's mental condition, so as to get completely his own point of view, and thus be able to treat his case with true sympathy. A very close observer might perhaps have noticed that a slight tremor ran through his frame after he had held the hand for a few seconds.

"Tell me quite frankly, Mr. Pender," he said soothingly, releasing the hand, and with deep attention in his manner, "tell me all the steps that led to the beginning of this invasion. I mean tell me what the particular drug was, and why you took it, and how it affected you——"

"Then you know it began with a drug!" cried the author, with undisguised astonishment.

"I only know from what I observe in you, and in its effect upon myself. You are in a surprising psychical condition. Certain portions of your atmosphere are vibrating at a far greater rate than others. This is the effect of a drug, but of no ordinary drug. Allow me to finish, please. If the higher rate of vibration spreads all over, you will become, of course, permanently cognizant of a much larger world than the one you know normally. If, on the other hand, the rapid portion sinks back to the usual rate, you will lose these occasional increased perceptions you now have."

"You amaze me!" exclaimed the author; "for your words exactly describe what I have been feeling——"

"I mention this only in passing, and to give you confidence before you approach the account of your real affliction," continued the doctor. "All perception, as you know, is the result of vibrations; and clairvoyance simply means becoming sensitive to an increased scale of vibrations. The awakening of the inner senses we hear so much about means no more than that. Your partial clairvoyance is easily explained. The only thing that puzzles me is how you managed to procure the drug, for it is not easy to get in pure form, and no adulterated tincture could have given you the terrific impetus I see you have acquired. But, please proceed now and tell me your story in your own way."

"This *Cannabis indica*," the author went on, "came into my possession last autumn while my wife was away. I need not explain how I got it, for that has no importance; but it was the genuine fluid extract, and I could not resist the temptation to make an experiment. One of its effects, as you know, is to induce torrential laughter——"

"Yes; sometimes."

"——I am a writer of humorous tales, and I wished to increase my own sense of laughter—to see the ludicrous from an abnormal point of view. I wished to study it a bit, if possible, and——"

"Tell me!"

"I took an experimental dose. I starved for six hours to hasten the effect, locked myself into this room, and gave orders not to be disturbed. Then I swallowed the stuff and waited."

"And the effect?"

"I waited one hour, two, three, four, five hours. Nothing happened. No laughter came, but only a great weariness instead. Nothing in the room or in my thoughts came within a hundred miles of a humorous aspect."

"Always a most uncertain drug," interrupted the doctor. "We make very small use of it on that account."

"At two o'clock in the morning I felt so hungry and tired that I decided to give up the experiment and wait no longer. I drank some milk and went upstairs to bed. I felt flat and disappointed. I fell asleep at once and must have slept for about an hour, when I awoke suddenly with a great noise in my ears. It was the noise of my own

laughter! I was simply shaking with merriment. At first I was bewildered and thought I had been laughing in dreams, but a moment
later I remembered the drug, and was delighted to think that after
all I had got an effect. It had been working all along, only I had
miscalculated the time. The only unpleasant thing *then* was an odd
feeling that I had not waked naturally, but had been wakened by
someone else—deliberately. This came to me as a certainty in the
middle of my noisy laughter and distressed me."

"Any impression who it could have been?" asked the doctor, now
listening with close attention to every word, very much on the alert.

Pender hesitated and tried to smile. He brushed his hair from his
forehead with a nervous gesture.

"You must tell me all your impressions, even your fancies; they
are quite as important as your certainties."

"I had a vague idea that it was someone connected with my forgotten dream, someone who had been at me in my sleep, someone
of great strength and great ability—of great force—quite an unusual
personality—and, I was certain, too—a woman."

"A good woman?" asked John Silence quietly.

Pender started a little at the question and his sallow face flushed;
it seemed to surprise him. But he shook his head quickly with an
indefinable look of horror.

"Evil," he answered briefly, "appallingly evil, and yet mingled
with the sheer wickedness of it was also a certain perverseness—the
perversity of the unbalanced mind."

He hesitated a moment and looked up sharply at his interlocutor.
A shade of suspicion showed itself in his eyes.

"No," laughed the doctor, "you need not fear that I'm merely
humouring you, or think you mad. Far from it. Your story interests
me exceedingly and you furnish me unconsciously with a number
of clues as you tell it. You see, I possess some knowledge of my own
as to these psychic byways."

"I was shaking with such violent laughter," continued the nar-
rator, reassured in a moment, "though with no clear idea what was
amusing me, that I had the greatest difficulty in getting up for the
matches, and was afraid I should frighten the servants overhead
with my explosions. When the gas was lit I found the room empty,
of course, and the door locked as usual. Then I half dressed and
went out on to the landing, my hilarity better under control, and

proceeded to go downstairs. I wished to record my sensations. I stuffed a handkerchief into my mouth so as not to scream aloud and communicate my hysterics to the entire household."

"And the presence of this—this——?"

"It was hanging about me all the time," said Pender, "but for the moment it seemed to have withdrawn. Probably, too, my laughter killed all other emotions."

"And how long did you take getting downstairs?"

"I was just coming to that. I see you know all my 'symptoms' in advance, as it were; for, of course, I thought I should never get to the bottom. Each step seemed to take five minutes, and crossing the narrow hall at the foot of the stairs—well, I could have sworn it was half an hour's journey had not my watch certified that it was a few seconds. Yet I walked fast and tried to push on. It was no good. I walked apparently without advancing, and at that rate it would have taken me a week to get down Putney Hill."

"An experimental dose radically alters the scale of time and space sometimes—"

"But, when at last I got into my study and lit the gas, the change came horridly, and sudden as a flash of lightning. It was like a douche of icy water, and in the middle of this storm of laughter—"

"Yes; what?" asked the doctor, leaning forward and peering into his eyes.

"—I was overwhelmed with terror," said Pender, lowering his reedy voice at the mere recollection of it.

He paused a moment and mopped his forehead. The scared, hunted look in his eyes now dominated the whole face. Yet, all the time, the corners of his mouth hinted of possible laughter as though the recollection of that merriment still amused him. The combination of fear and laughter in his face was very curious, and lent great conviction to his story; it also lent a bizarre expression of horror to his gestures.

"Terror, was it?" repeated the doctor soothingly.

"Yes, terror; for, though the Thing that woke me seemed to have gone, the memory of it still frightened me, and I collapsed into a chair. Then I locked the door and tried to reason with myself, but the drug made my movements so prolonged that it took me five minutes to reach the door, and another five to get back to the chair again. The laughter, too, kept bubbling up inside me—great whole-

some laughter that shook me like gusts of wind—so that even my
terror almost made me laugh. Oh, but I may tell you, Dr. Silence, it
was altogether vile, that mixture of fear and laughter, altogether
vile!

"Then, all at once, the things in the room again presented their
funny side to me and set me off laughing more furiously than ever.
The bookcase was ludicrous, the armchair a perfect clown, the
way the clock looked at me on the mantelpiece too comic for words;
the arrangement of papers and inkstand on the desk tickled me till
I roared and shook and held my sides and the tears streamed down
my cheeks. And that footstool! Oh, that absurd' footstool!"

He lay back in his chair, laughing to himself and holding up his
hands at the thought of it, and at the sight of him Dr. Silence broke
into laughter also.

"Go on, please," he said, "I quite understand. I know something
myself of the hashish laughter."

The author pulled himself together and resumed, his face growing quickly grave again.

"So, you see, side by side with this extravagant, apparently causeless merriment, there was also an extravagant, apparently causeless
terror. The drug produced the laughter, I knew; but what brought
in the terror I could not imagine. Everywhere behind the fun lay
the fear. It was terror masked by cap and bells; and I became the
playground for two opposing emotions, armed and fighting to the
death. Gradually, then, the impression grew in me that this fear
was caused by the invasion—so you called it just now—of the 'person' who had wakened me: she was utterly evil; inimical to my soul,
or at least to all in me that wished for good. There I stood, sweating
and trembling, laughing at everything in the room, yet all the while
with this white terror mastering my heart. And this creature was
putting—putting her—"

He hesitated again, using his handkerchief freely.

"Putting what?"

"Putting ideas into my mind," he went on, glancing nervously
about the room. "Actually tapping my thought-stream so as to
switch off the usual current and inject her own. How mad that
sounds! I know it, but it's true. It's the only way I can express it.
Moreover, while the operation terrified me, the skill with which it
was accomplished filled me afresh with laughter at the clumsiness

of men by comparison. Our ignorant, bungling methods of teaching
the minds of others, of inculcating ideas, and so on, overwhelmed
me with laughter when I understood this superior and diabolical
method. Yet my laughter seemed hollow and ghastly, and ideas of
evil and tragedy trod close upon the heels of the comic. Oh, doctor,
I tell you again, it was unnerving!"

John Silence sat with his head thrust forward to catch every word
of the story which the other continued to pour out in nervous,
jerky sentences and lowered voice.

"You *saw* nothing—no one—all this time?" he asked.

"Not with my eyes. There was no visual hallucination. But in my
mind there began to grow the vivid picture of a woman—large, dark-
skinned, with white teeth and masculine features, and one eye—the
left—so drooping as to appear almost closed. Oh, such a face—!"

"A face you would recognise again?"

Pender laughed dreadfully.

"I wish I could forget it," he whispered, "I only wish I could forget it!" Then he sat forward in his chair suddenly, and grasped the
doctor's hand with an emotional gesture.

"I *must* tell you how grateful I am for your patience and sympathy," he cried, with a tremor in his voice, "and—that you do not
think me mad. I have told no one else a quarter of all this, and
the mere freedom of speech—the relief of sharing my affliction with
another—has helped me already more than I can possibly say."

Dr. Silence pressed his hand and looked steadily into the frightened eyes. His voice was very gentle when he replied.

"Your case, you know, is very singular, but of absorbing interest
to me," he said, "for it threatens, not your physical existence, but
the temple of your psychical existence—the inner life. Your mind
would not be permanently affected here and now, in this world; but
in the existence after the body is left behind, you might wake up
with your spirit so twisted, so distorted, so befouled, that you would
be *spiritually insane*—a far more radical condition than merely
being insane here."

There came a strange hush over the room, and between the two
men sitting there facing one another.

"Do you really mean—Good Lord!" stammered the author as
soon as he could find his tongue.

"What I mean in detail will keep till a little later, and I need only say now that I should not have spoken in this way unless I were quite positive of being able to help you. Oh, there's no doubt as to that, believe me. In the first place, I am very familiar with the workings of this extraordinary drug, this drug which has had the chance effect of opening you up to the forces of another region; and, in the second, I have a firm belief in the reality of super-sensuous occurrences as well as considerable knowledge of psychic processes acquired by long and painful experiment. The rest is, or should be, merely sympathetic treatment and practical application. The hashish has partially opened another world to you by increasing your rate of psychical vibration, and thus rendering you abnormally sensitive. Ancient forces attached to this house have attacked you. For the moment I am only puzzled as to their precise nature; for were they of an ordinary character, I should myself be psychic enough to feel them. Yet I am conscious of feeling nothing as yet. But now, please continue, Mr. Pender, and tell me the rest of your wonderful story; and when you have finished, I will talk about the means of cure."

Pender shifted his chair a little closer to the friendly doctor and then went on in the same nervous voice with his narrative.

"After making some notes of my impressions I finally got upstairs again to bed. It was four o'clock in the morning. I laughed all the way up—at the grotesque banisters, the droll physiognomy of the staircase window, the burlesque grouping of the furniture, and the memory of that outrageous footstool in the room below; but nothing more happened to alarm or disturb me, and I woke late in the morning after a dreamless sleep, none the worse for my experiment except for a slight headache and a coldness of the extremities due to lowered circulation."

"Fear gone, too?" asked the doctor.

"I seemed to have forgotten it, or at least ascribed it to mere nervousness. Its reality had gone, anyhow for the time, and all that day I wrote and wrote and wrote. My sense of laughter seemed wonderfully quickened and my characters acted without effort out of the heart of true humour. I was exceedingly pleased with this result of my experiment. But when the stenographer had taken her departure and I came to read over the pages she had typed out, I recalled her sudden glances of surprise and the odd way she had looked up at me while I was dictating. I was amazed at what I read and could hardly believe I had uttered it."

"And why?"

"It was so distorted. The words, indeed, were mine so far as I could remember, but the meanings seemed strange. It frightened me. The sense was so altered. At the very places where my characters were intended to tickle the ribs, only curious emotions of sinister amusement resulted. Dreadful innuendoes had managed to creep into the phrases. There was laughter of a kind, but it was bizarre, horrible, distressing; and my attempt at analysis only increased my dismay. The story, as it read then, made me shudder, for by virtue of these slight changes it had come somehow to hold the soul of horror, of horror disguised as merriment. The framework of humour was there, if you understand me, but the characters had turned sinister, and their laughter was evil."

"Can you show me this writing?"

The author shook his head.

"I destroyed it," he whispered. "But, in the end, though of course much perturbed about it, I persuaded myself that it was due to some after-effect of the drug, a sort of reaction that gave a twist to my mind and made me read macabre interpretations into words and situations that did not properly hold them."

"And, meanwhile, did the presence of this person leave you?"

"No; that stayed more or less. When my mind was actively employed I forgot it, but when idle, dreaming, or doing nothing in particular, there she was beside me, influencing my mind horribly—"

"In what way, precisely?" interrupted the doctor.

"Evil, scheming thoughts came to me, visions of crime, hateful pictures of wickedness, and the kind of bad imagination that so far has been foreign, indeed impossible, to my normal nature——"

"The pressure of the Dark Powers upon the personality," murmured the doctor, making a quick note.

"Eh? I didn't quite catch——"

"Pray, go on. I am merely making notes; you shall know their purport fully later."

"Even when my wife returned I was still aware of this Presence in the house; it associated itself with my inner personality in most intimate fashion; and outwardly I always felt oddly constrained to be polite and respectful towards it—to open doors, provide chairs and hold myself carefully deferential when it was about. It became very compelling at last, and, if I failed in any little particular, I seemed to know that it pursued me about the house, from one room to another, haunting my very soul in its inmost abode. It certainly came before my wife so far as my attentions were concerned.

"But, let me first finish the story of my experimental dose, for I took it again the third night, and underwent a very similar experience, delayed like the first in coming, and then carrying me off my feet when it did come with a rush of this false demon-laughter. This time, however, there was a reversal of the changed scale of space and time; it shortened, instead of lengthened, so that I dressed and got downstairs in about twenty seconds, and the couple of hours I stayed and worked in the study passed literally like a period of ten minutes."

"That is often true of an overdose," interjected the doctor, "and you may go a mile in a few minutes, or a few yards in a quarter of an hour. It is quite incomprehensible to those who have never experienced it, and is a curious proof that time and space are merely forms of thought.

"This time," Pender went on, talking more and more rapidly in his excitement, "another extraordinary effect came to me, and I experienced a curious changing of the senses, so that I perceived external things through one large main sense-channel instead of through the five divisions known as sight, smell, touch, and so forth. You will, I know, understand me when I tell you that I *heard* sights and *saw* sounds. No language can make this comprehensible, of course, and I can only say, for instance, that the striking of the clock I saw as a visible picture in the air before me. I saw the sounds of the tinkling bell. And in precisely the same way I heard the colours in the room, especially the colours of those books in the shelf behind you. Those red bindings I heard in deep sounds, and the yellow covers of the French bindings next to them made a shrill, piercing note not unlike the chattering of starlings. That brown bookcase muttered, and those green curtains opposite kept up a constant sort of rippling sound like the lower notes of a wood-horn. But I only was conscious of these sounds when I looked steadily at the different objects, and thought about them. The room, you understand, was not full of a chorus of notes; but when I concentrated my mind upon a colour, I heard, as well as saw, it."

"That is a known, though rarely obtained, effect of *Cannabis indica*," observed the doctor. "And it provoked laughter again, did it?"

"Only the muttering of the cupboard-bookcase made me laugh. It was so like a great animal trying to get itself noticed, and made me think of a performing bear—which is full of a kind of pathetic humour, you know. But this mingling of the senses produced no confusion in my brain. On the contrary, I was unusually clear-headed and experienced an intensification of consciousness, and felt marvellously alive and keen-minded.

"Moreover, when I took up a pencil in obedience to an impulse to sketch—a talent not normally mine—I found that I could draw nothing but heads, nothing, in fact, but one head—always the same —the head of a dark-skinned woman, with huge and terrible features and a very drooping left eye; and so well drawn, too, that I was amazed, as you may imagine—"

"And the expression of the face—?"

Pender hesitated a moment for words, casting about with his hands in the air and hunching his shoulders. A perceptible shudder ran over him.

"What I can only describe as—*blackness*," he replied in a low tone; "the face of a dark and evil soul."

"You destroyed that, too?" queried the doctor sharply.

"No; I have kept the drawings," he said, with a laugh, and rose to get them from a drawer in the writing-desk behind him.

"Here is all that remains of the pictures, you see," he added, pushing a number of loose sheets under the doctor's eyes; "nothing but a few scrawly lines. That's all I found the next morning. I had really drawn no heads at all—nothing but those lines and blots and wriggles. The pictures were entirely subjective, and existed only in my mind which constructed them out of a few wild strokes of the pen. Like the altered scale of space and time it was a complete de-lusion. These all passed, of course, with the passing of the drug's effects. But the other thing did not pass. I mean, the presence of that Dark Soul remained with me. It is here still. It is real. I don't know how I can escape from it."

"It is attached to the house, not to you personally. You must leave the house."

"Yes. Only I cannot afford to leave the house, for my work is my sole means of support, and—well, you see, since this change I cannot even write. They are horrible, these mirthless tales I now write, with their mockery of laughter, their diabolical suggestion. Horrible! I shall go mad if this continues."

He screwed his face up and looked about the room as though he expected to see some haunting shape.

"The influence in this house, induced by my experiment, has killed in a flash, in a sudden stroke, the sources of my humour, and, though I still go on writing funny tales—I have a certain name, you know—my inspiration has dried up, and much of what I write I have to burn—yes, doctor, to burn, before anyone sees it."

"As utterly alien to your own mind and personality?"

"Utterly! As though someone else had written it——"

"Ah!"

"And shocking!" He passed his hand over his eyes a moment and let the breath escape softly through his teeth. "Yet most damnably clever in the consummate way the vile suggestions are insinuated under cover of a kind of high drollery. My stenographer left me, of course—and I've been afraid to take another——"

John Silence got up and began to walk about the room leisurely, without speaking; he appeared to be examining the pictures on the wall and reading the names of the books lying about. Presently he paused on the hearthrug, with his back to the fire, and turned to look his patient quietly in the eyes. Pender's face was grey and drawn; the hunted expression dominated it; the long recital had told upon him.

"Thank you, Mr. Pender," he said, a curious glow showing about his fine, quiet face, "thank you for the sincerity and frankness of your account. But I think now there is nothing further I need ask you." He indulged in a long scrutiny of the author's haggard features, drawing purposely the man's eyes to his own and then meeting them with a look of power and confidence calculated to inspire even the feeblest soul with courage. "And, to begin with," he added, smiling pleasantly, "let me assure you without delay that you need have no alarm, for you are no more insane or deluded than I myself am——"

Pender heaved a deep sigh and tried to return the smile.

"——and this is simply a case, so far as I can judge at present, of a very singular psychical invasion, and a very sinister one, too, if you perhaps understand what I mean—"

"It's an odd expression; you used it before, you know," said the author wearily, yet eagerly listening to every word of the diagnosis, and deeply touched by the intelligent sympathy which did not at once indicate the lunatic asylum.

"Possibly," returned the other, "and an odd affliction too, you'll allow, yet one not unknown to the nations of antiquity, nor to those moderns, perhaps, who recognise the freedom of action under certain pathogenic conditions between this world and another."

"And you think," asked Pender hastily, "that it is all primarily due to the *Cannabis*? There is nothing radically amiss with myself—nothing incurable, or—?"

"Due entirely to the overdose," Dr. Silence replied emphatically, "to the drug's direct action upon your psychical being. It rendered you ultra-sensitive and made you respond to an increased rate of vibration. And, let me tell you, Mr. Pender, that your experiment might have had results far more dire. It has brought you into touch with a somewhat singular class of Invisible, but of one, I think, chiefly human in character. You might, however, just as easily have been drawn out of human range altogether, and the results of such a contingency would have been exceedingly terrible. Indeed, you would not now be here to tell the tale. I need not alarm you on that score, but mention it as a warning you will not misunderstand or underrate after what you have been through.

"You look puzzled. You do not quite gather what I am driving at; and it is not to be expected that you should, for you, I suppose, are the nominal Christian with the nominal Christian's lofty standard of ethics, and his utter ignorance of spiritual possibilities. Beyond a somewhat childish understanding of 'spiritual wickedness in high places,' you probably have no conception of what is possible once you break down the slender gulf that is mercifully fixed between you and that Outer World. But my studies and training have taken me far outside these orthodox trips, and I have made experiments that I could scarcely speak to you about in language that would be intelligible to you."

He paused a moment to note the breathless interest of Pender's face and manner. Every word he uttered was calculated; he knew exactly the value and effect of the emotions he desired to wake in the heart of the afflicted being before him.

"And from certain knowledge I have gained through various experiences," he continued calmly, "I can diagnose your case as I said before to be one of psychical invasion."

"And the nature of this—er—invasion?" stammered the bewildered writer of humorous tales.

"There is no reason why I should not say at once that I do not yet quite know," replied Dr. Silence. "I may first have to make one or two experiments——"

"On me?" gasped Pender, catching his breath.

"Not exactly," the doctor said, with a grave smile, "but with your assistance, perhaps. I shall want to test the conditions of the house—to ascertain, if possible, the character of the forces, of this strange personality that has been haunting you—"

"At present you have no idea exactly who—what—why—" asked the other in a wild flurry of interest, dread and amazement.

"I have a very good idea, but no proof rather," returned the doctor. "The effects of the drug in altering the scale of time and space, and merging the senses have nothing primarily to do with the invasion. They come to anyone who is fool enough to take an experimental dose. It is the other features of your case that are unusual. You see, you are now in touch with certain violent emotions, desires, purposes, still active in this house, that were produced in the past by some powerful and evil personality that lived here. How long ago, or why they still persist so forcibly, I cannot positively say. But I should judge that they are merely forces acting automatically with the momentum of their terrific original impetus."

"Not directed by a living being, a conscious will, you mean?"

"Possibly not—but none the less dangerous on that account, and more difficult to deal with. I cannot explain to you in a few minutes the nature of such things, for you have not made the studies that would enable you to follow me; but I have reason to believe that on the dissolution at death of a human being, its forces may still persist and continue to act in a blind, unconscious fashion. As a rule they speedily dissipate themselves, but in the case of a very powerful personality they may last a long time. And, in some cases—of which I incline to think this is one—these forces may coalesce with certain non-human entities who thus continue their life indefinitely and increase their strength to an unbelievable degree. If the original personality was evil, the beings attracted to the left-over forces will also be evil. In this case, I think there has been an unusual and dreadful aggrandisement of the thoughts and purposes left behind long ago by a woman of consummate wickedness and great personal power of character and intellect. Now, do you begin to see what I am driving at a little?"

Pender stared fixedly at his companion, plain horror showing in his eyes. But he found nothing to say, and the doctor continued:

"In your case, predisposed by the action of the drug, you have experienced the rush of these forces in undiluted strength. They wholly obliterate in you the sense of humour, fancy, imagination— all that makes for cheerfulness and hope. They seek, though perhaps automatically only, to oust your own thoughts and establish themselves in their place. You are the victim of a psychical invasion. At the same time, you have become clairvoyant in the true sense. You are also a clairvoyant victim."

Pender mopped his face and sighed. He left his chair and went over to the fireplace to warm himself.

"You must think me a quack to talk like this, or a madman," laughed Dr. Silence. "But never mind that. I have come to help you, and I can help you if you will do what I tell you. It is very simple; you must leave this house at once. Oh, never mind the difficulties; we will deal with those together. I can place another house at your disposal, or I would take the lease here off your hands, and later have it pulled down. Your case interests me greatly, and I mean to see you through, so that you have no anxiety, and can drop back into your old groove of work to-morrow! The drug has provided you, and therefore me, with a short-cut to a very interesting experience. I'm grateful to you."

The author poked the fire vigorously, emotion rising in him like a tide. He glanced towards the door nervously.

"There is no need to alarm your wife or to tell her the details of our conversation," pursued the other quietly. "Let her know that you will soon be in possession again of your sense of humour and your health, and explain that I am lending you another house for six months. Meanwhile I may have the right to use this house for a night or two for my experiment. Is that understood between us?"

"I can only thank you from the bottom of my heart," stammered Pender, unable to find words to express his gratitude.

Then he hesitated for a moment, searching the doctor's face anxiously.

"And your experiment with the house?" he said at length.

"Of the simplest character, my dear Mr. Pender. Although I am myself an artificially trained psychic, and consequently aware of the presence of discarnate entities as a rule, I have so far felt nothing here at all. This makes me sure that the forces acting here are of an unusual description. What I propose to do is to make an experiment with a view of drawing out this evil, coaxing it from its lair, so to speak, in order that it may *exhaust itself through me* and become dissipated for ever. I have already been inoculated," he added; "I consider myself to be immune."

"Heavens above!" gasped the author, collapsing on to a chair.

"Hell beneath! might be a more appropriate exclamation," the doctor laughed. "But, seriously, Mr. Pender, this is what I propose to do—with your permission."

"Of course, of course," cried the other, "you have my permission and my best wishes for success. I can see no possible objection, but—"

"But what?"

"I pray to Heaven you will not understake this experiment alone, will you?"

"Oh dear, no; not alone."

"You will take a companion with good nerves, and reliable in case of disaster, won't you?"

"I shall bring two companions," the doctor said.

"Ah, that's better. I feel easier. I am sure you must have among your acquaintances men who—"

"I shall not think of bringing men, Mr. Pender."

The other looked up sharply.

"No, or women either; or children."

"I don't understand. Who will you bring, then?"

"Animals," explained the doctor, unable to prevent a smile at his companion's expression of surprise—"two animals, a cat and a dog."

Pender stared as if his eyes would drop out upon the floor, and then led the way without another word into the adjoining room where his wife was awaiting them for tea.

A few days later the humorist and his wife, with minds greatly relieved, moved into a small furnished house placed at their free disposal in another part of London; and John Silence, intent upon his approaching experiment, made ready to spend a night in the empty house on top of Putney Hill. Only two rooms were prepared for occupation: the study on the ground floor and the bedroom immediately above it; all other doors were to be locked, and no servant was to be left in the house. The car had orders to call for him at nine o'clock the following morning.

And, meanwhile, his secretary had instructions to look up the past history and associations of the place, and learn everything he could concerning the character of former occupants, recent or remote.

The animals, by whose sensitiveness he intended to test any unusual conditions in the atmosphere of the building, Dr. Silence selected with care and judgment. He believed (and had already made curious experiments to prove it) that animals were more often, and more truly, clairvoyant than human beings. Many of them, he felt convinced, possessed powers of perception far superior to that mere keenness of the senses common to all dwellers in the wilds where the senses grow specially alert; they had what he termed "animal clairvoyance," and from his experiments with horses, dogs, cats, and even birds, he had drawn certain deductions, which, however, need not be referred to in detail here.

Cats, in particular, he believed, were almost continuously conscious of a larger field of vision, too detailed even for a photographic camera, and quite beyond the reach of normal human organs. He had, further, observed that while dogs were usually terrified in the presence of such phenomena, cats on the other hand were soothed and satisfied. They welcomed manifestations as something belonging peculiarly to their own region.

He selected his animals, therefore, with wisdom, so that they might afford a differing test, each in its own way, and that one should not merely communicate its own excitement to the other. He took a dog and a cat.

The cat he chose, now full grown, had lived with him since kittenhood, a kittenhood of perplexing sweetness and audacious mischief. Wayward it was and fanciful, ever playing its own mysterious games in the corners of the room, jumping at invisible nothings, leaping sideways into the air and falling with tiny moccasined feet on to another part of the carpet, yet with an air of dignified earnestness which showed that the performance was necessary to its own well-being, and not done merely to impress a stupid human audience. In the middle of elaborate washing it would look up, startled, as though to stare at the approach of some Invisible, cocking its little head sideways and putting out a velvet pad to inspect cautiously. Then it would get absent-minded, and stare with equal intentness in another direction (just to confuse the onlookers), and suddenly go on furiously washing its body again, but in quite a new place. Except for a white patch on its breast it was coal black. And its name was—Smoke.

"Smoke" described its temperament as well as its appearance. Its movements, its individuality, its posing as a little furry mass of concealed mysteries, its elfin-like elusiveness, all combined to justify its name; and a subtle painter might have pictured it as a wisp of floating smoke, the fire below betraying itself at two points only— the glowing eyes.

All its forces ran to intelligence—secret intelligence, the wordless, incalculable intuition of the Cat. It was, indeed, *the* cat for the business in hand.

The selection of the dog was not so simple, for the doctor owned many; but after much deliberation he chose a collie, called Flame from his yellow coat. True, it was a trifle old, and stiff in the joints, and even beginning to grow deaf, but, on the other hand, it was a very particular friend of Smoke's, and had fathered it from kitten-hood upwards so that a subtle understanding existed between them. It was this that turned the balance in its favour, this and its courage. Moreover, though good-tempered, it was a terrible fighter, and its anger when provoked by a righteous cause was a fury of fire, and irresistible.

It had come to him quite young, straight from the shepherd, with the air of the hills yet in its nostrils, and was then little more than skin and bones and teeth. For a collie it was sturdily built, its nose blunter than most, its yellow hair stiff rather than silky, and it had full eyes, unlike the slit eyes of its breed. Only its master could touch it, for it ignored strangers, and despised their pattings—when any dared to pat it. There was something patriarchal about the old beast. He was in earnest, and went through life with tremendous energy and big things in view, as though he had the reputation of his whole race to uphold. And to watch him fighting against odds was to understand why he was terrible.

In his relations with Smoke he was always absurdly gentle; also he was fatherly; and at the same time betrayed a certain diffidence or shyness. He recognised that Smoke called for strong yet respectful management. The cat's circuitous methods puzzled him, and his elaborate pretences perhaps shocked the dog's liking for direct, undisguised action. Yet, while he failed to comprehend these tortuous feline mysteries, he was never contemptuous or condescending; and he presided over the safety of his furry black friend somewhat as a father, loving but intuitive, might superintend the vagaries of a wayward and talented child. And, in return, Smoke rewarded him with exhibitions of fascinating and audacious mischief.

And these brief descriptions of their characters are necessary for the proper understanding of what subsequently took place.

With Smoke sleeping in the folds of his fur coat, and the collie lying watchful on the seat opposite, John Silence went down in his motor after dinner on the night of November 15th.

And the fog was so dense that they were obliged to travel at quarter speed the entire way.

.   .   .   .   .   .

It was after ten o'clock when he dismissed the motor and entered the dingy little house with the latch-key provided by Pender. He found the hall gas turned low, and a fire in the study. Books and food had also been placed ready by the servant according to instructions. Coils of fog rushed in after him through the opened door and filled the hall and passage with its cold discomfort.

The first thing Dr. Silence did was to lock up Smoke in the study with a saucer of milk before the fire, and then make a search of the house with Flame. The dog ran cheerfully behind him all the way while he tried the doors of the other rooms to make sure they were locked. He nosed about into corners and made little excursions on his own account. His manner was expectant. He knew there must be something unusual about the proceedings, because it was contrary to the habits of his whole life not to be asleep at this hour on the mat in front of the fire. He kept looking up into his master's face, as door after door was tried, with an expression of intelligent sympathy, but at the same time a certain air of disapproval. Yet everything his master did was good in his eyes, and he betrayed as little impatience as possible with all this unnecessary journeying to and fro. If the doctor was pleased to play this sort of game at such an hour of the night, it was surely not for him to object. So he played it too; and was very busy and earnest about it into the bargain.

After an uneventful search they came down again to the study, and here Dr. Silence discovered Smoke washing his face calmly in front of the fire. The saucer of milk was licked dry and clean; the preliminary examination that cats always make in new surroundings had evidently been satisfactorily concluded. He drew an arm-chair up to the fire, stirred the coals into a blaze, arranged the table and lamp to his satisfaction for reading, and then prepared surreptitiously to watch the animals. He wished to observe them carefully without their being aware of it.

Now, in spite of their respective ages, it was the regular custom of these two to play together every night before sleep. Smoke always made the advances, beginning with grave impudence to pat the dog's tail, and Flame played cumbrously with condescension. It was his duty, rather than pleasure; he was glad when it was over, and sometimes he was very determined and refused to play at all.

And this night was one of the occasions on which he was firm.

The doctor, looking cautiously over the top of his book, watched the cat begin the performance. It started by gazing with an innocent expression at the dog where he lay with nose on paws and eyes wide open in the middle of the floor. Then it got up and made as though it meant to walk to the door, going deliberately and very softly. Flame's eyes followed it until it was beyond the range of sight, and then the cat turned sharply and began patting his tail tentatively with one paw. The tail moved slightly in reply, and Smoke changed paws and tapped it again. The dog, however, did not rise to play as was his wont, and the cat fell to patting it briskly with both paws. Flame still lay motionless.

This puzzled and bored the cat, and it went round and stared hard into its friend's face to see what was the matter. Perhaps some inarticulate message flashed from the dog's eyes into its own little brain, making it understand that the programme for the night had better not begin with play. Perhaps it only realised that its friend was immovable. But, whatever the reason, its usual persistence thenceforward deserted it, and it made no further attempts at persuasion. Smoke yielded at once to the dog's mood; it sat down where it was and began to wash.

But the washing, the doctor noted, was by no means its real purpose; it only used it to mask something else; it stopped at the most busy and furious moments and began to stare about the room. Its thoughts wandered absurdly. It peered intently at the curtains; at the shadowy corners; at empty space above; leaving its body in curiously awkward positions for whole minutes together. Then it turned sharply and stared with a sudden signal of intelligence at the dog, and Flame at once rose somewhat stiffly to his feet and began to wander aimlessly and restlessly to and fro about the floor. Smoke followed him, padding quietly at his heels. Between them they made what seemed to be a deliberate search of the room.

And, here, as he watched them, noting carefully every detail of the performance over the top of his book, yet making no effort to interfere, it seemed to the doctor that the first beginnings of a faint distress betrayed themselves in the collie, and in the cat the stirrings of a vague excitement.

He observed them closely. The fog was thick in the air, and the tobacco smoke from his pipe added to its density; the furniture at the far end stood mistily, and where the shadows congregated in hanging clouds under the ceiling, it was difficult to see clearly at all; the lamplight only reached to a level of five feet from the floor, above which came layers of comparative darkness, so that the room appeared twice as lofty as it actually was. By means of the lamp and the fire, however, the carpet was everywhere clearly visible.

The animals made their silent tour of the floor, sometimes the dog leading, sometimes the cat; occasionally they looked at one another as though exchanging signals; and once or twice, in spite of the limited space, he lost sight of one or other among the fog and the shadows. Their curiosity, it appeared to him, was something more than the excitement lurking in the unknown territory of a strange room; yet, so far, it was impossible to test this, and he purposely kept his mind quietly receptive lest the smallest mental excitement on his part should communicate itself to the animals and thus destroy the value of their independent behaviour.

They made a very thorough journey leaving no piece of furniture unexamined, or unsmelt. Flame led the way, walking slowly with lowered ear, and Smoke followed demurely at his heels, making a transparent pretence of not being interested, yet missing nothing. And, at length, they returned, the old collie first, and came to rest on the mat before the fire. Flame rested his muzzle on his master's knee, smiling beatifically while he patted the yellow head and spoke his name; and Smoke, coming a little later pretending he came by chance, looked from the empty saucer to his face, lapped up the milk when it was given him to the last drop, and then sprang upon his knees and curled round for the sleep it had fully earned and intended to enjoy.

Silence descended upon the room. Only the breathing of the dog upon the mat came through the deep stillness, like the pulse of time marking the minutes; and the steady drip, drip of the fog outside upon the window-ledges dismally testified to the inclemency of the night beyond. And the soft crashings of the coals as the fire settled down into the grate became less and less audible as the fire sank and the flames resigned their fierceness.

It was now well after eleven o'clock, and Dr. Silence devoted himself again to his book. He read the words on the printed page and took in their meaning superficially, yet without starting into life the correlations of thought and suggestion that should accompany interesting reading. Underneath, all the while, his mental energies were absorbed in watching, listening, waiting for what might come. He was not over-sanguine himself, yet he did not wish to be taken by surprise. Moreover, the animals, his sensitive barometers, had incontinently gone to sleep.

After reading a dozen pages, however, he realised that his mind was really occupied in reviewing the features of Pender's extraordinary story, and that it was no longer necessary to steady his imagination by studying the dull paragraphs detailed in the pages before him. He laid down his book accordingly, and allowed his thoughts to dwell upon the features of the case. Speculations as to the meaning, however, he rigorously suppressed, knowing that such thoughts would act upon his imagination like wind upon the glowing embers of a fire.

As the night wore on the silence grew deeper and deeper, and only at rare intervals he heard the sound of wheels on the main road a hundred yards away, where the horses went at a walking pace owing to the density of the fog. The echo of pedestrian footsteps no longer reached him, the clamour of occasional voices no longer

came down the side street. The night, muffled by fog, shrouded by
veils of ultimate mystery, hung about the haunted villa like a doom.
Nothing in the house stirred. Stillness, in a thick blanket, lay over
the upper stories. Only the mist in the room grew more dense, he
thought, and the damp cold more penetrating. Certainly, from time
to time, he shivered.

The collie, now deep in slumber, moved occasionally—grunted,
sighed, or twitched his legs in dreams. Smoke lay on his knees, a
pool of warm, black fur, only the closest observation detecting the
movement of his sleek sides. It was difficult to distinguish exactly
where his head and body joined in that circle of glistening hair;
only a black satin nose and a tiny tip of pink tongue betrayed the
secret.

Dr. Silence watched him, and felt comfortable. The collie's
breathing was soothing. The fire was well built, and would burn
for another two hours without attention. He was not conscious of
the least nervousness. He particularly wished to remain in his ordinary and normal state of mind, and to force nothing. If sleep came
naturally, he would let it come—and even welcome it. The coldness
of the room, when the fire died down later, would be sure to wake
him again; and it would then be time enough to carry these sleeping barometers up to bed. From various psychic premonitions he
knew quite well that the night would not pass without adventure;
but he did not wish to force its arrival; and he wished to remain
normal, and let the animals remain normal, so that, when it came,
it would be unattended by excitement or by any straining of attention. Many experiments had made him wise. And, for the rest, he
had no fear.

Accordingly, after a time, he did fall asleep as he had expected,
and the last thing he remembered, before oblivion slipped up over
his eyes like soft wool, was the picture of Flame stretching all four
legs at once, and sighing noisily as he sought a more comfortable
position for his paws and muzzle upon the mat.

      ·   ·   ·   ·   ·   ·

It was a good deal later when he became aware that a weight
lay upon his chest, and that something was pencilling over his face
and mouth. A soft touch on the cheek woke him. Something was
patting him.

He sat up with a jerk, and found himself staring straight into a pair of brilliant eyes, half green, half black. Smoke's face lay level with his own; and the cat had climbed up with its front paws upon his chest.

The lamp had burned low and the fire was nearly out, yet Dr. Silence saw in a moment that the cat was in an excited state. It kneaded with its front paws into his chest, shifting from one to the other. He felt them prodding against him. It lifted a leg very carefully and patted his cheek gingerly. Its fur, he saw, was standing ridgewise upon its back; the ears were flattened back somewhat; the tail was switching sharply. The cat, of course, had wakened him with a purpose, and the instant he realised this, he set it upon the arm of the chair and sprang up with a quick turn to face the empty room behind him. By some curious instinct, his arms of their own accord assumed an attitude of defence in front of him, as though to ward off something that threatened his safety. Yet nothing was visible. Only shapes of fog hung about rather heavily in the air, moving slightly to and fro.

His mind was now fully alert, and the last vestiges of sleep gone. He turned the lamp higher and peered about him. Two things he became aware of at once: one, that Smoke, while excited, was *pleasurably* excited; the other, that the collie was no longer visible upon the mat at his feet. He had crept away to the corner of the wall farthest from the window, and lay watching the room with wide-open eyes, in which lurked plainly something of alarm.

Something in the dog's behaviour instantly struck Dr. Silence as unusual, and, calling him by name, he moved across to pat him. Flame got up, wagged his tail, and came over slowly to the rug, uttering a low sound that was half growl, half whine. He was evidently perturbed about something, and his master was proceeding to administer comfort when his attention was suddenly drawn to the antics of his other four-footed companion, the cat.

And what he saw filled him with something like amazement.

Smoke had jumped down from the back of the armchair and now occupied the middle of the carpet, where, with tail erect and legs stiff as ramrods, it was steadily pacing backwards and forwards in a narrow space, uttering, as it did so, those curious little guttural sounds of pleasure that only an animal of the feline species knows how to make expressive of supreme happiness. Its stiffened legs and arched back made it appear longer than usual, and the black visage wore a smile of beatific joy. Its eyes blazed magnificently; it was in an ecstasy.

At the end of every few paces it turned sharply and stalked back again along the same line, padding softly, and purring like a roll of little muffled drums. It behaved precisely as though it was rubbing against the ankles of someone who remained invisible. A thrill ran down the doctor's spine as he stood and stared. His experiment was growing interesting at last.

He called the collie's attention to his friend's performance to see whether he too was aware of anything standing there upon the carpet, and the dog's behaviour was significant and corroborative. He came as far as his master's knees and then stopped dead, refusing to investigate closely. In vain Dr. Silence urged him; he wagged his tail, whined a little, and stood in a half-crouching attitude, staring alternately at the cat and at his master's face. He was, apparently, both puzzled and alarmed, and the whine went deeper and deeper down into his throat till it changed into an ugly snarl of awakening anger.

Then the doctor called to him in a tone of command he had never known to be disregarded; but still the dog, though springing up in response, declined to move nearer. He made tentative motions, pranced a little like a dog about to take to water, pretended to bark, and ran to and fro on the carpet. So far there was no actual fear in his manner, but he was uneasy and anxious, and nothing would induce him to go within touching distance of the walking cat. Once he made a complete circuit, but always carefully out of reach; and in the end he returned to his master's legs and rubbed vigorously against him. Flame did not like the performance at all: that much was quite clear.

For several minutes John Silence watched the performance of the cat with profound attention and without interfering. Then he called to the animal by name.

"Smoke, you mysterious beastie, what in the world are you about?" he said, in a coaxing tone.

The cat looked up at him for a moment, smiling in its ecstasy, blinking its eyes, but too happy to pause. He spoke to it again. He called to it several times, and each time it turned upon him its blazing eyes, drunk with inner delight, opening and shutting its lips, its body large and rigid with excitement. Yet it never for one instant paused in its short journeys to and fro.

He noted exactly what it did: it walked, he saw, the same number of paces each time, some six or seven steps, and then it turned sharply and retraced them. By the pattern of the great roses in the carpet he measured it. It kept to the same direction and the same line. It behaved precisely as though it were rubbing against something solid. Undoubtedly, there was something standing there on that strip of carpet, something invisible to the doctor, something that alarmed the dog, yet caused the cat unspeakable pleasure.

"Smokie!" he called again, "Smokie, you black mystery, what is it excites you so?"

Again the cat looked up at him for a brief second, and then continued its sentry-walk, blissfully happy, intensely preoccupied. And, for an instant, as he watched it, the doctor was aware that a faint uneasiness stirred in the depths of his own being, focusing itself for the moment upon this curious behaviour of the uncanny creature before him.

There rose in him quite a new realisation of the mystery connected with the whole feline tribe, but especially with that common member of it, the domestic cat—their hidden lives, their strange aloofness, their incalculable subtlety. How utterly remote from anything that human beings understood lay the sources of their elusive activities. As he watched the indescribable bearing of the little creature mincing along the strip of carpet under his eyes, coquetting with the powers of darkness, welcoming, maybe, some fearsome visitor, there stirred in his heart a feeling strangely akin to awe. Its indifference to human kind, its serene superiority to the obvious, struck him forcibly with fresh meaning; so remote, so inaccessible seemed the secret purposes of its real life, so alien to the blundering honesty of other animals. Its absolute poise of bearing brought into his mind the opium-eater's words that "no dignity is perfect which does not at some point ally itself with the mysterious"; and he became suddenly aware that the presence of the dog in this foggy, haunted room on the top of Putney Hill was uncommonly welcome to him. He was glad to feel that Flame's dependable personality was with him. The savage growling at his heels was a pleasant sound. He was glad to hear it. That marching cat made him uneasy.

Finding that Smoke paid no further attention to his words, the doctor decided upon action. Would it rub against his leg, too? He would take it by surprise and see.

He stepped quickly forward and placed himself upon the exact strip of carpet where it walked.

But no cat is ever taken by surprise! The moment he occupied the space of the Intruder, setting his feet on the woven roses midway in the line of travel, Smoke suddenly stopped purring and sat down. It lifted up its face with the most innocent stare imaginable of its green eyes. He could have sworn it laughed. It was a perfect child again. In a single second it had resumed its simple, domestic manner; and it gazed at him in such a way that he almost felt Smoke was the normal being, and *his* was the eccentric behaviour that was being watched. It was consummate, the manner in which it brought about this change so easily and so quickly.

"Superb little actor;" he laughed in spite of himself, and stooped to stroke the shining black back. But, in a flash, as he touched its fur, the cat turned and spat at him viciously, striking at his hand with one paw. Then, with a hurried scutter of feet, it shot like a shadow across the floor and a moment later was calmly sitting over by the window-curtains washing its face as though nothing interested it in the whole world but the cleanness of its cheeks and whiskers.

John Silence straightened himself up and drew a long breath. He realised that the performance was temporarily at an end. The collie, meanwhile, who had watched the whole proceeding with marked disapproval, had now lain down again upon the mat by the fire, no longer growling. It seemed to the doctor just as though something that had entered the room while he slept, alarming the dog, yet bringing happiness to the cat, had now gone out again, leaving all as it was before. Whatever it was that excited its blissful attentions had retreated for the moment.

He realised this intuitively. Smoke evidently realised it, too, for presently he deigned to march back to the fireplace and jump upon his master's knees. Dr. Silence, patient and determined, settled down once more to his book. The animals soon slept; the fire blazed cheerfully; and the cold fog from outside poured into the room through every available chink and cranny.

For a long time silence and peace reigned in the room and Dr. silence availed himself of the quietness to make careful notes of what had happened. He entered for future use in other cases an exhaustive analysis of what he had observed, especially with regard to the effect upon the two animals. It is impossible here, nor would it be intelligible to the reader unversed in the knowledge of the region known to a scientifically trained psychic like Dr. Silence, to detail these observations. But to him it was clear, up to a certain point—and for the rest he must still wait and watch. So far, at least, he realised that while he slept in the chair—that is, while his will was dormant—the room had suffered intrusion from what he recognised as an intensely active Force, and might later be forced to acknowledge as something more than merely a blind force, namely, a distinct personality.

So far it had affected himself scarcely at all, but had acted directly upon the simpler organisms of animals. It stimulated keenly the centres of the cat's psychic being, inducing a state of instant happiness (intensifying its consciousness probably in the same way a drug or stimulant intensifies that of a human being); whereas it alarmed the less sensitive dog, causing it to feel a vague apprehension and distress.

His own sudden action and exhibition of energy had served to disperse it temporarily, yet he felt convinced—the indications were not lacking even while he sat there making notes—that it still remained near to him, conditionally if not spatially, and was, as it were, gathering force for a second attack.

And, further, he intuitively understood that the relations between the two animals had undergone a subtle change: that the cat had become immeasurably superior, confident, sure of itself in its own peculiar region, whereas Flame had been weakened by an attack he could not comprehend and knew not how to reply to. Though not yet afraid, he was defiant—ready to act against a fear that he felt to be approaching. He was no longer fatherly and protective towards the cat. Smoke held the key to the situation; and both he and the cat knew it.

Thus, as the minutes passed, John Silence sat and waited, keenly on the alert, wondering how soon the attack would be renewed, and at what point it would be diverted from the animals and directed upon himself.

The book lay on the floor beside him, his notes were complete. With one hand on the cat's fur, and the dog's front paws resting against his feet, the three of them dozed comfortably before the hot fire while the night wore on and the silence deepened towards midnight.

It was well after one o'clock in the morning when Dr. Silence turned the lamp out and lighted the candle preparatory to going up to bed. Then Smoke suddenly woke with a loud sharp purr and sat up. It neither stretched, washed nor turned; it listened. And the doctor, watching it, realised that a certain indefinable change had come about that very moment in the room. A swift readjustment of the forces within the four walls had taken place—a new disposition of their personal equations. The balance was destroyed, the former harmony gone. Smoke, most sensitive of barometers, had been the first to feel it, but the dog was not slow to follow suit, for on looking down he noted that Flame was no longer asleep. He was lying with eyes wide open, and that same instant he sat up on his great haunches and began to growl.

Dr. Silence was in the act of taking the matches to re-light the lamp when an audible movement in the room behind made him pause. Smoke leaped down from his knee and moved forward a few paces across the carpet. Then it stopped and stared fixedly; and the doctor stood up on the rug to watch.

As he rose the sound was repeated, and he discovered that it was not in the room as he first thought, but outside, and that it came from more directions than one. There was a rushing, sweeping noise against the window-panes, and simultaneously a sound of something brushing against the door—out in the hall. Smoke advanced sedately across the carpet, twitching his tail, and sat down within a foot of the door. The influence that had destroyed the harmonious conditions of the room had apparently moved in advance of its cause. Clearly, something was about to happen.

For the first time that night John Silence hesitated; the thought of that dark narrow hall-way, choked with fog, and destitute of human comfort, was unpleasant. He became aware of a faint creeping of his flesh. He knew, of course, that the actual opening of the door was not necessary to the invasion of the room that was about to take place, since neither doors nor windows, nor any other solid barriers could interpose an obstacle to what was seeking entrance. Yet the opening of the door would be significant and symbolic, and he distinctly shrank from it.

But for a moment only. Smoke, turning with a show of impatience, recalled him to his purpose, and he moved past the sitting, watching creature, and deliberately opened the door to its full width.

What subsequently happened, happened in the feeble and flickering light of the solitary candle on the mantelpiece.

Through the opened door he saw the hall, dimly lit and thick with fog. Nothing, of course, was visible—nothing but the hat-stand, the African spears in dark lines upon the wall and the high-backed wooden chair standing grotesquely underneath on the oilcloth floor. For one instant the fog seemed to move and thicken oddly; but he set that down to the score of imagination. The door had opened upon nothing.

Yet Smoke apparently thought otherwise, and the deep growling of the collie from the mat at the back of the room seemed to confirm his judgment.

For, proud and self-possessed, the cat had again risen to his feet, and having advanced to the door, was now ushering someone slowly into the room. Nothing could have been more evident. He passed from side to side, bowing his little head with great *empressement* and holding his stiffened tail aloft like a flagstaff. He turned this way and that, mincing to and fro, and showing signs of supreme satisfaction. He was in his element. He welcomed the intrusion, and apparently reckoned that his companions, the doctor and the dog, would welcome it likewise.

The Intruder had returned for a second attack.

Dr. Silence moved slowly backwards and took up his position on the hearthrug, keying himself up to a condition of concentrated attention.

He noted that Flame stood beside him, facing the room, with body motionless, and head moving swiftly from side to side with a curious swaying movement. His eyes were wide open, his back rigid, his neck and jaws thrust forward, his legs tense and ready to leap. Savage, ready for attack or defence, yet dreadfully puzzled and perhaps already a little cowed, he stood and stared, the hair on his spine and sides positively bristling outwards as though a wind played through them. In the dim firelight he looked like a great yellow-haired wolf, silent, eyes shooting dark fire, exceedingly formidable. It was Flame, the terrible.

Smoke, meanwhile, advanced from the door towards the middle
of the room, adopting the very slow pace of an invisible companion.
A few feet away it stopped and began to smile and blink its eyes.
There was something deliberately coaxing in its attitude as it stood
there undecided on the carpet, clearly wishing to effect some sort of
introduction between the Intruder and its canine friend and ally. It
assumed its most winning manners, purring, smiling, looking per-
suasively from one to the other, and making quick tentative steps
first in one direction and then in the other. There had always existed such perfect understanding between them in everything. Surely
Flame would appreciate Smoke's intentions now, and acquiesce.

. But the old collie made no advances. He bared his teeth, lifting
his lips till the gums showed, and stood stockstill with fixed eyes
and heaving sides. The doctor moved a little farther back, watching
intently the smallest movement, and it was just then he divined
suddenly from the cat's behaviour and attitude that it was not only
a single companion it had ushered·into the room, but *several*. It
kept crossing over from one to the other, looking up at each in turn.
It sought to win over the dog to friendliness with them all. The
original Intruder had come back with reinforcements. And at the
same time he further realised that the Intruder was something more
than a blindly acting force, impersonal though destructive. It was a
Personality, and moreover a great personality. And it was accompanied for the purposes of assistance by a host of other personalities,
minor in degree, but similar in kind.

He braced himself in the corner against the mantelpiece and
waited, his whole being roused to defence, for he was now fully
aware that the attack had spread to include himself as well as the
animals, and he must be on the alert. He strained his eyes through
the foggy atmosphere, tying in vain to see what the cat and dog
saw; but the candlelight threw an uncertain and flickering light
across the room and his eyes discerned nothing. On the floor Smoke
moved softly in front of him like a black shadow, his eyes gleaming
as he turned his head, still trying with many insinuating gestures
and much purring to bring about the introductions he desired.

But it was all in vain. Flame stood riveted to one spot, motionless
as a figure carved in stone.

Some minutes passed, during which only the cat moved, and then
there came a sharp change. Flame began to back towards the wall.

He moved his head from side to side as he went, sometimes turning to snap at something almost behind him. *They* were advancing upon him, trying to surround him. His distress became very marked from now onwards, and it seemed to the doctor that his anger merged into genuine terror and became overwhelmed by it. The savage growl sounded perilously like a whine, and more than once he tried to dive past his masters' legs, as though hunting for a way to escape. He was trying to avoid something that everywhere blocked the way.

This terror of the indomitable fighter impressed the doctor enormously; yet also painfully; stirring his impatience; for he had never before seen the dog show signs of giving in, and it distressed him to witness it. He knew, however, that he was not giving in easily, and understood that it was really impossible for him to gauge the animal's sensations properly at all. What Flame felt, and saw, must be terrible indeed to turn him all at once into a coward. He faced something that made him afraid of more than his life merely. The doctor spoke a few quick words of encouragement to him, and stroked the bristling hair. But without much success.

The collie seemed already beyond the reach of comfort such as that, and the collapse of the old dog followed indeed very speedily after this.

And Smoke, meanwhile, remained behind, watching the advance, but not joining in it; sitting, pleased and expectant, considering that all was going well and as it wished. It was kneading on the carpet with its front paws—slowly, laboriously, as though its feet were dipped in treacle. The sound its claws made as they caught in the threads was distinctly audible. It was still smiling, blinking, purring.

Suddenly the collie uttered a poignant short bark and leaped heavily to one side. His bared teeth traced a line of whiteness through the gloom. The next instant he dashed past his master's legs, almost upsetting his balance, and shot out into the room, where he went blundering wildly against walls and furniture. But that bark was significant; the doctor had heard it before and knew what it meant: for it was the cry of the fighter against odds and it meant that the old beast had found his courage again. Possibly it was only the courage of despair, but at any rate the fighting would be terrific. And Dr. Silence understood, too, that he dared not interfere. Flame must fight his own enemies in his own way.

But the cat, too, had heard that dreadful bark; and it, too, had understood. This was more than it had bargained for. Across the dim shadows of that haunted room there must have passed some secret signal of distress between the animals. Smoke stood up and looked swiftly about him. He uttered a piteous meow and trotted smartly away into the greater darkness by the windows. What his object was only those endowed with the spirit-like intelligence of cats might know. But, at any rate, he had at last ranged himself on the side of his friend. And the little beast meant business.

At the same moment the collie managed to gain the door. The doctor saw him rush through into the hall like a flash of yellow light. He shot across the oilcloth, and tore up the stairs, but in another second he appeared again, flying down the steps and landing at the bottom in a tumbling heap, whining, cringing, terrified. The doctor saw him slink back into the room again and crawl round by the wall towards the cat. Was, then, even the staircase occupied? Did *They* stand also in the hall? Was the whole house crowded from floor to ceiling?

The thought came to add to the keen distress he felt at the sight of the collie's discomfiture. And, indeed, his own personal distress had increased in a marked degree during the past minutes, and continued to increase steadily to the climax. He recognised that the drain on his own vitality grew steadily, and that the attack was now directed against himself even more than against the defeated dog, and the too much deceived cat.

It all seemed so rapid and uncalculated after that—the events that took place in this little modern room at the top of Putney Hill between midnight and sunrise—that Dr. Silence was hardly able to follow and remember it all. It came about with such uncanny swiftness and terror; the light was so uncertain; the movements of the black cat so difficult to follow on the dark carpet, and the doctor himself so weary and taken by surprise—that he found it almost impossible to observe accurately, or to recall afterwards precisely what it was he had seen or in what order the incidents had taken place. He never could understand what defect of vision on his part made it seem as though the cat had duplicated itself at first, and then increased indefinitely, so that there were at least a dozen of them darting silently about the floor, leaping softly on to chairs and tables, passing like shadows from the open door to the end of the room, all black as sin, with brilliant green eyes flashing fire in all directions. It was like the reflections from a score of mirrors placed round the walls at different angles. Nor could he make out at the time why the size of the room seemed to have altered, grown much larger, and why it extended away behind him where ordinarily the wall should have been. The snarling of the enraged and terrified collie sounded sometimes so far away; the ceiling seemed to have raised itself so much higher than before, and much of the furniture had changed in appearance and shifted marvellously.

It was all so confused and confusing, as though the little room he knew had become merged and transformed into the dimensions of quite another chamber, that came to him, with its host of cats and its strange distances, in a sort of vision.

But these changes came about a little later and at a time when his attention was so concentrated upon the proceedings of Smoke and the collie, that he only observed them, as it were, subconsciously. And the excitement, the flickering candle-light, the distress he felt for the collie, and the distorting atmosphere of fog were the poorest possible allies to careful observation.

At first he was only aware that the dog was repeating his short dangerous bark from time to time, snapping viciously at the empty air, a foot or so from the ground. Once, indeed, he sprang upwards and forwards, working furiously with teeth and paws, and with a noise like wolves fighting, but only to dash back the next minute against the wall behind him. Then, after lying still for a bit, he rose to a crouching position as though to spring again, snarling horribly and making short half-circles with lowered head. And Smoke all the while meowed piteously by the window as though trying to draw the attack upon himself.

Then it was that the rush of the whole dreadful business seemed to turn aside from the dog and direct itself upon his own person. The collie had made another spring and fallen back with a crash into the corner, where he made noise enough in his savage rage to waken the dead before he fell to whining and then finally lay still. And directly afterwards the doctor's own distress became intolerably acute. He had made a half movement forward to come to the rescue when a veil that was denser than mere fog seemed to drop down over the scene, draping room, walls, animals and fire in a mist of darkness and folding also about his own mind. Other forms moved silently across the field of vision, forms that he recognised from previous experiments, and welcomed not. Unholy thoughts began to crowd into his brain, sinister suggestions of evil presented themselves seductively. Ice seemed to settle about his heart, and his mind trembled. He began to lose memory—memory of his identity, of where he was, of what he ought to do. The very foundations of his strength were shaken. His will seemed paralysed.

And it was then that the room filled with this horde of cats, all dark as the night, all silent, all with lamping eyes of green fire. The dimensions of the place altered and shifted. He was in a much larger space. The whining of the dog sounded far away, and all about him the cats flew busily to and fro, silently playing their tearing, rushing game of evil, weaving the pattern of their dark purpose upon the floor. He strove hard to collect himself and remember the words of power he had made use of before in similar dread positions where his dangerous practice had sometimes led; but he could recall nothing consecutively; a mist lay over his mind and memory; he felt dazed and his forces scattered. The deeps within were too troubled for healing power to come out of them.

It was glamour, of course, he realized afterwards, the strong glamour thrown upon his imagination by some powerful personality behind the veil; but at the time he was not sufficiently aware of this and, as with all true glamour, was unable to grasp where the true ended and the false began. He was caught momentarily in the same vortex that had sought to lure the cat to destruction through its delight, and threatened utterly to overwhelm the dog through its terror.

There came a sound in the chimney behind him like wind booming and tearing its way down. The windows rattled. The candle flickered and went out. The glacial atmosphere closed round him with the cold of death, and a great rushing sound swept by overhead as though the ceiling had lifted to great height. He heard the. door shut. Far away it sounded. He felt lost, shelterless in the depths of his soul. Yet still he held out and resisted while the climax of the fight came nearer and nearer. . . . He had stepped into the stream of forces awakened by Pender and he knew that he must withstand them to the end or come to a conclusion that it was not good for a man to come to. Something from the region of utter cold was upon him.

And then quite suddenly, through the confused mists about him, there slowly rose up the Personality that had been all the time directing the battle. Some force entered his being that shook him as the tempest takes a leaf, and close against his eyes—clean level with his face—he found himself staring into the wreck of a vast dark Countenance, a countenance that was terrible even in its ruin.

For ruined it was, and terrible it was, and the mark of spiritual evil was branded everywhere upon its broken features. Eyes, face and hair rose level with his own, and for a space of time he never could properly measure, or determine, these two, a man and a woman, looked straight into each other's visages and down into each other's hearts.

And John Silence, the soul with the good, unselfish motive, held his own against the dark discarnate woman whose motive was pure evil, and whose soul was on the side of the Dark Powers.

It was the climax that touched the depth of power within him and began to restore him slowly to his own. He was conscious, of course, of effort, and yet it seemed no superhuman one, for he had recognised the character of his opponent's power, and he called upon the good within him to meet and overcome it. The inner forces stirred and trembled in response to his call. They did not at first come readily as was their habit, for under the spell of glamour they had already been diabolically lulled into inactivity, but come they eventually did, rising out of the inner spiritual nature he had learned with so much time and pain to awaken to life. And power and confidence came with them. He began to breathe deeply and regularly, and at the same time to absorb into himself the forces opposed to him, and to *turn them to his own account*. By ceasing to resist, and allowing the deadly stream to pour into him unopposed, he used the very power supplied by his adversary and thus enormously increased his own.

For this spiritual alchemy he had learned. He understood that force ultimately is everywhere one and the same; it is the motive behind that makes it good or evil; and his motive was entirely unselfish. He knew—provided he was not first robbed of self-control—how vicariously to absorb these evil radiations into himself and change them magically into his own good purposes. And, since his motive was pure and his soul fearless, they could not work him harm.

Thus he stood in the main stream of evil unwittingly attracted by Pender, deflecting its course upon himself; and after passing through the purifying filter of his own unselfishness these energies could only add to his store of experience, of knowledge, and therefore of power. And, as his self-control returned to him, he gradually accomplished this purpose, even though trembling while he did so.

Yet the struggle was severe, and in spite of the freezing chill of the air, the perspiration poured down his face. Then, by slow degrees, the dark and dreadful countenance faded, the glamour passed from his soul, the normal proportions returned to walls and ceiling, the forms melted back into the fog, and the whirl of rushing shadow-cats disappeared whence they came.

And with the return of the consciousness of his own identity John Silence was restored to the full control of his own will-power. In a deep, modulated voice he began to utter certain rhythmical sounds that slowly rolled through the air like a rising sea, filling the room with powerful vibratory activities that whelmed all irregularities of lesser vibrations in its own swelling tone. He made certain signals, gestures and movements at the same time. For several minutes he continued to utter these words, until at length the growing volume dominated the whole room and mastered the manifestation of all that opposed it. For just as he understood the spiritual alchemy that can transmute evil forces by raising them into higher channels, so he knew from long study the occult use of sound, and its direct effect upon the plastic region wherein the powers of spiritual evil work their fell purposes. Harmony was restored first of all to his own soul, and thence to the room and all its occupants.

And, after himself, the first to recognise it was the old dog lying in his corner. Flame began suddenly uttering sounds of pleasure, that "something" between a growl and a grunt that dogs make upon being restored to their master's confidence. Dr. Silence heard the thumping of the collie's tail against the ground. And the grunt and the thumping touched the depth of affection in the man's heart, and gave him some inkling of what agonies the dumb creature had suffered.

Next, from the shadows by the window, a somewhat shrill purring announced the restoration of the cat to its normal state. Smoke was advancing across the carpet. He seemed very pleased with himself, and smiled with an expression of supreme innocence. He was no shadow-cat, but real and full of his usual and perfect self-possession. He marched along, picking his way delicately, but with a stately dignity that suggested his ancestry with the majesty of Egypt. His eyes no longer glared; they shone steadily before him; they radiated, not excitement, but knowledge. Clearly he was anxious to make amends for the mischief to which he had unwittingly lent himself owing to his subtle and electric constitution.

Still uttering his sharp high purrings he marched up to his master and rubbed vigorously against his legs. Then he stood on his hind feet and pawed his knees and stared beseechingly up into his face. He turned his head towards the corner where the collie still lay, thumping his tail feebly and pathetically.

John Silence understood. He bent down and stroked the creature's living fur, noting the line of bright blue sparks that followed the motion of his hand down its back. And then they advanced together towards the corner where the dog was.

Smoke went first and put his nose gently against his friend's muzzle, purring while he rubbed, and uttering little soft sounds of affection in his throat. The doctor lit the candle and brought it over. He saw the collie lying on its side against the wall; it was utterly exhausted, and foam still hung about its jaws. Its tail and eyes responded to the sound of its name, but it was evidently very weak and overcome. Smoke continued to rub against its cheek and nose and eyes, sometimes even standing on its body and kneading into the thick yellow hair. Flame replied from time to time by little licks of the tongue, most of them curiously misdirected.

But Dr. Silence felt intuitively that something disastrous had happened, and his heart was wrung. He stroked the dear body, feeling it over for bruises or broken bones, but finding none. He fed it with what remained of the sandwiches and milk, but the creature clumsily upset the saucer and lost the sandwiches between its paws, so that the doctor had to feed it with his own hand. And all the while Smoke meowed piteously.

Then John Silence began to understand. He went across to the farther side of the room and called aloud to it.

"Flame, old man! come!"

At any other time the dog would have been upon him in an instant, barking and leaping to the shoulder. And even now he got up, though heavily and awkwardly, to his feet. He started to run, wagging his tail more briskly. He collided first with a chair, and then ran straight into a table. Smoke trotted close at his side, trying his very best to guide him. But it was useless. Dr. Silence had to lift him up into his own arms and carry him like a baby. For he was blind.

It was a week later when John Silence called to see the author in his new house, and found him well on the way to recovery and already busy again with his writing. The haunted look had left his eyes, and he seemed cheerful and confident.

"Humour restored?" laughed the doctor, as soon as they were comfortably settled in the room overlooking the Park.

"I've had no trouble since I left that dreadful place," returned Pender gratefully; "and thanks to you——"

The doctor stopped him with a gesture.

"Never mind that," he said, "we'll discuss your new plans afterwards, and my scheme for relieving you of the house and helping you settle elsewhere. Of course it must be pulled down, for it's not fit for any sensitive person to live in, and any other tenant might be afflicted in the same way you were. Although, personally, I think the evil has exhausted itself by now."

He told the astonished author something of his experiences in it with the animals.

"I don't pretend to understand," Pender said, when the account was finished, "but I and my wife are intensely relieved to be free of it all. Only I must say I should like to know something of the former history of the house. When we took it six months ago I heard no word against it."

Dr. Silence drew a typewritten paper from his pocket.

"I can satisfy your curiosity to some extent," he said, running his eye over the sheets, and then replacing them in his coat; "for by my secretary's investigations I have been able to check certain information obtained in the hypnotic trance by a 'sensitive' who helps me in such cases. The former occupant who haunted you appears to have been a woman of singularly atrocious life and character who finally suffered death by hanging, after a series of crimes that appalled the whole of England and only came to light by the merest chance. She came to her end in the year 1798, for it was not this particular house she lived in, but a much larger one that then stood upon the site it now occupies, and was then, of course, not in London, but in the country. She was a person of intellect, possessed of a powerful, trained will, and of consummate audacity, and I am convinced availed herself of the resources of the lower magic to attain her ends. This goes far to explain the virulence of the attack upon yourself, and why she is still able to carry on after death the evil practices that formed her main purpose during life."

"You think that after death a soul can still consciously direct——" gasped the author.

"I think, as I told you before, that the forces of a powerful personality may still persist after death in the line of their original momentum," replied the doctor; "and that strong thoughts and purposes can still react upon suitably prepared brains long after their originators have passed away.

"If you knew anything of magic," he pursued, "you would know that thought is dynamic, and that it may call into existence forms and pictures that may well exist for hundreds of years. For, not far removed from the region of our human life, is another region where floats the waste and drift of all the centuries, the limbo of the shells of the dead; a densely populated region crammed with horror and abomination of all descriptions, and sometimes galvanised into active life again by the will of a trained manipulator, a mind versed in the practices of lower magic. That this woman understood its vile commerce, I am persuaded, and the forces she set going during her life have simply been accumulating ever since, and would have continued to do so had they not been drawn down upon yourself, and afterwards discharged and satisfied through me.

"Anything might have brought down the attack, for, besides drugs, there are certain violent emotions, certain moods of the soul, certain spiritual fevers, if I may so call them, which directly open the inner being to a cognisance of this astral region I have mentioned. In your case it happened to be a peculiarly potent drug which had this peculiar effect on you.

"But now, tell me," he added, after a pause, handing to the perplexed author a pencil drawing he had made of the dark countenance that had appeared to him during the night on Putney Hill—"tell me if you recognise this face?"

Pender looked at the drawing closely, greatly astonished. He shuddered a little as he looked.

"Undoubtedly," he said, "it is the face I kept trying to draw—dark, with the great mouth and jaw, and the drooping eye. That is the woman."

Dr. Silence then produced from his pocket-book an old-fashioned woodcut of the same person which his secretary had unearthed from the records of the Newgate Calendar. The woodcut and the pencil drawing were two different aspects of the same dreadful visage. The men compared them for some moments in silence.

"It makes me thank God for the limitations of our senses," said Pender quietly, with a sigh; "continuous clairvoyance must be a sore affliction."

"It is indeed," returned John Silence significantly, "and if all the people nowadays who claim to be clairvoyant were really so, the statistics of suicide and lunacy would be considerably higher than they are. It is little wonder," he added, "that your sense of humour was clouded, with the mind-forces of that dead monster trying to use your brain for their dissemination. You have had an interesting adventure, Mr. Felix Pender, and, let me add, a fortunate escape."

The author was about to renew his thanks when there came a sound of scratching at the door, and the doctor sprang up quickly.

"It's time for me to go. I left my dog on the step, but I suppose——"

Before he had time to open the door, it had yielded to the pressure behind it and flew wide open to admit a great yellow-haired collie. The dog, wagging his tail and contorting his whole body with delight, tore across the floor and tried to leap up upon its owner's breast. And there was laughter and happiness in the old eyes; for they were clear again as the day.

Back for Christmas

BY

JOHN COLLIER

"Doctor," said Major Sinclair, "we certainly must have you with us for Christmas." It was afternoon and the Carpenters' living room was filled with friends who had come to say last-minute farewells to the Doctor and his wife.

"He shall be back," said Mrs. Carpenter. "I promise you."

"It's hardly certain," said Dr. Carpenter. "I'd like nothing better, of course."

"After all," said Mr. Hewitt, "you've contracted to lecture only for three months."

"Anything may happen," said Dr. Carpenter.

"Whatever happens," said Mrs. Carpenter, beaming at them, "he shall be back in England for Christmas. You may all believe me."

They all believed her. The Doctor himself almost believed her. For ten years she had been promising him for dinner parties, garden parties, committees, heaven knows what, and the promises had always been kept.

The farewells began. There was a fluting of compliments on dear Hermione's marvellous arrangements. She and her husband would drive to Southampton that evening. They would embark the following day. No trains, no bustle, no last-minute worries. Certainly the Doctor was marvellously looked after. He would be a great success in America. Especially with Hermione to see to everything. She would have a wonderful time, too. She would see the skyscrapers. Nothing like that in Little Godwearing. But she must be very sure to bring him back. "Yes, I will bring him back. You may rely upon it." He mustn't be persuaded. No extensions. No wonderful post at some super-American hospital. Our infirmary needs him. And he must be back by Christmas. "Yes," Mrs. Carpenter called to the last departing guest, "I shall see to it. He shall be back by Christmas."

The final arrangements for closing the house were very well managed. The maids soon had the tea things washed up; they came in, said good-bye, and were in time to catch the afternoon bus to Devizes.

Nothing remained but odds and ends, locking doors, seeing that everything was tidy. "Go upstairs," said Hermione, "and change into your brown tweeds. Empty the pockets of that suit before you put it in your bag. I'll see to everything else. All you have to do is not to get in the way."

The Doctor went upstairs and took off the suit he was wearing, but instead of the brown tweeds, he put on an old, dirty bath gown, which he took from the back of his wardrobe. Then, after making one or two little arrangements, he leaned over the head of the stairs and called to his wife, "Hermione! Have you a moment to spare?"

"Of course, dear. I'm just finished."

"Just come up here for a moment. There's something rather extraordinary up here."

Hermione immediately came up. "Good heavens, my dear man!" she said when she saw her husband. "What are you lounging about in that filthy old thing for? I told you to have it burned long ago."

"Who in the world," said the Doctor, "has dropped a gold chain down the bathtub drain?"

"Nobody has, of course," said Hermione. "Nobody wears such a thing."

"Then what is it doing there?" said the Doctor. "Take this flashlight. If you lean right over, you can see it shining, deep down."

"Some Woolworth's bangle off one of the maids," said Hermione. "It can be nothing else." However, she took the flashlight and leaned over, squinting into the drain. The Doctor, raising a short length of lead pipe, struck two or three times with great force and precision, and tilting the body by the knees, tumbled it into the tub.

He then slipped off the bathrobe and, standing completely naked, unwrapped a towel full of implements and put them into the washbasin. He spread several sheets of newspaper on the floor and turned once more to his victim.

She was dead, of course—horribly doubled up, like a somersaulter, at one end of the tub. He stood looking at her for a very long time, thinking of absolutely nothing at all. Then he saw how much blood there was and his mind began to move again.

First he pushed and pulled until she lay straight in the bath, then he removed her clothing. In a narrow bathtub this was an extremely clumsy business, but he managed it at last and then turned on the taps. The water rushed into the tub, then dwindled, then died away, and the last of it gurgled down the drain.

"Good God!" he said. "She turned it off at the main."

There was only one thing to do: the Doctor hastily wiped his hands on a towel, opened the bathroom door with a clean corner of the towel, threw it back onto the bath stool, and ran downstairs, barefoot, light as a cat. The cellar door was in a corner of the entrance hall, under the stairs. He knew just where the cut-off was. He had reason to: he had been pottering about down there for some time past—trying to scrape out a bin for wine, he had told Hermione. He pushed open the cellar door, went down the steep steps, and just before the closing door plunged the cellar into pitch darkness, he put his hand on the tap and turned it on. Then he felt his way back along the grimy wall till he came to the steps. He was about to ascend them when the bell rang.

The Doctor was scarcely aware of the ringing as a sound. It was like a spike of iron pushed slowly up through his stomach. It went on until it reached his brain. Then something broke. He threw himself down in the coal dust on the floor and said, "I'm through. I'm through."

"They've got no right to come. Fools!" he said. Then he heard himself panting. "None of this," he said to himself. "None of this."

He began to revive. He got to his feet, and when the bell rang again the sound passed through him almost painlessly. "Let them go away," he said. Then he heard the front door open. He said, "I don't care." His shoulder came up, like that of a boxer, to shield his face. "I give up," he said.

He heard people calling. "Herbert!" "Hermione!" It was the Wallingfords. "Damn them! They come butting in. People anxious to get off. All naked! And blood and coal dust! I'm done! I'm through! I can't do it."

"Herbert!"

"Hermione!"

"Where the dickens can they be?"

"The car's there."

"Maybe they've popped round to Mrs. Liddell's."

"We must see them."

"Or to the shops, maybe. Something at the last minute."

"Not Hermione. I say, listen! Isn't that someone having a bath? Shall I shout? What about whanging on the door?"

"Sh-h-h! Don't. It might not be tactful."

"No harm in a shout."

"Look, dear. Let's come in on our way back. Hermione said they wouldn't be leaving before seven. They're dining on the way, in Salisbury."

"Think so? All right. Only I want a last drink with old Herbert. He'd be hurt."

"Let's hurry. We can be back by half past six."

The Doctor heard them walk out and the front door close quietly behind them. He thought, "Half past six. I can do it."

He crossed the hall, sprang the latch of the front door, went upstairs, and taking his instruments from the washbasin, finished what he had to do. He came down again, clad in his bath gown, carrying parcel after parcel of towelling or newspaper neatly secured with safety pins. These he packed carefully into the narrow, deep hole he had made in the corner of the cellar, shovelled in the soil, spread coal dust over all, satisfied himself that everything was in order, and went upstairs again. He then thoroughly cleansed the bath, and himself, and the bath again, dressed, and took his wife's clothing and his bath gown to the incinerator.

One or two more little touches and everything was in order. It was only quarter past six. The Wallingfords were always late; he had only to get into the car and drive off. It was a pity he couldn't wait till after dusk, but he could make a detour to avoid passing through the main street, and even if he was seen driving alone, people would only think Hermione had gone on ahead for some reason and they would forget about it.

Still, he was glad when he had finally got away, entirely unobserved, on the open road, driving into the gathering dusk. He had to drive very carefully; he found himself unable to judge distances, his reactions were abnormally delayed, but that was a detail. When it was quite dark he allowed himself to stop the car on the top of the downs, in order to think.

The stars were superb. He could see the lights of one or two little towns far away on the plain below him. He was exultant. Everything that was to follow was perfectly simple. Marion was waiting in Chicago. She already believed him to be a widower. The lecture people could be put off with a word. He had nothing to do but establish himself in some thriving out-of-the-way town in America and he was safe forever. There were Hermione's clothes, of course, in the suitcases: they could be disposed of through the porthole. Thank heaven she wrote her letters on the typewriter—a little thing like handwriting might have prevented everything. "But there you are," he said. "She was up-to-date, efficient all along the line. Managed everything. Managed herself to death, damn her!"

"There's no reason to get excited," he thought. "I'll write a few letters for her, then fewer and fewer. Write myself—always expecting to get back, never quite able to. Keep the house one year, then another, then another; they'll get used to it. Might even come back alone in a year or two and clear it up properly. Nothing easier. But not for Christmas!" He started up the engine and was off.

In New York he felt free at last, really free. He was safe. He could look back with pleasure—at least after a meal, lighting his cigarette, he could look back with a sort of pleasure—to the minute he had passed in the cellar listening to the bell, the door, and the voices. He could look forward to Marion.

As he strolled through the lobby of his hotel, the clerk, smiling, held up letters for him. It was the first batch from England. Well, what did that matter? It would be fun dashing off the typewritten sheets in Hermione's downright style, signing them with her squiggle, telling everyone what a success his first lecture had been, how thrilled he was with America but how certainly she'd bring him back for Christmas. Doubts could creep in later.

He glanced over the letters. Most were for Hermione. From the Sinclair's, the Wallingfords, the vicar, and a business letter from Holt & Sons, Builders and Decorators.

He stood in the lounge, people brushing by him. He opened the letters with his thumb, reading here and there, smiling. They all seemed very confident he would be back for Christmas. They relied on Hermione. "That's where they make their big mistake," said the Doctor, who had taken to American phrases. The builder's letter he kept to the last. Some bill, probably. It was:

Dear Madam,

We are in receipt of your kind acceptance of estimate as below, and also of key.

We beg to repeat you may have every confidence in same being ready in ample time for Christmas present as stated. We are setting men to work this week.

We are, Madam,

Yours faithfully,

Paul Holt & Sons

To excavating, building up, suitably lining one sunken wine bin in cellar as indicated, using best materials, making good, etc.

........£18/0/0

Couching at the Door

BY

D. K. BROSTER

CHAPTER ONE

THE FIRST inkling which Augustine Marchant had of the matter
was on one fine summer morning about three weeks after his
visit to Prague, that is to say, in June, 1898. He was reclining, as his
custom was when writing his poetry, on the very comfortable sofa
in his library at Abbot's Medding, near the French windows, one of
which was open to the garden. Pausing for inspiration—he was
nearly at the end of his poem, *Salutation to All Unbeliefs*—he let
his eyes wander round the beautifully appointed room, with its
cloisonné and Satsuma, Buhl and first editions, and then allowed
them to stray toward the sunlight outside. And so, between the edge
of the costly Herat carpet and the sill of the open window, across the
strip of polished oak flooring, he observed what he took to be a
small piece of dark fluff blowing in the draft; and instantly made a
note to speak to his housekeeper about the parlormaid. There was
slackness somewhere; and in Augustine Marchant's house no one
was allowed to be slack but himself.

There had been a time when the poet would not for a moment
have been received, as he was now, in country and even county society—those days, even before the advent of *The Yellow Book* and
The Savoy, when he had lived in London, writing the plays and
poems which had so startled and shocked all but the "decadent" and
the "advanced," *Pomegranates of Sin, Queen Theodora and Queen
Marozia, The Nights of the Tour de Nesle, Amor Cypriacus* and
the rest. But when, as the 'nineties began to wane, he inherited
Abbot's Medding from a distant cousin and came to live there,
being then at the height of an almost international reputation,

Wiltshire society at first tolerated him for his kinship with the late Lord Medding, and then, placated by the excellence of his dinners and further mollified by the patent staidness of his private life, decided that, in his personal conduct at any rate, he must have turned over a new leaf. Perhaps indeed he had never been as bad as he was painted, and if his writings continued to be no less scandalously free and freethinking than before, and needed to be just as rigidly kept out of the hands of daughters, well, no country gentleman in the neighborhood was obliged to read them!

And indeed Augustine Marchant in his fifty-first year was too keenly alive to the value of the good opinion of county society to risk shocking it by any overt doings of his. He kept his license for his pen. When he went abroad, as he did at least twice a year—but that was another matter altogether. The nose of Mrs. Grundy was not sharp enough to smell out his occupations in Warsaw or Berlin or Naples, her eyes long-sighted enough to discern what kind of society he frequented even so near home as Paris. At Abbot's Medding his reputation for being "wicked" was fast declining into just enough of a sensation to titillate a croquet party. He had charming manners, could be witty at moments (though he could not keep it up), still retained his hyacinthine locks (by means of hair restorers), wore his excellently cut velvet coats and flowing ties with just the right air—half poet, half man of the world—and really had, at Abbot's Medding, no dark secret to hide beyond the fact, sedulously concealed by him for five-and-twenty years, that he had never been christened Augustine. Between Augustus and Augustine, what a gulf! But he had crossed it, and his French poems (which had to be smuggled into his native land) were signed Augustin—Augustin Lemarchant.

Removing his gaze from the objectionable evidence of domestic carelessness upon the floor Mr. Marchant now fixed it meditatively upon the ruby-set end of the gold pencil which he was using. Rossell & Ward, his publishers, were about to bring out an édition de luxe of *Queen Theodora and Queen Marozia* with illustrations by a hitherto unknown young artist—if they were not too daring. It would be a sumptuous affair in a limited edition. And as he thought of this the remembrance of his recent stay in Prague returned to the poet. He smiled to himself, as a man smiles when he looks at a rare wine, and thought, "Yes, if these blunt-witted Pharisees round

Abbot's Medding only knew!" It was a good thing that the up-holders of British petty morality were seldom great travelers; a dispensation of . . . ahem, Providence!

Twiddling his gold pencil between plump fingers, Augustine Marchant returned to his ode, weighing one epithet against another. Except in summer he was no advocate of open windows, and even in summer he considered that to get the most out of that delicate and precious instrument, his brain, his feet must always be kept thoroughly warm; he had therefore cast over them, before settling into his semi-reclining position, a beautiful rose-colored Indian *sari* of the purest and thickest silk, leaving the ends trailing on the floor. And he became aware, with surprise and annoyance, that the piece of brown fluff or whatever it was down there, traveling in the draft from the window, had reached the nearest end of the *sari* and was now, impelled by the same current, traveling up it.

The master of Abbot's Medding reached out for the silver hand-bell on the table by his side. There must be more breeze coming in than he had realized, and he might take cold, a catastrophe against which he guarded himself as against the plague. Then he saw that the upward progress of the dark blot—it was about the size of a farthing—could not by any possibility be assigned to any other agency than its own. It was *climbing* up—some horrible insect, plainly, some disgusting kind of almost legless and very hairy spider, round and vague in outline. The poet sat up and shook the *sari* violently. When he looked again the invader was gone. He had obviously shaken it on to the floor, and on the floor somewhere it must still be. The idea perturbed him, and he decided to take his writing out to the summer-house, and give orders later that the library was to be thoroughly swept out.

Ah! it was good to be out of doors and in a pleasance so delight-fully laid out, so exquisitely kept, as his! In the basin of the fountain the sea-nymphs of rosy-veined marble clustered round a Thetis as beautiful as Aphrodite herself; the lightest and featheriest of acacia-trees swayed near. And as the owner of all this went past over the weedless turf he repeated snatches of Verlaine to himself about "sveltes jets d'eau" and "sanglots d'extase."

Then, turning his head to look back at the fountain, he became aware of a little dark-brown object about the size of a half-penny running toward him over the velvet-smooth sward. . . .

He believed afterward that he must first have had a glimpse of the truth at that instant in the garden, or he would not have acted so instinctively as he did and so promptly. For a moment later he was standing at the edge of the basin of Thetis, his face blanched in the sunshine, his hand firmly clenched. Inside that closed hand something feather-soft pulsated. . . . Holding back as best he could the disgust and the something more which clutched at him, Augustine Marchant stooped and plunged his whole fist into the bubbling water, and let the stream of the fountain whirl away what he had picked up. Then with uncertain steps he went and sat down on the nearest seat and shut his eyes. After a while he took out his lawn handkerchief and carefully dried his hand with the intaglio ring, dried it and then looked curiously at the palm. "I did not know I had so much courage," he was thinking; "so much courage and good sense!" . . . It would doubtless drown very quickly.

Burrows, his butler, was coming over the lawn. "Mr. and Mrs. Morrison have arrived, sir."

"Ah, yes; I had forgotten for the moment." Augustine Marchant got up and walked toward the house and his guests, throwing back his shoulders and practicing his famous enigmatic smile, for Mrs. Morrison was a woman worth impressing.

(But what had it been exactly? Why, just what it had looked—a tuft of fur blowing over the grass, a tuft of fur! Sheer imagination that it had moved in his closed hand with a life of its own. . . . Then why had he shut his eyes as he stooped and made a grab at it? Thank God, thank God, it was nothing now but a drenched smear swirling round the nymphs of Thetis!)

"Ah, dear lady, you must forgive me! Unpardonable of me not to be in to receive you!" He was in the drawing-room now, fragrant with its banks of hothouse flowers, bending over the hand of the fashionably attired guest on the sofa, in her tight bodice and voluminous sleeves, with a flyaway hat perched at a rakish angle on her gold-brown hair.

"Your man told us that you were writing in the garden," said her goggle-eyed husband reverently.

"*Cher maître*, it is we who ought not to be interrupting your rendezvous with the Muse," returned Mrs. Morrison in her sweet, high voice. "Terrible to bring you from such company into that of mere visitors!"

Running his hand through his carefully tended locks the *cher maître* replied, "Between a visit from the Muse and one from Beauty's self no true poet would hesitate!—Moreover, luncheon awaits us, and I trust it is a good one."

He liked faintly to shock fair admirers by admitting that he cared for the pleasures of the table; it was quite safe to do so, since none of them had sufficient acumen to see that it was true.

The luncheon was excellent, for Augustine kept an admirable cook. Afterward he showed his guests over the library—yes, even though it had not received the sweeping which would not be necessary now—and round the garden; and in the summer-house was prevailed upon to read some of *Amor Cypriacus* aloud. And Mrs. Frances (nowadays Francesca) Morrison was thereafter able to recount to envious friends how the Poet himself had read her stanza after stanza from that most *daring* poem of his; and how poor Fred, fanning himself meanwhile with his straw hat—not from the torridity of the verse but because of the afternoon heat—said afterward that he had not understood a single word. A good thing, perhaps. . . .

When they had gone Augustine Marchant reflected rather cynically, "All that was just so much bunkum when I wrote it." For ten years ago, in spite of those audacious, glowing verses, he was an ignorant neophyte. Of course, since then . . . He smiled, a private, sly, self-satisfied smile. It was certainly pleasant to know oneself no longer a fraud!

Returning to the summer-house to fetch his poems he saw what he took to be Mrs. Morrison's fur boa lying on the floor just by the basket chair which she had occupied. Odd of her not to have missed it on departure—a tribute to his verses perhaps. His housekeeper must send it after her by post. But just at that moment his head gardener approached, desiring some instructions, and when the matter was settled, and Augustine Marchant turned once more to enter the summer-house, he found that he had been mistaken about the dropped boa, for there was nothing on the floor.

Besides, he remembered now that Mrs. Morrison's boa had been a rope of gray feathers, not of dark fur. As he took up *Amor Cypriacus* he asked himself lazily what could have led him to imagine a woman's boa there at all, much less a fur one.

Suddenly he knew why. A lattice in the house of memory had

opened, and he remained rigid, staring out at the jets of the fountain rising and falling in the afternoon sun. Yes; of that glamorous, wonderful, abominable night in Prague, the part he least wished to recall was connected—incidentally but undeniably—with a fur boa— a long boa of dark fur. . . .

He had to go up to town next day to a dinner in his honor. There and then he decided to go up that same night by a late train, a most unusual proceeding, and most disturbing to his valet, who knew that it was doubtful whether he could at such short notice procure him a first-class carriage to himself. However, Augustine Marchant went, and even, to the man's amazement, deliberately chose a compartment with another occupant when he might, after all, have had an empty one.

The dinner was brilliant; Augustine had never spoken better. Next day he went round to the little street not far from the British Museum where he found Lawrence Storey, his new illustrator, working feverishly at his drawings for *Queen Theodora and Queen Marozia,* and quite overwhelmed at the honor of a personal visit. Augustine was very kind to him, and, while offering a few criticisms, highly praised his delineation of those two Messalinas of tenth-century Rome, their long supple hands, their heavy eyes, their full, almost repellent mouths. Storey had followed the same type for mother and daughter, but with a subtle difference.

"They were certainly two most evil women, especially the younger," he observed ingenuously. "But I suppose that, from an artistic point of view, that doesn't matter nowadays!"

Augustine, smoking one of his special cigarettes, made a delicate little gesture. "My dear fellow, Art has nothing whatever to do with what is called 'morality'; happily we know that at last! Show me how you thought of depicting the scene where Marozia orders the execution of her mother's papal paramour. Good, very good! Yes, the lines there, even the fall of that loose sleeve from the extended arm, express with clarity what I had in mind. You have great gifts!"

"I have tried to make her look wicked," said the young man, reddening with pleasure. "But," he added deprecatingly, "it is very hard for a ridiculously inexperienced person like myself to have the right artistic vision. For to you, Mr. Marchant, who have penetrated into such wonderful arcana of the forbidden, it would be foolish to pretend to be other than I am."

"How do you know that I have penetrated into any such arcana?" inquired the poet, half-shutting his eyes and looking (though not to the almost worshiping gaze of young Storey) like a great cat being stroked.

"Why, one has only to read you!"

"You must come down and stay with me soon," were Augustine Marchant's parting words. (He would give the boy a few days' good living, for which he would be none the worse; let him drink some decent wine.) "How soon do you think you will be able to finish the rough sketches for the rest, and the designs for the *culs de lampe?* A fortnight or three weeks? Good; I shall look to see you then. Good-by, my dear fellow; I am very, very much pleased with what you have shown me!"

The worst of going up to London from the country was that one was apt to catch a cold in town. When he got back Augustine Marchant was almost sure that this misfortune had befallen him, so he ordered a fire in his bedroom, despite the season, and consumed a *recherché* little supper in seclusion. And, as the cold turned out to have been imaginary, he was very comfortable, sitting there in his silken dressing-gown, toasting his toes and holding up a glass of golden Tokay to the flames. Really *Theodora and Marozia* would make as much sensation when it came out with these illustrations as when it first appeared!

All at once he set down his glass. Not far away on his left stood a big cheval mirror, like a woman's in which a good portion of the bed behind him was reflected. And, in this mirror, he had just seen the valance of the bed move. There could be no draft to speak of in this warm room, he never allowed a cat in the house, and it was quite impossible that there should be a rat about. If after all some stray cat should have got in it must be ejected at once. Augustine hitched round in his chair to look at the actual bedhanging.

Yes, the topaz-hued silk valance again swung very slightly outward as though it were being pushed. Augustine bent forward to the bell-pull to summon his valet. Then the flask of Tokay rolled over on the table as he leapt from his chair instead. Something like a huge, dark caterpillar was emerging very slowly from under his bed, moving as a caterpillar moves, with undulations running over it. Where its head should have been was merely a tapering end smaller than the rest of it, but of like substance. It was a dark fur boa.

Augustine Marchant felt that he screamed, but he could not have done so, for his tongue clave to the roof of his mouth. He merely stood staring, staring, all the blood gone from his heart. Still very slowly the thing continued to creep out from under the valance, waving that eyeless, tapering end to and fro, as though uncertain where to proceed. "I am going mad, mad, mad!" thought Augustine, and then, with a revulsion, "No, it can't be! It's a real snake of some kind!"

That could be dealt with. He snatched up the poker as the boa-thing, still swaying the head which was no head, kept pouring steadily out from under the lifted yellow frill, until quite three feet were clear of the bed. Then he fell upon it furiously, with blow after blow.

But they had no effect on the furry, spineless thing; it merely gave under them and rippled up in another place. Augustine hit the bed, the floor; at last, really screaming, he threw down his weapon and fell upon the thick, hairy rope with both hands, crushing it together into a mass—there was little if any resistance in it—and hurled it into the fire and, panting, kept it down with shovel and tongs. The flames licked up instantly and, with a roar, made short work of it, though there seemed to be some slight effort to escape, which was perhaps only the effect of the heat. A moment later there was a very strong smell of burnt hair, and that was all.

Augustine Marchant seized the fallen flask of Tokay and drained from its mouth what little was left in the bottom ere, staggering to the bed, he flung himself upon it and buried his face in the pillows, even heaping them over his head as if he could thus stifle the memory of what he had seen.

He kept his bed next morning; the supposed cold afforded a good pretext. Long before the maid came in to re-lay the fire he had crawled out to make sure that there were no traces left of . . . what he had burnt there. There were none. A nightmare could not have left a trace, he told himself. But well he knew that it was not a nightmare.

And now he could think of nothing but that room in Prague and the long fur boa of the woman. Some department of his mind (he supposed) must have projected that thing, scarcely noticed at the time, scarcely remembered, into the present and the here. It was terrible to think that one's mind possessed such dark, unknown powers. But not so terrible as if the . . . apparition . . . had been endowed with an entirely separate objective existence. In a day or two he would consult his doctor and ask him to give him a tonic.

But, expostulated an uncomfortably lucid part of his brain, you are trying to run with the hare and hunt with the hounds. Is it not better to believe that the thing *had* an objective existence, for you have burnt it to nothing? Well and good! But if it is merely a projection from your own mind, what is to prevent it from reappearing, like the phœnix, from ashes?

There seemed no answer to that, save in an attempt to persuade himself that he had been feverish last night. Work was the best antidote. So Augustine Marchant rose, and was surprised and delighted to find the atmosphere of his study unusually soothing and inspiring, and that day, against all expectation, *Salutation to All Unbeliefs* was completed by some stanzas with which he was not too ill-pleased. Realizing nevertheless that he should be glad of company that evening, he had earlier sent round a note to the local solicitor, a good fellow, to come and dine with him; played a game of billiards with the lawyer afterward and retired to bed after some vintage port and a good stiff whisky and soda with scarcely a thought of the visitant of the previous night.

He woke at that hour when the thrushes in early summer punctually greet the new day—three o'clock. They were greeting it even vociferously, and Augustine Marchant was annoyed with their enthusiasm. His golden damask window-curtains kept out all but a glimmer of the new day, yet as, lying upon his back, the poet opened his eyes for a moment, his only half-awakened sense of vision reported something swinging to and fro in the dimness like a pendulum of rope. It was indistinct but seemed to be hanging from the tester of the bed. And, wide awake in an instant, with an unspeakable anguish of premonition tearing through him, he felt, next moment, a light thud on the coverlet about the level of his knees. Something had arrived on the bed. . . .

And Augustine Marchant neither shrieked nor leapt from his bed; he could not. Yet, now that his eyes were grown used to the twilight of the room, he saw it clearly, the fur rope which he had burnt to extinction two nights ago, dark and shining as before, rippling with a gentle movement as it coiled itself neatly together in the place where it had struck the bed and subsided there in a symmetrical round, with only that tapering end a little raised and, as it were, looking at him—only, eyeless and featureless, it could not look. One thought of disgusted relief, that it was not at any rate going to attack him, and Augustine Marchant fainted.

Yet his swoon must have merged into sleep, for he woke in a more or less ordinary fashion to find his man placing his early tea-tray beside him and inquiring when he should draw his bath. There was nothing on the bed.

"I shall change my bedroom," thought Augustine to himself, looking at the haggard, fallen-eyed man who faced him in the mirror as he shaved. "No, better still, I will go away for a change. Then I shall not have these . . . dreams. I'll go to old Edgar Fortescue for a few days; he begged me again not long ago to come any time."

So to the house of that old Mæcenas he went. He was much too great a man now to be in need of Sir Edgar's patronage. It was homage which he received there, both from host and guests. The stay did much to soothe his scarified nerves. Unfortunately the last day undid the good of all the foregoing ones.

Sir Edgar possessed a pretty young wife—his third—and, among other charms of his place in Somerset, an apple orchard underplanted with flowers. And in the cool of the evening Augustine walked there with his host and hostess almost as if he were the Almighty with the dwellers in Eden. Presently they sat down upon a rustic seat (but a very comfortable one) under the shade of the apple boughs, amid the incongruous but pleasant parterres.

"You have come at the wrong season for these apple-trees, Marchant," observed Sir Edgar after a while, taking out his cigar. "Blossom-time or apple-time—they are showy at either, in spite of the underplanting. What is attracting you on that tree—a tit? We have all kinds here, pretty, destructive little beggars!"

"I did not know that I was looking . . . it's nothing . . . thinking of something else," stammered the poet. Surely, surely he had been mistaken in thinking that he had seen a sinuous, dark furry thing undulating like a caterpillar down the stem of that particular apple-tree at a few yards' distance?

Talk went on, even his; there was safety in it. It was only the breeze which faintly rustled that bed of heliotrope behind the seat. Augustine wanted desperately to get up and leave the orchard, but neither Sir Edgar nor his wife seemed disposed to move, and so the poet remained at his end of the seat, his left hand playing nervously with a long bent of grass which had escaped the scythe.

All at once he felt a tickling sensation on the back of his hand, looked down and saw that featureless snout of fur protruding upward from underneath the rustic bench and sweeping itself backward and forward against his hand with a movement which was almost caressing. He was on his feet in a flash.

"Do you mind if I go in?" he asked abruptly. "I'm not . . . feeling very well."

If the thing could follow him it was of no use to go away. He returned to Abbot's Medding looking so much the worse for his change of air that Burrows expressed a respectful hope that he was not indisposed. And almost the first thing that occurred, when Augustine sat down at his writing-table to attend to his correspondence, was the unwinding of itself from one of its curved legs, of a soft, brown, oscillating serpent which slowly waved an end at him as if in welcome. . . .

In welcome, yes, that was it! The creature, incredible though it was, the creature seemed glad to see him! Standing at the other end of the room, his hands pressed over his eyes—for what was the use of attempting to hurt or destroy it—Augustine Marchant thought shudderingly that, like a witch's cat, a "familiar" would not, presumably, be ill disposed toward its master. Its master! Oh, God!

The hysteria which he had been trying to keep down began to mount uncontrollably when, removing his hand, Augustine glanced again toward his writing-table and saw that the boa had coiled itself in his chair and was sweeping its end to and fro over the back, somewhat in the way that a cat, purring meanwhile, rubs itself against furniture or a human leg in real or simulated affection.

"Oh, go, go away from there!" he suddenly screamed at it, advancing with outstretched hand. "In the devil's name, get out!"

To his utter amazement, he was obeyed. The rhythmic movements ceased, the fur snake poured itself down out of the chair and writhed toward the door. Venturing back to his writing-table after a moment Augustine saw it coiled on the threshold, the blind end turned toward him as usual, as though watching. And he began to laugh. What would happen if he rang and someone came; would the opening door scrape it aside . . . would it vanish? Had it, in short, an existence for anyone else but himself?

But he dared not make the experiment. He left the room by the French window, feeling that he could never enter the house again. And perhaps, had it not been for the horrible knowledge just acquired that it could follow him, he might easily have gone away for good from Abbott's Meddling and all his treasures and comforts. But of what use would that be—and how should he account for so extraordinary an action? No; he must think and plan while he yet remained sane.

To what, then, could he have recourse? The black magic in which he had dabbled with such disastrous consequences might possibly help him. Left to himself he was but an amateur, but he had a number of books. . . . There was also that other realm whose boundaries sometimes marched side by side with magic—religion. But how could he pray to a Deity in whom he did not believe? Rather pray to the Evil which had sent this curse upon him to show him how to banish it. Yet since he had deliberately followed what religion stigmatized as sin, what even the world would label as lust and necromancy, supplication to the dark powers was not likely to deliver him from them. They must somehow be outwitted, circumvented.

He kept his *grimoires* and books of the kind in a locked bookcase in another room, not in his study; in that room he sat up till midnight. But the spells which he read were useless; moreover, he did not really believe in them. The irony of the situation was that, in a sense, he had only played at sorcery; it had but lent a spice to sensuality. He wandered wretchedly about the room dreading at any moment to see his "familiar" wreathed round some object in it. At last he stopped at a small bookcase which held some old forgotten books of his mother's—Longfellow and Mrs. Hemans, *John Halifax, Gentleman,* and a good many volumes of sermons and mild essays. And when he looked at that blameless assembly a cloud seemed to pass over Augustine Marchant's vision, and he saw his mother, gentle and lace-capped as years and years ago she used to sit, hearing his lessons, in an antimacassared chair. She had been everything to him then, the little boy whose soul was not smirched. He called

silently to her now: "Mamma, Mamma, can't you help me? Can't
you send this thing away?"

When the cloud had passed he found that he had stretched out
his hand and removed a big book. Looking at it he saw that it was
her Bible, with "Sarah Amelia Marchant" on the faded yellow flyleaf. Her spirit *was* going to help him! He turned over a page or
two, and out of the largish print there sprang instantly at him:
Now the serpent was more subtle than any beast of the field. Augustine shuddered and almost put the Bible back, but the conviction that there was help there urged him to go on. He turned a few
more pages of Genesis and his eyes were caught by this verse, which
he had never seen before in his life.

> *"And if thou doest well, shalt thou not be accepted? And if
> thou doest not well, sin lieth at the door. And unto thee shall
> be his desire, and thou shalt rule over him."*

What strange words! What could they possibly mean? Was there
light for him in them? "Unto thee shall be his desire." That Thing,
the loathsome semblance of affection which hung about it. . . .
"Thou shalt rule over him." It *had* obeyed him, up to a point.
. . . Was this Book, of all others, showing him the way to be free?
But the meaning of the verse was so obscure! He had not, naturally,
such a thing as a commentary in the house. Yet, when he came to
think of it, he remembered that some pious and anonymous person,
soon after the publication of *Pomegranates of Sin,* had sent him a
Bible in the Revised Version, with an inscription recommending
him to read it. He had it somewhere, though he had always meant
to get rid of it.

After twenty minutes' search through the sleeping house he found
it in one of the spare bedrooms. But it gave him little enlighten-
ment, for there was scant difference in the rendering, save that for,
"lieth at the door," this version had, "coucheth," and that the
margin held an alternaive translation for the end of the verse: "And
unto thee is its desire, but thou shouldst rule over it."

Nevertheless, Augustine Marchant stood after midnight in this
silent, sheeted guest-chamber repeating, *"But thou shouldst rule
over it."*

And all at once he thought of a way of escape.

CHAPTER TWO

It was going to be a marvelous experience, staying with Augustine Marchant. Sometimes Lawrence Storey hoped there would be no other guests at Abbot's Medding; at other times he hoped there would be. A *tête-à-tête* of four days with the great poet—could he sustain his share worthily? For Lawrence, despite the remarkable artistic gifts which were finding their first real flowering in these illustrations to Augustine's poem, was still unspoilt, still capable of wonder and admiration, still humble and almost naïf. It was still astonishing to him that he, an architect's assistant, should have been snatched away, as Ganymede by the eagle, from the lower world of elevations and drains to serve on Olympus. It was not, indeed, Augustine Marchant who had first discovered him, but it was Augustine Marchant who was going to make him famous.

The telegraph poles flitted past the second-class carriage window and more than one traveler glanced with a certain envy and admiration at the fair, good-looking young man who diffused such an impression of happiness and candor, and had such a charming smile on his boyish lips. He carried with him a portfolio which he never let out of reach of his hand; the oldish couple opposite, speculating upon its contents, might have changed their opinion of him had they seen them.

But no shadow of the dark weariness of things unlawful rested on Lawrence Storey; to know Augustine Marchant, to be illustrating his great poem, to have learnt from him that art and morality had no kinship, this was to plunge into a new realm of freedom and enlarging experience. Augustine Marchant's poetry, he felt, had already taught his hand what his brain and heart knew nothing of.

There was a dogcart to meet him at the station, and in the scented June evening he was driven with a beating heart past meadows and hayfields to his destination.

Mr. Marchant, awaiting him in the hall, was at his most charming. "My dear fellow, are those the drawings? Come, let us lock them away at once in my safe! If you had brought me diamonds I should not be one quarter so concerned about thieves. And did you have a comfortable journey? I have had you put in the orange room; it is next to mine. There is no one else staying here, but there are a few people coming to dinner to meet you."

There was only just time to dress for dinner, so that Lawrence did not get an opportunity to study his host until he saw him seated at the head of the table. Then he was immediately struck by the fact that he looked curiously ill. His face—ordinarily by no means attenuated—seemed to have fallen in, there were dark circles under his eyes, and the perturbed Lawrence, observing him as the meal progressed, thought that his manner too seemed strange and once or twice quite absent-minded. And there was one moment when, though the lady on his right was addressing him, he sharply turned his head away and looked down at the side of his chair just as if he saw something on the floor. Then he apologized, saying that he had a horror of cats, and that sometimes the tiresome animal from the stables . . . But after that he continued to entertain his guests in his own inimitable way, and, even to the shy Lawrence, the evening proved very pleasant.

The three ensuing days were wonderful and exciting to the young artist—days of uninterrupted contact with a master mind which acknowledged, as the poet himself admitted, none of the petty barriers which man, for his own convenience, had set up between alleged right and wrong. Lawrence had learned why his host did not look well; it was loss of sleep, the price exacted by inspiration. He had a new poetic drama shaping in his mind which would scale heights that he had not yet attempted.

There was almost a touch of fever in the young man's dreams to-night—his last night but one. He had several. First he was standing by the edge of a sort of mere, inexpressibly desolate and unfriendly, a place he had never seen in his life, which yet seemed in some way familiar; and something said to him, "You will never go away from here!" He was alarmed, and woke, but went to sleep again almost immediately, and this time was back, oddly enough, in the church where in his earliest years he had been taken to service by the aunt who had brought him up—a large church full of pitch-pine pews with narrow ledges for hymn-books, which ledges he used surreptitiously to lick during the long dull periods of occultation upon his knees. But most of all he remembered the window with Adam and Eve in the Garden of Eden, on either side of an apple-tree round whose trunk was coiled a monstrous snake with a semi-human head. Lawrence had hated and dreaded that window, and because of it he would never go near an orchard and had no temptation to steal apples. . . . Now he was back in that church again, staring at the window, lit up with some infernal glow from behind. He woke again, little short of terrified—he, a grown man! But again he went to sleep quite quickly.

His third dream had for background, as sometimes happens in nightmares, the very room in which he lay. He dreamed that a door opened in the wall, and in the doorway, quite plain against the light from another room behind him, stood Augustine Marchant in his dressing-gown. He was looking down at something on the ground which Lawrence did not see, but his hand was pointing at Lawrence in the bed, and he was saying in a voice of command, "Go to him, do you hear? Go to him! Go to *him!* Am I not your master?" And Lawrence, who could neither move nor utter a syllable, wondered uneasily what this could be which was thus commanded, but his attention was chiefly focused on Augustine Marchant's face. After he had said these words several times, and apparently without result, a dreadful change came upon it, a look of the most unutterable despair. It seemed visibly to age and wither; he said, in a loud, penetrating whisper, "Is there no escape then?" covered his ravaged face a moment with his hands, and then went back and softly closed the door. At that Lawrence woke; but in the morning he had forgotten all three dreams.

The *tête-à-tête* dinner on the last night of his stay would have lingered in a gourmet's memory, so that it was a pity the young man did not know in the least what he was eating. At last there was happening what he had scarcely dared hope for; the great poet of the sensuous was revealing to him some of the unimaginably strange and secret sources of his inspiration. In the shaded rosy candlelight, his elbows on the table among trails of flowers he, who was not even a neophyte, listened like a man learning for the first time of some spell or spring which will make him more than mortal.

"Yes," said Augustine Marchant, after a long pause, "yes, it was a marvelous, an undying experience . . . one that is not given to many. It opened doors, it—but I despair of doing it justice in mere words." His look was transfigured, almost dreamy.

"But she . . . the woman . . . how did you . . . ?" asked Lawrence Storey in a hushed voice.

"Oh, the woman?" said Augustine, suddenly finishing off his wine. "The woman was only a common street-walker."

A moment or two later Lawrence was looking at his host wonderingly and wistfully. "But this was in Prague. Prague is a long way off."

"One does not need to go so far, in reality. Even in Paris——"

"One could . . . have that experience in Paris?"

"If you knew where to go. And of course, it is necessary to have credentials. I mean that—like all such enlightenments—it has to be kept secret, most secret, from the vulgar minds who lay their restrictions on the finer. That is self-evident."

"Of course," said the young man, and sighed deeply. His host looked at him affectionately.

"You, my dear Lawrence—I may call you Lawrence?—want just that touch of . . . what shall I call them—*les choses cachées*—to liberate your immense artistic gifts from the shackles which still bind them. Through that gateway you would find the possibility of their full fruition! It would fertilize your genius to a still finer blossoming. . . . But you would have scruples . . . and you are very young."

"You know," said Lawrence in a low and trembling tone, "what I feel about your poetry. You know how I ache to lay the best that is in me at your feet. If only I could make my drawings for the Two Queens more worthy—already it is an honor which overwhelms me that you should have selected me to do them—but they are not what they should be. I am *not* sufficiently liberated. . . ."

Augustine leaned forward on the flower-decked table. His eyes were glowing.

"Do you truly desire to be?"

The young man nodded, too full of emotion to find his voice.

The poet got up, went over to a cabinet in a corner and unlocked it. Lawrence watched his fine figure in a sort of trance. Then he half-rose with an exclamation.

"What is it?" asked Augustine very sharply, facing round.

"Oh, nothing, sir—only that I believe you hate cats, and I thought I saw one, or rather its tail, disappearing into that corner."

"There's no cat here," said Augustine quickly. His face had become all shiny and mottled, but Lawrence did not notice it. The poet stood a moment looking at the carpet; one might almost have thought that he was gathering resolution to cross it; then he came swiftly back to the table.

"Sit down again," he commanded. "Have you a pocket-book with you, a pocket-book which you never leave about? Good! Then write *this* in one place; and *this* on another page . . . write it small . . . among other entries is best . . . not on a blank page . . . write it in Greek characters if you know them. . . ."

"What . . . what is it?" asked Lawrence, all at once intolerably excited, his eyes fixed on the piece of paper in Augustine's hand.

"The two halves of the address in Paris."

CHAPTER THREE

Augustine Marchant kept a diary in those days, a locked diary, written in cipher. And for more than a month after Lawrence Storey's visit the tenor of the entries there was almost identical:

"No change . . . Always with me . . . How much longer can I endure it? The alteration in my looks is being remarked upon to my face. I shall have to get rid of Thornton [his man] on some pretext or other, for I begin to think that he has seen It. No wonder, since it follows me about like a dog. When It is visible to everyone it will be the end. . . . I found It in bed with me this morning, pressed up against me as if for warmth. . . ."

But there was a different class of entry also, appearing at intervals with an ever-increasing note of impatience.

"Will L.S. go there? . . . When shall I hear from L.S.? . . . Will the experiment do what I think? It is my last hope."

Then, suddenly, after five weeks had elapsed, an entry in a trembling hand:

"For twenty-four hours I have seen no sign of It! Can it be possible?"

And next day:

"Still nothing. I begin to live again.—This evening has just come an ecstatic letter from L.S., from Paris, telling me that he had 'presented his credentials' and was to have the experience next day. He has had it by now—by yesterday, in fact. Have I really freed myself? It looks like it!"

In one week from the date of that last entry it was remarked in Abbot's Medding how much better Mr. Marchant was looking again. Of late he had not seemed at all himself; his cheeks had fallen in, his clothes seemed to hang loosely upon him, who had generally filled them so well, and he appeared nervous. Now he was as before, cheery, courtly, debonair. And last Sunday, will you believe it, he went to church! The Rector was so astonished when he first became aware of him from the pulpit that he nearly forgot to give out his text. And the poet joined in the hymns, too! Several observed this amazing phenomenon.

It was the day after this unwonted appearance at St. Peter's. Augustine was strolling in his garden. The air had a new savor, the sun a new light; he could look again with pleasure at Thetis and her nymphs of the fountain, could work undisturbed in the summerhouse. Free, free! All the world was good to the senses once again, and the hues and scents of early autumn better, in truth, than the brilliance of that summer month which had seen his curse descend upon him.

The butler brought him out a letter with a French stamp. From Lawrence Storey, of course; to tell him—what? Where had he caught his first glimpse of it? In one of those oppressively furnished French bedrooms? And how had he taken it?

At first, however, Augustine was not sure that the letter was from Storey. The writing was very different, cramped instead of flowing, and, in places, spluttering, the pen having dug into the paper as if the hand which held it had not been entirely under control—almost, thought Augustine, his eyes shining with excitement, almost as though something had been twined, liana-like, round the wrist. (He had a sudden sick recollection of a day when that had happened to him, quickly submerged in a gush of eager anticipation.) Sitting down upon the edge of the fountain he read—not quite what he had looked for.

"I don't know what is happening to me," began the letter without other opening. "Yesterday I was in a café by myself, and had just ordered some absinthe—though I do not like it. And quite suddenly, although I knew that I was in the café, I realized that I was also back in *that room*. I could see every feature of it, but I could see the café too, with all the people in it; the one was, as it were, superimposed upon the other, the room, which was a good deal smaller than the café, being inside the latter, as a box may be within a larger box. And all the while the room was growing clearer, the café fading. I saw the glass of absinthe suddenly standing on nothing, as it were. All the furniture of *the room,* all the accessories you know of, were mixed up with the chairs and tables of the café. I do not know how I managed to find my way to the *comptoir,* pay and get out. I took a *fiacre* back to my hotel. By the time I arrived there I was all right. I suppose that it was only the after effects of a very strange and violent emotional experience. But I hope to God that it will not recur!"

"How interesting!" said Augustine Marchant, dabbling his hand in the swirling water where he had once drowned a piece of dark fluff. "And why indeed should I have expected that It would couch at his door in the same form as at mine?"

Four days more of new-found peace and he was reading this:

"In God's name—or the Devil's—come over and help me! I have hardly an hour now by night or day when I am sure of my whereabouts. I could not risk the journey back to England alone. It is like being imprisoned in some kind of infernal half-transparent box, always growing a little smaller. Wherever I go now I carry it about with me; when I am in the street I hardly know which is the pavement and which is the roadway, because I am always treading on that black carpet with the cabalistic designs; if I speak to anyone they may suddenly disappear from sight. To attempt to work is naturally useless. I would consult a doctor, but that would mean telling him everything. . . ."

"I hope to God he won't do that!" muttered Augustine uneasily. "He can't—he swore to absolute secrecy. I hadn't bargained, however, for his ceasing work. Suppose he finds himself unable to complete the designs for *Theodora and Marozia!* That would be serious. . . . However, to have freed myself is worth *any* sacrifice. . . . But Storey cannot, obviously, go on living indefinitely on two planes at once. . . . Artistically, though, it might inspire him to something quite unprecedented. I'll write to him and point that out; it might encourage him. But go near him in person—is it likely!"

The next day was one of great literary activity. Augustine was so deeply immersed in his new poetical drama that he neglected his correspondence and almost his meals—except his dinner, which seemed that evening to be shared most agreeably and excitingly by these new creations of his brain. Such, in fact was his preoccupation with them that it was not until he had finished the savory and poured out a glass of his superlative port that he remembered a telegram which had been handed to him as he came into dinner. It still lay unopened by his plate. Now, tearing apart the envelope, he read with growing bewilderment these words above his publishers' names:

"Please inform us immediately what steps to take are prepared send to France recover drawings if possible what suggestions can you make as to successor Rossell and Ward."

Augustine was more than bewildered; he was stupefied. Had some accident befallen Lawrence Storey of which he knew nothing? But he had opened all his letters this morning though he had not answered any. A prey to a sudden very nasty anxiety he got up and rang the bell.

"Burrows, bring me *The Times* from the library."

The newspaper came, unopened. Augustine, now in a frenzy of uneasiness, scanned the pages rapidly. But it was some seconds before he came upon the headline: "TRAGIC DEATH OF A YOUNG ENGLISH ARTIST," and read the following, furnished by the Paris correspondent:

"Connoisseurs who were looking forward to the appearance of the superb illustrated edition of Mr. Augustine Marchant's *Queen Theodora and Queen Marozia* will learn with great regret of the death by drowning of the gifted young artist, Mr. Lawrence Storey, who was engaged upon the designs for it. Mr. Storey had recently been staying in Paris, but left one day last week for a remote spot in Brittany, it was supposed in pursuance of his work. On Friday last his body was discovered floating in a lonely pool near Carhaix. It is hard to see how Mr. Storey could have fallen in, since this piece of water—the Mare de Plougouven—has a completely level shore surrounded by reeds, and is not in itself very deep, nor is there any boat upon it. It is said that the unfortunate young Englishman had been somewhat strange in his manner recently and complained of hallucinations; it is therefore possible that under their influence he deliberately waded out into the Mare de Plougouven. A strange feature of the case is that he had fastened round him under his coat the finished drawings for Mr. Marchant's book, which were of course completely spoiled by the water before the body was found. It is to be hoped that they were not the only——"

Augustine threw *The Times* furiously from him and struck the dinner-table with his clenched fist.

"Upon my soul, that is too much! It is criminal! My property—and I who had done so much for him! Fastened them round himself—he must have been crazy!"

But had he been so crazy? When his wrath had subsided a little Augustine could not but ask himself whether the young artist had not in some awful moment of insight guessed the truth, or a part of it—that his patron had deliberately corrupted him? It looked almost like it. But, if he had really taken all the finished drawings with him to this place in Brittany, what an unspeakably mean trick of revenge thus to destroy them! . . . Yet, even if it were so, he must regard their loss as the price of his own deliverance, since, from his point of view, the desperate expedient of passing on his "familiar" had been a complete success. By getting someone else to plunge even deeper than he had done into the unlawful (for he had seen to it that Lawrence Storey should do that) he had proved, as that verse in Genesis said, that he *had* rule over . . . what had pursued him in tangible form as a consequence of his own night in Prague. He could not be too thankful. The literary world might well be thankful too. For his own art was of infinitely more importance than the subservient, the parasitic art of an illustrator. He could with a little search find half a dozen just as gifted as that poor hallucination-ridden Storey to finish *Theodora and Marozia*—even, if necessary, to begin an entirely fresh set of drawings. And meanwhile, in the new lease of creative energy which this unfortunate but necessary sacrifice had made possible for him, he would begin to put on paper the masterpiece which was now taking brilliant shape in his liberated mind. A final glass, and then an evening in the work-shop!

Augustine poured out some port, and was raising the glass, prepared to drink to his own success, when he thought he heard a sound near the door. He looked over his shoulder. Next instant the stem of the wineglass had snapped in his hand and he had sprung back to the farthest limit of the room.

Reared up for quite five feet against the door, huge, dark, sleeked with wet and flecked with bits of green waterweed, was something half-python, half-gigantic cobra, its head drawn back as if to strike . . . its head, for in its former featureless tapering end were now two reddish eyes, such as furriers put into the heads of stuffed creatures. And they were fixed in an unwavering and malevolent glare upon him, as he cowered there clutching the bowl of the broken wineglass, the crumpled copy of *The Times* lying at his feet.

The Disappearance of Doctor Parkman

BY

EDMUND PEARSON

Doctor Parkman was walking—rapidly, as usual—through the streets of Boston, on his way to keep an appointment. He wore a black frock coat and trousers, a purple silk vest, black stock, and high hat, and his lean figure would have made him noticeable, even if his peculiar countenance had not attracted attention by itself. Boys pointed him out to other boys:

"There goes Doctor Parkman!"

Women who passed him on the street went home and told their families that they had seen "Chin." The Doctor had a protruding lower jaw, and his mouth was fitted with some conspicuous false teeth. That chin was not meaningless; he was a determined man, on his way to put an end to a long-drawn-out and vexatious business affair. Plainly there was going to be trouble for someone.

Doctor Parkman was always in a hurry, and today he was in more of a hurry than ever. He was so impatient a man, says one account, that when riding he would sometimes leave his horse in the street, and hurry ahead on foot. This morning he had been at the Merchants' Bank on State Street, and at various other places. He bought a lettuce for his invalid daughter, and left it in a bag at Holland's grocery at the corner of Blossom and Vine Streets, where he said he would soon return. Then he pushed on to his appointment, at half-past one, at the Medical College. He must get this business over, and return promptly to his dinner at half-past two—for this was the year 1849, when gentlemen dined early in the afternoon. He hoped that to-day Professor Webster would really do something to settle this infernal debt and cease putting him off with evasions, excuses, and subterfuges.

Professor Webster! The name was enough to make Doctor Parkman snarl. This was a man who held a lectureship in a medical college built on land which he—Doctor Parkman—had provided. The Parkman Chair of Anatomy in the College—occupied by Oliver Wendell Holmes—was named in Doctor Parkman's honour, as acknowledgment of the gift. And here was Webster, twice a professor, since he was also Erving Professor of Chemistry and Mineralogy at Harvard, and yet he was nothing but a defaulting, dishonourable debtor! Doctor Parkman had told him as much to his face, and to make sure that Professor Webster should be in no doubt about it, had sent him a message to the same effect within a week.

Doctor Parkman had cause to be indignant. Professor Webster, who had quickly run through the fortune inherited from his father, liked to live well and to entertain his friends. Even in Cambridge, and at that date, it was not easy to do this—and incidentally to support a wife and three daughters—on the $1,200 a year which the University paid him, with a slender addition from the sale of tickets for his lectures at the Medical College. Seven years earlier, Parkman had lent Webster $400, taking a note secured by the mortgage of some personal property. In 1847, when the loan was not fully repaid, Doctor Parkman had been one of a group of men to lend the Professor a larger sum, taking this time a note for $2,432, secured by a mortgage of all Webster's personal property, including his household furniture and his cabinet of minerals. The next year, Professor Webster, still embarrassed for lack of money, went to Doctor Parkman's brother-in-law, Robert Gould Shaw, told a pathetic tale of sheriffs and attachments, and prevailed upon that gentleman to buy the cabinet of minerals for $1,200—omitting all mention of the fact that this collection was already in pawn to Doctor Parkman. The transaction happened to come out in conversation between the brothers-in-law, and Doctor Parkman was furious.

"Those minerals are not his to sell," he exclaimed; "I have a mortgage on them, and I can show it to you!"

The Doctor was prompt and punctilious, and he expected others to be like him. He began to pursue the Professor for the debt. I do not know whether the story is true that he used to come to Webster's lectures, sit in the front row, glare at the unhappy man, and confuse him by the sight of that prognathous jaw and those shining

teeth. Webster, in the months to come, did all he could to represent
Parkman as an overbearing and violent persecutor of a struggling
scholar, and it may be that this was merely his corroborative detail.
He furnished a great amount of corroborative detail, once started,
and some of it was like Pooh Bah's description of the execution of
Nanki Poo, everything added for the sake of artistic verisimilitude.
But Doctor Parkman certainly moved upon another source of Webster's income—the sale of lecture tickets—and after he had been
fobbed off once more, threatened legal processes to get at this source
of cash. On Monday night of this week he had called at the Massachusetts Medical College. Here is the scene and here is the interview, as they were described by Littlefield, the janitor.

It was in Doctor Webster's back private room. It was somewhat dark in that room. . . . I was helping Doctor Webster, who
had three or four candles burning. The Doctor stood at a table,
looking at a chemical book, and appeared to be reading—his
back toward the door. I stood by the stove, stirring some water,
in which a solution was to be made. I never heard a footstep;
but the first I saw, Doctor Parkman came into the back room.
. . . Doctor Webster looked round, and appeared surprised to
see him enter so suddenly. The first words he said were:
"Doctor Webster, are you ready for me to-night?"
Doctor Parkman spoke quick and loud. Doctor Webster
made answer:
"No, I am not ready, to-night, Doctor."
Doctor Parkman said something else. . . . He either accused
Doctor Webster of selling something that had been mortgaged
before . . . or something like that. He took some papers out of
his pocket. Doctor Parkman said:
"It is so, and you know it."
Doctor Webster told him:
"I will see you to-morrow, Doctor."
Doctor Parkman stood near the door; he put his hand up,
and said:
"Doctor, something must be accomplished to-morrow."
He then went out and it was the last time I saw him in the
building.

Nothing, however, was accomplished on the morrow toward settling the trouble between the two doctors, and now it is four days

later, Friday, November 23d, in the week before Thanksgiving. An unlucky Friday for both men. Professor Webster has paid a sudden and rather mysterious call at Doctor Parkman's house before nine o'clock this morning, and made an appointment to see his creditor at the College at half-past one. Could a settlement be made at the College near an anatomical theatre, and amid the "pieces of sour mortality"—as Dickens afterward described some of the furniture of the place—which could not be done at Doctor Parkman's home? Evidently both men thought so, for here is Doctor Parkman hastening to the appointment. It is quarter before two; he is seen near the building and going toward it. He enters—or so it is supposed—and then, nobody sees him again.

Such a man as Doctor Parkman could not casually disappear from the streets of Boston, in broad daylight, without causing excitement. He was too prominent and too highly connected. He does not seem to have practised as a physician (although he was M.D. of the University of Aberdeen), but, instead, he devoted himself, too energetically, to business and finance. He was willing to accommodate an acquaintance with an advance of money, and he was not above bedevilling the debtor who seemed to be evading payment. His brother was the Reverend Doctor Parkman; but his nephew, then a young man, recently from college, was to become more distinguished than any of them, as Francis Parkman, the historian. He also had the family characteristic of determination, and it was most nobly exercised. Doctor Parkman lived in a substantial and rather gloomy-looking house, still standing at Number 8 Walnut Street. When he did not come home to dinner that Friday afternoon his family were alarmed, and by the next day were in great agitation and distress. Advertisements offering rewards were put in the newspapers, the river was dredged, empty buildings and cellars were searched.

On Sunday afternoon, Professor Webster paid a sudden and surprising visit at the Reverend Doctor Parkman's house and aroused astonishment by his abrupt manner. The Professor acknowledged having had an interview with the missing man on Friday afternoon. According to this account, they had parted at the end of the interview. To other persons about the College the Professor said that he had met the Doctor by appointment, had paid him $483, and that the Doctor had rushed out with this money in his hand. The inference served to bolster up the popular theory that Doctor Parkman had been waylaid somewhere, robbed, and murdered.

Professor Webster's actions were strange, both before and after the disappearance of Doctor Parkman, and at last he completely astounded the janitor, on Tuesday, by giving him an order for a Thanksgiving turkey. It was the first gift he had ever made to Littlefield in an acquaintance of seven years. Finally, Littlefield became tired of hearing on the street that Doctor Parkman would be found in the College, and he resolved to investigate a vault below Professor Webster's own apartments. Only superficial examination of the College had been made so far, in the searches which were going on all over Boston and Cambridge. But the janitor, with crowbars and chisels, and with his wife on guard to warn him of the approach of Webster, put in parts of two or three days trying to break through a brick wall, and inspect the contents of the vault. Thanksgiving was a gloomy day with him, in spite of Professor Webster's turkey, for he spent the morning cleaning up his own cellar, and the afternoon pounding and prying at the tough courses of brick in the vault. He had some relief at night, however, when he went to a ball given by the Sons of Temperance, where he stayed until four o'clock in the morning, and danced eighteen out of the twenty dances. Ah, there were janitors in those days!

On Friday, one week after Doctor Parkman's disappearance, Littlefield broke through the wall and looked into the vault.

"I held my light forward," he said, "and the first thing which I saw was the pelvis of a man and two parts of a leg. The water was running down on these remains from the sink. I knew it was no place for these things."

College officers and the city marshal were notified; three policemen were sent to Cambridge to bring Professor Webster to Boston, and put him under arrest.

The policemen told the Professor, when they reached his house, that a further search was to be made at the College, and that his presence was desired. He came willingly enough, and talked pleasantly with them, until he found that the carriage had been driven, not to the College, but to the jail. Then he asked:

"What does this mean?"

The officer replied:

"We have done looking for Doctor Parkman, and you are in custody for the murder of Doctor Parkman."

He became greatly agitated, requested water to drink, and then asked a torrent of questions:

"Have they found Doctor Parkman? Where did they find him? Did they find the whole of the body? How came they to suspect me? Oh! my children, what will they do? Oh! what will they think of me?"

The officer in charge told him that he must not ask questions which it would be improper for him to answer, and then asked Professor Webster if anybody had access to his private apartments in the College.

"Nobody," he replied, "except the porter who makes the fire."

He paused for a minute and then added:

"That villain! I am a ruined man!"

After a few moments spent in pacing the floor, he sat down, took something from his waistcoat pocket, and put it to his mouth. This was followed by a spasm, and he was soon helpless. The officers helped him to rise and assisted him to a cell, where he lay down. He had a series of violent spasms, but was able, about an hour afterward, to go to the College, in charge of the officers, while a further inspection was made. At a later date, Professor Webster said that before he left the carriage, he took a dose of strychnine, which he had already prepared. He supposed that his nervous condition prevented it from acting fatally, as he thought it was a large dose.

The excitement in Boston was intense when it became known that Professor Webster had been arrested. It is said that two companies of militia were ordered out, but for what purpose, I do not know.

The list of the academic distinctions of John White Webster is rather long. His college class was that of 1811. He was Master of Arts and Doctor of Medicine of Harvard; a member of the American Academy of Arts and Sciences; of the London Geological Society, and of other learned bodies. He had written and edited some books on chemistry, and another describing one of the Azores, where his married daughter dwelt. Senator Hoar, who attended his lectures, said that he seemed "a kind-hearted, fussy person," but that his lectures were the most tedious compositions to which he ever listened. Owing to the fact that he had insisted on having fireworks at the inauguration of President Everett, the students called him "Sky-rocket Jack."

At one of his chemistry lectures, there had been a violent explosion of a copper vessel, part of which flew into the back of the classroom, and except for the fact that a student was absent and there was a vacancy in the row where the metal fragment struck, one of his auditors might have been killed. The Professor had commented drily:

"The President sent for me and told me I must be more careful. He said I should feel very badly indeed if I had killed one of the students. And I should."

Professor Andrew Peabody, writing many years after the trial, said:

Of Professor Webster I have not an unkind word to say. I never supposed him to be a great man; and he certainly was not interesting as a teacher, nor was he often successful in his chemical experiments. But he was good-natured in the classroom; and during my tutorship I was often invited to his too hospitable house, and became acquainted with his charming family.

When he was brought to trial in March, many persons still believed him innocent. Others thought that the case against him would fail, for lack of proof that the remains were those of Doctor Parkman. Some of his friends tried to induce Rufus Choate to undertake the defence, but that great attorney, after hearing the evidence, refused to enter the case unless the Professor would admit the killing, and permit him to try to convince the jury that it was manslaughter, not murder. This, the Websters refused to consider. Those, who like Charles Sumner, still believed in the Professor's innocence, probably did not understand the strength of the evidence which was to be brought forward.

The trial, before Chief Justice Shaw, is one of the landmarks in the history of criminal law in Massachusetts. Everyone was impressed by the gravity of the occasion, and the proceedings were extremely dignified. The jury could not have been excelled for seriousness of purpose and religious demeanour if they had been chosen from the House of Bishops. To accommodate the great numbers of folk who wished to see something of the trial, the floor of the Court was closed to all but privileged spectators, while the general public were admitted to the gallery, where, it is astonishing to learn, a change of audience was effected by the police every ten minutes! "Except for two tumultuous movements," order and quiet were preserved, and *from 55,000 to 60,000 persons had a glimpse of the proceedings.* The trial lasted for eleven days, and the New York *Herald,* a paper of four pages, was one of many which adopted the extraordinary policy of reporting the events daily, in three or four closely printed columns, and on the front page.

The testimony of Littlefield was of great importance; he was examined for hours. He described the interview between the two doctors, and then said that on that same day Professor Webster had inquired of him about the condition of the vault where were placed the remains from the dissecting room. On Thursday, the day before Doctor Parkman disappeared, Professor Webster sent the witness to the Massachusetts General Hospital on an unsuccessful errand to get a jar of blood. Littlefield saw Doctor Parkman coming toward the College on the Friday, but did not see him enter. During the next few days, the Professor was locked in his apartments at hours which were not customary; unusual fires were burning in the furnace; a stream of water could be heard running in the sink. After the search for Doctor Parkman had begun, Webster told Littlefield that he had paid $483 and some cents to Doctor Parkman, who had hurried out with it.

The State produced evidence that the prisoner had performed a number of feats of juggling with checks and notes, which the defence could not explain. Professor Webster told Doctor Parkman's agent that he had "settled" with Doctor Parkman; as, indeed, he had, but not in the manner in which the agent was intended to understand the phrase. Fragments of false teeth were found in the furnace, and in addition to what had been discovered in the vault, other larger parts of a human body in a tea chest filled with tanbark. And Webster had had a quantity of tanbark brought in from Cambridge, during the week, by Sawin the expressman—name familiar to generations of Harvard students.

Prisoners, at that period, were not allowed to testify, but Professor Webster's counsel entered for him a complete denial. They raised doubts whether the pieces of a human frame were those of

Doctor Parkman, and suggested that, even if this were true, the fragments had been placed there by some person, unknown to Professor Webster, and perhaps in order to incriminate him. The tendency of the defence was to suggest the possible guilt of Littlefield. They tried to show, by witnesses, that Doctor Parkman had been seen later on that Friday, and in other parts of the city. Two or three witnesses appeared; some of them were mistaken as to the date, and others mistook a man of similar appearance for the Doctor.

Despite the strong net of circumstantial evidence closing around Professor Webster, the whole case for the State hinged on the proof of the identity of the remains, and in the final analysis this rested upon the evidence about the false teeth. When Doctor Nathan Keep, a friend of both men, who had made the teeth for Doctor Parkman, gave his positive evidence, and proved its correctness by fitting the mould, still in his possession, to the fragments found in the furnace, he burst into tears, as he realized that his testimony would hang the prisoner.

A large number of Professor Webster's neighbours, friends, and colleagues appeared in his behalf, and testified as to his good character. He was nearly sixty years of age, and since he was generally respected, even if not very well liked, it was difficult for the jury to believe him guilty of the offence. One of his character witnesses was Jared Sparks, president of Harvard. Oliver Wendell Holmes had testified for the State; he had been lecturing on anatomy in the room above Doctor Webster's at the time of the meeting with Doctor Parkman. Professor Webster was allowed to make a statement to the jury, and was so unwise as to accept the opportunity. He spoke for about fifteen minutes, criticizing his own counsel, and referring to details of the case brought against him. Chief Justice Shaw's charge to the jury is a celebrated address; parts of it, especially those relating to the nature and value of circumstantial evidence, are quoted in courts to-day. The case against Professor Webster was purely one of circumstantial evidence; nobody had seen the two men together at the time of the murder.

On the evening of the eleventh day of the trial, the jury went out for three hours and came in about midnight with a verdict of "guilty."

Professor Webster was sentenced to death, but the usual appeals were made in his behalf. When the application for a writ of error was dismissed, the Professor addressed the Governor and Council, and in the most solemn language, protested his innocence. He used such remarkable phrases as these:

"To Him who seeth in secret, and before Whom I may ere long be called to appear, would I appeal for the truth of what I now declare . . ." and "Repeating in the most solemn and positive manner, and under the fullest sense of my responsibility as a man and as a Christian, that I am wholly innocent of this charge, to the truth of which the Searcher of all hearts is a witness. . . ."

Some weeks later, this address was withdrawn, and the wretched man made a long confession, maintaining that the murder was not premeditated. Professor Webster described his call on the doctor on the Friday morning, and their appointment to meet that afternoon, at the College. He then wrote:

He came, accordingly, between half-past one and two. He came in at the lecture-room door. I was engaged in removing some glasses from my lecture-room table into the room in the rear, called the upper laboratory. He came rapidly down the steps and followed me into the laboratory. He immediately addressed me with great energy.

"Are you ready for me, sir? Have you got the money?"

I replied:

"No, Doctor Parkman," and was then beginning to state my condition and make my appeal to him. He would not listen to me, but interrupted me with much vehemence. He called me "scoundrel" and "liar," and went on heaping upon me the most bitter taunts and opprobrious epithets. While he was talking, he drew a handful of papers from his pocket, and took from among them my two notes, and also an old letter from Doctor Hosack, written many years ago, and congratulating him (Doctor P.) on his success in getting me appointed professor of chemistry.

"You see," he said, "I got you into your office, and now I will get you out of it."

He put back into his pocket all the papers, except the letter and the notes. I cannot tell how long the torrent of threats and invectives continued, and I can now recall to memory but a small portion of what he said.

At first I kept interposing, trying to pacify him, so that I might obtain the object for which I had sought the interview. But I could not stop him, and soon my own temper was up. I forgot everything. I felt nothing but the sting of his words. I was excited to the highest degree of passion; and while he was speaking and gesticulating in the most violent and menacing manner, thrusting the letter and his fist into my face, in my fury I seized whatever thing was handiest—it was a stick of wood—and dealt him an instantaneous blow with all the force that passion could give it. I did not know, nor think, nor care where I should hit him, nor how hard, nor what the effect would be. It was on the side of his head, and there was nothing to break the force of the blow. He fell instantly upon the pavement. There was no second blow. He did not move. I stooped down over him, and he seemed to be lifeless. Blood flowed from his mouth, and I got a sponge and wiped it away. I got some ammonia and applied it to his nose; but without effect.

Perhaps I spent ten minutes in attempts to resuscitate him; but I found that he was absolutely dead. In my horror and consternation I ran instinctively to the doors and bolted them—the doors of the lecture room and of the laboratory below. And then, what was I to do?

It never occurred to me to go out and declare what had been done and obtain assistance. I saw nothing but the alternative of a successful removal and concealment of the body, on the one hand, and of infamy and destruction on the other. The first thing I did, as soon as I could do anything, was to drag the body into the private room adjoining. There I took off the clothes, and began putting them into the fire which was burning in the upper laboratory. They were all consumed there that afternoon—with papers, pocketbook, or whatever else they may have contained. I did not examine the pockets, nor remove anything except the watch. I saw that, or the chain of it, hanging out; and I took it and threw it over the bridge as I went to Cambridge.

My next move was to get the body into the sink which stands in the small private room. By setting the body partially erect against the corner, and getting up into the sink myself, I succeeded in drawing it up. There it was entirely dismembered. It was quickly done, as a work of terrible and desperate necessity. The only instrument used was the knife found by the officers in the tea chest, and which I kept for cutting corks. I made no use of the Turkish knife, as it was called at the trial. . . .

While dismembering the body, a stream of (water) was running through the sink, carrying off the blood in a pipe that passed down through the lower laboratory. There must have been a leak in the pipe, for the ceiling below was stained immediately round it.

Professor Webster made a long and plausible appeal for commutation of sentence, basing his claim, not only on the assertion—quite possibly correct—that the blow had been struck in a momentary fit of anger,* but upon his argument that every act of his own showed there had been no premeditation. His call in the morning to make an appointment, so he declared, would have been an insane act if he had planned to kill Doctor Parkman.

The Governor, however, could not admit that the prisoner's word was entitled to credit, nor did his pastor, or some of his friends, venture to suggest that he could be believed. Professor Webster was hanged on the last Friday in August, 1850. He was calm and apparently resigned. He had apologized humbly to Littlefield for the attempts to throw suspicion upon him, and he wrote a letter, in a spirit of deep contrition, to the Reverend Doctor Parkman, to make what peace he could with the family he had wronged.

Was it a coldly premeditated murder, or can it be considered manslaughter, done in a sudden passion and under provocation? The question about the vault, the attempt to get the blood, and, perhaps, the appointment with Parkman at the College point to a plan. On the other hand, he gave more or less plausible explanations of all these things, and the absurdity of any hope to make away with such a man as Doctor Parkman, and conceal the crime, is so great as to cast doubts upon the theory of premeditation. The question seems to me impossible to answer.

The murder shows these things clearly: that a hitherto highly respectable person may commit a crime of this nature; that he may solemnly lie in the name of God, to escape punishment; and that a just conviction may be had upon circumstantial evidence. Even after the trial there were many who were unconvinced of the Professor's guilt, and A. Oakey Hall, afterward Mayor of New York, was one of those who wrote pamphlets to protest against the conviction. Mr. Hall was very severe upon what he denounced as the result of "Puritan bigotry" and "Bostonian snobbishness," but what

* Professor Peabody, in the book already quoted, expresses his firm belief that this was true. Many persons have always held the same opinion.

course he took after the prisoner had confessed does not appear at this date.

The Webster-Parkman case has hardly been displaced as America's most celebrated murder, and the one which lives longest in the books of reminiscences. It will be recalled that Artemus Ward's show had "wax figgers" of "Doctor Webster in the act of killin' Doctor Parkman." Few writers of the time failed to mention the murder. Of the anecdotes which are told about it, the story related by Longfellow is perhaps the most remarkable. This was told at a dinner given to Charles Dickens, during his visit in 1869. Dickens, during the day, had visited the scene of the murder, with Doctor Holmes. A year or two before the murder, Longfellow had been one of the guests at a men's dinner at Professor Webster's, to meet a foreign visitor, interested in science. Toward the end of the evening, the Professor had the lights in the room lowered and a servant bring in a bowl of burning chemicals, which shed a ghastly glow upon the faces of the men about the table. Professor Webster rose, and producing a rope, cast it around his own neck like a noose. He then leaned over the hell fires which came from the bowl, lolled his head upon one side, and protruded his tongue in the manner of a man who had been hanged!

After the execution, it is said that the Webster family removed to Fayal, where a married daughter lived. Some years later, at a dinner party, there was a glib guest who had not caught the names of some of the Websters who were present, but merely knew that they had come from Boston. In order to make himself agreeable, he suddenly remarked:

"Oh, by the way, what ever became of that Professor Webster who killed Doctor Parkman? Did they hang him?"

Another similarly gentle yarn is of a later date. Benjamin Butler was cross-examining a witness in Court, and treating him, so the Judge thought, with unnecessary brusqueness. He reminded the lawyer that the witness was a Harvard professor.

"Yes, I know, your Honour. We hanged one of them the other day!"

But Ben Butler always had a sinful dislike of Harvard. They had refused to give him an LL.D.

I'll Be Waiting

BY

RAYMOND CHANDLER

AT ONE O'CLOCK in the morning, Carl, the night porter, turned down the last of three table lamps in the main lobby of the Windermere Hotel. The blue carpet darkened a shade or two and the walls drew back into remoteness. The chairs filled with shadowy loungers. In the corners were memories like cobwebs.

Tony Reseck yawned. He put his head on one side and listened to the frail, twittery music from the radio room beyond a dim arch at the far side of the lobby. He frowned. That should be his radio room after one A.M. Nobody should be in it. That red-haired girl was spoiling his nights.

The frown passed and a miniature of a smile quirked at the corners of his lips. He sat relaxed, a short, pale, paunchy, middle-aged man with long, delicate fingers clasped on the elk's tooth on his watch chain; the long delicate fingers of a sleight-of-hand artist, fingers with shiny, molded nails and tapering first joints, fingers a little spatulate at the ends. Handsome fingers. Tony Reseck rubbed them gently together and there was peace in his quiet sea-gray eyes.

The frown came back on his face. The music annoyed him. He got up with a curious litheness, all in one piece, without moving his clasped hands from the watch chain. At one moment he was leaning back relaxed, and the next he was standing balanced on his feet, perfectly still, so that the movement of rising seemed to be a thing imperfectly perceived, an error of vision.

He walked with small, polished shoes delicately across the blue carpet and under the arch. The music was louder. It contained the hot, acid blare, the frenetic, jittering runs of a jam session. It was too loud. The red-haired girl sat there and stared silently at the fretted part of the big radio cabinet as though she could see the

607

band with its fixed professional grin and the sweat running down its back. She was curled up with her feet under her on a davenport which seemed to contain most of the cushions in the room. She was tucked among them carefully, like a corsage in the florist's tissue paper.

She didn't turn her head. She leaned there, one hand in a small fist on her peach-colored knee. She was wearing lounging pajamas of heavy ribbed silk embroidered with black lotus buds.

"You like Goodman, Miss Cressy?" Tony Reseck asked.

The girl moved her eyes slowly. The light in there was dim, but the violet of her eyes almost hurt. They were large, deep eyes without a trace of thought in them. Her face was classical and without expression.

She said nothing.

Tony smiled and moved his fingers at his sides, one by one, feeling them move. "You like Goodman, Miss Cressy?" he repeated gently.

"Not to cry over," the girl said tonelessly.

Tony rocked back on his heels and looked at her eyes. Large, deep, empty eyes. Or were they? He reached down and muted the radio.

"Don't get me wrong," the girl said. "Goodman makes money, and a lad that makes legitimate money these days is a lad you have to respect. But this jitterbug music gives me the backdrop of a beer flat. I like something with roses in it."

"Maybe you like Mozart," Tony said.

"Go on, kid me," the girl said.

"I wasn't kidding you, Miss Cressy. I think Mozart was the greatest man that ever lived—and Toscanini is his prophet."

"I thought you were the house dick." She put her head back on a pillow and stared at him through her lashes. "Make me some of that Mozart," she added.

"It's too late," Tony sighed. "You can't get it now."

She gave him another long lucid glance. "Got the eye on me, haven't you, flatfoot?" She laughed a little, almost under her breath. "What did I do wrong?"

Tony smiled his toy smile. "Nothing, Miss Cressy. Nothing at all. But you need some fresh air. You've been five days in this hotel and you haven't been outdoors. And you have a tower room."

She laughed again. "Make me a story about it. I'm bored."

"There was a girl here once had your suite. She stayed in the hotel a whole week, like you. Without going out at all, I mean. She didn't speak to anybody hardly. What do you think she did then?"

The girl eyed him gravely. "She jumped her bill."

He put his long delicate hand out and turned it slowly, fluttering the fingers, with an effect almost like a lazy wave breaking. "Unh-uh. She sent down for her bill and paid it. Then she told the hop to be back in half an hour for her suitcases. Then she went out on her balcony."

The girl leaned forward a little, her eyes still grave, one hand capping her peach-colored knee. "What did you say your name was?"

"Tony Reseck."

"Sounds like a hunky."

"Yeah," Tony said. "Polish."

"Go on, Tony."

"All the tower suites have private balconies, Miss Cressy. The walls of them are too low, for fourteen stories above the street. It was a dark night, that night, high clouds." He dropped his hand with a final gesture, a farewell gesture. "Nobody saw her jump. But when she hit, it was like a big gun going off."

"You're making it up, Tony." Her voice was a clean dry whisper of sound.

He smiled his toy smile. His quiet sea-gray eyes seemed almost to be smoothing the long waves of her hair. "Eve Cressy," he said musingly. "A name waiting for lights to be in."

"Waiting for a tall dark guy that's no good, Tony. You wouldn't care why. I was married to him once. I might be married to him again. You can make a lot of mistakes in just one lifetime." The hand on her knee opened slowly until the fingers were strained back as far as they would go. Then they closed quickly and tightly, and even in that dim light the knuckles shone like little polished bones. "I played him a low trick once. I put him in a bad place—without meaning to. You wouldn't care about that either. It's just that I owe him something."

He leaned over softly and turned the knob on the radio. A waltz formed itself dimly on the warm air. A tinsel waltz, but a waltz. He turned the volume up. The music gushed from the loud-speaker in a swirl of shadowed melody. Since Vienna died, all waltzes are shadowed.

The girl put her head on one side and hummed three or four bars and stopped with a sudden tightening of her mouth.

"Eve Cressy," she said. "It was in lights once. At a bum night club. A dive. They raided it and the lights went out."

He smiled at her almost mockingly. "It was no dive while you were there, Miss Cressy. . . . That's the waltz the orchestra always played when the old porter walked up and down in front of the hotel entrance, all swelled up with his medals on his chest. The Last Laugh. Emil Jannings. You wouldn't remember that one, Miss Cressy."

"Spring, Beautiful Spring," she said. "No, I never saw it."

He walked three steps away from her and turned. "I have to go upstairs and palm door-knobs. I hope I didn't bother you. You ought to go to bed now. It's pretty late."

The tinsel waltz stopped and a voice began to talk. The girl spoke through the voice, "You really thought something like that—about the balcony?"

He nodded. "I might have," he said softly. "I don't any more."

"No chance, Tony." Her smile was a dim lost leaf. "Come and talk to me some more. Redheads don't jump, Tony. They hang on—and wither."

He looked at her gravely for a moment and then moved away over the carpet. The porter was standing in the archway that led to the main lobby. Tony hadn't looked that way yet, but he knew somebody was there. He always knew if anybody was close to him. He could hear the grass grow, like the donkey in The Blue Bird.

The porter jerked his chin at him urgently. His broad face above the uniform collar looked sweaty and excited. Tony stepped up close to him and they went together through the arch and out to the middle of the dim lobby.

"Trouble?" Tony asked wearily.

"There's a guy outside to see you, Tony. He won't come in. I'm doing a wipe-off on the plate glass of the doors and he comes up beside me, a tall guy. 'Get Tony,' he says, out of the side of his mouth."

Tony said: "Uh-huh," and looked at the porter's pale blue eyes. "Who was it?"

"Al, he said to say he was."

Tony's face became as expressionless as dough. "Okey." He started to move off.

The porter caught his sleeve. "Listen, Tony. You got any enemies?"

Tony laughed politely, his face still like dough.

"Listen, Tony." The porter held his sleeve tightly. "There's a big black car down the block, the other way from the hacks. There's a guy standing beside it with his foot on the running board. This guy that spoke to me, he wears a dark-colored, wrap-around overcoat with a high collar turned up against his ears. His hat's way low. You can't hardly see his face. He says, 'Get Tony,' out of the side of his mouth. You ain't got any enemies, have you, Tony?"

"Only the finance company," Tony said. "Beat it."

He walked slowly and a little stiffly across the blue carpet, up the three shallow steps to the entrance lobby with the three elevators on one side and the desk on the other. Only one elevator was working. Beside the open doors, his arms folded, the night operator stood silent in a neat blue uniform with silver facings. A lean, dark Mexican named Gomez. A new boy, breaking in on the night shift.

The other side was the desk, rose marble, with the night clerk leaning on it delicately. A small neat man with a wispy reddish mustache and cheeks so rosy they looked roughed. He stared at Tony and poked a nail at his mustache.

Tony pointed a stiff index finger at him, folded the other three fingers tight to his palm, and flicked his thumb up and down on the stiff finger. The clerk touched the other side of his mustache and looked bored.

Tony went on past the closed and darkened newsstand and the side entrance to the drugstore, out to the brassbound plate-glass doors. He stopped just inside them and took a deep, hard breath. He squared his shoulders, pushed the doors open and stepped out into the cold, damp, night air.

The street was dark, silent. The rumble of traffic on Wilshire, two blocks away, had no body, no meaning. To the left were two taxis. Their drivers leaned against a fender, side by side, smoking. Tony walked the other way. The big dark car was a third of a block from the hotel entrance. Its lights were dimmed and it was only when he was almost up to it that he heard the gentle sound of its engine turning over.

A tall figure detached itself from the body of the car and strolled toward him, both hands in the pockets of the dark overcoat with the high collar. From the man's mouth a cigarette tip glowed faintly, a rusty pearl.

They stopped two feet from each other.

The tall man said: "Hi, Tony. Long time no see."

"Hello, Al. How's it going?"

"Can't complain." The tall man started to take his right hand out of his overcoat pocket, then stopped and laughed quietly. "I forgot. Guess you don't want to shake hands."

"That don't mean anything," Tony said. "Shaking hands. Monkeys can shake hands. What's on your mind, Al?"

"Still the funny little fat guy, eh, Tony?"

"I guess." Tony winked his eyes tight. His throat felt tight.

"You like your job back there?"

"It's a job."

Al laughed his quiet laugh again. "You take it slow, Tony. I'll take it fast. So it's a job and you want to hold it. Oke. There's a girl named Eve Cressy flopping in your quiet hotel. Get her out. Fast and right now."

"What's the trouble?"

The tall man looked up and down the street. A man behind in the car coughed lightly. "She's hooked with a wrong number. Nothing against her personal, but she'll lead trouble to you. Get her out, Tony. You got maybe an hour."

"Sure," Tony said aimlessly, without meaning.

Al took his hand out of his pocket and stretched it against Tony's chest. He gave him a light lazy push. "I wouldn't be telling you just for the hell of it, little fat brother. Get her out of there."

"Okey," Tony said, without any tone in his voice.

The tall man took back his hand and reached for the car door. He opened it and started to slip in like a lean black shadow.

Then he stopped and said something to the men in the car and got out again. He came back to where Tony stood silent, his pale eyes catching a little dim light from the street.

"Listen, Tony. You always kept your nose clean. You're a good brother, Tony."

Tony didn't speak.

Al leaned toward him, a long urgent shadow, the high collar almost touching his ears. "It's trouble business, Tony. The boys won't like it, but I'm telling you just the same. This Cressy was married to a lad named Johnny Ralls. Ralls is out of Quentin two, three days, or a week. He did a three-spot for manslaughter. The girl put him there. He ran down an old man one night when he was drunk, and she was with him. He wouldn't stop. She told him to go in and tell it, or else. He didn't go in. So the Johns come for him."

Tony said, "That's too bad."

"It's kosher, kid. It's my business to know. This Ralls flapped his mouth in stir about how the girl would be waiting for him when he got out, all set to forgive and forget, and he was going straight to her."

Tony said: "What's he to you?" His voice had a dry, stiff crackle, like thick paper.

Al laughed. "The trouble boys want to see him. He ran a table at a spot on the Strip and figured out a scheme. He and another guy took the house for fifty grand. The other lad coughed up, but we still need Johnny's twenty-five. The trouble boys don't get paid to forget."

Tony looked up and down the dark street. One of the taxi drivers flicked a cigarette stub in a long arc over the top of one of the cabs. Tony watched it fall and spark on the pavement. He listened to the quiet sound of the big car's motor.

"I don't want any part of it," he said. "I'll get her out."

Al backed away from him, nodding. "Wise kid. How's mom these days?"

"Okey," Tony said.

"Tell her I was asking for her."

"Asking for her isn't anything," Tony said.

Al turned quickly and got into the car. The car curved lazily in the middle of the block and drifted back toward the corner. Its lights went up and sprayed on a wall. It turned a corner and was gone. The lingering smell of its exhaust drifted past Tony's nose. He turned and walked back to the hotel, and into it. He went along to the radio room.

The radio still muttered, but the girl was gone from the davenport in front of it. The pressed cushions were hollowed out by her body. Tony reached down and touched them. He thought they were still warm. He turned the radio off and stood there, turning a thumb slowly in front of his body, his hand flat against his stomach. Then he went back through the lobby toward the elevator bank and stood beside a majolica jar of white sand. The clerk fussed behind a pebbled-glass screen at one end of the desk. The air was dead.

The elevator bank was dark. Tony looked at the indicator of the middle car and saw that it was at 14.

"Gone to bed," he said under his breath.

The door of the porter's room beside the elevators opened and the little Mexican night operator came out in street clothes. He looked at Tony with a quiet sidewise look out of eyes the color of dried-out chestnuts.

"Good night, boss."

"Yeah," Tony said absently.

He took a thin dappled cigar out of his vest pocket and smelled it. He examined it slowly, turning it around in his neat fingers. There was a small tear along the side. He frowned at that and put the cigar away.

There was a distant sound and the hand on the indicator began to steal around the bronze dial. Light glittered up in the shaft and the straight line of the car floor dissolved the darkness below. The car stopped and the doors opened, and Carl came out of it.

His eyes caught Tony's with a kind of jump and he walked over to him, his head on one side, a thin shine along his pink upper lip.

"Listen, Tony."

Tony took his arm in a hard swift hand and turned him. He pushed him quickly, yet somehow casually, down the steps to the dim main lobby and steered him into a corner. He let go of the arm. His throat tightened again, for no reason he could think of.

"Well?" he said darkly. "Listen to what?"

The porter reached into a pocket and hauled out a dollar bill. "He gimme this," he said loosely. His glittering eyes looked past Tony's shoulder at nothing. They winked rapidly. "Ice and ginger ale."

"Don't stall," Tony growled.

"Guy in 14B," the porter said.

"Lemme smell your breath."

The porter leaned toward him obediently.

"Liquor," Tony said harshly.

"He gimme a drink."

Tony looked down at the dollar bill. "Nobody's in 14B. Not on my list," he said.

"Yeah. There is." The porter licked his lips and his eyes opened and shut several times. "Tall dark guy."

"All right," Tony said crossly. "All right. There's a tall dark guy in 14B and he gave you a buck and a drink. Then what?"

"Gat under his arm," Carl said, and blinked.

Tony smiled, but his eyes had taken on the lifeless glitter of thick ice. "You take Miss Cressy up to her room?"

Carl shook his head. "Gomez. I saw her go up."

"Get away from me," Tony said between his teeth. "And don't accept any more drinks from the guests."

He didn't move until Carl had gone back into his cubbyhole by the elevators and shut the door. Then he moved silently up the three steps and stood in front of the desk, looking at the veined rose marble, the onyx pen set, the fresh registration card in its leather frame. He lifted a hand and smacked it down hard on the marble. The clerk popped out from behind the glass screen like a chipmunk coming out of its hole.

Tony took a flimsy out of his breast pocket and spread it on the desk. "No 14B on this," he said in a bitter voice.

The clerk wisped politely at his mustache. "So sorry. You must have been out to supper when he checked in."

"Who?"

"Registered as James Watterson, San Diego." The clerk yawned.

"Ask for anybody?"

The clerk stopped in the middle of the yawn and looked at the top of Tony's head. "Why, yes. He asked for a swing band. Why?"

"Smart, fast and funny," Tony said. "If you like 'em that way." He wrote on his flimsy and stuffed it back into his pocket. "I'm going upstairs and palm doorknobs. There's four tower rooms you ain't rented yet. Get up on your toes, son. You're slipping."

"I make out," the clerk drawled, and completed his yawn. "Hurry back, pop. I don't know how I'll get through the time."

"You could shave that pink fuzz off your lip," Tony said, and went across to the elevators.

He opened up a dark one and lit the dome light and shot the car up to fourteen. He darkened it again, stepped out and closed the doors. This lobby was smaller than any other, except the one imme-

diately below it. It had a single blue-paneled door in each of the
walls other than the elevator wall. On each door was a gold number
and letter with a gold wreath around it. Tony walked over to 14A
and put his ear to the panel. He heard nothing. Eve Cressy might be
in bed asleep, or in the bathroom, or out on the balcony. Or she
might be sitting there in the room, a few feet from the door, looking
at the wall. Well, he wouldn't expect to be able to hear her sit and
look at the wall. He went over to 14B and put his ear to that panel.
This was different. There was a sound in there. A man coughed. It
sounded somehow like a solitary cough. There were no voices. Tony
pressed the small nacre button beside the door.

Steps came without hurry. A thickened voice spoke through the
panel. Tony made no answer, no sound. The thickened voice repeated the question. Lightly, maliciously, Tony pressed the bell
again.

Mr. James Watterson, of San Diego, should now open the door
and give forth noise. He didn't. A silence fell beyond that door that
was like the silence of a glacier. Once more Tony put his ear to the
wood. Silence utterly.

He got out a master key on a chain and pushed it delicately into
the lock of the door. He turned it, pushed the door inward three
inches and withdrew the key. Then he waited.

"All right," the voice said harshly. "Come in and get it."

Tony pushed the door wide and stood there, framed against the
light from the lobby. The man was tall, black-haired, angular and
white-faced. He held a gun. He held it as though he knew about
guns.

"Step right in," he drawled.

Tony went in through the door and pushed it shut with his shoulder. He kept his hands a little out from his sides, the clever fingers
curled and slack. He smiled his quiet little smile.

"Mr. Watterson?"

"And after that what?"

"I'm the house detective here."

"It slays me."

The tall, white-faced, somehow handsome and somehow not handsome man backed slowly into the room. It was a large room with a
low balcony around two sides of it. French doors opened out on the
little, private, open-air balcony that each of the tower rooms had.

There was a grate set for a log fire behind a paneled screen in front of a cheerful davenport. A tall misted glass stood on a hotel tray beside a deep, cozy chair. The man backed toward this and stood in front of it. The large, glistening gun drooped and pointed at the floor.

"It slays me," he said. "I'm in the dump an hour and the house copper gives me the buzz. Okey, sweetheart, look in the closet and bathroom. But she just left."

"You didn't see her yet," Tony said.

The man's bleached face filled with unexpected lines. His thickened voice edged toward a snarl. "Yeah? Who didn't I see yet?"

"A girl named Eve Cressy."

The man swallowed. He put his gun down on the table beside the tray. He let himself down into the chair backwards, stiffly, like a man with a touch of lumbago. Then he leaned forward and put his hands on his kneecaps and smiled brightly between his teeth. "So she got here, huh? I didn't ask about her yet. I'm a careful guy. I didn't ask yet."

"She's been here five days," Tony said. "Waiting for you. She hasn't left the hotel a minute."

The man's mouth worked a little. His smile had a knowing tilt to it. "I got delayed a little up north," he said smoothly. "You know how it is. Visiting old friends. You seem to know a lot about my business, copper."

"That's right, Mr. Ralls."

The man lunged to his feet and his hand snapped at the gun. He stood leaning over, holding it on the table, staring. "Dames talk too much," he said with a muffed sound in his voice, as though he held something soft between his teeth and talked through it.

"Not dames, Mr. Ralls."

"Huh?" The gun slithered on the hard wood of the table. "Talk it up, copper. My mind reader just quit."

"Not dames. Guys. Guys with guns."

The glacier silence fell between them again. The man straightened his body slowly. His face was washed clean of expression, but his eyes were haunted. Tony leaned in front of him, a shortish plump man with a quiet, pale, friendly face and eyes as simple as forest water.

"They never run out of gas—those boys," Johnny Ralls said, and licked at his lip. "Early and late, they work. The old firm never sleeps."

"You know who they are?" Tony said softly.

"I could maybe give nine guesses. And twelve of them would be right."

"The trouble boys," Tony said, and smiled a brittle smile.

"Where is she?" Johnny Ralls asked harshly.

"Right next door to you."

The man walked to the wall and left his gun lying on the table. He stood in front of the wall, studying it. He reached up and gripped the grillwork of the balcony railing. When he dropped his hand and turned, his face had lost some of its lines. His eyes had a quieter glint. He moved back to Tony and stood over him.

"I've got a stake," he said. "Eve sent me some dough and I built it up with a touch I made up north. Case dough, what I mean. The trouble boys talk about twenty-five grand." He smiled crookedly. "Five C's I can count. I'd have a lot of fun making them believe that, I would."

"What did you do with it?" Tony asked indifferently.

"I never had it, copper. Leave that lay. I'm the only guy in the world that believes it. It was a little deal I got suckered on."

"I'll believe it," Tony said.

"They don't kill often. But they can be awful tough."

"Mugs," Tony said with a sudden bitter contempt. "Guys with guns. Just mugs."

Johnny Ralls reached for his glass and drained it empty. The ice cubes tinkled softly as he put it down. He picked his gun up, danced it on his palm, then tucked it, nose down, into an inner breast pocket. He stared at the carpet.

"How come you're telling me this, copper?"

"I thought maybe you'd give her a break."

"And if I wouldn't?"

"I kind of think you will," Tony said.

Johnny Ralls nodded quietly. "Can I get out of here?"

"You could take the service elevator to the garage. You could rent a car. I can give you a card to the garage-man."

"You're a funny little guy," Johnny Ralls said.

Tony took out a worn ostrich-skin billfold and scribbled on a printed card. Johnny Ralls read it, and stood holding it, tapping it against a thumbnail.

"I could take her with me," he said, his eyes narrow.

"You could take a ride in a basket too," Tony said. "She's been here five days, I told you. She's been spotted. A guy I know called me up and told me to get her out of here. Told me what it was all about. So I'm getting you out instead."

"They'll love that," Johnny Ralls said. "They'll send you violets."

"I'll weep about it on my day off."

Johnny Ralls turned his hand over and stared at the palm. "I could see her, anyway. Before I blow. Next door to here, you said?"

Tony turned on his heel and started for the door. He said over his shoulder, "Don't waste a lot of time, handsome. I might change my mind."

The man said, almost gently: "You might be spotting me right now, for all I know."

Tony didn't turn his head. "That's a chance you have to take."

He went on to the door and passed out of the room. He shut it carefully, silently, looked once at the door of 14A and got into his dark elevator. He rode it down to the linen-room floor and got out to remove the basket that held the service elevator open at that floor. The door slid quietly shut. He held it so that it made no noise. Down the corridor, light came from the open door of the housekeeper's office. Tony got back into his elevator and went on down to the lobby.

The little clerk was out of sight behind his pebbled-glass screen, auditing accounts. Tony went through the main lobby and turned into the radio room. The radio was on again, soft. She was there, curled on the davenport again. The speaker hummed to her, a vague sound so low that what it said was as wordless as the murmur of trees. She turned her head slowly and smiled at him.

"Finished palming doorknobs? I couldn't sleep worth a nickel. So I came down again. Okey?"

He smiled and nodded. He sat down in a green chair and patted the plump brocade arms of it. "Sure, Miss Cressy."

"Waiting is the hardest kind of work, isn't it? I wish you'd talk to that radio. It sounds like a pretzel being bent."

Tony fiddled with it, got nothing he liked, set it back where it had been.

"Beer-parlor drunks are all the customers now."

She smiled at him again.

"I don't bother you being here, Miss Cressy?"

"I like it. You're a sweet little guy, Tony."

He looked stiffly at the floor and a ripple touched his spine. He waited for it to go away. It went slowly. Then he sat back, relaxed again, his neat fingers clasped on his elk's tooth. He listened. Not to the radio—to far-off, uncertain things, menacing things. And perhaps to just the safe whir of wheels going away into a strange night.

"Nobody's all bad," he said out loud.

The girl looked at him lazily. "I've met two or three I was wrong on, then."

He nodded. "Yeah," he admitted judiciously. "I guess there's some that are."

The girl yawned and her deep violet eyes half closed. She nestled back into the cushions. "Sit there a while, Tony. Maybe I could nap."

"Sure. Not a thing for me to do. Don't know why they pay me."

She slept quickly and with complete stillness, like a child. Tony hardly breathed for ten minutes. He just watched her, his mouth a little open. There was a quiet fascination in his limpid eyes, as if he was looking at an altar.

Then he stood up with infinite care and padded away under the arch to the entrance lobby and the desk. He stood at the desk listening for a little while. He heard a pen rustling out of sight. He went around the corner to the row of house phones in little glass cubbyholes. He lifted one and asked the night operator for the garage.

It rang three or four times and then a boyish voice answered; "Windermere Hotel. Garage speaking."

"This is Tony Reseck. That guy Watterson I gave a card to. He leave?"

"Sure, Tony. Half an hour almost. Is it your charge?"

"Yeah," Tony said. "My party. Thanks. Be seein' you."

He hung up and scratched his neck. He went back to the desk and slapped a hand on it. The clerk wafted himself around the screen with his greeter's smile in place. It dropped when he saw Tony.

"Can't a guy catch up on his work?" he grumbled.

"What's the professional rate on 14B?"

The clerk stared morosely. "There's no professional rate in the tower."

"Make one. The fellow left already. Was there only an hour."

"Well, well," the clerk said airily. "So the personality didn't click tonight. We get a skip-out."

"Will five bucks satisfy you?"

"Friend of yours?"

"No. Just a drunk with delusions of grandeur and no dough."

"Guess we'll have to let it ride, Tony. How did he get out?"

"I took him down the service elevator. You was asleep. Will five bucks satisfy you?"

"Why?"

The worn ostrich-skin wallet came out and a weedy five slipped across the marble. "All I could shake him for," Tony said loosely.

The clerk took the five and looked puzzled. "You're the boss," he said, and shrugged. The phone shrilled on the desk and he reached for it. He listened and then pushed it toward Tony. "For you."

Tony took the phone and cuddled it close to his chest. He put his mouth close to the transmitter. The voice was strange to him. It had a metallic sound. Its syllables were meticulously anonymous.

"Tony? Tony Reseck?"

"Talking."

"A message from Al. Shoot?"

Tony looked at the clerk. "Be a pal," he said over the mouthpiece. The clerk flicked a narrow smile at him and went away. "Shoot," Tony said into the phone.

"We had a little business with a guy in your place. Picked him up scramming. Al had a hunch you'd run him out. Tailed him and took him to the curb. Not so good. Backfire."

Tony held the phone very tight and his temples chilled with the evaporation of moisture. "Go on," he said. "I guess there's more."

"A little. The guy stopped the big one. Cold. Al—Al said to tell you good-by."

Tony leaned hard against the desk. His mouth made a sound that was not speech.

"Get it?" The metallic voice sounded impatient, a little bored. "This guy had him a rod. He used it. Al won't be phoning anybody any more."

Tony lurched at the phone, and the base of it shook on the rose marble. His mouth was a hard dry knot.

The voice said: "That's as far as we go, bud. G'night." The phone clicked dryly, like a pebble hitting a wall.

Tony put the phone down in its cradle very carefully, so as not to make any sound. He looked at the clenched palm of his left hand. He took a handkerchief out and rubbed the palm softly and straightened the fingers out with his other hand. Then he wiped his forehead. The clerk came around the screen again and looked at him with glinting eyes.

"I'm off Friday. How about lending me that phone number?"

Tony nodded at the clerk and smiled a minute frail smile. He put his handkerchief away and patted the pocket he had put it in. He turned and walked away from the desk, across the entrance lobby, down the three shallow steps, along the shadowy reaches of the main lobby, and so in through the arch to the radio room once more. He walked softly, like a man moving in a room where somebody is very sick. He reached the chair he had sat in before and lowered himself into it inch by inch. The girl slept on, motionless, in that curled-up looseness achieved by some women and all cats. Her breath made no slightest sound against the vague murmur of the radio.

Tony Reseck leaned back in the chair and clasped his hands on his elk's tooth and quietly closed his eyes.

5
POETRY

Dover Beach

The sea is calm to-night.
The tide is full, the moon lies fair
Upon the straits;—on the French coast the light
Gleams and is gone; the cliffs of England stand,
Glimmering and vast, out in the tranquil bay.
Come to the window, sweet is the night-air!
Only, from the long line of spray
Where the sea meets the moon-blanched land,
Listen! you hear the grating roar
Of pebbles which the waves draw back, and fling,
At their return, up the high strand,
Begin, and cease, and then again begin,
With tremulous cadence slow, and bring
The eternal note of sadness in.

Sophocles long ago
Heard it on the Ægean, and it brought
Into his mind the turbid ebb and flow
Of human misery; we
Find also in the sound a thought,
Hearing it by this distant northern sea.
The Sea of Faith
Was once, too, at the full, and round earth's shore
Lay like the folds of a bright girdle furled.
But now I only hear
Its melancholy, long, withdrawing roar,
Retreating, to the breath
Of the night-wind, down the vast edges drear
And naked shingles of the world.

Ah, love, let us be true
To one another! for the world, which seems
To lie before us like a land of dreams,
So various, so beautiful, so new,
Hath really neither joy, nor love, nor light,

Nor certitude, nor peace, nor help for pain;
And we are here as on a darkling plain
Swept with confused alarms of struggle and flight,
Where ignorant armies clash by night.

—Matthew Arnold

As I Walked Out One Evening

As I walked out one evening,
  Walking down Bristol Street,
The crowds upon the pavement
  Were fields of harvest wheat.

And down by the brimming river
  I heard a lover sing
Under an arch of the railway:
  "Love has no ending.

I'll love you, dear, I'll love you
  Till China and Africa meet
And the river jumps over the mountain
  And the salmon sing in the street.

I'll love you till the ocean
  Is folded and hung up to dry
And the seven stars go squawking
  Like geese about the sky.

The years shall run like rabbits
  For in my arms I hold
The Flower of the Ages
  And the first love of the world."

But all the clocks in the city
  Began to whirr and chime:
"O let not Time deceive you,
  You cannot conquer Time.

In the burrows of the Nightmare
  Where Justice naked is,
Time watches from the shadow
  And coughs when you would kiss.

In headaches and in worry
 Vaguely life leaks away,
And Time will have his fancy
 To-morrow or to-day.

Into many a green valley
 Drifts the appalling snow;
Time breaks the threaded dances
 And the diver's brilliant bow.

O plunge your hands in water,
 Plunge them in up to the wrist;
Stare, stare in the basin
 And wonder what you've missed.

The glacier knocks in the cupboard,
 The desert sighs in the bed,
And the crack in the tea-cup opens
 A lane to the land of the dead.

Where the beggars raffle the banknotes
 And the Giant is enchanting to Jack,
And the Lily-white Boy is a Roarer
 And Jill goes down on her back.

O look, look in the mirror,
 O look in your distress;
Life remains a blessing
 Although you cannot bless.

O stand, stand at the window
 As the tears scald and start:
You shall love your crooked neighbour
 With your crooked heart."

It was late, late in the evening,
 The lovers they were gone;
The clocks had ceased their chiming
 And the deep river ran on.

                              —*W. H. Auden*

The Ballad of William Sycamore

My father, he was a mountaineer,
His fist was a knotty hammer;
He was quick on his feet as a running deer,
And he spoke with a Yankee stammer.

My mother, she was merry and brave,
And so she came to her labor,
With a tall green fir for her doctor grave
And a stream for her comforting neighbor.

And some are wrapped in the linen fine,
And some like a godling's scion;
But I was cradled on twigs of pine
In the skin of a mountain lion.

And some remember a white, starched lap
And a ewer with silver handles;
But I remember a coonskin cap
And the smell of bayberry candles.

The cabin logs, with the bark still rough,
And my mother who laughed at trifles,
And the tall, lank visitors, brown as snuff,
With their long, straight squirrel-rifles.

I can hear them dance, like a foggy song,
Through the deepest one of my slumbers,
The fiddle squeaking the boots along
And my father calling the numbers.

The quick feet shaking the puncheon-floor,
The fiddle squeaking and squealing,
Till the dried herbs rattled above the door
And the dust went up to the ceiling.

There are children lucky from dawn till dusk,
But never a child so lucky!
For I cut my teeth on "Money Musk"
In the Bloody Ground of Kentucky!

When I grew tall as the Indian corn,
My father had little to lend me,
But he gave me his great, old powder-horn
And his woodsman's skill to befriend me.

With a leather shirt to cover my back,
And a redskin nose to unravel
Each forest sign, I carried my pack
As far as a scout could travel.

Till I lost my boyhood and found my wife,
A girl like a Salem clipper!
A woman straight as a hunting-knife
With eyes as bright as the Dipper!

We cleared our camp where the buffalo feed,
Unheard-of streams were our flagons;
And I sowed my sons like apple-seed
On the trail of the Western wagons.

They were right, tight boys, never sulky or slow,
A fruitful, a goodly muster.
The eldest died at the Alamo.
The youngest fell with Custer.

The letter that told it burned my hand.
Yet we smiled and said, "So be it!"
But I could not live when they fenced the land,
For it broke my heart to see it.

I saddled a red, unbroken colt
And rode him into the day there;
And he threw me down like a thunderbolt
And rolled on me as I lay there.

The hunter's whistle hummed in my ear
As the city-men tried to move me,
And I died in my boots like a pioneer
With the whole wide sky above me.

Now I lie in the heart of the fat, black soil,
Like the seed of a prairie-thistle;
It has washed my bones with honey and oil
And picked them clean as a whistle.

And my youth returns, like the rains of Spring,
And my sons, like the wild-geese flying;
And I lie and hear the meadow-lark sing
And have much content in my dying.

Go play with the towns you have built of blocks
The towns where you would have bound me!
I sleep in my earth like a tired fox,
And my buffalo have found me.

—Stephen Vincent Benét

Heaven

Fish (fly-replete, in depth of June,
Dawdling away their wat'ry noon)
Ponder deep wisdom, dark or clear,
Each secret fishy hope or fear.
Fish say, they have their Stream and Pond;
But is there anything Beyond?
This life cannot be All, they swear,
For how unpleasant, if it were!
One may not doubt that, somehow, Good
Shall come of Water and of Mud;
And, sure, the reverent eye must see
A Purpose in Liquidity.
We darkly know, by Faith we cry,
The future is not Wholly Dry.
Mud unto mud!—Death eddies near—
Not here the appointed End, not here!
But somewhere, beyond Space and Time.
Is wetter water, slimier slime!
And there (they trust) there swimmeth One
Who swam ere rivers were begun,
Immense, of fishy form and mind,
Squamous, omnipotent, and kind;
And under that Almighty Fin,
The littlest fish may enter in.
Oh! never fly conceals a hook,
Fish say, in the Eternal Brook,
But more than mundane weeds are there,
And mud, celestially fair;

Fat caterpillars drift around,
And Paradisal grubs are found;
Unfading moths, immortal flies,
And the worm that never dies.
And in that Heaven of all their wish,
There shall be no more land, say fish.

—Rupert Brooke

We'll Go No More A-Roving

So, we'll go no more a-roving
  So late into the night,
Though the heart be still as loving,
  And the moon be still as bright.

For the sword outwears its sheath,
  And the soul wears out the breast,
And the heart must pause to breathe,
  And love itself have rest.

Though the night was made for loving,
  And the day returns too soon,
Yet we'll go no more a-roving
  By the light of the moon.

—Lord Byron

Break of Day

Stay, O sweet, and do not rise;
The light that shines comes from thine eyes;
The day breaks not, it is my heart,
Because that you and I must part.
  Stay, or else my joys will die
  And perish in their infancy.

—John Donne

Go and Catch a Falling Star

Go and catch a falling star,
  Get with child a mandrake root,
Tell me where all past years are,
  Or who cleft the devil's foot;
Teach me to hear mermaids singing,
Or to keep off envy's stinging,
    And find
    What wind
Serves to advance an honest mind.

If thou be'st born to strange sights,
  Things invisible go see,
Ride ten thousand days and nights
  Till Age snow white hairs on thee;
Thou, when thou return'st, wilt tell me
All strange wonders that befell thee,
    And swear
    No where
Lives a woman true and fair.

If thou find'st one, let me know;
  Such a pilgrimage were sweet.
Yet do not; I would not go,
  Though at next door we might meet.
Though she were true when you met her,
And last till you write your letter,
    Yet she
    Will be
False, ere I come, to two or three.

                              —*John Donne*

The Road Not Taken

Two roads diverged in a yellow wood,
And sorry I could not travel both
And be one traveler, long I stood
And looked down one as far as I could
To where it bent in the undergrowth;

Then took the other, as just as fair,
And having perhaps the better claim,
Because it was grassy and wanted wear;
Though as for that the passing there
Had worn them really about the same,

And both that morning equally lay
In leaves no step had trodden black.
Oh, I kept the first for another day!
Yet knowing how way leads on to way,
I doubted if I should ever come back.

I shall be telling this with a sigh
Somewhere ages and ages hence:
Two roads diverged in a wood, and I—
I took the one less traveled by,
And that has made all the difference.

—*Robert Frost*

Delight in Disorder

A sweet disorder in the dress
Kindles in clothes a wantonness:
A lawn about the shoulders thrown
Into a fine distraction,
An erring lace, which here and there
Enthrals the crimson stomacher,
A cuff neglectful, and thereby
Ribbands to flow confusedly,
A winning wave (deserving note)
In the tempestuous petticoat,
A careless shoe-string, in whose tie
I see a wild civility,
Do more bewitch me, than when art
Is too precise in every part.

—*Robert Herrick*

To the Virgins, to Make Much of Time

Gather ye rosebuds while ye may,
  Old Time is still a-flying:
And this same flower that smiles to-day
  To-morrow will be dying.

The glorious lamp of heaven, the sun,
  The higher he's a-getting,
The sooner will his race be run,
  And nearer he's to setting.

That age is best which is the first,
  When youth and blood are warmer;
But being spent, the worse, and worst
  Times still succeed the former.

Then be not coy, but use your time,
  And while ye may, go marry:
For having lost but once your prime,
  You may for ever tarry.
                                    —*Robert Herrick*

Six Poems from A. E. Housman's
"A Shropshire Lad"

REVEILLE

Wake: the silver dusk returning
  Up the beach of darkness brims,
And the ship of sunrise burning
  Strands upon the eastern rims.

Wake: the vaulted shadow shatters,
  Trampled to the floor it spanned,
And the tent of night in tatters
  Straws the sky-pavilioned land.

Up, lad, up, 'tis late for lying:
    Hear the drums of morning play;
Hark, the empty highways crying
    'Who'll beyond the hills away?'

Towns and countries woo together,
    Forelands beacon, belfries call;
Never lad that trod on leather
    Lived to feast his heart with all.

Up, lad: thews that lie and cumber
    Sunlit pallets never thrive;
Morns abed and daylight slumber
    Were not meant for man alive.

Clay lies still, but blood's a rover;
    Breath's a ware that will not keep.
Up, lad: when the journey's over
    There'll be time enough to sleep.

2

When I was one-and-twenty
    I heard a wise man say,
'Give crowns and pounds and guineas
    But not your heart away;
Give pearls away and rubies
    But keep your fancy free.'
But I was one-and-twenty,
    No use to talk to me.

When I was one-and-twenty
    I heard him say again,
'The heart out of the bosom
    Was never given in vain;
'Tis paid with sighs a plenty
    And sold for endless rue.'
And I am two-and-twenty,
    And oh, 'tis true, 'tis true.

THE MERRY GUIDE

Once in the wind of morning
　I ranged the thymy wold;
The world-wide air was azure
　And all the brooks ran gold.

There through the dews beside me
　Behold a youth that trod,
With feathered cap on forehead,
　And poised a golden rod.

With mien to match the morning
　And gay delightful guise
And friendly brows and laughter
　He looked me in the eyes.

Oh whence, I asked, and whither?
　He smiled and would not say,
And looked at me and beckoned
　And laughed and led the way.

And with kind looks and laughter
　And nought to say beside
We two went on together,
　I and my happy guide.

Across the glittering pastures
　And empty upland still
And solitude of shepherds
　High in the folded hill,

By hanging woods and hamlets
　That gaze through orchards down
On many a windmill turning
　And far-discovered town,

With gay regards of promise
　And sure unslackened stride
And smiles and nothing spoken
　Led on my merry guide.

By blowing realms of woodland
With sunstruck vanes afield
And cloud-led shadows sailing
About the windy weald,

By valley-guarded granges
And silver waters wide,
Content at heart I followed
With my delightful guide.

And like the cloudy shadows
Across the country blown
We two fare on for ever,
But not we two alone.

With the great gale we journey
That breathes from gardens thinned,
Borne in the drift of blossoms
Whose petals throng the wind;

Buoyed on the heaven-heard whisper
Of dancing leaflets whirled
From all the woods that autumn
Bereaves in all the world.

And midst the fluttering legion
Of all that ever died
I follow, and before us
Goes the delightful guide,

With lips that brim with laughter
But never once respond,
And feet that fly on feathers,
And serpent-circled wand.

4

Be still, my soul, be still; the arms you bear are brittle,
  Earth and high heaven are fixt of old and founded strong.
Think rather,—call to thought, if now you grieve a little,
  The days when we had rest, O soul, for they were long.

Men loved unkindness then, but lightless in the quarry
  I slept and saw not; tears fell down, I did not mourn;
Sweat ran and blood sprang out and I was never sorry:
  Then it was well with me, in days ere I was born.

Now, and I muse for why and never find the reason,
  I pace the earth, and drink the air, and feel the sun.
Be still, be still, my soul; it is but for a season:
  Let us endure an hour and see injustice done.

Ay, look: high heaven and earth ail from the prime foundation;
  All thoughts to rive the heart are here, and all are vain:
Horror and scorn and hate and fear and indignation—
  Oh why did I awake? when shall I sleep again?

5

Think no more, lad; laugh, be jolly:
  Why should men make haste to die?
Empty heads and tongues a-talking
Make the rough road easy walking,
And the feather pate of folly
  Bears the falling sky.

Oh, 'tis jesting, dancing, drinking
  Spins the heavy world around.
If young hearts were not so clever,
Oh, they would be young for ever:
Think no more; 'tis only thinking
  Lays lads underground.

6

With rue my heart is laden
  For golden friends I had,
For many a rose-lipt maiden
  And many a lightfoot lad.

By brooks too broad for leaping
  The lightfoot boys are laid;
The rose-lipt girls are sleeping
  In fields where roses fade.

—*A. E. Housman*

"To One Who Has Been Long in City Pent"

To one who has been long in city pent,
   'Tis very sweet to look into the fair
   And open face of heaven,—to breathe a prayer
Full in the smile of the blue firmament.
Who is more happy, when, with heart's content,
   Fatigued he sinks into some pleasant lair
   Of wavy grass, and reads a debonair
And gentle tale of love and languishment?
Returning home at evening, with an ear
   Catching the notes of Philomel,—an eye
Watching the sailing cloudlet's bright career,
   He mourns that day so soon has glided by:
E'en like the passage of an angel's tear
   That falls through the clear ether silently.

—John Keats

The Long Trail

There's a whisper down the field where the year has shot her yield,
   And the ricks stand grey to the sun,
Singing: "Over then, come over, for the bee has quit the clover,
   "And your English summer's done."

   You have heard the beat of the off-shore wind,
      And the thresh of the deep-sea rain;
   You have heard the song—how long? how long?
   Pull out on the trail again!
Ha' done with the Tents of Shem, dear lass,
   We've seen the seasons through,
And it's time to turn on the old trail, our own trail, the out
   trail,
Pull out, pull out, on the Long Trail—the trail that is always
   new!

It's North you may run to the rime-ringed sun
   Or South to the blind Horn's hate;

Or East all the way into Mississippi Bay,
  Or West to the Golden Gate—
    Where the blindest bluffs hold good, dear lass,
    And the wildest tales are true,
    And the men bulk big on the old trail, our own trail, the out
      trail,
    And life runs large on the Long Trail—the trail that is
      always new.

The days are sick and cold, and the skies are grey and old,
  And the twice-breathed airs blow damp;
And I'd sell my tired soul for the bucking beam-sea roll
  Of a black Bilbao tramp,
    With her load-line over her hatch, dear lass,
    And a drunken Dago crew,
    And her nose held down on the old trail, our own trail, the
      out trail
    From Cadiz south on the Long Trail—the trail that is always
      new.

There be triple ways to take, of the eagle or the snake,
  Or the way of a man with a maid;
But the sweetest way to me is a ship's upon the sea
  In the heel of the North-East Trade.
    Can you hear the crash on her bows, dear lass,
    And the drum of the racing screw,
    As she ships it green on the old trail, our own trail, the out
      trail,
    As she lifts and 'scends on the Long Trail—the trail that is
      always new?

See the shaking funnels roar, with the Peter at the fore,
  And the fenders grind and heave,
And the derricks clack and grate, as the tackle hooks the crate,
  And the fall-rope whines through the sheave;
    It's "Gang-plank up and in," dear lass,
    It's "Hawsers warp her through!"
    And it's "All clear aft" on the old trail, our own trail, the
      out trail,
    We're backing down on the Long Trail—the trail that is
      is always new.

O the mutter overside, when the port-fog holds us tied,
  And the sirens hoot their dread,
When foot by foot we creep o'er the hueless viewless deep
    To the sob of the questing lead!
        It's down by the Lower Hope, dear lass,
        With the Gunfleet Sands in view,
        Till the Mouse swings green on the old trail, our own trail,
          the out trail,
        And the Gull Light lifts on the Long Trail—the trail that is
          always new.

O the blazing tropic night, when the wake's a welt of light
  That holds the hot sky tame,
And the steady fore-foot snores through the planet-powdered floors
  Where the scared whale flukes in flame!
        Her plates are flaked by the sun, dear lass,
        And her ropes are taut with the dew,
        For we're booming down on the old trail, our own trail, the
          out trail,
        We're sagging south on the Long Trail—the trail that is
          always new.

Then home, get her home, where the drunken rollers comb,
  And the shouting seas drive by,
And the engines stamp and ring, and the wet bows reel and swing,
  And the Southern Cross rides high!
        Yes, the old lost stars wheel back, dear lass,
        That blaze in the velvet blue.
        They're all old friends on the old trail, our own trail, the
          out trail,
        They're God's own guide on the Long Trail—the trail that is
          always new.

Fly forward, O my heart, from the Foreland to the Start—
  We're steaming all too slow,
And it's twenty thousand mile to our little lazy isle
  Where the trumpet-orchids blow!
        You have heard the call of the off-shore wind
        And the voice of the deep-sea rain;
        You have heard the song. How long—how long?
        Pull out on the trail again!

The Lord knows what we may find, dear lass,
And The Deuce knows what we may do—
But we're back once more on the old trail, our own trail, the out
    trail,
We're down, hull-down, on the Long Trail—the trail that is always
    new!

—Rudyard Kipling

The Flower-Fed Buffaloes

The flower-fed buffaloes of the spring
In the days of long ago,
Ranged where the locomotives sing
And the prairie flowers lie low;
The tossing, blooming, perfumed grass
Is swept away by wheat,
Wheels and wheels and wheels spin by
In the spring that still is sweet.
But the flower-fed buffaloes of the spring
Left us long ago.
They gore no more, they bellow no more,
They trundle around the hills no more:—
With the Blackfeet lying low,
With the Pawnees lying low.

—Vachel Lindsay

My Lost Youth

Often I think of the beautiful town
    That is seated by the sea;
Often in thought go up and down
The pleasant streets of that dear old town,
    And my youth comes back to me,
        And a verse of a Lapland song
        Is haunting my memory still:
    "A boy's will is the wind's will,
    And the thoughts of youth are long, long thoughts."

I can see the shadowy lines of its trees,
  And catch, in sudden gleams,
The sheen of the far-surrounding seas,
And islands that were the Hesperides
  Of all my boyish dreams.
    And the burden of that old song,
    It murmurs and whispers still:
  "A boy's will is the wind's will,
And the thoughts of youth are long, long thoughts."

I remember the black wharves and the slips,
  And the sea-tides tossing free;
And Spanish sailors with bearded lips,
And the beauty and mystery of the ships,
  And the magic of the sea.
    And the voice of that wayward song,
    Is singing and saying still:
  "A boy's will is the wind's will,
And the thoughts of youth are long, long thoughts."

I remember the bulwarks by the shore,
  And the fort upon the hill;
The sunrise gun, with its hollow roar,
The drum-beat repeated o'er and o'er,
  And the bugle wild and shrill.
    And the music of that old song
    Throbs in my memory still;
  "A boy's will is the wind's will,
And the thoughts of youth are long, long thoughts."

I remember the sea-fight far away,
  How it thundered o'er the tide!
And the dead captains, as they lay
In their graves, o'erlooking the tranquil bay,
  Where they in battle died.
    And the sound of that mournful song
    Goes through me with a thrill:
  "A boy's will is the wind's will,
And the thoughts of youth are long, long thoughts."

I can see the breezy dome of groves,
  The shadows of Deering's Woods;
And the friendships old and the early loves
Come back with a Sabbath sound, as of doves

In quiet neighbourhoods.
   And the verse of that sweet old song,
     It flutters and murmurs still:
"A boy's will is the wind's will,
And the thoughts of youth are long, long thoughts."

I remember the gleams and glooms that dart
   Across the schoolboy's brain;
The song and the silence in the heart,
That in part are prophecies, and in part
   Are longings wild and vain.
     And the voice of that fitful song
     Sings on, and is never still:
"A boy's will is the wind's will,
And the thoughts of youth are long, long thoughts."

There are things of which I may not speak;
   There are dreams that cannot die;
There are thoughts that make the strong heart weak,
And bring a pallor into the cheek,
   And a mist before the eye.
     And the words of that fatal song
     Come over me like a chill:
"A boy's will is the wind's will,
And the thoughts of youth are long, long thoughts."

Strange to me now are the forms I meet
   When I visit the dear old town;
But the native air is pure and sweet,
And the trees that o'ershadow each well-known street,
   As they balance up and down,
     Are singing the beautiful song,
     Are sighing and whispering still:
"A boy's will is the wind's will,
And the thoughts of youth are long, long thoughts."

And Deering's Woods are fresh and fair,
   And with joy that is almost pain
My heart goes back to wander there,
And among the dreams of the days that were,
   I find my lost youth again.

And the strange and beautiful song,
The groves are repeating it still:
"A boy's will is the wind's will,
And the thoughts of youth are long, long thoughts."
—*Henry Wadsworth Longfellow*

To His Coy Mistress

Had we but world enough, and time,
This coyness, Lady, were no crime.
We would sit down, and think which way
To walk, and pass our long love's day.
Thou by the Indian Ganges' side
Shouldst rubies find; I by the tide
Of Humber would complain. I would
Love you ten years before the Flood;
And you should, if you please, refuse
Till the conversion of the Jews.
My vegetable love should grow
Vaster than empires, and more slow;
An hundred years should go to praise
Thine eyes and on thy forehead gaze;
Two hundred to adore each breast;
But thirty thousand to the rest:
An age, at least, to every part,
And the last age should show your heart.
For, Lady, you deserve this state;
Nor would I love at lower rate.
    But, at my back, I always hear
Time's winged chariot hurrying near:
And yonder, all before us lie
Deserts of vast eternity.
Thy beauty shall no more be found;
Nor, in thy marble vault, shall sound
My echoing song. Then worms shall try
That long preserved virginity:
And your quaint honour turn to dust;
And into ashes all my lust.
The grave's a fine and private place,
But none, I think, do there embrace.

Now, therefore, while the youthful hue
Sits on thy skin like morning dew,
And while thy willing soul transpires
At every pore with instant fires,
Now let us sport us while we may;
And now, like armorous birds of prey,
Rather at once our time devour,
Than languish in his slow-chapt power.
Let us roll all our strength, and all
Our sweetness, up into one ball;
And tear our pleasures, with rough strife,
Thorough the iron gates of life.
Thus, though we cannot make our sun
Stand still, yet we will make him run.

—Andrew Marvell

Sea Fever

I must go down to the seas again, to the lonely sea and the sky,
And all I ask is a tall ship and a star to steer her by;
And the wheel's kick and the wind's song and the white sails shaking,
And a grey mist on the sea's face, and a grey dawn breaking,

I must go down to the seas again, for the call of the running tide
Is a wild call and a clear call that may not be denied;
And all I ask is a windy day with the white clouds flying,
And the flung spray and the blown spume, and the sea-gulls crying.

I must go down to the seas again, to the vagrant gypsy life,
To the gull's way and the whale's way where the wind's like a
      whetted knife;
And all I ask is a merry yarn from a laughing fellow-rover,
And quiet sleep and a sweet dream when the long trick's over.

—John Masefield

You, Andrew Marvell

And here face down beneath the sun
And here upon earth's noonward height
To feel the always coming on
The always rising of the night

To feel creep up the curving east
The earthly chill of dusk and slow
Upon those under lands the vast
And ever-climbing shadow grow

And strange at Ecbatan the trees
Take leaf by leaf the evening strange
The flooding dark about their knees
The mountains over Persia change

And now at Kermanshah the gate
Dark empty and the withered grass
And through the twilight now the late
Few travelers in the westward pass

And Baghdad darken and the bridge
Across the silent river gone
And through Arabia the edge
Of evening widen and steal on

And deepen on Palmyra's street
The wheel rut in the ruined stone
And Lebanon fade out and Crete
High through the clouds and overblown

And over Sicily the air
Still flashing with the landward gulls
And loom and slowly disappear
The sails above the shadowy hulls

And Spain go under and the shore
Of Africa the gilded sand
And evening vanish and no more
The low pale light across that land

Nor now the long light on the sea—
And here face downward in the sun
To feel how swift how secretly
The shadow of the night comes on. . . .

—Archibald Macleish

The Penitent

I had a little Sorrow,
Born of a little Sin,
I found a room all damp with gloom
    And shut us all within;
And, "Little Sorrow, weep," said I,
"And, Little Sin, pray God to die,
And I upon the floor will lie
    And think how bad I've been!"

Alas for pious planning—
    It mattered not a whit!
As far as gloom went in that room,
    The lamp might have been lit!
My Little Sorrow would not weep,
My Little Sin would go to sleep—
To save my soul I could not keep
    My graceless mind on it!

So up I got in anger,
    And took a book I had,
And put a ribbon on my hair
    To please a passing lad.
And, "One thing there's no getting by—
I've been a wicked girl," said I;
"But if I can't be sorry, why,
    I might as well be glad!"
        —Edna St. Vincent Millay

Eight Sonnets
by William Shakespeare

1

When I consider every thing that grows
Holds in perfection but a little moment,
That this huge stage presenteth nought but shows
Whereon the stars in secret influence comment;
When I perceive that men as plants increase,
Cheered and checked even by the self-same sky,

Vaunt in their youthful sap, at height decrease,
And wear their brave state out of memory;
Then the conceit of this inconstant stay
Sets you most rich in youth before my sight,
Where wasteful Time debateth with Decay,
To change your day of youth to sullied night;
 And all in war with Time for love of you,
 As he takes from you, I engraft you new.

2

Shall I compare thee to a summer's day?
Thou art more lovely and more temperate:
Rough winds do shake the darling buds of May,
And summer's lease hath all too short a date:
Sometime too hot the eye of heaven shines,
And often is his gold complexion dimmed;
And every fair from fair sometime declines,
By chance or nature's changing course untrimmed;
But thy eternal summer shall not fade,
Nor lose possession of that fair thou owest;
Nor shall Death brag thou wander'st in his shade,
When in eternal lines to time thou grow'st:
 So long as men can breathe or eyes can see,
 So long lives this, and this gives life to thee.

3

When in disgrace with fortune and men's eyes,
I all alone beweep my outcast state,
And trouble deaf heaven with my bootless cries,
And look upon myself, and curse my fate,
Wishing me like to one more rich in hope,
Featured like him, like him with friends possessed,
Desiring this man's art and that man's scope,
With what I most enjoy contented least;
Yet in these thoughts myself almost despising,
Haply I think on thee, and then my state,
Like to the lark at break of day arising
From sullen earth, sings hymns at heaven's gate;
 For thy sweet love remembered such wealth brings
 That then I scorn to change my state with kings.

4

When to the sessions of sweet silent thought
I summon up remembrance of things past,
I sigh the lack of many a thing I sought,
And with old woes new wail my dear time's waste:
Then can I drown an eye, unused to flow,
For precious friends hid in death's dateless night,
And weep afresh love's long since cancelled woe,
And moan the expense of many a vanished sight:
Then can I grieve at grievances foregone,
And heavily from woe to woe tell o'er
The sad account of fore-bemoaned moan,
Which I new pay as if not paid before.
   But if the while I think on thee, dear friend,
   All losses are restored and sorrows end.

5

Full many a glorious morning have I seen
Flatter the mountain-tops with sovereign eye,
Kissing with golden face the meadows green,
Gilding pale streams with heavenly alchemy;
Anon permit the basest clouds to ride
With ugly rack on his celestial face,
And from the forlorn world his visage hide,
Stealing unseen to west with this disgrace:
Even so my sun one early morn did shine
With all-triumphant splendor on my brow;
But, out, alack! he was but one hour mine,
The region cloud hath masked him from me now.
   Yet him for this my love no whit disdaineth;
   Suns of the world may stain when heaven's sun staineth.

6

When in the chronicle of wasted time
I see descriptions of the fairest wights,
And beauty making beautiful old rhyme
In praise of ladies dead and lovely knights,
Then in the blazon of sweet beauty's best,
Of hand, of foot, of lip, of eye, of brow,

I see their antique pen would have expressed
Even such a beauty as you master now.
So all their praises are but prophecies
Of this our time, all you prefiguring;
And, for they looked but with divining eyes,
They had not skill enough your worth to sing:
    For we which now behold these present days,
    Have eyes to wonder, but lack tongues to praise.

7

Not mine own fears, nor the prophetic soul
Of the wide world dreaming on things to come,
Can yet the lease of my true love control,
Supposed as forfeit to a confined doom.
The mortal moon hath her eclipse endured,
And the sad augurs mock their own presage;
Incertainties now crown themselves assured,
And peace proclaims olives of endless age.
Now with the drops of this most balmy time
My love looks fresh, and Death to me subscribes,
Since spite of him I'll live in this poor rhyme,
While he insults o'er dull and speechless tribes:
    And thou in this shalt find thy monument,
    When tyrants' crests and tombs of brass are spent.

8

Let me not to the marriage of true minds
Admit impediments. Love is not love
Which alters when it alteration finds,
Or bends with the remover to remove:
O, no! it is an ever-fixèd mark,
That looks on tempests and is never shaken;
It is the star to every wandering bark,
Whose worth's unknown, although his height be taken.
Love's not Time's fool, though rosy lips and cheeks
Within his bending sickle's compass come;
Love alters not with his brief hours and weeks,
But bears it out even to the edge of doom.
    If this be error and upon me proved,
    I never writ, nor no man ever loved.
                    —William Shakespeare

Good-Night

Good-night? ah! no; the hour is ill
  Which severs those it should unite;
Let us remain together still,
  Then it will be *good* night.

How can I call the lone night good,
  Though thy sweet wishes wing its flight?
Be it not said, thought, understood,
  Then it will be *good* night.

To hearts which near each other move
  From evening close to morning light,
The night is good; because, my love,
  They never *say* good-night.

          —*Percy Bysshe Shelley*

The Express

After the first powerful plain manifesto
The black statement of pistons, without more fuss
But gliding like a queen, she leaves the station.
Without bowing and with restrained unconcern
She passes the houses which humbly crowd outside,
The gasworks and at last the heavy page
Of death, printed by gravestones in the cemetery.
Beyond the town there lies the open country
Where, gathering speed, she acquires mystery,
The luminous self-possession of ships on ocean.
It is now she begins to sing—at first quite low,
Then loud, and at last with a jazzy madness—
The song of her whistle screaming at curves,
Of deafening tunnels, brakes, innumerable bolts.
And always light, aerial underneath,
Goes the elate metre of her wheels.
Steaming through metal landscape on her lines
She plunges new eras of wild happiness
Where speed throws up strange shapes, broad curves
And parallels clean like the steel of guns.

At last, further than Edinburgh or Rome,
Beyond the crest of the world, she reaches night
Where only a low streamline brightness
Of phosphorus on the tossing hills is white.
Ah, like a comet through flame, she moves entranced
Wrapt in her music no bird song, no, nor bough
Breaking with honey buds, shall ever equal.

—*Stephen Spender*

Why So Pale and Wan?

Why so pale and wan, fond lover?
    Prithee, why so pale?
Will, when looking well can't move her,
    Looking ill prevail?
    Prithee, why so pale?

Why so dull and mute, young sinner?
    Prithee, why so mute?
Will, when speaking well can't win her,
    Saying nothing do 't?
    Prithee, why so mute?

Quit, quit for shame! This will not move;
    This cannot take her.
If of herself she will not love,
    Nothing can make her.
    The devil take her!

—*John Suckling*

Earth

Grasshopper, your fairy song
And my poem alike belong
To the dark and silent earth
From which all poetry has birth.

All we say and all we sing
Is but as the murmuring
Of that drowsy heart of hers
When from her deep dream she stirs:
If we sorrow, or rejoice,
You and I are but her voice.

Deftly does the dust express
In mind her hidden loveliness,
And from her cool silence stream
The cricket's cry and Dante's dream;
For the earth that breeds the trees
Breeds cities too, and symphonies.
Equally her beauty flows
Into a savior, or a rose—

Looks down in dream, and from above
Smiles at herself in Jesus' love.
Christ's love and Homer's art
Are but the workings of her heart;
Through Leonardo's hand she seeks
Herself, and through Beethoven speaks
In holy thunderings around
The awful message of the ground.

The serene and humble mold
Does in herself all selves enfold—
Kingdoms, destinies, and creeds,
Great dreams, and dauntless deeds,
Science that metes the firmament,
The high, inflexible intent
Of one for many sacrificed—
Plato's brain, the heart of Christ;
All love, all legend, and all lore
Are in the dust forevermore.

Even as the growing grass,
Up from the soil religions pass,
And the field that bears the rye
Bears parables and prophecy.
Out of the earth the poem grows
Like the lily, or the rose;
And all man is, or yet may be,

Is but herself in agony
Toiling up the steep ascent
Toward the complete accomplishment
When all dust shall be, the whole
Universe, one conscious soul.

Yea, the quiet and cool sod
Bears in her breast the dream of God.
If you would know what earth is, scan
The intricate, proud heart of man,
Which is the earth articulate,
And learn how holy and how great,
How limitless and how profound
Is the nature of the ground—
How without terror or demur
We may entrust ourselves to her
When we are wearied out and lay
Our faces in the common clay.

For she is pity, she is love,
All wisdom, she, all thoughts that move
About her everlasting breast
Till she gathers them to rest:
All tenderness of all the ages,
Seraphic secrets of the sages,
Vision and hope of all the seers,
All prayer, all anguish, and all tears
Are but the dust that from her dream
Awakes, and knows herself supreme—
Are but earth, when she reveals
All that her secret heart conceals
Down in the dark and silent loam,
Which is ourselves, asleep, at home.
Yea, and this, my poem, too,
Is part of her as dust and dew,
Wherein herself she doth declare
Through my lips, and say her prayer.

                              —*John Hall Wheelock*

Song of the Open Road

1

Afoot and light-hearted, I take to the open road,
Healthy, free, the world before me,
The long brown path before me, leading wherever I choose.

Henceforth I ask not good-fortune—I myself am good-fortune;
Henceforth I whimper no more, postpone no more, need nothing,
Strong and content, I travel the open road.

The earth—that is sufficient;
I do not want the constellations any nearer;
I know they are very well where they are;
I know they suffice for those who belong to them.

Still here I carry my old delicious burdens;
I carry them, men and women—I carry them with me wherever I go;
I swear it is impossible for me to get rid of them;
I am fill'd with them, and I will fill them in return.

2

You road I enter upon and look around! I believe you are not all
    that is here;
I believe that much unseen is also here.

Here is the profound lesson of reception, neither preference or
    denial;
The black with his woolly head, the felon, the diseas'd, the illiterate
    person, are not denied;
The birth, the hasting after the physician, the beggar's tramp, the
    drunkard's stagger, the laughing party of mechanics,
The escaped youth, the rich person's carriage, the fop, the eloping
    couple,
The early market-man, the hearse, the moving of furniture into the
    town, the return back from the town,
They pass, I also pass, anything passes—none can be interdicted,
None but are accepted, none but are dear to me.

3

You air that serves me with breath to speak!
You objects that call from diffusion my meanings and give them
    shape!
You light that wraps me and all things in delicate equable showers!
You animals moving serenely over the earth!
You birds that wing yourselves through the air! you insects!
You sprouting growths from the farmers' fields! you stalks and
    weeds by the fences!
You paths worn in the irregular hollows by the roadsides!
I think you are latent with unseen existences—you are so dear to me.

You flagg'd walks of the cities! you strong curbs at the edges!
You ferries! you planks and posts of wharves! you timber-lined
    sides! you distant ships!
You rows of houses! you window-pierc'd façades! you roofs!
You porches and entrances! you copings and iron guards!
You windows whose transparent shells might expose so much!
You doors and ascending steps! you arches!
You gray stones of interminable pavements! you trodden crossings!
From all that has been near you, I believe you have imparted to
    yourselves, and now would impart the same secretly to me;
From the living and the dead I think you have peopled your im-
    passive surfaces, and the spirits thereof would be evidence and
    amicable with me.

4

The earth expanding right hand and left hand,
The picture alive, every part in its best light,
The music falling in where it is wanted, and stopping where it is
    not wanted,
The cheerful voice of the public road—the gay fresh sentiment of
    the road.

O highway I travel! O public road! do you say to me, Do not leave
    me?
Do you say, Venture not? If you leave me, you are lost?
Do you say, I am already prepared—I am well-beaten and undenied
    —adhere to me?

O public road! I say back, I am not afraid to leave you—yet I love
    you;
You express me better than I can express myself;
You shall be more to me than my poem.

I think heroic deeds were all conceiv'd in the open air;
I think I could stop here myself, and do miracles;
I think whatever I shall meet on the road I shall like, and whoever
    beholds me shall like me;
I think whoever I see must be happy.

5

From this hour, freedom!
From this hour I ordain myself loosed of limits and imaginary lines,
Going where I list—my own master, total and absolute,
Listening to others, and considering well what they say,
Pausing, searching, receiving, contemplating,
Gently, but with undeniable will, divesting myself of the holds that
    would hold me.

I inhale great draughts of air;
The east and the west are mine, and the north and the south are
    mine.

I am larger than I thought;
I did not know I held so much goodness.

All seems beautiful to me;
I can repeat over to men and women, You have done such good to
    me, I would do the same to you.

I will recruit for myself and you as I go;
I will scatter myself among men and women as I go;
I will toss the new gladness and roughness among them;
Whoever denies me, it shall not trouble me;
Whoever accepts me, he or she shall be blessed, and shall bless me.

6

Now if a thousand perfect men were to appear, it would not amaze
    me;
Now if a thousand beautiful forms of women appear'd, it would not
    astonish me.

Now I see the secret of the making of the best persons,
It is to grow in the open air, and to eat and sleep with the earth.

Here is space—here a great personal deed has room;
A great deed seizes upon the hearts of the whole race of men,
Its effusion of strength and will overwhelms law, and mocks all
    authority and all argument against it.
Here is the test of wisdom;
Wisdom is not finally tested in schools;
Wisdom cannot be pass'd from one having it, to another not hav-
    ing it;
Wisdom is of the Soul, is not susceptible of proof, is its own proof,
Applies to all stages and objects and qualities, and is content,
Is the certainty of the reality and immortality of things, and the
    excellence of things;
Something there is in the float of the sight of things that provokes it
    out of the Soul.

Now I reëxamine philosophies and religions,
They may prove well in lecture-rooms, yet not prove at all under the
    spacious clouds, and along the landscape and flowing currents.

Here is realization;
Here is a man tallied—he realizes here what he has in him;
The animals, the past, the future, light, space, majesty, love, if they
    are vacant of you, you are vacant of them.

Only the kernel of every object nourishes;
Where is he who tears off the husks for you and me?
Where is he that undoes stratagems and envelopes for you and me?

Here is adhesiveness—it is not previously fashion'd—it is apropos;
Do you know what it is, as you pass, to be loved by strangers?
Do you know the talk of those turning eye-balls?

7

Here is the efflux of the Soul;
The efflux of the Soul comes from within, through embower'd gates,
    ever provoking questions:
These yearnings, why are they? These thoughts in the darkness, why
    are they?

Why are there men and women that while they are nigh me, the
    sun-light expands my blood?
Why, when they leave me, do my pennants of joy sink flat and lank?
Why are there trees I never walk under, but large and melodious
    thoughts descend upon me?
(I think they hang there winter and summer on those trees, and
    always drop fruit as I pass;)
What is it I interchange so suddenly with strangers?
What with some driver, as I ride on the seat by his side?
What with some fisherman, drawing his seine by the shore, as I walk
    by, and pause?
What gives me to be free to a woman's or man's goodwill? What
    gives them to be free to mine?

8

The efflux of the Soul is happiness—here is happiness;
I think it pervades the air, waiting at all times;
Now it flows into us—we are rightly charged.

Here rises the fluid and attaching character;
The fluid and attaching character is the freshness and sweetness of
    man and woman;
(The herbs of the morning sprout no fresher and sweeter every day
    out of the roots of themselves, than it sprouts fresh and sweet
    continually out of itself.)

Toward the fluid and attaching character exudes the sweat of the
    love of young and old;
From it falls distill'd the charm that mocks beauty and attainments;
Toward it heaves the shuddering longing ache of contact.

9

Allons! whoever you are, come travel with me!
Traveling with me, you find what never tires.

The earth never tires;
The earth is rude, silent, incomprehensible at first—Nature is rude
    and incomprehensible at first;
Be not discouraged—keep on—there are divine things, well en-
    velop'd;
I swear to you there are divine things more beautiful than words
    can tell.

Allons! We must not stop here!
However sweet these laid-up stores—however convenient this dwell-
    ing, we cannot remain here;
However shelter'd this port, and however calm these waters, we
    must not anchor here;
However welcome the hospitality that surrounds us, we are per-
    mitted to receive it but a little while.

10

Allons! The inducements shall be great to you;
We will sail pathless and wild seas;
We will go where winds blow, waves dash, and the Yankee clipper
    speeds by under full sail.
Allons! With power, liberty, the earth, the elements!
Health, defiance, gayety, self-esteem, curiosity;
Allons! from all formules!
From your formules, O bat-eyed and materialistic priests!

The stale cadaver blocks up the passage—the burial waits no longer.
Allons! Yet take warning!
He traveling with me needs the best blood, thews, endurance;
None may come to the trial, till he or she bring courage and health.

Come not here if you have already spent the best of yourself;
Only those may come, who come in sweet and determin'd bodies;
No diseas'd person—no rum-drinker or venereal taint is permitted
    here.

I and mine do not convince by arguments, similes, rhymes;
We convince by our presence.

11

Listen! I will be honest with you;
I do not offer the old smooth prizes, but offer rough new prizes;
These are the days that must happen to you:

You shall not heap up what is call'd riches,
You shall scatter with lavish hand all that you earn or achieve,
You but arrive at the city to which you were destined—you hardly
    settle yourself to satisfaction, before you are call'd by an irre-
    sistible call to depart,

You shall be treated to the ironical smiles and mockings of those
    who remain behind you;
What beckonings of love you receive, you shall only answer with
    passionate kisses of parting,
You shall not allow the hold of those who spread their reach'd
    hands toward you.

12

Allons! After the GREAT COMPANIONS! and to belong to them!
They too are on the road! they are the swift and majestic men! they
    are the greatest women.

Over that which hinder'd them—over that which retarded—passing
    impediments large or small,
Committers of crimes, committers of many beautiful virtues,
Enjoyers of calms of seas, and storms of seas,
Sailors of many a ship, walkers of many a mile of land,
Habitués of many different countries, habitués of far-distant dwell-
    ings,
Trusters of men and women, observers of cities, solitary toilers,
Pausers and contemplators of tufts, blossoms, shells of the shore,
Dancers at wedding-dances, kissers of brides, tender helpers of chil-
    dren, bearers of children,
Soldiers of revolts, standers by gaping graves, lowerers down of cof-
    fins,
Journeyers over consecutive seasons, over the years—the curious
    years, each emerging from that which preceded it,
Journeyers as with companions, namely, their own diverse phases,
Forth-steppers from the latent unrealized baby-days,
Journeyers gayly with their own youth—Journeyers with their
    bearded and well-grain'd manhood,
Journeyers with their womanhood, ample, unsurpass'd, content,
Journeyers with their own sublime old age of manhood or woman-
    hood,
Old age, calm, expanded, broad with the haughty breadth of the
    universe,
Old age, flowing free with the delicious near-by freedom of death.

13

Allons! To that which is endless, as it was beginningless,
To undergo much, tramps of days, rests of nights,

To merge all in the travel they tend to, and the days and nights
they tend to,
Again to merge them in the start of superior journeys;
To see nothing anywhere but what you may reach it and pass it,
To conceive no time, however distant, but what you may reach it
and pass it,
To look up or down no road but it stretches and waits for you—
however long, but it stretches and waits for you;
To see no being, not God's or any, but you also go thither,
To see no possession but you may possess it—enjoying all without
labor or purchase—abstracting the feast, yet not abstracting one
particle of it;
To take the best of the farmer's farm and the rich man's elegant
villa, and the chaste blessings of the well-married couple, and
the fruits of orchards and flowers of gardens,
To take to your use out of the compact cities as you pass through,
To carry buildings and streets with you afterward wherever you go,
To gather the minds of men out of their brains as you encounter
them—to gather the love out of their hearts,
To take your lovers on the road with you, for all that you leave
them behind you,
To know the universe itself as a road—as many roads—as roads for
traveling souls.

14

The soul travels;
The body does not travel as much as the soul;
The body has just as great a work as the soul, and parts away at last
for the journeys of the soul.

All parts away for the progress of souls;
All religion, all solid things, arts, governments,—all that was or is
apparent upon this globe or any globe, falls into niches and
corners before the procession of Souls along the grand roads of
the universe.

Of the progress of the souls of men and women along the grand
roads of the universe, all other progress is the needed emblem
and sustenance.

Forever alive, forever forward,
Stately, solemn, sad, withdrawn, baffled, mad, turbulent, feeble, dis-
satisfied.

Desperate, proud, fond, sick, accepted by men, rejected by men,
They go; they go; I know that they go, but I know not where they
     go;
But I know that they go toward the best—toward something great.

15

Allons! Whoever you are! come forth!
You must not stay sleeping and dallying there in the house, though
     you built it, or though it has been built for you.

Allons! out of the dark confinement!
It is useless to protest—I know all, and expose it.
Behold, through you as bad as the rest,
Through the laughter, dancing, dining, supping, of people,
Inside of dresses and ornaments, inside of those wash'd and trimm'd
     faces,
Behold a secret silent loathing and despair.

No husband, no wife, no friend, trusted to hear the confession;
Another self, a duplicate of every one, skulking and hiding it goes,
Formless and wordless through the streets of the cities, polite and
     bland in the parlors,
In the cars of rail-roads, in steamboats, in the public assembly,
Home to the houses of men and women, at the table, in the bed-
     room, everywhere,
Smartly attired, countenance smiling, form upright, death under the
     breast-bones, hell under the skull-bones,
Under the broadcloth and gloves, under the ribbons and artificial
     flowers,
Keeping fair with the customs, speaking not a syllable of itself,
Speaking of anything else, but never of itself.

16

Allons! Through struggles and wars!
The goal that was named cannot be countermanded.

Have the past struggles succeeded?
What has succeeded? Yourself? Your nation? Nature?
Now understand me well—It is provided in the essence of things,
     that from any fruition of success, no matter what, shall come
     forth something to make a greater struggle necessary.

My call is the call of battle—I nourish active rebellion.
He going with me must go well armed;
He going with me goes often with spare diet, poverty, angry ene-
mies, desertions.

17

Allons! The road is before us!
It is safe—I have tried it—my own feet have tried it well.
Allons! Be not detain'd!
Let the paper remain on the desk unwritten, and the book on the
shelf unopen'd!
Let the tools remain in the workshop! let the money remain un-
earn'd!
Let the school stand! mind not the cry of the teacher!
Let the preacher preach in his pulpit! let the lawyer plead in the
court, and the judge expound the law.

Mon enfant! I give you my hand!
I give you my love, more precious than money,
I give you myself, before preaching or law;
Will you give me yourself? Will you come travel with me?
Shall we stick by each other as long as we live?

—*Walt Whitman*

The World Is Too Much with Us

The world is too much with us: late and soon,
Getting and spending, we lay waste our powers:
Little we see in Nature that is ours;
We have given our hearts away, a sordid boon!
The sea that bares her bosom to the moon;
The winds that will be howling at all hours,
And are up-gathered now like sleeping flowers;
For this, for everything, we are out of tune;
It moves us not.—Great God! I'd rather be
A Pagan suckled in a creed outworn;
So might I, standing on this pleasant lea,
Have glimpses that would make me less forlorn;
Have sight of Proteus rising from the sea;
Or hear old Triton blow his wreathèd horn.

—*William Wordsworth*

The Solitary Reaper

Behold her, single in the field,
Yon solitary Highland Lass!
Reaping and singing by herself;
Stop here, or gently pass!
Alone she cuts and binds the grain,
And sings a melancholy strain;
O listen! for the Vale profound
Is overflowing with the sound.

No Nightingale did ever chaunt
More welcome notes to weary bands
Of travellers in some shady haunt,
Among Arabian sands:
A voice so thrilling ne'er was heard
In spring-time from the Cuckoo-bird,
Breaking the silence of the seas
Among the farthest Hebrides.

Will no one tell me what she sings?—
Perhaps the plaintive numbers flow
For old, unhappy, far-off things,
And battles long ago:
Or is it some more humble lay,
Familiar matter of to-day?
Some natural sorrow, loss, or pain,
That has been, and may be again?

Whate'er the theme, the Maiden sang
As if her song could have no ending;
I saw her singing at her work,
And o'er the sickle bending;—
I listened, motionless and still;
And, as I mounted up the hill,
The music in my heart I bore,
Long after it was heard no more.

—*William Wordsworth*

Wild Peaches

1

When the world turns completely upside down
You say we'll emigrate to the Eastern Shore
Aboard a river-boat from Baltimore;
We'll live among wild peach trees, miles from town,
You'll wear a coonskin cap, and I a gown
Homespun, dyed butternut's dark gold colour.
Lost, like your lotus-eating ancestor,
We'll swim in milk and honey till we drown.

The winter will be short, the summer long,
The autumn amber-hued, sunny and hot,
Tasting of cider and of scuppernong;
All seasons sweet, but autumn best of all.
The squirrels in their silver fur will fall
Like falling leaves, like fruit, before your shot.

2

The autumn frosts will lie upon the grass
Like bloom on grapes of purple-brown and gold.
The misted early mornings will be cold;
The little puddles will be roofed with glass.
The sun, which burns from copper into brass,
Melts these at noon, and makes the boys unfold
Their knitted mufflers; full as they can hold,
Fat pockets dribble chestnuts as they pass.

Peaches grow wild, and pigs can live in clover;
A barrel of salted herrings lasts a year;
The spring begins before the winter's over.
By February you may find the skins
Of garter snakes and water moccasins
Dwindled and harsh, dead-white and cloudy-clear.

3

When April pours the colours of a shell
Upon the hills, when every little creek

Is shot with silver from the Chesapeake
In shoals new-minted by the ocean swell,
When strawberries go begging, and the sleek
Blue plums lie open to the blackbird's beak,
We shall live well—we shall live very well.

The months between the cherries and the peaches
Are brimming cornucopias which spill
Fruits red and purple, sombre-bloomed and black;
Then, down rich fields and frosty river beaches
We'll trample bright persimmons, while you kill
Bronze partridge, speckled quail, and canvasback.

4

Down to the Puritan marrow of my bones
There's something in this richness that I hate.
I love the look, austere, immaculate,
Of landscapes drawn in pearly monotones.
There's something in my very blood that owns
Bare hills, cold silver on a sky of slate,
A thread of water, churned to milky spate
Streaming through slanted pastures fenced with stones.

I love those skies, thin blue or snowy gray,
Those fields sparse-planted, rendering meagre sheaves;
That spring, briefer than apple-blossom's breath,
Summer, so much too beautiful to stay,
Swift autumn, like a bonfire of leaves,
And sleepy winter, like the sleep of death.

                                        —*Elinor Wylie*

The Lake Isle of Innisfree

I will arise and go now, and go to Innisfree,
And a small cabin build there, of clay and wattles made;
Nine bean rows will I have there, a hive for the honey bee,
And live alone in the bee-loud glade.

And I shall have some peace there, for peace comes dropping slow,
Dropping from the veils of the morning to where the cricket sings;
There midnight's all a glimmer, and noon a purple glow,
    And evening full of the linnet's wings.

I will arise and go now, for always night and day
I hear lake water lapping with low sounds by the shore;
While I stand on the roadway, or on the pavements gray,
    I hear it in the deep heart's core.

—William Butler Yeats

6
EATING
AND DRINKING

A Mess of Clams

BY

JOSEPH MITCHELL

P RACTICALLY all the littleneck and cherrystone clams served on the half shell in New York restaurants come out of the black mud of the Long Island bays. They are the saltiest, cleanest, and biggest-bellied clams in the world. The most abundant beds are in Great South Bay and are owned by the towns of Islip and Babylon. Right after dawn every weekday about seventy licensed clammers from these towns go out on the Bay in a fleet of dilapidated sloops and cat boats and spread out over the beds. They work over the sides of their anchored boats, using long-handled tongs and rakes; the clams are bedded in bottoms which lie under eight to ten feet of water. At noon the buy-boats of two clam-shipping firms—Still & Clock of Bay Shore, and G. Vander Borgh & Son of West Sayville —go out and anchor near the fleet, and from then until 4 P.M. the clammers bring their catches to the buy-boats in bushel bags and sell them over the rail for cash.

One muggy June day I made a trip to the South Bay beds with Captain Archie M. Clock, who commands the Still & Clock buy-boat. This boat is the Jennie Tucker, a battered, stripped-down, 38-foot sloop powered with a motor the Captain took out of an old Chrysler. Captain Clock and his partner, Louis Still, are members of families which have fished, oyster-farmed, and clammed on the South Shore since the middle of the eighteenth century. I arrived at their weather-beaten clam shed on Homan Avenue Creek in Bay Shore at ten in the morning and found Captain Clock on the narrow wharf at the rear. He was sitting on an overturned clam bucket, smoking his pipe. A man I know who runs a wholesale shell-fish business in Fulton Fish Market had written me a note of introduction to the Captain, and I handed it to him. He read it, grunted, and said, "You picked a good day to see the beds. We're going out a little early." He motioned toward a bucket with the stem of his pipe. "Have a seat and make yourself at home," he said. "Do you care much for clams?"

I sat down on the bucket and told him that one Sunday afternoon in August, 1937, I placed third in a clam-eating tournament at a Block Island clambake, eating eighty-four cherries. I told him that I regard this as one of the few worth-while achievements of my life.

"Well, you can eat yourself a bellyful today," he said. "I feel like having a few myself. They tell me brewers sometimes get so they hate beer, and sometimes I get so I can't stand the sight of a clam, but I'm real hungry this morning."

The Jennie Tucker was lying alongside the wharf, and the mate, a muscular young man named Charlie Bollinger, was sloshing down her decks with buckets of water. "Give her plenty of water, Charlie," the Captain told him. He turned to me and said, "You have to be extra clean when you're handling clams. Let a few dead clams lie around and you'll breed up a smell that'll make a strong man weak, a smell that'll knock your hat off, unravel the knot in your necktie, and tear holes in your shirt." He stood up, yawned, spat, and went into a little office in the shed. When he returned he carried an armful of gear which included a lunch bucket, a tattered old ledger, and a green metal box. Later I learned that this box contained the cash with which he would buy the day's load.

"Everything O.K., Charlie?" he asked.

"She's clean as a whistle, Archie," said the mate.

"Let's get going then," he said. We went aboard and the Captain stowed his gear in the sloop's tiny cabin. The Captain was stocky, slow-moving, and sleepy-eyed. He was deeply tanned, but he had smeared some white salve on his nose and ears to guard against sunburn. He was roughly dressed; he wore patched pants, a blue work shirt, and a long-visored swordfisherman's cap. He took the tiller, which he handled expertly, until we were well out in the Bay. Then he turned it over to Bollinger, got his ledger, and sat down beside me on the hatch. "The beds they're clamming lie about four miles down the Bay," he said, motioning with his head in the direction of Babylon. He opened the ledger and got a new page ready, writing down the names of the clammers. The wind from the ocean ruffled the pages as he worked. Most of the names he wrote down were old Long Island ones like Doxsee, Ricketts, Baldwin, Crowell, and Tooker.

"Most of the clammers come from families that have been around this bay so many generations they long since lost track," he said. "The bulk of them are of English descent or Holland Dutch, and there's quite a few squareheads. They know the bottom of the Bay like they know their wife's face. Clamming is back-breaking, but a man can get a living if his muscle holds out. I looked through this ledger last night and figured I paid one clammer eighty-some-odd dollars last week, but that's unusual. Most of them average between five and ten bucks a day. It's all according to how good a man can handle the tongs."

He laid his ledger on the hatch, stretched his arms, and yawned. The morning had been cloudy, but the sun came out soon after we left the wharf and now it was burning off the haze on the Bay. After it had been shining fifteen minutes, we could see the striped Fire Island lighthouse and the long, glistening dunes on Oak and Cap-tree Islands. I asked the Captain if any bayman can go out to the beds and clam.

"He cannot," the Captain said. "He has to get a Conservation Department license that costs two and a half, and he has to be a resident of the town that owns the beds he works. A Babylon man can't clam in Islip water, and vice versa. In fact, they're always fussing among themselves about the division line. That's a fuss that'll go on as long as there's a clam left in the mud."

"How much do you pay for a bushel?" I asked.

"The price is based on the size of the clam and the demand in Fulton Market," the Captain said. "Prices may fluctuate as much as a dollar in a single season, but right now I'm paying the boys two dollars a bushel for littlenecks and a dollar and a half for cherry-stones. That's for the half-shell trade. For the big ones—what we call chowders—I pay a dollar a bushel.

"The bulk of the clams in South Bay are hard-shells—they're called quahogs in New England. There's a few soft-shells, or steam-ers, around the shores of the Bay, but we don't bother with them. Most of the steam clams you see in the city come from New England. The hard-shell is the king of the clams. He can be baked, fried, steamed, put into chowder, or served on the half shell. I *will* say that the best chowder is made with a mixture of softs and hards.

Out here we believe in Manhattan-style chowder, a couple of tomatoes to every quart of shucked clams. Our chowder clams are
around four years old, a couple of years older than littlenecks. We
truck our necks and cherries to dealers in Fulton Market and to
restaurants in Manhattan and Brooklyn, and we truck the chowders
to the Campbell's soup factory in Camden, New Jersey. They take
around fifteen hundred bushels of chowders off us every week." He
turned to the mate. "I'll take her now, Charlie," he said.

Soon after Captain Clock took the tiller, we approached the fleet.
The little boats were laying with the wind and the tide about two
miles southeast of Babylon. Captain Clock said the majority of the
boats were anchored near the imaginary line dividing the beds, and
that some were hugging it. "Human nature," he said. "The boys
from Islip just itch to work the Babylon water, and the Babylon
boys think they could tong up twice as many if they could get over
on the Islip territory." A few of the boats carried two clammers,
one for each side, but one man to a boat seemed to be the rule.
When we were about fifty yards from the nearest clammer, the
Captain ducked into the cabin and cut off the motor. Bollinger
hurried to the bow and threw out the anchor.

"Now I'll show you how to clam," said Captain Clock. "We'll
tong up a few pecks for us to eat."

He rolled up his shirtsleeves and picked up a pair of tongs, an
implement with two sets of teeth fixed to the ends of two four-
teen-foot handles. He lowered the tongs into the water, which was
nine feet deep, and pushed the opened teeth into the mud; then he
brought the handles together scissors-fashion, closing the teeth. Just
before hauling the tongs over the rail, he doused the closed teeth
in the water several times, washing out the mud. He opened the
teeth on the deck and out dropped a dazed spider crab, two bunches
of scarlet oyster sponge, a handful of empty shells, and twelve
beautiful clams. The shells of the clams were steel blue, the color
of the Bay water.

"A good haul," he said. "I got four cherries, two necks, two chowders and four peanuts." He said that a state law forbids the sale of
clams less than an inch thick and that such undersized clams are
called peanuts. He tossed the peanuts and the crab back into the
water. Then he put the tongs overboard again. He sent the teeth
into the mud seven times and brought up forty-three clams. Then

he laid aside the tongs and got two clam knives off a shelf in the cabin. He gave me one and we squatted on the deck and went to work opening the cherries. When the valves were pried apart, the rich clam liquor dribbled out. The flesh of the cherries was a delicate pink. On the cups of some of the shells were splotches of deep purple; Indians used to hack such splotches out of clamshells for wampum. Fresh from the coal-black mud and uncontaminated by ketchup or sauce, they were the best clams I had ever eaten. The mate sat on the hatch and watched us.

"Aren't you going to have any?" I asked.

"I wouldn't put one of them goddamn things in my mouth if I was perishing to death," he said. "I'm working on this buy-boat ten years and I'm yet to eat a clam."

He scornfully watched us eat for a few moments; then he went into the cabin and came out with a portable radio, which he placed on the cabin roof, and tuned in on a news broadcast. While the Captain and I opened and ate clams we looked out at the fleet and watched the clammers. The Captain said that a clammer works both sides of his boat until the tongs start coming up empty; then he lets out slack in his anchor cable and drifts into unworked territory. "Most of them are patient," he said, "but some will be lifting and dropping their anchors all day long. When a man does that we say he's got the runs." The fleet was made up largely of catboats stripped of their rigs and powered with old automobile motors. The majority of the men were tonging, but here and there a man worked with a rake. The Captain said that rakes are used only on stretches of soft bottom. "The handle of a rake is twenty-two feet long," he said, "and it takes a Joe Louis to pull it." Some of the clammers were stripped to their belts, but most of them worked in their undershirts. Occasionally a man would lay aside his tongs or rake and squat in the bottom of the boat and bag up his clams. Captain Clock said it is customary for the clammers to sell their catches in the early-afternoon hours, so the shippers will have time to cull and barrel the clams for trucking in the evening.

The Captain and I were finishing the last of the forty-three clams when a whistle in Babylon blew for noon. "We better eat dinner, Archie," Bollinger said. "They'll start bringing their loads over pretty soon now." Intent on his last clam, the Captain nodded. Bollinger brought out their lunch buckets and a thermos jug of iced tea. I had bought a couple of sandwiches in Bay Shore and I got them out of my raincoat. Bollinger tuned in on a program of waltzes broadcast from a Manhattan hotel. We sat on peck baskets in the hot sun and ate and listened to the waltzes. We were drinking tea out of tin cups when the first of the clammers came alongside. Bollinger jumped up, tossed the clammer a rope, and helped him make fast to the Jennie Tucker. The clammer was a small, spry old man in hip boots.

"What you got?" Captain Clock asked him.

"Nothing to speak of," he said. "Just a mess of clams. I been scratch-raking off Grass Island. I got two bushels of cherries, a bushel of necks, and two bushels of chowders." Gripping the bags by their ears, he passed them to Bollinger. Captain Clock took a five and two ones out of his cashbox and handed them to the clammer, who carefully placed them in an old-fashioned snap purse. Then he picked up two conches from the bottom of his boat and tossed them to Bollinger.

"I was about to forget your konks," he said. He threw aside the ropes, pushed off, and started his engine.

"Be good," yelled Captain Clock.

"I'm getting so old," the clammer said, "I can't be anything else."

Bollinger deposited the conches in a rusty wire basket. "Konks are my racket," he said. "They get caught in the tongs and the boys save them for me instead of throwing them back. One of the truck-drivers takes them in and sells them to Italian clam stands in downtown New York and we divvy up. It's just cigarette money. The Italians boil the konks and make something called *scungili*."

We drank some more tea, and then another clammer, a gloomy-eyed, sunburned young man, pulled alongside. He was in a cat-boat that had been patched with tin in a dozen places.

"Hello, Tarzan," said Bollinger. "Didn't that old eelpot sink yet? How many clams you got?"

"I been croshaying the mud for six hours and I barely took enough to bait a hook," the young man said. "They was thin where I was tonging."

"Quit bellyaching," said Bollinger. "If it was to rain clams, you wouldn't be satisfied." The young man passed over a bushel of necks, two bushels of cherries, a scanty peck of chowders, and three conches. Captain Clock handed him five ones and twenty cents. He folded the bills into a wad and stuffed it in his watch pocket. "Another day, another dollar," he said. "My back feels like it was run over by a load of bricks." He cranked his engine and moved off, heading for Babylon. "He'll get drunk tonight," Captain Clock said. "I can tell by the way he was talking." The Captain bent over a bag of cherries. He scooped a double handful out of the mouth of the bag and spread them on the deck. "Beauties," he said. "Uniform as peas in a pod. The shells are blue now, but they'll turn gray or white before we get them to town." He opened a cherry and balanced it on his palm. He looked at it admiringly. "A spawner," he said. "Now, that's the beauty of a clam. He doesn't make a bit of fuss about spawning. An oyster's just the opposite. He spawns from May through August—the months without an 'r' in them—and he gets so milky you can't eat him on the half shell. You can fry him, but you can't eat him raw. A clam is better behaved. He never gets milky enough to notice and he's just as good in the midsummer months, when he's spawning, as he is on the coldest day of the winter."

Captain Clock said that once a year the town of Islip buys a couple of truckloads of hardshells from Massachusetts or New Jersey to scatter on its beds. "Foreign clams put new life in the natives," he said. "They improve the breed. The spawn mixes and we get a better set. Hey, Charlie, hand me a knife. I'm going to try some of these chowders." The Captain opened a dozen chowders and arranged them in a semicircle on the hatch. We were eating them when Bollinger suddenly shouted, "Here come the cops!" He pointed in the direction of Babylon, and I saw a launch flying a green flag. In a minute it cut the water just off our bow, heading for the fleet. The clammers stopped work and commenced yelling. "They're warning each other," Bollinger said. "That's the police boat from Babylon. The cops go through the beds every day or so. You never know when they'll show up. If they spy an Islip man in Babylon water, they give him a ticket and he has to go to court and get fined." The clammers leaned on their tong and rake handles while the police boat slowly picked its way through the fleet. It did not halt; evidently the clammers were behaving themselves.

Presently another clammer called it a day and came alongside. He was a gaunt, stooped man, who silently handed over four bushels of necks, three bushels of cherries, and a bushel and a peck of chowders. He collected thirteen dollars and seventy-five cents, bit a chew of tobacco off a plug he took from his hip pocket, mumbled "Good night, Cap," and pushed off. "He's one of the best clammers on Long Island," said Captain Clock. "I bet he's got ten thousand dollars in the bank, and he's so saving he gets his wife to cut his hair." The gaunt clammer's departure from the beds appeared to be a signal to the others. Soon after he left, they began moving toward the buy-boat in two and threes. In twenty minutes the Jennie Tucker was surrounded by loaded boats, waiting their turns to come alongside. "They all have to come at once," Bollinger said indignantly. Captain Clock stood at the stern, hunched over his ledger, which he had placed on the cabin roof. Bollinger helped the clammers heft their bags over the rail. He piled the chowders aft, the cherries on the hatch, and the necks forward. When a boat finished unloading he would call out the number of bushels, and the Captain would make a notation in his ledger and then pay off the clammer.·

To get out of Bollinger's way, I went to the bow and sat on a bale of empty bags. Standing in their boats, the waiting clammers smoked cigarettes and shouted insults at each other. I couldn't tell if the insults were good-natured or genuine. "If I was you, I'd take that old cement-mixer home and set fire to it," one yelled at his neighbor. "I wouldn't be caught dead in that dirty old boat." "Well, it's paid for," said the master of the cement-mixer, "and that's more'n you can say." "Paid for!" screamed the first man. "You mean you stole it off the beach. Nothing's safe when you're around. Why, by God, you'd steal a tick off a widow's belly!" Most of the clammers seemed to be irritable. "Hello, Pop," a young clammer said to the man in an adjoining boat, a sullen old man in wet overalls, "how's your hammer hanging?" "Shut up!" said the old man. The young clammer snickered and said, "Didn't get your share of clams today, did you, Pop?" "Shut up!" said the old man. "Why, hell," said the young clammer, "I was just passing the time of day." "Shut up!" said the old man.

At a quarter after four the last clammer finished unloading, cast off, and made for home. The Captain snapped his cashbox shut and we sat down and drained the iced tea in the thermos jug. Then Bollinger hoisted the anchor, started the motor, and pointed the

Jennie Tucker for her wharf. The decks were piled high. "A regular floating clam mountain," said Bollinger. The Captain rearranged some bags on the hatch, clearing away a space to sit. He lit his pipe and added up the row of figures in his ledger.

"We took a hundred and forty-five bushels," he said. "One day I took two hundred bushels. I emptied my cashbox for that load. The stern was awash on the trip in." He pointed toward Oak Island. "See those boats over there? Some of the boys are still out, but they don't sell over the rail like the others. They have bigger boats and they stay out until late in the afternoon and bring their loads right to our shed. We buy every clam that's offered, no matter if there's a glut in New York or a big demand. Some days we buy more clams than we can get rid of, and we take the surplus out to some lots of water we lease from the town of Islip and shovel them overboard. In the last five weeks we've planted thirteen hundred bushels of cherries and five hundred bushels of necks in those lots. When we need them, we go out and tong them up. No waste that way. In the old days, when clams were very dear, we used to have clam pirates. They would steal up at night and tong our lots, but not any more. We keep a watchman, just in case."

At five o'clock, the Jennie Tucker puttered up to her wharf. Mr. Still, the senior partner of the firm, was standing in the back doorway of the shed, waiting. He looks after the office end of the business. He is a shellfish expert and belongs to the family which once ran Still's, a renowned sea-food restaurant and hang-out for Tammany gluttons on Third Avenue, and which still runs a thriving oyster business in a scow anchored in Pike Slip, beneath Manhattan Bridge. When the Jennie Tucker scraped against the wharf, Mr. Still shouted, "Here she is," and four men came out of the shed. The moment the buy-boat was tied up, two of these men leaped aboard and began lifting the bags to the wharf. The others placed them on handtrucks and wheeled them into the culling room. This was a long, cool room, which smelled like a clean cellar. There the clams were poured in great heaps on tables built against the walls. The tables and the cement floor had recently been hosed down and they were wet and immaculate. Captain Clock, Mr. Still, and Bollinger took places at the tables and culled the clams, tossing aside those with broken shells or gapped-open lips.

After they had been culled, the clams were poured into woven-wire baskets and dipped in a tank of tap water in which an anti-septic solution had been poured. Then some were emptied into great, three-bushel barrels and others into tubs holding three pecks. Soon the room was crowded with loaded barrels, and Mr. Still got a hammer out of the roll-top desk in the little office adjoining the culling room. He tacked tags on the heads of the barrels, addressing them to various restaurants and Fulton Market dealers. Then they were wheeled into one of the company's three trucks. At seven o'clock, this truck contained sixty-five barrels and twenty-two tubs. "She's ready to roll," said Mr. Still. "If you're a mind to, you can ride into the city with this load." He introduced me to Paul Boice, the driver, and I climbed into the cab of the truck. It was one of those massive, aluminum-painted trucks.

We took the Sunrise Highway. At Valley Stream, we stopped at a diner for hamburgers and coffee. The counterman knew Boice. "Care for some clams tonight, Paul?" he asked, grinning. "How about a dozen nice clams for supper?" The driver laughed per-functorily. Evidently it was an old joke. "When I want clams for supper," he said, "I'll notify you. Fix me a hamburger." We did not tarry long in the diner. In Brooklyn the driver deftly guided the heavy truck through a maze of side streets. "I've been hauling clams over this route eight years and I know every short cut there is," he said. "Clams are nowhere near as perishable as oysters, but I don't like to dawdle." When we rolled off Manhattan Bridge he glanced at his watch. "Took less than two hours," he said. "That's good time."

He made his first delivery at Vincent's Clam Bar, at Mott and Hester Streets, unloading three clam tubs and the basket of *scungili* conches Bollinger had gathered during the day. The proprietor brought Boice a goblet of red wine. "I get a drink on the house every time I hit this place," he said. He drove down Mott Street, passing slowly through Chinatown. Entering South Street, he had to climb out of the cab and drag a sleeping drunk out of the road. "Truck-drivers have to slow-poke through here just because of drunks," he said. "I drag one out of my way at least once a week." The Fulton Market sheds were dark, deserted, and locked up when we arrived. "I make four deliveries in the Market," Boice said, "and then I head uptown and make stops at big restaurants in the the-atrical district." He backed the truck up to the door of a shellfish wholesaler and we climbed out of the cab. We looked up and down the street and did not see a soul. "There's a night watchman down here who helps me unload," Boice said, "and I always have to wait for him to show up." We sat down on the steps of the wholesale house and lit cigarettes. Across the street, on top of a pile of broken lobster barrels, three overfed fishhouse cats were screeching at each other. We sat for fifteen minutes, watching the cats screech and fight, and then I said goodbye. "If you order clams or chowder tomorrow," Boice said, peering up the dark street for the night watchman, "like as not you'll eat some of the ones we hauled in tonight."

The Days of the Giants

BY

H. L. MENCKEN

Not infrequently I am asked by young college folk, sometimes male and sometimes female, whether there has been any significant change, in my time, in the bacchanalian virtuosity of the American people. They always expect me, of course, to say that boozing is now at an all-time high, for they are a proud generation, and have been brought up to believe that Prohibition brought in refinements unparalleled on earth since the fall of Babylon. But when I speak for that thesis it is only to please them, for I know very well that the facts run the other way. My actual belief is that Americans reached the peak of their alcoholic puissance in the closing years of the last century. Along about 1903 there was a sudden and marked letting up—partly due, I suppose, to the accelerating pace and hazard of life in a civilization growing more and more mechanized, but also partly to be blamed on the lugubrious warnings of the medical men, who were then first learning how to reinforce their hocus-pocus with the alarms of the uplift.

In my early days as a reporter they had no more sense of civic responsibility than so many stockbrokers or policemen. A doctor of any standing not only had nothing to say against the use of stimulants; he was himself, nine times out of ten, a steady patron of them, and argued openly that they sustained him in his arduous and irregular life. Dr. Z. K. Wiley, our family practitioner, always took a snifter with my father when he dropped in to dose my brother Charlie and me with castor oil, and whenever, by some unusual accident of his heavy practise, he had any free time afterward, he and my father gave it over to quiet wrestling with the decanters. His favorite prescription for a cold was rock-and-rye, and he believed and taught that a shot of Maryland whiskey was the best preventive of pneumonia in the *R* months. If you object here that Dr. Wiley was a Southerner, then I answer at once that Dr. Oliver Wendell Holmes was a Yankee of the Yankees, and yet held exactly the same views. Every schoolboy, I suppose, has heard by this time of Dr. Holmes's famous address before the Massachusetts Medical Society on May 30, 1860, in which he argued that "if the whole materia medica, as now used, could be sunk to the bottom of the sea, it would be all the better for mankind—and all the worse for the fishes"; but what the pedagogues always fail to tell their poor dupes is that he made a categorical exception of wine, which he ranked with opium, quinine, anesthetics and mercury among the sovereign and invaluable boons to humanity.

I was thus greatly surprised when I first heard a medical man talk to the contrary. This was in the Winter of 1899–1900, and the place was a saloon near a messy downtown fire. I was helping my betters to cover the fire, and followed them into the saloon for a prophylactic drink. The doctor, who was a fire department surgeon, thereupon made a speech arguing that alcohol was not a stimulant but a depressant, and advising us to keep off it until the fire was out and we were relaxing in preparation for bed. "You think it warms you," he said, sipping a hot milk, "but it really cools you, and you are seventeen point eight per cent. more likely to catch pneumonia at the present minute than you were when you came into this doggery." This heresy naturally outraged the older reporters, and they became so prejudiced against the doctor that they induced the Fire Board, shortly afterward, to can him—as I recall it, by reporting that he was always drunk on duty. But his words made a deep impression on my innocence, and continue to lurk in my mind to this day. In consequence, I am what may be called a somewhat cagey drinker. That is to say, I never touch the stuff by daylight if I can help it, and I employ it of an evening, not to hooch up my faculties, but to let them down after work. Not in years have I ever written anything with so much as a glass of beer in my system. My compositions, I gather, sometimes seem boozy to the nobility and gentry, but they are actually done as soberly as those of William Dean Howells.

But this craven policy is not general among the literati, nor was it to be noted among the journalists of my apprentice days. Between 1899 and 1904 there was only one reporter south of the Mason &

Dixon Line who did not drink at all, and he was considered insane.
In New York, so far as I could make out, there was not even one.
On my first Christmas Eve on the *Herald* but two sober persons
were to be found in the office—one of them a Seventh Day Adventist
office-boy in the editorial rooms, and the other a superannuated
stereotyper who sold lunches to the printers in the composing-
room. There was a printer on the payroll who was reputed to be a
teetotaler—indeed his singularity gave him the nickname of the
Moral Element—, but Christmas Eve happened to be his night off.
All the rest were full of what they called hand-set whiskey. This
powerful drug was sold in a saloon next door to the *Herald* office,
and was reputed to be made in the cellar by the proprietor in person—of wood alcohol, snuff, tabasco sauce, and coffin varnish. The
printers liked it, and got down a great many shots of it. On the
Christmas Eve I speak of its effects were such that more than half
the linotype machines in the composing-room broke down, and one
of the apprentices ran his shirt-tail through the proof-press. Down
in the press-room four or five pressmen got hurt, and the city edition
was nearly an hour late.

Nobody cared, for the head of the whole establishment, the rev-
ered managing editor, Colonel Cunningham, was locked up in his
office with a case of Bourbon. At irregular intervals he would throw
a wad of copy-paper over the partition which separated him from
the editorial writers, and when this wad was smoothed out it always
turned out to be part of an interminable editorial against General
Felix Angus, editor of the *American*. The General was a hero of the
Civil War, with so much lead in his system that he was said to rattle
as he walked, but Colonel Cunningham always hooted at his war
record, and was fond of alleging—without any ground whatsoever—
that he had come to America from his native France in the pussy-
like character of a barber. The editorial that he was writing that
Christmas Eve was headed, in fact, "The Barber of Seville." It never
got into the paper, for it was running beyond three columns by
press-time, and the night editor, Isidor Goodman, killed it for fear
that its point was still to come. When the Colonel inquired about
it two or three days afterwards he was told that a truck had upset in
the composing-room, and pied it.

The hero of the *Herald* composing-room in those days was a fat
printer named Bill, who was reputed to be the champion beer-

drinker of the Western Hemisphere. Bill was a first-rate linotype operator, and never resorted to his avocation in working-hours, but the instant his time was up he would hustle on his coat and go to a beer-house in the neighborhood, and there give what he called a setting. He made no charge for admission, but the spectators, of course, were supposed to pay for the beer. One night in 1902 I saw him get down thirty-two bottles in a row. Perhaps, in your wanderings, you have seen the same—but have you ever heard of a champion who could do it *without once retiring from his place at the bar?* Well, that is what Bill did, and on another occasion, when I was not present, he reached forty. Physiologists tell me that these prodigies must have been optical delusions, for there is not room enough in the coils and recesses of man for so much liquid, but I can only reply *Pfui* to that, for a record is a record. Bill avoided the door marked "Gents" as diligently as if he had been a débutante of the era, or the sign on it had been "For Ladies Only." He would have been humiliated beyond endurance if anyone had ever seen him slink through it.

In the year 1904, when the *Herald* office was destroyed in the great Baltimore fire, and we had to print the paper, for five weeks, in Philadelphia, I was told off to find accommodation for the printers. I found it in one of those old-fashioned $1-a-day hotels that were all bar on the first floor. The proprietor, a German with goat whiskers, was somewhat reluctant to come to terms, for he had heard that printers were wild fellows who might be expected to break up his furniture and work their wicked will upon his chambermaids, but when I told him that a beer-champion was among them he showed a more friendly interest, and when I began to brag about Bill's extraordinary talents his doubts disappeared and he proposed amiably that some Philadelphia foam-jumpers be invited in to make it a race. The first heat was run the very next night, and Bill won hands down. In fact, he won so easily that he offered grandly to go until he had drunk *twice* as much as the next best entry. We restrained him and got him to bed, for there had been some ominous whispering among the other starters, and it was plain that they were planning to call in help. The next night it appeared in the shape of a tall, knotty man from Allentown, Pa., who was introduced as the champion of the Lehigh Valley. He claimed to be not only a beer-drinker of high gifts, but also a member of the Bach Choir at

Bethlehem; and when he got down his first dozen mugs—the boys were drinking from the wood—he cut loose with an exultant yodel that he said was one of Bach's forgotten minor works. But he might very well have saved his wind, for Bill soon had him, and at the end of the setting he was four or five mugs behind, and in a state resembling suffocation. The next afternoon I saw his disconsolate fans taking him home, a sadder and much less melodious man.

On the first two nights there had been only slim galleries, but on the third the bar was jammed, and anyone could see that something desperate was afoot. It turned out to be the introduction of two super-champions, the one a short, saturnine Welshman from Wilkes-Barré, and the other a hearty blond young fellow from one of the Philadelphia suburbs, who said that he was half German and half Irish. The Welshman was introduced as the man who had twice drunk Otto the Brewery Horse under the table, and we were supposed to know who Otto was, though we didn't. The mongrel had a committee with him, and the chairman thereof offered to lay $25 on him at even money. The printers in Bill's corner made up the money at once, and their stake had grown to $50 in forty minutes by the clock, for the hybrid took only that long to blow up. The Welshman lasted much better, and there were some uneasy moments when he seemed destined to make history again by adding Bill to Otto, but in the end he succumbed so suddenly that it seemed like a bang, and his friends laid him out on the floor and began fanning him with bar-towels.

Bill was very cocky after that, and talked grandiosely of taking on two champions at a time, in marathon series. There were no takers for several nights, but after that they began to filter in from the remoter wilds of the Pennsylvania Dutch country, and the whole *Herald* staff was kept busy guarding Bill by day, to make sure that he did not waste any of his libido for malt liquor in the afternoons. He knocked off twenty or thirty challengers during the ensuing weeks, including two more Welshmen from the hard-coal country, a Scotsman with an ear missing, and a bearded Dunkard from Lancaster county. They were mainly pushovers, but now and then there was a tough one. Bill did not let this heavy going interfere with the practise of his profession. He set type every night from 6 P.M. to midnight in the office of the *Evening Telegraph,* where we were printing the *Herald,* and never began his combats until 12.30. By two o'clock he was commonly in bed, with another wreath of laurels hanging on the gas-jet.

To ease your suspense I'll tell you at once that he was never beaten. Germans, Irishmen, Welshmen and Scotsmen went down before him like so many Sunday-school superintendents, and he bowled over everyday Americans with such facility that only two of them ever lasted more than half an hour. But I should add in candor that he was out of service during the last week of our stay in Philadelphia. What fetched him is still a subject of debate among the pathologists at the Johns Hopkins Medical School, to whom the facts were presented officially on our return to Baltimore. The only visible symptom was a complete loss of speech. Bill showed up one night talking hoarsely, the next night he could manage only whispers, and the third night he was as mute as a shad-fish. There was absolutely no other sign of distress. He was all for going on with his derisive harrying of the Pennsylvania lushers, but a young doctor who hung about the saloon and served as surgeon at the bouts forbade it on unstated medical grounds. The Johns Hopkins experts in morbid anatomy have never been able to agree about the case. Some argue that Bill's potations must have dissolved the gummy coating of his pharyngeal plexus, and thus paralyzed his vocal cords; the rest laugh at this as nonsense savoring of quackery, and lay the whole thing to an intercurrent laryngitis, induced by insufficient bedclothes on very cold nights. I suppose that no one will ever know the truth. Bill recovered his voice in a couple of months, and soon afterward left Baltimore. Of the prodigies, if any, that marked his later career I can't tell you.

He was but one of a notable series of giants who flourished in Baltimore at the turn of the century, bringing the city a friendly publicity and causing the theory to get about that life there must be delightful. They appeared in all the ranks of society. The Maryland Club had its champions, and the cops had theirs. Some were drinkers pure and simple; others specialized in eating. One of the latter was an old man of easy means who lived at the Rennert Hotel, then the undisputed capital of gastronomy in the terrapin and oyster country. But for some reason that I can't tell you he never did his eating there; instead, he always took dinner at Tommy McPherson's eating-house, six or eight blocks away. He would leave the hotel every evening at seven o'clock, elegantly arrayed in a long-

tailed black coat and a white waistcoat, and carrying a gold-headed
cane, and would walk the whole way. Tommy's place was arranged
in two layers, with tables for men only alongside the bar downstairs,
and a series of small rooms upstairs to which ladies might be invited.
The cops, goaded by vice crusaders, had forced him to take the
doors off these rooms, but he had substituted heavy portières, and
his colored waiters were instructed to make a noise as they shuffled
down the hall, and to enter every room backward. The old fellow I
speak of, though there were tales about his wild youth, had by now
got beyond thought of sin, and all his eating was done downstairs. It
consisted of the same dishes precisely every night of the week, year
in and year out. First he would throw in three straight whiskeys,
and then he would sit down to *two* double porterhouse steaks, with
two large plates of peas, *two* of French fried potatoes, *two* of cole-
slaw, and a mountain of rye-bread. This vast meal he would eat to
the last speck, and not infrequently he called for more potatoes or
bread. He washed it down with two quarts of Burgundy, and at its
end threw in three more straight whiskeys. Then he would light
a cigar, and amble back to the Rennert, to spend the rest of the evening conversing with the politicoes who made their headquarters in
its lobby.

One day a report reached the *Herald* office that he was beginning
to break up, and Max Ways sent me to take a look. He had, by
then, been on his diet for no less than twelve years. When I opened
the subject delicately he hooted at the notion that he was not up to
par. He was, he told me, in magnificent health, and expected to live
at least twenty years longer. His excellent condition, he went on to
say, was due wholly to his lifelong abstemiousness. He ate only a
sparing breakfast, and no lunch at all, and he had not been drunk
for fifteen years—that is, in the sense of losing all control of himself.
He told me that people who ate pork dug their graves with their
teeth, and praised the Jews for avoiding it. He also said that he regarded all sea-food as poisonous, on the ground that it contained
too much phosphorus, and that fowl was almost as bad. There was,
in his view, only one perfectly safe and wholesome victual, and that
was beef. It had everything. It was nourishing, palatable and salu-
brious. The last bite tasted as good as the first. Even the bones had
a pleasant flavor. He ate peas and potatoes with it, he said, mainly
to give it some company: if he were ever cast on a desert island he

could do without them. The cole-slaw went along as a sort of gesture of politeness to the grass that had produced the beef, and he
ate rye-bread instead of wheat because rye was the bone and sinew
of Maryland whiskey, the most healthful appetizer yet discovered by
man. He would not affront me by presuming to discuss the virtues
of Burgundy: they were mentioned in the Bible, and all humanity
knew them.

The old boy never made his twenty years, but neither did he ever
change his regimen. As the uplift gradually penetrated medicine
various doctors of his acquaintance began to warn him that he was
headed for a bad end, but he laughed at them in his quiet way, and
went on going to Tommy's place every night, and devouring his two
double porterhouses. What took him off at last was not his eating,
but a trifling accident. He was knocked down by a bicycle in front
of the Rennert, developed pneumonia, and was dead in three days.
The resurrection men at both the Johns Hopkins and the University
of Maryland tried to get his body for autopsy, and were all set to
dig out of it a whole series of pathological monstrosities of a moral
tendency, but his lawyer forbade any knifeplay until his only heir,
a niece, could be consulted, and when she roared in from Eufaula,
Ala., it turned out that she was a Christian Scientist, with a hate
against anatomy. So he was buried without yielding any lessons for
science. If he had any real rival, in those declining years of Baltimore gastronomy, it must have been John Wilson, a cop: I have
always regretted that they were never brought together in a match.
Once, at a cop party, I saw John eat thirty fried hard crabs at a
sitting—no mean feat, I assure you, for though the claws are pulled
off a crab before it is fried, all the body-meat remains. More, he not
only ate the crabs, but sucked the shells. On another occasion, on a
bet, he ate a ham and a cabbage in half an hour by the clock, but I
was not present at that performance. When, a little later, he
dropped dead in the old Central station-house, the police surgeons
laid it to a pulmonary embolus, then a recent novelty in pathology.

Madame Is Pleased

BY

M. F. K. FISHER

THAT early spring [1936] I met a young servant in northern
Burgundy who was almost fanatical about food, like a medieval
woman possessed by the devil. Her obsession engulfed even my appreciation of the dishes she served, until I grew uncomfortable.

It was the off season at the old mill which a Parisian chef had
bought and turned into one of France's most famous restaurants,
and my mad waitress was the only servant. In spite of that she was
neatly uniformed, and showed no surprise at my unannounced arrival and my hot dusty walking clothes.

She smiled discreetly at me, said, "Oh, but certainly!" when I
asked if I could lunch there, and led me without more words to a
dark bedroom bulging with First Empire furniture, and a new white
bathroom.

When I went into the dining room it was empty of humans . . . a
cheerful ugly room still showing traces of the *petit-bourgeois* parlor
it had been. There were aspidistras on the mantel; several small
white tables were laid with those imitation "peasant-ware" plates
that one sees in Paris china stores, and very good crystal glasses; a
cat folded under some ferns by the window ledge hardly looked at
me; and the air was softly hurried with the sound of high waters
from the stream outside.

I waited for the maid to come back. I knew I should eat well and
slowly, and suddenly the idea of dry sherry, unknown in all the village *bistrots* of the last few days, stung my throat smoothly. I tried
not to think of it; it would be impossible to realize. Dubonnet would
do. But not as well. I longed for sherry.

The little maid came into the silent room. I looked at her stocky

young body, and her butter-colored hair, and noticed her odd pale
voluptuous mouth before I said, "Mademoiselle, I shall drink an
apéritif. Have you by any chance—"

"Let me suggest," she interrupted firmly, "our special dry sherry.
It is chosen in Spain for Monsieur Paul."

And before I could agree she was gone, discreet and smooth.

She's a funny one, I thought, and waited in a pleasant warm tired-
ness for the wine.

It was good. I smiled approval at her, and she lowered her eyes,
and then looked searchingly at me again. I realized suddenly that in
this land of trained nonchalant waiters I was to be served by a small
waitress who took her duties seriously. I felt much amused, and
matched her solemn searching gaze.

"Today, Madame, you may eat shoulder of lamb in the English
style, with baked potatoes, green beans, and a sweet."

My heart sank. I felt dismal, and hot and weary, and still grateful
for the sherry.

But she was almost grinning at me, her lips curved triumphantly,
and her eyes less palely blue.

"Oh, in *that* case a trout, of course—a *truite au bleu* as only Mon-
seiur Paul can prepare it!"

She glanced hurriedly at my face, and hastened on. "With the
trout, one or two young potatoes—oh, very delicately boiled," she
added before I could protest, "very light."

I felt better. I agreed. "Perhaps a leaf or two of salad after the
fish," I suggested. She almost snapped at me. "Of course, of course!
And naturally our *hors d'oeuvres* to commence." She started away.

"No!" I called, feeling that I must assert myself now or be forever
lost. "No!"

She turned back, and spoke to me very gently. "But Madame has
never tasted our *hors d'oeuvres.* I am sure that Madame will be
pleased. They are our specialty, made by Monsieur Paul himself. I
am sure," and she looked reproachfully at me, her mouth tender and
sad, "I am sure that Madame would be very much pleased."

I smiled weakly at her, and she left. A little cloud of hurt gentleness seemed to hang in the air where she had last stood.

I comforted myself with sherry, feeling increasing irritation with
my own feeble self. Hell! I loathed *hors d'oeuvres!* I conjured disgusting visions of square glass plates of oily fish, of soggy vegetables

glued together with cheap mayonnaise, of rank radishes and tasteless butter. No, Monsieur Paul or not, sad young pale-faced waitress or not, I hated *hors d'oeuvres*.

I glanced victoriously across the room at the cat, whose eyes seemed closed.

II

Several minutes passed. I was really very hungry.

The door banged open, and my girl came in again, less discreet this time. She hurried toward me.

"Madame, the wine! Before Monsieur Paul can go on—" Her eyes watched my face, which I perversely kept rather glum.

"I think," I said ponderously, daring her to interrupt me, "I think that today, since I am in Burgundy and about to eat a trout," and here I hoped she noticed that I did not mention *hors d'oeuvres*, "I think I shall drink a bottle of Chablis 1929—*not* Chablis Village 1929."

For a second her whole face blazed with joy, and then subsided into a trained mask. I knew that I had chosen well, had somehow satisfied her in a secret and incomprehensible way. She nodded politely and scuttled off, only for another second glancing impatiently at me as I called after her, "Well cooled, please, but not iced."

I'm a fool, I thought, to order a whole bottle. I'm a fool, here all alone and with more miles to walk before I reach Avallon and my fresh clothes and a bed. Then I smiled at myself and leaned back in my solid wide-seated chair, looking obliquely at the prints of Gibson girls, English tavern scenes, and hideous countrysides that hung on the papered walls. The room was warm; I could hear my companion cat purring under the ferns.

The girl rushed in, with flat baking dishes piled up her arms on napkins, like the plates of a Japanese juggler. She slid them off neatly in two rows on to the table, where they lay steaming up at me, darkly and infinitely appetizing.

"*Mon Dieu!* All for me?" I peered at her. She nodded, her discretion quite gone now and a look of ecstatic worry on her pale face and eyes and lips.

There were at least eight dishes. I felt almost embarrassed, and sat for a minute looking weakly at the fork and spoon in my hand.

"Perhaps Madame would care to start with the pickled herring? It is not like any other. Monsieur Paul prepares it himself, in his own vinegar and wines. It is very good."

I dug out two or three brown filets from the dish, and tasted. They were truly unlike any others, truly the best I had ever eaten, mild, pungent, meaty as fresh nuts.

I realized the maid had stopped breathing, and looked up at her. She was watching me, or rather a gastronomic X-ray of the herring inside me, with a hypnotized glaze in her eyes.

"Madame is pleased?" she whispered softly.

I said I was. She sighed, and pushed a sizzling plate of broiled endive toward me, and disappeared.

I had put a few dull green lentils on my plate, lentils scattered with minced fresh herbs and probably marinated in tarragon vinegar and walnut oil, when she came into the dining room again with the bottle of Chablis in a wine basket.

"Madame should be eating the little baked onions while they are hot," she remarked over her shoulder as she held the bottle in a napkin and uncorked it. I obeyed meekly, and while I watched her I ate several more than I had meant to. They were delicious, simmered first in strong meat broth, I think, and then drained and broiled with olive oil and new-ground pepper.

I was fascinated by her method of uncorking a vintage wine. Instead of the Burgundian procedure of infinite and often exaggerated precautions against touching or tipping or jarring the bottle, she handled it quite nonchalantly, and seemed to be careful only to keep her hands from the cool bottle itself, holding it sometimes by the basket and sometimes in a napkin. The cork was very tight, and I thought for a minute that she would break it. So did she; her face grew tense, and did not loosen until she had slowly worked out the cork and wiped the lip. Then she poured an inch of wine in a glass, turned her back to me like a priest taking Communion, and drank it down. Finally some was poured for me, and she stood with the bottle in her hand and her full lips drooping until I nodded a satisfied yes. Then she pushed another of the plates toward me, and almost rushed from the room.

I ate slowly, knowing that I should not be as hungry as I ought to be for the trout, but knowing too that I had never tasted such delicate savory morsels. Some were hot, some cold. The wine was light and cool. The room, warm and agreeably empty under the rushing sound of the stream, became smaller as I grew used to it.

My girl hurried in again, with another row of plates up·one arm, and a large bucket dragging at the other. She slid the plates deftly on to the table, and drew a deep breath as she let the bucket down against the table leg.

"Your trout, Madame," she said excitedly. I looked down at the gleam of the fish curving through its limited water. "But first a good slice of Monsieur Paul's *pâté*. Oh yes, oh yes, you will be very sorry if you miss this. It is rich, but appetizing, and not at all too heavy. Just this one morsel!"

And willy-nilly I accepted the large gouge she dug from a terrine. I prayed for ten normal appetites and thought with amused nostalgia of my usual lunch of cold milk and fruit as I broke off a crust of bread and patted it smooth with the paste. Then I forgot everything but the exciting faint decadent flavor in my mouth.

I beamed up at the girl. She nodded, but from habit asked if I was satisfied. I beamed again, and asked, simply to please her, "Is there not a faint hint of *marc*, or perhaps cognac?"

"*Marc*, Madame!" And she awarded me the proud look of a teacher whose pupil has showed unexpected intelligence. "Monsieur Paul, after he has taken equal parts of goose breast and the finest pork, and broken a certain number of egg yolks into them, and ground them *very*, very fine, cooks all with seasoning for some three hours. But," she pushed her face nearer, and looked with ferocious gloating at the *pâté* inside me, her eyes like X-rays, "he never stops stirring it! Figure to yourself the work of it—stir, stir, never stopping!

"Then he grinds in a suspicion of nutmeg, and then adds, very thoroughly, a glass of *marc* for each hundred grams of *pâté*. And is Madame not pleased?"

Again I agreed, rather timidly, that Madame was much pleased, that Madame had never, indeed, tasted such an unctuous and exciting *pâté*. The girl wet her lips delicately, and then started as if she had been pin-struck.

"But the trout! My God, the trout!" She grabbed the bucket, and her voice grew higher and more rushed.

"Here is the trout, Madame. You are to eat it *au bleu*, and you should never do so if you had not seen it alive. For if the trout were

dead when it was plunged into the *court bouillon* it would not turn
blue. So, naturally, it must be living."

I knew all this, more or less, but I was fascinated by her absorption in the momentary problem. I felt quite ignorant, and asked her
with sincerity, "What about the trout? Do you take out its guts
before or after?"

"Oh, the trout!" She sounded scornful. "Any trout is glad, truly
glad, to be prepared by Monsieur Paul. His little gills are pinched,
with one flash of the knife he is empty, and then he curls in agony
in the *bouillon* and all is over. And it is the curl you must judge,
Madame. A false *truite au bleu* cannot curl."

She panted triumph at me, and hurried out with the bucket.

III

She *is* a funny one, I thought, and for not more than two or
three minutes I drank wine and mused over her. Then she darted
in, with the trout correctly blue and agonizingly curled on a platter,
and on her crooked arm a plate of tiny boiled potatoes and a bowl.

When I had been served and had cut off her anxious breathings
with an assurance that the fish was the best I had ever tasted, she
peered again at me and at the sauce in the bowl. I obediently put
some of it on the potatoes: no fool I, to ruin *truite au bleu* with a
hot concoction! There was more silence.

"Ah!" she sighed at last. "I knew Madame would feel thus! Is it
not the most beautiful sauce in the world with the flesh of a trout?"

I nodded incredulous agreement.

"Would you like to know how it is done?"

I remembered all the legends of chefs who guarded favorite
recipes with their very lives, and murmured yes.

She wore the exalted look of a believer describing a miracle at
Lourdes as she told me, in a rush, how Monsieur Paul threw
chopped chives into hot sweet butter and then poured the butter
off, how he added another nut of butter and a tablespoonful of
thick cream for each person, stirred the mixture for a few minutes
over a slow fire, and then rushed it to the table.

"So simple?" I asked softly, watching her lighted eyes and the
tender lustful lines of her strange mouth.

"So simple, Madame! But," she shrugged, "you know, with a mas-ter—"

I was relieved to see her go; such avid interest in my eating wore on me. I felt released when the door closed behind her, free for a minute or so from her victimization. What would she have done, I wondered, if I had been ignorant or unconscious of any fine flavors?

She was right, though, about Monsieur Paul. Only a master could live in this isolated mill and preserve his gastronomic dignity through loneliness and the sure financial loss of unused butter and addled eggs. Of course, there was the stream for his fish, and I knew his *pâtés* would grow even more edible with age; but how could he manage to have a thing like roasted lamb ready for any chance patron? Was the consuming interest of his one maid enough fuel for his flame?

I tasted the last sweet nugget of trout, the one nearest the blued tail, and poked somnolently at the minute white billiard balls that had been eyes. Fate could not harm me, I remembered winily, for I had indeed dined today, and dined well. Now for a leaf of crisp salad, and I'd be on my way.

The girl slid into the room. She asked me again, in a respectful but gossipy manner, how I had liked this and that and the other things, and then talked on as she mixed dressing for the endive.

"And now," she announced, after I had eaten one green sprig and dutifully pronounced it excellent, "now Madame is going to taste Monsieur Paul's special terrine, one that is not even on the summer menu, when a hundred covers are laid here daily and we have a headwaiter and a wine waiter, and cabinet ministers telegraph for tables! Madame will be pleased."

And heedless of my low moans of the walk still before me, of my appreciation and my unhappily human and limited capacity, she cut a thick heady slice from the terrine of meat and stood over me while I ate it, telling me with almost hysterical pleasure of the wild ducks, the spices, the wines that went into it. Even surfeit could not make me deny that it was a rare dish. I ate it all, knowing my luck, and wishing only that I had red wine to drink with it.

I was beginning, though, to feel almost frightened, realizing my-self an accidental victim of these stranded gourmets, Monsieur Paul and his handmaiden. I began to feel that they were using me for a safety valve, much as a thwarted woman relieves herself with tantrums or a fit of weeping. I was serving a purpose, and perhaps a noble one, but I resented it in a way approaching panic.

I protested only to myself when one of Monsieur Paul's special cheeses was cut for me, and ate it doggedly, like a slave. When the girl said that Monsieur Paul himself was preparing a special filter of coffee for me, I smiled servile acceptance; wine and the weight of food and my own character could not force me to argue with maniacs. When, before the coffee came, Monsieur Paul presented me, through his idolater, with the most beautiful apple tart I had ever seen, I allowed it to be cut and served to me. Not a wince or a murmur showed the waitress my distressed fearfulness. With a stuffed careful smile on my face, and a clear nightmare in my head of trussed wanderers prepared for his altar by this hermit-priest of gastronomy, I listened to the girl's passionate plea for fresh pastry dough.

"You cannot, you cannot, Madame, serve old pastry!" She seemed ready to beat her breast as she leaned across the table. "Look at that delicate crust! You may feel that you have eaten too much." (I nodded idiotic agreement.) "But this pastry is like feathers—it is like snow. It is in fact good for you, a digestive! And why?" She glared sternly at me. "Because Monsieur Paul did not even open the flour bin until he saw you coming! He could not, he could not have baked you one of his special apple tarts with old dough!"

She laughed, tossing her head and curling her mouth voluptuously.

IV

Somehow I managed to refuse a second slice, but I trembled under her surmise that I was ready for my special filter.

The wine and the fortitude had fled me, and I drank the hot coffee as a suffering man gulps ether, deeply and gratefully.

I remember, then, chatting with surprising glibness, and sending to Monsieur Paul flowery compliments, all of them sincere and well won, and I remember feeling only amusement when a vast glass of *marc* appeared before me and then gradually disappeared, like the light in the warm room full of water-sounds. I felt surprise to be alive still, and suddenly very grateful to the wild-lipped waitress, as if her presence had sustained me through duress. We discussed food and wine. I wondered bemusedly why I had been frightened.

The *marc* was gone. I went into the crowded bedroom for my jacket. She met me in the darkening hall when I came out, and I paid my bill, a large one. I started to thank her, but she took my hand, drew me into the dining room, and without words poured more spirits into my glass. I drank to Monsieur Paul while she watched me intently, her pale eyes bulging in the dimness and her lips pressed inward as if she too tasted the hot, aged *marc*.

The cat rose from his ferny bed, and walked contemptuously out of the room.

Suddenly the girl began to laugh, in a soft shy breathless way, and came close to me.

"Permit me!" she said, and I thought she was going to kiss me. But instead she pinned a tiny bunch of snowdrops and dark bruised cyclamens against my stiff jacket, very quickly and deftly, and then ran from the room with her head down.

I waited for a minute. No sounds came from anywhere in the old mill, but the endless rushing of the full stream seemed to strengthen, like the timid blare of an orchestra under a falling curtain.

She's a *funny* one, I thought. I touched the cool blossoms on my coat and went out, like a ghost from ruins, across the courtyard toward the dim road to Avallon.

Vouvray, Terrines, and the Slopes of Gold

BY

G. B. STERN

THE WEATHER and the landscape that we passed through on the first stage of our northward journey from Libourne to Burgundy was autumn and spring whimsically entangled, crisp as autumn, and languid as spring; pear-trees and lilac actually in bloom, contrasted with patches of tall Jerusalem artichokes in yellow flower, with Indian corn and dahlias and scarlet salvias, dabbling the quiet blue sky with bright colour; and shining pomegranate-trees that arched their boughs of gold-copper fruit over most of the cottage doorways. An occasional baby château, with miniature towers, completed the peaceful pattern of the tapestry.

We were surprised to hear that Jerusalem artichokes are not looked on as a delectable food, in France. The roots are given to beasts, or made into alcohol for hairwash!

We lunched at the Grand Hôtel de France, Chalais. Let no one be misled by the pompous name. It was a very small inn, trees planted close about it; and a long, narrow dining-room, with a wooden floor, and one set of knives and forks to be used for all the courses. Our meal, which was served us by an extraordinarily deft and pretty girl, was typical of what one may expect in almost any small place in France; not of the trout-and-partridge grade, but just below it, where they shyly suggest omelet and veal, and you take it for granted that these will be well cooked and quickly dished up; and that, in addition, there will be hors-d'œuvres, vegetables, cheese, fruit, and coffee. We drank *vin ordinaire,* a really good light white wine, with a rounded flavour; and the bill for the four of us, including all these things, and probably four vermouths and a couple of *fines,* amounted to seventy-six francs—about nine shillings.

That lunch was a pleasant memory; and so was our arrival

towards evening, at Angoulême, at the Nouvel Hôtel des Trois Piliers, where we were received in the joyful spirit of an old nurse welcoming back her bairns after twenty years, when they are grown men and women. We had sent a wire, announcing that we intended to spend a night there; so, according to previous request, they had prepared *homard thermidor* for three of us, and delicious fried soles for one—the one being myself. I have never really cared for lobster since, in Cornwall, I went lobster-glutto! The outposts of the meal, at either end, were our old friends, that excellent white *vin ordinaire,* and the 1873 Cognac, which should be spoken of with bared head, and in a voice of reverence. But in between we drank a bottle of Château Latour 1918—a very promising wine, but young, and therefore crude in the after-taste. In twenty years, perhaps . . .

But meanwhile: "Not *very* good, dear, I'm afraid," said Rosemary, gently. Humphrey said never a word. . . .

> *—Es ist eine alte Geschichte,*
> *Doch bleibt sie immer neu;*
> *Und wem sie just passieret,*
> *Dem bricht das Herz entzwei!*

Our lunch the next day, at Saint-Jean-d'Angely, in contrast to the lunch at Chalais, was most sinister: we had to drive the car up a long, cobbled alley; and directly we stopped, a hag, grey and thin and angry, rushed out from one of the doorways, and began mopping and mowing, and making wide-flung melodramatic gestures of despair, reminding us of what Sybil Thorndike would have been, in the part of any Dumb Old Woman, at the Guignol. However, as there seemed no other spot to park the car, we had to ignore Dumb Old Woman, who, with one final fatalistic gesture of her skinny arms, sweeping us downwards and away, out of all luck and light, disappeared again under the arch of her doorway, next to the hotel.

The dining-room at the hotel was sinister, too. Those who waited upon us were silent and joyless, their movements mechanical, their eyes sullen. Lunch was almost uneatable, and the only literally bright spot in it was quite an agreeable *vin rosé.*

But the outside world was a compensation, for no gloom could last long on that cold, brilliant autumn day. Thouars, where we had arranged to spend that first night of our northward journey to Burgundy, proved to be a small ramparted town, standing solitary on a hill. It was there, at the Hôtel du Cheval Blanc on the very crest of the hill, that we tasted, at dinner, our first Vouvray: a Château Moncontour 1920; I think, from later experience, that this is the only dry Vouvray. I had heard much of this wine, having been told that it was wonderful when drunk in its own region, and utterly unlike any other wine; so that we took our first sip with keen curiosity.

Its bouquet, certainly, was distinctive. Humphrey said it reminded him of wet iron. I have never noticed the bouquet of wet iron, but I cannot imagine that it has anything like the delicate crispness of Vouvray. Vouvray tastes more like Rhine wine than French. I know of no better wine to encourage a mood of gay exhilaration. In this it is like really lilting waltz music, not heavy, mawkish, melancholy waltzes, but Schubert, Johann Strauss, Lehar, and Fall. Wine gaiety should halt, laughing, just on the brink of intoxication. I remember a wine in Italy which induced this evanescent happiness, this rapture with all things, not as they were, but as I, for the moment, thought them. It was called Soave Veronese; and I drank it, most appropriately, sitting outside a café, opposite the amphitheatre at Verona, on a blazing September day. It was not an elfin, elusive white wine, like Vouvray; but crimson, and mellow, and, as its name indicates, suave.

. . . Presently I found myself swaggering down an arcade in Verona, with watch-shops on either side of me. I had never seen so many beautiful watches. The Arcade of the Jewelled Watches!—it sounded as romantic as the Street of Swords in Toledo. I vowed, then, that when I was richer—not if, but *when,* for I was confident with Soave Veronese—I would return here and buy a watch. Two years later a friend of mine was going to Verona, and, being then "in purse," I commissioned her to buy me a watch. I described to her the arcade, with watch-shops one beside the other for the whole length and on either side. "You can't miss it!" I said—but it transpired that she could. There was, indeed, no arcade entirely composed of watchmongers in all Verona. It did not exist. She could not even find so many as two watch-shops side by side. She bought for me quite a pretty little watch, the sort that you can easily find in any jeweller's in any town of a certain size. . . . But I had been happy in an arcade in Verona, I had drunk Soave Veronese, and walked with the gods, and on either side of me were watch-shops, thousands of watch-shops, millions of watches, all gloriously ticking away the vermilion hours. . . .

Funny thing, wine! A mere germ that creeps into and foments the juice of a grape, and then . . . "It's a good thing God thought of it," said Humphrey, one day; "because *I* shouldn't have!"

So that night, after dinner, at Thouars, instead of feeling, as we usually did, lumpish and sleepy from our day of fast driving and rushing air, we felt joyful and enterprising; and went swinging out to explore, down the hill, through the town, and on to the ramparts. It was a night of black velvet, with cold flashing stars, and Thouars felt like mediæval France. Somehow we found ourselves thinking of the fine old names that once embroidered the map— Acquitaine, Gascony, Touraine. . . . Of old wars, too! Of archers and the first cannons. We walked round the tower of the Black Prince, where he had sojourned for some months during his victories in France; and I remembered learning about him from *Little Arthur's History of England,* and being bidden to admire him for his infernally priggish act in bringing home the captive King John on a great white horse, while he himself rode meekly beside him on a small pony. Even as a child, it had struck me that the Black Prince would have been nicer still if he had allowed King John to remain somewhere in quiet obscurity, instead of dragging him through the streets, conspicuous on an immense charger. Viewed from an adult and psychological standpoint, it is, of course, quite obvious that our modest Black Prince was an adept at stage-managing himself effectively.

. . . Presently, scrambling up and down steep cobbled lanes, past dark entries that led we knew not whither, we passed under an archway that was certainly one of the old gates of the town, and found ourselves on the walls, with the road running below, and the fortifications like cliffs behind us.

Old wars . . . old magic. . . . The air was like black wine. We could only dimly see each other's faces. Suddenly, among the ruins, above or below us, you could hardly tell which, came heavy steps, then the crumbling and sliding of stones . . . steps again, whispering, and silence. A sentry, maybe, had left his post for a few minutes for a kiss from Mademoiselle, who had slipped away from her father's vigilance. But he should be on duty. At any moment the English archers might attack. . . .

Well, these were old wars.

Our journey the next day was through what is known as the château country. By unspoken consent we did not enter a single one of the famous castles, though we passed Chinon, and Loche, Loudain, Tours, and finally Amboise, where we slept that night; but somehow we felt that a wine-tour would be rather overloaded if it actually involved getting out of the car and taking an intelligent interest in the insides of some seven or eight castles of different periods and centuries and histories. Besides, seeing each great château, first as a shape on the skyline, high on a hill, or washed by the river; drawing nearer and nearer; and then just not alighting, is a distinct sensation of its own, not without pleasure—the perverse pleasure, I suppose, which lies in missed opportunities.

Humphrey was smoking Wills' Gold Flake cigarettes at that time, which contained in each packet a picture from the Famous Châteaux series; and he held firmly to the opinion that this was the least exhausting and the most satisfactory way of "doing" the châteaux. I am afraid it is quite evident that the leading characteristic of our quartet was laziness—

> Lazy—I want to be lazy . . .
> I want to be out in the sun
> With no work to be done,
> Under that awning
> They call the sky. . . .

And "under that awning they call the sky" we sat at Vouvray, in the garden of the Hôtel du Pont de Cisse, drinking Château Moncontour again, *très sec*, 1920; an exquisitely luxurious sensation. It was a pale Chablis, greenish-gold, and the rhythm of our happy mood danced down on us again, and carried us buoyantly through the day. Rosemary, who sometimes drove the car, now drove it, after drinking Vouvray, as though it were the only car in the world on the only road, confidently, carelessly, and singing as she drove. . . .

We lunched at Chinon, on the River Vienne, and drank Grand Vin de Chinon, Clos d'Argenson, a pleasant, light, but undistinguished wine. But the Castle of Chinon I shall remember always, with its long greyhound lines, high above the river; the most lovely and legendary of all the châteaux. The massive strength of Loudain, with walls so thick that it seemed nothing could overthrow them, with moat, portcullis, and drawbridge, in all the best traditions of castle fame and castle legends, was, in its own way, as impressive. Chinon had slipped out from between the pages of the Book of Old, Old French Fairy-Tales; but Loudain we used to build out of sand, and it took a whole morning to build it strong enough to resist the incoming tide. . . .

Our way lay along the north bank of the Loire, a wide unemotional river with many shallows and islands; and we were puzzled by the curious troglodytic houses, like caves, built into the cliff, lower than the road, and lower, it seemed than the river, between Saint-Mars, Lapille, and Tours, as far as Vouvray. It was as though a race of dwarfs had burrowed their dwelling here, preferring the semi-darkness.

The château at Amboise was far too ornate and over-decorated to be beautiful; and, moreover, an atmosphere of char-à-bancs hung all about it. We crossed the bridge on to the south bank, and went to the excellent Hôtel de France et Cheval Blanc, where the view, the food, and the staff were all full of charm; and Johnny discovered an excellent quality of wolfdog—though not quite as good as the one at Thouars, he said; and indeed she had been a little darling at Thouars, almost as graceful and capricious as our own Tessa, left behind in Italy.

At Thouars we had all been very stupid; for there they kept a fox-cub unhappily in a cage, and we had longed to kidnap it, and carry it away in a sack, and let it run free and wild again in the green and russet rich-smelling woods that we passed on today's run. We had only *not* stolen it and carried it off in this arbitrary fashion because of the difficulties that had naturally arisen from the entire staff of a hotel, including the proprietor, and half the village, standing round in the courtyard to wave us farewell. But now that it was too late, now that we were already in Amboise, and a day's swift travel away, it occurred to us that we could quite simply and honestly have *bought* the fox-cub. They would surely have sold it to us, rejoicing, for less than a hundred francs; and then we could have seen it plunge into the undergrowth and vanish like a red-brown streak, never, perhaps, to be caught again—at all events, not without a run for it. It is curious that the honest method of acquiring it did not first occur to us!

With our dinner, at Amboise, we drank a wine we had never yet heard of, a Saint Nicholas Bourgeuil, 1921; here in the Loire region they export very little, and the wine-lists are exciting and unfamiliar. Saint Nicholas Bourgeuil was a good drink, clear ruby colour, soft and pleasant to the palate. We followed it up by a Vouvray 1893—thirty-three years is a good age, and we did not mind that this veteran was slightly sweet, for we drank it as a dessert wine; it was a sparkling, rich deep gold, mellow in flavour, and with plenty of character.

If, when you lunch at the Hôtel de l'Écu de Bretagne, at Beaugency, the *maître d'hôtel* should prove to be busy and bad-tempered, should he domineer over your wishes with terrifying bursts of *"Sapristi!"* and *"N'om d'un chien!"*—remember always that he is a lamb with a lion's moustache; for if I had found this out at the beginning, instead of at the end, of our most succulent lunch, I should not have sat quaking and apologetic, from the vermouth to the *fine*.

It was, as a matter of fact, the vermouth which began the trouble. The *maître d'hôtel*, when we entered, was charging about among his beseeching clients like an enraged but confident bull who has learnt not to break the china. . . . These zoological comparisons will occur! I must say for the man, however, that he did not keep us waiting. *"Quatre vermouths français!"* we said, quickly, for he made no attempt to conceal, as he stood by our table, that he was chafing to be off again. In a flash he was back, arranged the glasses, poured out half a vermouth—*"Pah!"* No! The bottle was finished; these were the dregs. Impatiently he substituted another bottle, pulled the cork, poured out four vermouths. . . . Then suddenly and suspiciously raised the bottle to his nose, shook his head, muttered an oath, swept away the four full glasses and the bottle, and disappeared.

Before we had had much time to speculate on the meaning of this, he reappeared with yet another bottle, and four more glasses. This time he seemed satisfied. Humphrey, however, was not.

"Esker c'est vermouth français?" he asked, in that style of French which will for ever maintain the reputation of the Englishman abroad.

The *maître d'hôtel* glared at him. *"Vermouth italien!"* he rapped back.

"S'il vous plaît," said our slow and imperturbable Humphrey, *"s'il vous plaît, nong. Vermouth français!"*

. . . I do not care to remember in detail that panic-stricken moment, though it is easy to divine that Johnny's hand, under the
table, had stolen swiftly to his hip-pocket. . . . The *maître d'hôtel*
seemed to gather himself as for some mighty explosion; but *"Sapr—r
—risti!"* was all he growled; *"Ça m'énerve à la fin!"*

"Nous aimong," intrepid Humphrey went on, *"vermouth français.
Pas italien. Trop dooss. Français!"*

—The *maître d'hôtel* went away. He returned with a bottle of
vermouth français; Noilly Pratt, in fact, which we always preferred,
as an *apéritif,* by itself, though Italian vermouth is necessary to mix
in cocktails. He also brought four more glasses. He poured out the
Noilly, and left us to drink it. . . .

"Have you read *The Virginian?"* asked Johnny of the rest of us,
reminiscently. "There's a wonderful bit in it about a cow-boy who
went into a small restaurant, where he was handed a menu including all sorts of delicacies, among them being 'Frogs' Legs *à la*
Delmonico,' which the cow-boy ordered. The proprietor of the
restaurant then produced two revolvers, which he pointed at the
cow-boy, saying: *'You'll 'ave 'ash!'* "

"You'll 'ave *terrine!"*—or words to that effect, said the *maître
d'hôtel,* reappearing suddenly before us.

We did 'ave *terrine.* If *terrine* rhymed with "dream," I would
make a poem about it. It was *"terrine de la maison,"* and, as the
chef afterwards told me, the main ingredients were crushed partridges. We ranked it, with the *brandade* at Avignon, the *crêpes
bordelais* at Bordeaux, and the *pâté de lièvre* at Châteauneuf-du-
Pape, as one of the great culinary experiences of our tour. Timidly,
oh, but very timidly, I whispered something of this to the *maître
d'hôtel* when he came round again with the dish. He seemed slightly
mollified, and, almost without pausing in his stride, gave us each
another large slice.

After the *terrine* came omelet, a beauty, served in a fiery sauce,
licked by transparent blue flame. Then we had the tenderest Cha-
teaubriand steak that France had as yet given me.

The wine was not quite up to the level of the food. We began
with Cheverney 1919, a quite well-behaved white wine; and this was
followed by a Beaugency *décanté,* 1921. The Beaugency might have
been a very good wine indeed, had it not been so rigidly frozen that
no flavour at all was perceptible. On a bright cold day, like this

twenty-ninth of September, you do prefer your red wine to be somewhat *chambré*. Never has wine been so cuddled as was this Beaugency by us in our efforts to unfreeze it. We treated it like an almost drowned kitten whom we were attempting to restore to life; but in spite of everything, the cold weather won, and we still do not know the taste of Beaugency 1921.

Resigned, we turned away from it to an eau-de-vie, very different from any other kind, with a strong bouquet, and a taste of schnapps.

The bill, when it was brought, proved that this extraordinarily good meal was also extraordinarily cheap.

Waiting while Humphrey brought the car round, I encountered the *maître d'hôtel* again, just outside the door. He was talking to the chef. The luncheon rush was over. He was smiling amiably; so was the chef, a meek little man in white linen, with a pointed beard. I went up to them, and faltered my compliments. The *maître d'hôtel* was very pleased. Encouraged, I went on to tell him how afraid I had been at the beginning of the meal. He patted my hand:

"*Mais non!* you must not be afraid of Papa—" (I forget his nickname—Papa something.) "What was there to be afraid of? I am very fond of the ladies, I!" And then followed a well-chosen compliment. He introduced me to the chef. The chef introduced me to the *terrine de la maison*. We all bowed, and approved of one another. The chef told me how many stars and decorations he had. I, in return, told him how many more I would give him had I the bestowal in my power. We were all very happy. I liked the Hôtel de l'Écu de Bretagne, at Beaugency.

Our good lunch, followed by four hours of high-speed motoring through the snapping, brilliant, cold afternoon, made us all drowsy. At sunset we saw the little, fortified town of Sancerre on the summit of a hill that was golden and red with vines. The hill stood up alone in a flat landscape of vines, all ruddy and autumn-coloured, and through it the white road looped and ran and lost itself again, and went up and up till it disappeared behind the topmost wall. Seen thus across the plains, Sancerre had all the silent enchantment of a scene worked on tapestry.

On an impulse, for we had meant to go as far as Pouilly-sur-Loire that night, we decided to mount that spiralling white road, up and up, to Sancerre.

It was a mistake, of course. Not a bad mistake. We found a reasonably comfortable hotel, and dined reasonably well. The wine of Sancerre is not particularly distinguished; though I believe it was here, at the Hôtel du Point du Jour et de l'Écu, that the proprietor brought out a really old vermouth which had lain a long time in wood, and a still longer time in bottle. Up till then, funnily enough, it had never occurred to me that vermouth would gain handsomely by the same respectful treatment that we accord to wine.

But never again, not that evening, nor the next morning, when we drove away again, nor from within the walls of the town, did Sancerre ever appear to us with the glamour of that moment when we first saw her, at sunset, on the hill, across the red-gold vineyards.

THE SLOPES OF GOLD

The invisible Master of Ceremonies who directed our entrance into Burgundy was aware of the value of pageantry. In Bordeaux no one had been aware of it. There is a famous road which runs from Chagny to Dijon, and all along are planted the grand vineyards; most of the more royal growths of Burgundy lie on the further side of Beaune—Romanée-Conti, Richebourg, Clos de Vougeot; but as we licked up the superb stretch of reinforced concrete on the last lap of our journey, the names which flashed past from the low walls—Grand Auxey, Meursault, Pommard, Volnay, were familiar enough to excite us.

When we entered the Côte d'Or, the hills far ahead in the east were drenched and misted in fabulous hues of pale gold, so that they looked like a myth told about hills long ago; but to our right and left, where the sun had already withdrawn, the colour of the ranges had ebbed and ebbed, from flame to damson, and from deep warm damson to indigo. The vines, here in this more northern region, had already been well stung by the cold, and their leaves ran chromatically through all the yellows, bronzes, chestnuts, and dark purples of their final flaunting array before they wither and fall. I was envious of all this pomp for Burgundy. In this fashion, and no other, should the big vineyards of the world make their impression on pilgrims from a country which grows no wine.

Nearly everyone who goes to Beaune stays at the Hôtel de la Poste. Here, too, they understand skilful staging of their effects. The proprietor, or rather, as we afterwards discovered, the proprietor's son-in-law, came forward as we entered the dining-room, and asked us if we would dine well, or dine table d'hôte. When it was put to us like that, we rather naturally answered that we would dine well! He approved our decision, and murmured something about *poulet au Chambertin*. That did not sound bad. Then we asked for the wine-list, and Humphrey fell upon it; Johnny and I remaining suitably in the background on this occasion.

Being human beings and not angels, we were not altogether displeased at seeing a slight cloud of disappointment on Humphrey's brow. "There seems to be nothing older than 1919," he said, slowly. Rosemary called up the proprietor: "We wanted to consult you," she began charmingly, "about the wine——" Here he rushed in before she had time to go any further. He told us that Burgundy was not the same as Bordeaux; and that it made a difference in wine which year you chose; also that one vintage differed in taste and flavour from another. . . .

"Tiens?" said Rosemary, a little piqued; and indeed it did seem as though the stamp of our recent studies and experiences should in some way be so marked upon us as to defend us from this sort of instruction. *"Mais nous sommes déjà un peu connoisseurs, vous savez."*

We chose for ourselves a Chablis de Clos, 1919, with a Chambertin 1919 to follow. The latter was the proprietor's choice. He said it would go well with the *poulet au Chambertin*. The staging of the wines, here, at this hotel, and indeed everywhere in the region, was again infinitely superior to the casual habits of the Bordelais, who slung their most precious wines about as though they were serving bottled lemonade. Here, the wines were carefully warmed and cradled, or, if necessary, iced, to exactly the right degree, carried as though they were the Holy Grail, and poured into gigantic tulip-shaped glasses with reverent ceremonial. As a matter of fact, I thought the glasses for the Chambertin were exaggeratedly immense. You had to tilt them practically upside down before any of the liquid at the bottom could reach your lips.

After the soup a gigantic fish was brought to us, lying voluptuously full length on a dish. Its name was *brochet meunière,* which translated itself as pike, disguised by art and a glorious sauce. The Chablis which we drank with this most excellent fellow brought bubbling to the surface again all my dormant springs of belief that Chablis was the best white wine in the world; better than Montrachet; better than Rhone wine, or either of the Pouillys; better than white Hermitage; and oh, how much better than Château Yquem! This Chablis had that rare pale effect of shot green and gold, and the fragrance and the flavour were unforgettable.

We had to wait a long time for our *poulet au Chambertin*, but it was a monumental dish when it arrived, and it would take hours to tell of all the delicacies which we found in the gravy. As for the Chambertin itself, it is not among my favourite Burgundies. This 1919 had a wonderful bouquet of violets, but the taste lingered a long way behind.

I must mention a special cheese called Minstère, like Camembert, only better, which they gave us here, and which we could get nowhere else. It immensely improved the flavour of the wine. As for the *fine de la maison* 1858, which, in a breathless hush, was slowly poured into glasses so overwhelmingly huge that any of them could have been used as a rose-bowl in the centre of a mayoral banquet, that brandy was almost an anæsthetic in bouquet. I believe in glasses of this size, for brandy; you can slowly inhale the rising perfume, and enjoy all the voluptuous pleasure of reeling back from it, dazed and incredulous.

Altogether a not undistinguished meal.

The next morning we went to see M. Jaboulet-Vercherre, who owns the old Clos de la Commaraine vineyard, and is a grower of good wines both at Hermitage and at the Côte d'Or. His specialty is Pommard. He very charmingly invited us all to lunch on the following day. So on this day we lunched at the Hôtel Terminus, Beaune, where I much enjoyed a Corton 1915, its hue a very glorious red when you lifted it to the rays of the sun. The name on the label, however, reminded me of a rather inglorious episode in my past, when I had just begun to know a little, a very little indeed, about wine. A good friend of mine, a perfect hostess, who always treats her guests with the delicate forethought of a loyalist making the ex-king of a lost cause believe that he is worthy of even better entertainment than a reigning king, once gave me white Corton 1915. Ungratefully, for it was a most delicious wine, I chid her for the date, pointing out that 1915 had been a poor year for Burgundy, and it should have been 1914. . . . Well, I am older, and,

fortunately, know less certainly about everything now than I did!
That 1915 white Corton was a peerless wine. 1915 was the right
year. I take this opportunity of apologizing to my hostess, with a
promise that I will be less bumptious next time!

It speaks powerfully for the effect of the Burgundy wines on my
sense of observation that I seem to recall nothing whatever of our
stay at Beaune except our meals; with the exception, perhaps, of
the eight dancing Siamese kittens, who lived with their Siamese
parents in the pantry of the hotel, and who were continually darting
out into the hall and dining-room, nimble as monkeys. Funny, fascinating little cats they were, with big blue eyes; their noses, ears,
tails, and paws, sombre splashes of mud-colour. We were so entranced by the spectacle of these kittens, tumbling in and out of
wine-cradles, or lying, when we would permit them, with Buddhist
faces and crossed paws in the hollow of our necks, motionless for
hours, that we bought two of the older litter, who were big enough
to travel, and arranged for the proprietor to send them to us by
train to Avignon, to reach us there on the day we left for home;
for we did not fancy the idea of having the rest of our leisurely
journeying accompanied day and night, in the car and out of it, by
the imperious, angry miaowings of this particular breed of cat; their
inflection was always more profane than sacred, and they clawfully
resented the slightest attention being paid to anything but themselves.

There is an interesting theory, which our own experience inclines
us to accept, that these cats used to be kept entirely in the Siamese
harems. This is supposed to account for the fact that they are never
quiet unless they are being petted and caressed; for the ladies of the
harem, presumably, had nothing better to do. Moreover, we have
noticed that their fur has a peculiar sweetish perfumè, which we
choose to believe is a survival of the scent favoured by the mistresses
of their ancestral past.

Satan and Sin, as we call them, are with us now; but unfortunately we were sent one kitten from each litter, instead of the two
we had originally chosen; and we have had the greatest trouble in
keeping poor little Sin alive, for she was much too young and frail
to leave her mother, and be sped on such a long journey, from
Beaune to the Italian Riviera. I am afraid that she will die at the
first nip of winter. Satan, however, grows in strength, in beauty, and

in evil, every day. He is a queer relic to have brought from a wine-tour; my only other "souvenirs" are a three-cornered jug in the dull green and blue pottery of Pouilly-sur-Loire; and a wave of flame and Chinese blue which was eventually to materialize on the bridge at Lyons.

Our dinner that night at the hotel was fully as good as the night before—*bisque d'écrevisses*, partridge, and a cheese *soufflé*. Johnny declared, however, that his *bisque* was just one shade in excellence behind the *bisque d'écrevisses* he had eaten at the Hotel Bristol at Vienna; and while I am on comparisons, I must mention that Humphrey declared that his best ham-and-eggs—*œufs au plat et jambon grillé*—for breakfast, from the beginning of the tour to the end, had been at the Grand Hôtel at Le Puy. These are subtleties of the highest importance.

We drank a bottle of the same Chablis as the night before, because we could not bear to think of it so near us in the cellar, and yet not in our glasses; and then, again on recommendation, we had Romanée-Conti 1920, very much too young for a final judgment to be passed on it; I told the proprietor, when he questioned me anxiously, that to drink it made me feel as though I were committing infanticide. He protested; wine, it appeared, was drunk young nowadays; much younger than of yore. The Romanée-Conti was at just the ripe age for drinking.

"*Tiens?*" said Rosemary. . . . He had implied that we were rather *démodé* victims of an old-fashioned fallacy.

So far, though we had drunk no Burgundy as definitely bad as some of the Bordeaux which had been served to us, the triumph of the Burgundians over the Bordelais had not been unbearable for Johnny and myself.

Humphrey and Rosemary were beginning to look bothered.

A Simple Christmas

BY

DELLA T. LUTES

CHRISTMAS, in the days of my childhood, was not the occasion for the orgy of spending and sophisticated entertainment that it now is. Santa Claus was to me neither a very real person nor a dominant myth. He was supposed to have had a hand in fashioning the renewed wardrobe of Annette, the only doll I ever owned, a mature and haughty creature with china head and elaborate chignon. But there was a certain familiarity about the fabrics from which her garments were made that was reminiscent of my mother's piece bag, a fact quite logically arousing some childish doubt.

An orange in the toe of the stocking, a well-polished apple oddly resembling those in our own cellar, a stick or two of pep'mint, cin'mon, or horehound candy, constituted the contents of the average stocking, and quite satisfying they were, too, to a generation of children not sated with useless, destructible, and often soul-destroying junk as are ours of to-day.

Christmas Day was lifted, in our home, only a few degrees above the plane of any other simple holiday. We had company, certainly, but because of the imminence of New Year's Day, my father's birthday, when the clan would congregate, this was confined to such relics of our immediate community as were likely to fare worse. Such, for instance, as Miz' Lou Esty, the itinerant seamstress who went from house to house to sew and mend, and who, after the unlamented demise of her husband some years before the time of my own memory, had no home other than a room in the Bouldry house, where she went, as she herself said, to catch her breath between seams.

Miz' Esty was an interesting person because of her intimate ac-

quaintance with neighborhood affairs, but not a woman of super-
stitions, as proved by her own related experience.

Some one of the neighbors had broken a mirror and Miz' Esty,
who had been present at the time, flouted the consternation of the
family and their trembling apprehension of the prophesied seven
years of bad luck.

"I've broke mirrors," said Miz' Esty with complacent assurance,
"and *I* never had no bad luck. I remember one time we was moving;
there was a big dresser in the back of the wagon and it bumped into
something and the glass smashed to pieces."

My mother, to whom, with my father, she was relating the incident at the supper table, said:—

"And you didn't have any bad luck?"

"Nothin' I can remember. Of course," she added negligently,
"Esty died that fall, but I wouldn't count that."

"Neither would I," my father agreed when, later, he and my
mother were laughing over Miz' Esty's evaluation of misfortune.
"Knowing Hod Esty, *I* wouldn't." For Hod Esty, as all the neighbors
knew, was a shiftless, worthless toper, refusing to work, and spending, when he could get his hands on it, the money which Miz' Esty
earned. Justified, as anyone would feel, was her curt summary of the
situation.

Old David H. was another derelict whom I remember sitting at
our Christmas board upon at least one occasion when Miz' Esty was
also a guest. David H. was a first-rate carpenter but one whose itch-
ing foot had become entangled in the treacherous vine, and whose
wife, her endurance finally exhausted, had turned her back upon his
bed and board, taking their one child, a little girl, with her.

My father was utterly intolerant of drunkenness, and, but for the
mellowing influence of his own approaching anniversary, would
probably never have listened to my mother's gentle plea for David
H. as a Christmas guest.

"What in tunket you want that old sot around on Christmas Day
for?" he demanded indignantly. "You already *got* Miz' Esty. If you
want more company, why don't you ask the Covell young-uns and
give 'em a square meal?"

To his surprise and apparent consternation, my mother took up
the challenge.

"I'm glad you thought of it, 'Lije," she said genially. "I'll ask 'em to-day."

And ask them she did, four half-starved little Covells, all girls, ranging in age from five to twelve, who stared greedily when my mother told them they were to come to dinner, and appeared on the eagerly anticipated day scrubbed and brushed and dressed in their poor best, two hours ahead of time.

Nevertheless, David H. was also invited, but my father himself did the asking. "Met old David H. down the road," he informed my mother largely one day, as having devised a creditable plan. "Asked him to dinner, Christmas. Keep him sober, *one* day, anyway."

David H., aside from being a man of skill in his craft, was a considerable character. He had some degree of education, was well spoken, and he had a mind. Pursued by propagandists of teetotalism, as he frequently was, he would shake his head and say, referring always to himself in the third person:—

"No, David H. ain't goin' to sign no pledge. When David H. puts his foot down *hisself,* he'll quit drinking. *But—David H. ain't goin' to put his foot down!*" However, he came soberly to Christmas dinner, sleekly shining, pomaded, and proud.

On the day before Christmas my father came home with a large, fat goose, dressed and drawn, dangling its long neck around his feet. The goose was singed, pin-feathered, and washed. Not merely rinsed with a dash of cold water, but put into a large dishpan of quite hot suds and scrubbed with soap and baking soda. A proceeding my mother accorded to most fowls, especially the large ones, turkeys, geese, and ducks.

"They're oily," she explained, "and then they wallow in the dirt. Nothing but soap and hot water'll get 'em clean."

From the soapy water, the goose was rinsed in hot and then cold water, which plumped her up and gave the skin a youthful appearance.

I once knew a spinster lady of uncertain but reasonably predictable years who, having set her heart upon gaining the attentions of a man considerably younger than herself, tried the same treatment upon her face.

"You take an old hen," she said, quite seriously, "and you dip her first in hot water and then in cold, and she'll plump up and her skin'll look as fresh as a daisy. I don't see," she added ingenuously, "why it wouldn't work on a human as well."

Apparently it did, for the nuptials were not long after announced.

My mother's reason for the hot and cold rinse, however, was not so much to give the semblance of youth, as to cleanse and freshen the skin.

The stuffing for the goose which was my father's favorite was made of mashed potato and onion. About a cupful of chopped onion was lightly fried in a piece of butter as big as a walnut, with salt and pepper, and added to the mashed potato which had been generously treated to a seasoning of cream, butter, pepper, and salt. It must not, however, be mushy. The cavities were stuffed with this and sewed; wings, legs, and neck were trussed. And then my mother mixed together salt, pepper, and a little finely crumbled sage, and with her fingers rubbed this over the surface of the fowl.

If the goose was over a year old it was parboiled or steamed before roasting. If a spring goose, it was put in the roasting pan with a cupful or so of water and some butter and frequently basted. The giblets were cooked separately, chopped, and added, with the water in which they were cooked, to the gravy made from the juices in the roasting pan *after* the excess fat had been poured off.

Of course this fat was saved and treasured, for "goose grease" was an invaluable remedy for cold-on-the-lungs, and equally useful as a lubricant for shoes that had been wet with snow.

Sundry herbs were grown in our own garden as they were in most farm gardens. The leaves were picked when full grown, dried and kept, to be finely crumbled as used. These were doubtless less convenient than the small containers of to-day and belong to that pleasant past when an attic garlanded with herbs and festooned with peppers was part of the accepted preparation for winter, but there are still those who believe in their greater potency, and a row of sage, savory, bay, marjoram, and thyme I would also urge, flanked by chives, shallots, scallions, mint, and parsley in every garden. With these and a few cloves of garlic at his hand, and an old, well-seasoned chopping bowl for his use, even the most finical gourmet should be able to fashion at least a few dishes to his liking.

Miz' Lou Esty came early to help with the dinner. Under my mother's direction she prepared a dish which was in our family a prime favorite chiefly as an accompaniment to roast pork, but which proved equally acceptable as an accessory to the dinner of roast goose. This was a combination of apple and onion, and for which I have no other name.

To make this you first gauge the amount of onion by your fondness for that vegetable, but as my family was—and is—what you might call onion-minded, we are never chary of that lusty bulb.

In my own practice I use a cast aluminum saucepan in lieu of the heavy iron spider which my mother had, and into this I put perhaps two tablespoonfuls of fat,—depending on the amount I am making,—either salt pork or bacon fat with another of butter. When this is hot, place a generous layer of thinly sliced onion on the bottom and let it cook until soft but not browned. This is salted and sprinkled with pepper. Now over the onion goes a thick layer of tart apple, unpeeled to keep the shape, cored and sliced across. This is sprinkled with sugar, the dish is covered, and the whole cooked until the apples are tender and the onions slightly browned on the bottom. If there is any danger of scorching, the dish must be stirred, of course, which will break the apples, but the taste will not be impaired. This can be used as a garnish or served separately.

Boiled onions there were too, for in spite of the apple combination, as well as the flavor of the stuffing, no poultry dinner would have been complete in our home without the dish of silvery globes dressed with a little cream, butter, and seasoning.

The table was spread with the second-best cloth of white linen, the best being reserved for the later, and greater, occasion of my father's birthday. Miz' Esty laid the plates one at each place, the way she said they were now doing in town, where she had recently been sewing, instead of piling them chin high before the server as was the usual country custom. We did not even use the gold-banded china for Christmas, but the sprigged rose pattern that my mother had bought not so long ago with carefully hoarded egg money.

The steel three-tined forks and knives with ivory handles lent their elegance. The bellflower goblets, sugar and creamer, and spoon holder, as well as the sauce dish of stewed cranberries (picked by my father in a neighboring bog), sparkled like jewels. Into the goblets Miz' Esty stuffed the napkins rolled cornucopia-fashion, another innovation from the city. That was one advantage in having Miz' Esty come—she brought new fashions, new customs and styles, into our more remote homes.

The centrepiece I remember well, for I had rubbed and polished every apple—Northern Spies, Jonathans, and Greenings—to a shining splendor, and heaped them in the latticework fruit dish of white glass.

A tumbler of wild grape jelly quivered upturned upon a small glass plate—wild grape because of the muskier tang. Pickled watermelon rind—translucent pink shading to opaque green—drenched in a luscious syrup of citron and lemon flavor reposed on a small dish shaped of two graceful hands (severed at the wrists) of alabaster white. Bread, moist, fresh, and creamy white, was piled on a round glass plate which had a sheaf of wheat in the centre, and the words, "Give Us This Day Our Daily Bread," embossed around the edge. A blue glass plug hat held toothpicks.

We knew nothing of salads, now considered indispensable, and we ate our nuts sitting around the evening fire instead of having them shelled and salted at the table. But even so I cannot feel that our table lacked in zestful relishes or accessories. Instead, I have a vision of plenty, appetizingly prepared.

Dessert, of course, on Christmas Day, consisted of plum pudding, and plum pudding only. On Thanksgiving there were pies—pumpkins and mince. On New Year's there would be pies, mince and apple and pumpkin, but on Christmas the pudding stood alone, a monarch amongst desserts.

It had been made weeks before, in fact at the same time that the mincemeat for Thanksgiving pies was in preparation. Contrary to her usual custom, my mother had a rule for making her plum pudding. In general her cookery was of so simple an order, consisting of dishes frequently repeated, as to need no rules, but this pudding was made but once a year, and so when the time came for its concoction she took down from its place beside the clock an old cookbook and opened it to a page slightly discolored from a tracing finger rich with fruity contact.

I think, perhaps, she also liked to read the words, for she spoke them aloud, and I can remember seeing my father draw his chair within hearing distance, adjust his spectacles, craftily lift a newspaper before his face, and give ear to the rich phrasing which fell alluringly upon the air:—

" 'Take of cold beef suet one pound, string it, and crumble into a wooden bowl and chop very fine. Mix with one cup of brown sugar. Into an earthen bowl put half a pound of currants, an equal amount of raisins, seeded; one-fourth pound each of candied citron, lemon, and orange peel, sliced to transparent thinness with a very sharp knife on a board; one ounce each of cinnamon, ginger, nutmeg, cloves; one teaspoonful salt (or more); cover these with one pound of flour and stir with fingers until fruit is coated.

" 'Now add two cups of fine bread crumbs, four eggs well beaten, one cup of milk, one-half cup of brandy. Mix and stir to a stiff dough. Now set this aside to *assimilate flavors* for two hours or more.

" 'Have ready a large flannel pudding bag, square in shape. Wet this, wring as dry as possible; lay the cloth on the table, butter the centre, and sprinkle with flour. Place this over a bowl and pour in the pudding. Tie firmly with string, leaving a little room for the swell but not much. Put a plate in bottom of a large kettle of boiling water, set the pudding on it, and let boil for seven hours. Serve on a round platter with a small amount of brandy poured over, to which a light is applied after the room is darkened. A sprig of holly adds to its tastiness. This pudding (*if not eaten*) will last for weeks and is as good cold as it was hot.' "

Could anything afford pleasanter reading than that? Is it any wonder that my father's newspaper drooped and sagged, or that his spectacles were pushed impatiently to the top of his head, the better to hear?

Upon one occasion I remember his remarking to my mother as her voice dropped, regretfully, the last phrase, "We might try that 'applying a light' sometime, maybe, 'Miry, huh?"

"Yes, and likely burn the whole pudding up," was her unsympathetic retort.

When the pudding, after the proper "assimilation of flavors," was finally consigned to the pot, the kitchen became of all rooms that could be imagined the most desirable. Every corner, every inch and ell, was permeated with the rich bouquet of "assimilated" raisins, currants, lemon, ginger, citron, and spice borne upon a cloud of steam, while the pudding on its plate, with its woolly ears protrud-

ing above the boisterous, ebullient seas of darkening water, danced
and bubbled, puffed and swelled, in its own juices. Perhaps it would
last for weeks "if not eaten," but its chances for longevity beyond
the date set for its proper consumption were slim indeed.

Awaiting its cue, then, for entrance upon the Christmas scene, the
pudding had sat during the intervening time upon the pantry shelf,
closely covered in an earthen jar.

My father was no great reader, but his attention had been known
to wander from the weekly *Citizen* while my mother was reading
aloud to me the *Christmas Carol,* as she did on the eve of the day I
am recalling. The enchanting picture of the Cratchits' dinner obviously aroused in him a certain envy, for on one of his too-frequent
visits to the kitchen in the midst of feverish activities, he said to my
mother, "What's a quartern, 'Miry?"

My mother, intent upon her culinary affairs, had lost all connec-
tive thread and looked up in surprise.

"I don't know," she said. "Where'd you get it?"

"Out of that story—Cratchits'. The pudding 'blazed in half a
quartern of brandy.' "

"Huh!" said my mother flatly, and pursued her tasks.

A few minutes later my father, who was constantly in and out of
the room, remarked:—

"You got any brandy around, 'Miry?"

My mother looked up sharply. "Yes," she said briefly. "You sick?"

"No," he replied shortly, "course not. I just thought maybe we
could do like they say—blaze the pudding, you know, and bedight
it with Christmas holly."

"Yes," said my mother in a scornful but muffled tone, since the
guests had already arrived, "and maybe bedight David H. too. I'm
goin' to put some in the sauce and that's enough."

If the Covells had not been his own unintentional contribution to
the occasion and David H. a guest of his own asking, my father
would doubtless have had something to say regarding the imposed
restrictions, but as it was he seemed robbed of argument and obliged
to content himself with the prospect of only the usual hard sauce as
accompaniment to his pudding.

David H. himself, however, had preconceived ideas about a
Christmas pudding, due, perhaps, to his own cultural pursuits. Of
a sudden my mother discovered him standing at her elbow in the

pantry, where she was moulding butter, sugar, and the yolk of egg into a foamy mass. Beside the bowl stood a generous bottle of brandy. David H. was licking his lips. "I'm glad to see, Miz' Thompson," he said genially, " 't you know how to dousel up a sauce. Nine women out o' ten'd stick in a little essence o' vanilla bean and think they'd flavored it. Pudding sauce calls for *brandy,* Miz' Thompson," he declared fervently, *"and it don't call for nothin' else."*

My mother, at the avidity in his eyes and the ardor of his voice, grew somewhat alarmed. Surreptitiously she slid the bottle inside the cupboard door, and tactfully edged David H. back into the front room, where the Covells sat stiffly upon upright chairs. My father had been out upon some last-minute chore, but, appearing at that moment, was haled by my mother into the pantry, the door pushed to.

"You keep David H. out o' here," she admonished him sharply. "I thought he's goin' to grab the brandy bottle 'fore I could get it out of sight."

"Huh," said my father unreasonably, "if you'd a listened to me you wouldn't had 'im around—old coot!"

"You asked him yourself," twitted my mother. "Now you keep him out the kitchen."

But keeping David H. out of the kitchen with a Christmas dinner under way was not so easily accomplished. In spite of my father's attempts to engage him in conversation, he shortly appeared at the door. "My!" he exclaimed. "It cer'nly does smell good here. 'Bout how long," he inquired ingratiatingly, "do you think it'll be afore we set down?"

"If you'll go into the front room, David H.," my mother told him not too patiently, "and keep out the way, it'll be about ten minutes."

"I'll jes' set this dish back in the cupboard," he said, picking up an unwanted pitcher that he had officiously brought out, "and then you won't hear another word out of me." With that he dashed into the pantry, where he was plainly heard rattling amongst its contents. With a grim determination my mother started toward the door, which was suddenly thrown open to catapult David H. tempestuously almost into her arms. He was visibly shaken, but bowed, scraped a foot, and begged her pardon.

"Hurrying," he explained volubly, "to get set down and out the way." My father appeared in the door.

"What in tunket's all this noise?" he wanted to know. "And how long before dinner's ready?"

"Dinner's ready now," my mother announced testily, "if you men'd stay out long enough to let us take it up. You may's well set down. Go'n tell the Covells."

"Allow *me!* Pray—allow *me!*" Before anyone else could make a move, David H. had dashed through the door, and while we continued to stare stupidly in the direction he had gone, he had lifted the oldest Covell girl literally from her chair with one hand, and the littlest one with the other. The baby he tossed to his shoulder, and with the older girl's arm tucked underneath his own he came tripping back, the girl's feet dragging awkwardly beside his, the two others following.

My mother stood with the dish of mashed potatoes upraised in her hands, the goose already upon the table. Miz' Esty was bringing the other dishes, while my father, his white hair bristling, looked as if he were about to bellow.

"Here we are!" cried David H. gayly. "Ol' Bob Cratchit, young Tim Cratchit—*all* the Tim Cratchits—God bless us every one!"

He deposited the youngest in the high chair placed for her, set the eldest down in hers, and, again bowing deeply to my mother, drew her chair for her.

Mechanically the dinner proceeded. The goose which graced this particular Christmas dinner of which I write was garnished with small spiced red crab apples, a flight of fancy on my mother's part which subjected her to derision.

"What in tunket you got these *crab* apples strung around on the platter for, 'Miry?" my father wanted to know. "You think David H. and I want to play marbles?"

David H. rose to their defense. "They look right pretty, Miz' Thompson," he said. "I think if things look pretty they taste better."

"What do you *do* with 'em?" my father insisted, as he poked them to one side. "Do you *eat* 'em, or play ball with 'em?"

"Don't pretend you never saw spiced crab apples before," my mother admonished him tranquilly. "Of course you eat 'em. Put one on each plate and hurry up."

My father served slices of hot, juicy goose, spoonfuls of mashed potato, onions, squash. Cranberries and jelly were passed. Not much was said. The Covells were plied with food. My mother made conversation with Miz' Esty. She discoursed upon the dinner. The squash was not as dry as some we had had. The onions were a mite too salt. The room, she thought, was terribly warm. She got up and opened a door. In a few minutes my father got up and shut it. He looked unhappy.

David H. ate with gusto, but absently. He seemed to be sunk in thought. No one talked. The Christmas dinner party was not turning out well. Tears were near my mother's eyes. Finally she and Miz' Esty got up and cleared the table. My mother brought the pudding, round and richly brown, with little puckers and creases where the cloth had been tied around the top. It steamed and smelled—well, it smelled for all the world like a Christmas pudding "sweetened with syrup, tinctured with spice." It bulged with raisins, citron, and the candied peel of orange. And she bore it proudly as one bringing a gift that should appease even the spleen of sullen men. She set it down before her and served it. Then she passed the sauce.

As the heady odor of brandy blended with golden egg and frothing butter reached her nose, her hand paused. Conscience and her responsibility as a cook held a moment's war. My father's shrewd questioning eyes were upon her. Her lips tightened. David H. glanced up at her with a curious dawn of comprehension on his face. He rose, bowed.

"Miz' Thompson," he said, and at the deep seriousness of his voice all eyes were turned upon him, "I c'n see 't you're bothered. You don't know whether you ort to pass that sauce to me or not. I'll tell you. I got to apologize to you. I went into your pantry and I found that bottle. I all but took a drink. *I couldn't hardly put the bottle down.* But—I says to myself, David H. may be a drunkard, but David H. ain't no sneak. It made me kind of weak. That was when I bumped into you. But I didn't touch it. So you can pass me the sauce, Miz' Thompson, and no harm done. And if the' was more women like you, David H.'d put his foot down."

He sat down and the sauce was passed. David H. helped himself—liberally. Miz' Esty surreptitiously wiped her eyes, for what reason

I do not know. My mother beamed. Her Christmas dinner was not a failure after all. "If you *should* ever put your foot down, David H.," she said warmly, "I know you'd never lift it up again."

My father chuckled. His keen eyes dwelt leniently upon the sinner. "Like to see you put your foot down, David H.," he said indulgently, "but I'd hate to see you put it down *that* hard."

The dinner was over. The little Covells were eager to go. Their mittened hands were full of gifts my mother had made them, cookies, apples, and a jar of mincemeat for pies ("although they'll probably come and borrow lard to make 'em with," she told Miz' Esty afterward), their stomachs full of food. Awkwardly and shyly they murmured their thank-yous and good-byes and hurried away.

Miz' Esty stayed to help with the dishes. She might even stay all night, since there was no sewing to be done until after New Year's.

David H., his worn old overcoat collar pulled up about his ears, his rusty coonskin cap in hand, stood to say good-bye. He had had the best Christmas dinner he ever tasted. He thanked my mother for his repast, my father for asking him. He put his thin, none too steady hand upon my head.

"David H.—had a little girl—once," he said huskily, and, opening the door hurriedly, was gone.

The day was drawing to its early close. The skies were lowering, gray and threatening. It would snow before night set in. My father went to the front room to nod and doze. My mother and Miz' Esty returned to the kitchen and lighted the lamps. The work was not quite finished. Miz' Esty, with a full-gathered gingham apron tied over an equally full-gathered and many-gored woolen skirt, washed the dishes while my mother dried and put them away. The room smelled pleasantly of food mingled with the odor of geranium leaves and damp earth. My mother had been pouring tea on her plants. A cat crouched over a plate near the door. Another cat could be seen stretched at length upon my father's knee. The dog, Shep, lay just outside upon the step, hopefully waiting for snow.

The women talked softly together. Their voices drifted in and out of the warmth of the room, the shadows from the lamp, the homely fragrance. The fire burned low in the stove. My mother opened the lid and thrust in a couple of sticks. It would be allowed, later, to go out for the night. We would eat bread and milk for supper.

It had been a good day, after all. Nothing to make history, but good to live, good to remember.

My father roused, put on his old fur cap, lighted the lantern.

"Want to go help with the chores, dawtie?" I hurriedly thrust myself into a coat, pulled on a woolen hood, took my little tin cup, into which my father would train a stream of milk straight from the cow. It was a nightly custom.

The dog jumped up to follow, barking. The horses, as we opened the door, neighed a throaty welcome and blew through their velvet nostrils. The cows gently mooed. The barn was warm with the breath of creatures dependent upon us for their comfort, and the musky sweetness of hay and grain.

The light from the kitchen streams out,—a lovely light,—soft, lambent, and golden like a heavenly road to peace and safety. Here in the barn there is security. Storms cannot enter. Nothing can harm us here, for my father is in charge. The animals trust him. I trust him.

Back there in the kitchen is safety, too. Warmth, and light, and food—and Mother.

Of Cheese in General

BY

OSBERT BURDETT

O NE OF the oldest, simplest, and most nourishing of foods, Cheese differs from other staple forms of nourishment in that all but its softest kinds are equally good for a whole meal, and that all serve for a final benediction to it. As if this were not enough to proclaim its virtue, Cheese has the further distinction of mating equally well with wine or with beer—with that which is the glory of drinks and that which is the finest of thirst-quenchers. The meat-eater and the vegetarian are at one in its praises, and to the latter it takes with eggs the place of meat. Thus the solid food of the simple or the meatless diner has been called the 'wine-drinker's biscuit'—so well does its astringent flavour set off the subtle delights of wine and create with each mouthful a new zest for sipping. Cheese can also make a rare sandwich. There is, in truth, no service for the appetite that Cheese cannot fulfil: the hungry man, the poor man, the hasty traveller and the epicure have severally found it their blessing.

What, then, is this product of the dairy, and how does it come to be what it is? Cheese is the curd of milk which has been coagulated by rennet, separated from the whey, and then (as a rule) pressed. Its original advantage was that it turned one of the most perishable of foods, milk, into a solid that could be kept, and eaten over a long period. The many modifications possible to the process, not to mention the different kinds of milk and the different degrees of fat in the same kind, explain its many varieties. As with wine, each cheese originally took its name from the place of its origin; and it is the misfortune of England not to have copied the French practice and protected by law the original product. This can scarcely ever be exactly copied away from its home. The consequence is that our local cheeses are disappearing, and some, like the Banbury, often mentioned by Shakespeare, now exist only as names.

The usual classification of Cheese is threefold: into hard, semi-hard, and soft varieties. Many people, however, think of it merely by colour, and are only consciously aware of the yellow, the red, and the green or blue. With local names now implying nothing preciser than a type, and with factories turning out more or less standard types, and these in very different and absolutely undefined qualities, people consider themselves to be ranging afield when they seek one of those cheeses still identified, more or less, with a particular place or country. Broadly speaking, the hard cheeses are best for a meal, the soft for a sweet or dessert, and the semi-hard, which include the green cheeses, for eating with wine at the end of dinner. This, like other matters of taste, will be disputed, and some even aver that the best place for cheese is where it is least often found, that is to say at the very beginning, as it were an hors-d'oeuvre to a meal. But hors-d'oeuvre is not French for Unemployment.

With what should cheese be eaten? Actually, for the hard and semi-hard cheeses, there is nothing better than plain bread, if we would savour our cheese and not use it to fill up an odd corner at the end of dinner. For these cheeses bread is better than biscuit, for the ideal accompaniment of biscuit is simply butter. With the creamiest kinds, however, most of which are mild, biscuits are preferable. The softness of the soft cheese invites its complement—the crispness of biscuit—but it will be found that the flavour of crust, especially the adorable flavour of crust browned to the verge of blackness, is too strong for them. This also rules out damp, white, soft, or usual toast.

It is an old question whether butter should be eaten with cheese. Not, surely, with the creamier, nor with the most pungent; and, unless we wish to indulge in the superfluously rich, butter is a superfluity with green cheese. With other cheeses it is a matter of choice, the inherent indication being that the drier cheeses, some would say Gruyère and (to my mind) generally Cheshire, are enhanced by butter. Old nurses used to enforce bread and butter before their charges were allowed to add jam; and it may be that it was not only parsimony that dictated the adage, which the French carefully endorse, that cheese should be eaten without butter. Whatever the

source, the adage exists, and traditions should be examined respectfully. They are the wisdom that has survived. Let us respect the
adage as a Principle of Reference, but act according to our whim.
Here, as elsewhere, the real mistake is to be fanatical about either.

The most difficult thing about common or popular cheese is to
buy what you pay for: to find the genuine article under the name it
bears, and to receive it in the condition without which you would
not choose it. Whether in hotels, restaurants, or shops, a few cheeses
are protected from substitutes; and who has not suffered from
Camemberts that are chalky instead of oozing, from Brie that has
staled to a condition of yellow dryness, from a solid Port Salut, an
india-rubber-like Bel Paese?

True Cheddar is the least discoverable of all, since the paradoxi-
cal effect of the factory and its standardisation has been to flood the
counter with such a number of concealed grades that the original
cheese has almost disappeared under a swarm of inferior semblances.
The only rule is to go where the best are professed to be sold, and
there too to be prepared for disappointments. What the tradesman
calls the West End taste has a standard of its own, of which a few
(men's) clubs are the last stronghold. The less exclusive shops, especially beyond the West End, cater mainly for the less particular,
who hate fine cheese, even though the variation in prices is not very
great. There are ten tastes and therefore ten markets for cheese;
and in the end the factory system makes a quick turnover paramount. Thus it is that the quickly made and the unmatured mo-
nopolise the grosser grocers.

On the other hand, the big shops generally supply some cheeses of
excellent quality, and among them the inquisitive may find sometimes one or more of the local cheeses that often cannot be found
in the towns nearest to their proper homes. The absence of complaint in regard to the haphazard quality of the common English
cheeses is probably due to the destruction of taste by the only avail-
ble and cheaper product: not to an original preference for insipid
substitutes. Destroy the memory of a good thing, and in time its
imitation under the old name will be preferred by most people.

This has happened to Cheddar, the most abused name in the
world.

At this the epicure will leave it; but though, from his point of
view, he is right, righteous indignation ignores something. If there

ever was, there has long ceased to be a uniform flavour for Cheddar. Does it not cover the facts, while protecting a cherished singularity, to admit that by this time Cheddar has become a word no more precisely descriptive than Sherry? As diverse flavours are now required of Cheddar cheese, and to some extent even of inimitable cheeses such as Stilton, as of the Jerez wines. Unfortunately, the differences are unreflected in nomenclature. Even the grocer's loose division of sherry into pale, golden, and brown, not to mention the individual names of the sherries included under each division, have no counterpart at a cheese-counter.

The epicure means the old, mellow, rich cheese that has been stored after ripening for a year, and to get it he must go, as a rule, to the traditional shops that scarcely offer any other. But even the young and mild cheeses have no true grading. The boasted uniformity of the factories achieves nothing more distinctively Cheddar than can be expected when a purchaser inquires after 'soap'. Buyer and seller must understand one another, and do in fact gravitate to counters where the same meaning is attached to the vaguest of English words.

Food and Drink

Why has our poetry eschewed
The rapture and response of food?
What hymns are sung, what praises said
For home-made miracles of bread?
Since what we love has always found
Expression in enduring sound,
Music and verse should be competing
To match the transient joy of eating.
There should be present in our songs
As many tastes as there are tongues;
There should be humbly celebrated
One passion that is never sated.
Let us begin it with the first
Distinction of a conscious thirst
When the collusion of the vine
Uplifted water into wine.
Let us give thanks before we turn
To other things of less concern
For all the poetry of the table:
Clams that parade their silent fable
Lobsters that have a rock for stable
Red-faced tomatoes ample as
A countryman's full-blossomed lass;
Plain-spoken turnips; honest beets;
The carnal gusto of red meats;
The insipidity of lamb;
The wood-fire pungence of smoked ham,
Young veal that's smooth as natural silk;
The lavish motherliness of milk;
Parsley and lemon-butter that add
Spring sweetness unto rivershad;
Thin flakes of halibut and cod,
Pickerel, flounder, snapper, scrod,
And every fish whose veins may be
Charged with the secrets of the sea;

Sweet-sour carp, beloved by Jews;
Pot-luck simplicity of stews;
Crabs, juciest of Nature's jokes;
The deep reserve of artichokes;
Mushrooms, whose taste is texture, loath
To tell of their mysterious growth;
Quick, mealy comfort glowing in
A baked potato's crackled skin;
The morning promise, hailed by man,
Of bacon crisping in the pan;
The sage compound of Hasenpfeffer
With dumplings born of flour and zephyr;
Spinach whose spirit is the soil;
Anchovies glorified in oil;
The slow-gold nectar maples yield;
Pale honey tasting of the field
Where every clover is Hymettus;
The cooling sanity of lettuce
And every other herbal green
Whose touch is calm, whose heart is clean;
Succulent bean-sprouts, bamboo-shoots;
The sapid catalogue of fruits:
Plebeian apple, caustic grape,
Quinces that have no gift for shape,
Dull plums that mind their own affairs,
Incurably bland and blunted pears,
Fantastic passion-fruit, frank lemons
With acid tongues as sharp as women's,
Exotic loquats, sly persimmons,
White currants, amber-fleshed sultanas,
(Miniature and sweetened mannas)
Expansive peaches, suave bananas,
Oranges ripening in crates,
Tight-bodied figs, sun-wrinkled dates,
Melons that have their own vagaries;
The bright astringency of berries;
Crepe-satin luxury of cream;
Wedding-cake that fulfils the dream;
Pepper, whose satire stings and cuts;
Raw liberality of nuts;
Sauces of complex mysteries;
Proverbial parsnips; muscular cheese;
Innocent eggs that scorn disguises;

Languid molasses; burning spices
In kitchen-oracles to Isis;
Thick sauerkraut's fat-bellied savour;
Anything with a chocolate flavour;
Large generosity of pies;
Hot puddings bursting to surprise;
The smug monotony of rice;
Raisins that doze in cinnamon buns;
Kentucky biscuits, Scottish scones;
Falstaffian tarts that mock the chaste
Rose-elegance of almond-paste;
Venison steaks that smack of cloisters;
Goose-liver for the soul that roisters;
Reticent prawn; Lucullan oysters;
Sausages, fragrant link on link;
The vast ambrosias of drink:
Tea, that domestic mandarin;
Bucolic cider; loose-lipped gin;
Coffee, extract of common sense,
Purgative of the night's pretense;
Cocoa's prim nursery; the male
Companionship of crusty ale;
Cognac as oily as a ferret;
The faintly iron thrust of claret;
Episcopal port, aged and austere;
Rebellious must of grape; the clear,
Bluff confraternity of beer—

All these are good, all are a part
Of man's imperative needs that start
Not in the palate but the heart.
Thus fat and fibre, root and leaf
Become quick fuel and slow grief.
These, through the chemistry of blood,
Sustain his hungering manhood,
Fulfilling passion, ripening pain,
Steel in his bone, fire at his brain . . .
So until man abjures the meats
Terrestrial and impermanent sweets,
Growing beyond the things he eats,
Let us be thankful for the good
Beauty and benison of food,
Let us join chiming vowel with vowel

To rhapsodize fish, flesh and fowl,
And let us thank God in our songs
There are as many tastes as tongues.

—Louis Untermeyer

The Ballad of Bouillabaisse

A street there is in Paris famous,
    For which no rhyme our language yields,
Rue Neuve des Petits Champs its name is—
    The New Street of the Little Fields.
And here's an inn, not rich and splendid,
    But still in comfortable case;
The which in youth I oft attended,
    To eat a bowl of Bouillabaisse.

This Bouillabaisse a noble dish is—
    A sort of soup or broth, or brew,
Or hotchpotch of all sorts of fishes,
    That Greenwich never could outdo;
Green herbs, red peppers, mussels, saffron,
    Soles, onions, garlic, roach, and dace:
All these you eat at Terré's tavern,
    In that one dish of Bouillabaisse.

Indeed, a rich and savoury stew 'tis;
    And true philosophers, methinks,
Who love all sorts of natural beauties,
    Should love good victuals and good drinks.
And Cordelier or Benedictine
    Might gladly, sure, his lot embrace,
Nor find a fast-day too afflicting,
    Which served him up a Bouillabaisse.

I wonder if the house still there is?
    Yes, here the lamp is, as before;
The smiling red-cheeked *écaillère* is
    Still opening oysters at the door.
Is Terré still alive and able?
    I recollect his droll grimace:

He'd come and sit before your table,
  And hope you liked your Bouillabaisse.

We enter—nothing's changed or older.
  "How's Monsieur Terré, waiter, pray?"
The waiter stares and shrugs his shoulder—
  "Monsieur is dead this many a day."
"It is the lot of saint and sinner,
  So honest Terré's run his race."
"What will Monsieur require for dinner?"
  "Say, do you still cook Bouillabaisse?"

"Oh, oui, Monsieur," 's the waiter's answer;
  "Quel vin Monsieur désire-t-il?"
"Tell me a good one."—"That I can, Sir;
  The Chambertin with yellow seal."
"So Terré's gone," I say, and sink in
  My old accustomed corner-place;
"He's done with feasting and with drinking,
  With Burgundy and Bouillabaisse."

My old accustomed corner here is,
  The table still is in the nook;
Ah! vanished many a busy year is
  This well-known chair since last I took.
When first I saw ye, *cari luoghi,*
  I'd scarce a beard upon my face,
And now a grizzled, grim old fogy,
  I sit and wait for Bouillabaisse.

Where are you, old companions trusty
  Of early days here met to dine?
Come, waiter! quick, a flagon crusty—
  I'll pledge them in the good old wine.
The kind old voices and old faces
  My memory can quick retrace;
Around the board they take their places,
  And share the wine and Bouillabaisse.

There's Jack has made a wondrous marriage;
  There's laughing Tom is laughing yet;
There's brave Augustus drives his carriage!
  There's poor old Fred in the *Gazette;*

On James's head the grass is growing:
   Good lord! the world has wagged apace
Since here we set the claret flowing,
   And drank, and ate the Bouillabaisse.

Ah me! how quick the days are flitting!
   I mind me of a time that's gone,
When here I'd sit, as now I'm sitting,
   In this same place—but not alone.
A fair young form was nestled near me,
   A dear, dear face looked fondly up,
And sweetly spoke and smiled to cheer me
   —There's no one now to share my cup.

I drink it as the Fates ordain it.
   Come, fill it, and have done with rhymes:
Fill up the lonely glass, and drain it
   In memory of dear old times.
Welcome the wine, whate'er the seal is;
   And sit you down, and say your grace
With thankful heart, whate'er the meal is.
   Here comes the smoking Bouillabaisse!
       —*William Makepeace Thackeray*

Ad Ministram

After Horace

Dear Lucy, you know what my wish is,—
   I hate all your Frenchified fuss;
Your silly entrées and made dishes
   Were never intended for us.
No footman in lace and in ruffles
   Need dangle behind my arm-chair;
And never mind seeking for truffles
   Although they be ever so rare.

But a plain leg of mutton, my Lucy,
   I prithee get ready at three:
Have it smoking, and tender and juicy,
   And what better meat can there be?

And when it has feasted the master,
'Twill amply suffice for the maid;
Meanwhile I will smoke my canaster,
And tipple my ale in the shade.
                    —*William Makepeace Thackeray*

Bacon and Eggs

Now blest be the Briton, his beef and his beer,
And all the strong waters that keep him in cheer,
But blest beyond cattle and blest beyond kegs
Is the brave British breakfast of bacon and eggs—

> *Bacon and eggs,*
> *Bacon and eggs;*
> *Sing bacon,*
> *Red bacon,*
> *Red bacon and eggs!*

Thus armed and thus engined, well-shaven and gay,
We leap to our labours and conquer the day,
While paltry pale foreigners, meagre as moles,
Must crawl through the morning on coffee and rolls—

> *Coffee and rolls,*
> *Barbarous rolls;*
> *Sing coffee,*
> *Black coffee,*
> *Vile coffee and rolls!*

What wonder the Frenchman, blown out with new bread,
Gesticulates oft and is light in the head!
Our perfect control of our arms and our legs
We owe to our ballast of bacon and eggs—

> *Bacon and eggs,*
> *Unemotional eggs;*
> *Sing bacon,*
> *Fat bacon,*
> *Brave bacon and eggs!*

What wonder that Fortune is careful to place
Her loveliest laurels on men of our race,
While sorrow is heaped upon Prussians and Poles
Who shame the glad morning with coffee and rolls—

> *Coffee and rolls,*
> *Ladylike rolls;*
> *Sing coffee,*
> *Pooh! coffee,*
> *Black coffee and rolls!*

What wonder the Russian looks redly because
Our England, old England, is much what it was!
We fight to the finish, we drink to the dregs
And dare to be Daniels on bacon and eggs—

> *Bacon and eggs,*
> *Masculine eggs;*
> *Sing bacon,*
> *Bring bacon,*
> *And fry me two eggs!*

But gross Europeans who constantly munch
Too little at breakfast, too freely at lunch,
Sit sated in *cafés,* incapable souls,
And go to the devil on coffee and rolls—

> *Coffee and rolls,*
> *Windy wet rolls;*
> *At coffee*
> *I'm scoffy,*
> *I execrate rolls!*

O breakfast! O breakfast! The meal of my heart!
Bring porridge, bring sausage, bring fish for a start,
Bring kidneys and mushrooms and partridges' legs,
But let the foundation be bacon and eggs—

> *Bacon and eggs,*
> *Bacon and eggs;*
> *Bring bacon,*
> *Crisp bacon,*
> *And let there be eggs!*

—A. P. Herbert

A Salad

To make this condiment, your poet begs
The pounded yellow of two hard-boiled eggs;
Two boiled potatoes, passed through kitchen sieve,
Smoothness and softness to the salad give;
Let onion atoms lurk within the bowl,
And, half-suspected, animate the whole.
Of mordant mustard add a single spoon,
Distrust the condiment that bites so soon;
But deem it not, thou man of herbs, a fault,
To add a double quantity of salt;
Four times the spoon with oil from Lucca drown,
And twice with vinegar procured from town;
And, lastly, o'er the flavored compound toss
A magic soupçon of anchovy sauce.
Oh, green and glorious! Oh, herbaceous treat!
'Twould tempt the dying anchorite to eat:
Back to the world he's turn his fleeting soul,
And plunge his fingers in the salad-bowl!
Serenely full, the epicure would say,
Fate cannot harm me, I have dined to-day.

—*Sydney Smith*

The Cheese-Mites

The cheese-mites asked how the cheese got there,
    And warmly debated the matter;
The orthodox said it came from the air,
    And the heretics said from the platter.

—*Anonymous*

Eating Song

*(Being a Rendering of the Fervours of our best Drink-
ing Songs into the equivalent terms of a kindred Art)*

If you want to drive wrinkles from belly and brow,
You must tighten the skin, as I tighten it now;

For at gobbets of bacon I sit at my ease,
And I button my mouth over dollops of cheese,
And I laugh at the Devil, who plays on his pipes
With the wind from a famishing traveller's tripes.
The French call it dining to peddle and peck,
But an Englishman's watchword is "Full to the neck!"
Does the parson deny it?—he's lean as a cat,
And the men that I like are all puffy and fat:
Perhaps you'll find music in heaven, but by George!·
You won't get a thundering suetty gorge. ·
So down with your victuals, and stuff till you burst,
And let him who refuses a morsel be curst!

                                    —*Sir Walter Raleigh*

Drinking

The thirsty earth soaks up the rain,
And drinks, and gapes for drink again.
The plants suck in the earth, and are
With constant drinking fresh and fair;
The sea itself—which one would think
Should have but little need of drink—
Drinks ten thousand rivers up,
So filled that they o'erflow the cup.
The busy sun—and one would guess
By's drunken fiery face no less—
Drinks up the sea, and when he's done,
The moon and stars drink up the sun:
They drink and dance by their own light;
They drink and revel all the night.
Nothing in nature's sober found,
But an eternal health goes round.
Fill up the bowl then, fill it high,
Fill up the glasses there; for why
Should every creature drink but I;
Why, man of morals, tell me why?

                                    —*Abraham Cowley*

7
THREE QUIZZES

The Country Quiz

1. Name one vegetable that improves in quality when the temperature drops below freezing.
2. There is a fish called crappie. To what family does it belong?
3. What common tree has three kinds of leaves at the same time?
4. If you were building a fence, which of the following woods would you prefer for the posts: elm, birch, locust, balsa, or beech?
5. If there were no roosters in the barnyard would the hens still lay eggs?
6. Twenty-two years before Pearl Harbor an armored invader from Japan landed in New Jersey and spread through neighboring states, causing great damage. Who was the invader?
7. Privet, trivet, civet—which is used in your fireplace?
8. Which of the following is not a vegetable: bean, tomato, radish, yam, spinach?
9. What have the following in common: Clydesdale, Morgan, Cleveland Bay, Palomino, Shetland?
10. Would you rather buy for $200 a piece of wood-land measuring 200 feet x 200 feet or one acre?
11. On this fine farm there are the following: a sheep-pen, a cow shed, a horse stable, and a pig-sty. Where would you put a foal, a ewe, a shoat, and a heifer?
12. Name an American town that produced great writers and grapes.
13. Name five upland game birds.
14. Name five varieties of wild duck.
15. What is wrong with this sentence: She spent a morning in the garden picking lilacs, dahlias, and bonitas.
16. Range in order of keenness the dog's senses of sight, smell, sound.
17. What is the most dangerous animal in North America?

745

18. He wanted to give her, at her housewarming party, a gift that he referred to as 12-gauge. Is it likely that he was talking about stockings, a new tin roof, a gun, or a machine tool?
19. As you walk down an American country road you see four snakes. The first has three stripes down its back. The second has a long, thin, pointed tail. The third is jet black in color. The fourth is bright green. Which is poisonous?
20. Of the following trees, which bear flowers: yellow poplar, hemlock, shadbush, hawthorne, catalpa.

The Ship and Sea Quiz

1. How long would you say a cable's length is: 6 feet, 60 feet, 600 feet, 6000 feet?
2. Pronounce the following: gunwale, boatswain, leeward.
3. What is the Western Ocean?
4. What is a white-ash breeze?
5. What are flotsam, jetsam, legan?
6. What's wrong with this statement: The schooner was 10 knots away.
7. Why were the horse latitudes so called?
8. On a ship how many bells designate noon, four o'clock, eight o'clock?
9. The plimsoll mark tells what—the depth of the water, clearance under a bridge, or the load line to indicate legal limit of submergence?
10. Define port and starboard.
11. What is leeward?
12. The tip of Africa and the tip of South America both have famous Capes. Name them.
13. If you were to read that a marooned sailor lived off penguin and polar bear meat, what would be wrong with that story?
14. What is Mother Carey's chicken: veal served to sailors under the guise of chicken, the stormy petrel, canned tuna fish, the flying fish, the youngest cabin boy aboard?
15. Who were the mooncursers?

16. Can you list five seas that are named by colors?
17. To box the compass means to put it in a wooden case to protect it when there's a heavy sea; to ship it to Greenwich for an annual inspection; to tell all its direction points in order—which?
18. The Bay of Fundy is noted for its coral reefs, its high tides, its unusual salinity—which?
19. What have the following great ports in common: New Orleans, London, Quebec, Hamburg, Antwerp?
20. When you sail through the Panama Canal from the Atlantic to the Pacific, in what direction are you going?

The Food and Drink Quiz

1. From what part of the cow do sweetbreads come?
2. What fruit or berry is used in Yorkshire pudding?
3. Everyone eats things prepared "au gratin." Define it.
4. What is café diabolo?
5. In English fiction you read about people eating bubble-and-squeak. What is it?
6. Whiskey is made from what grains?
7. There is a vegetable that can be prepared in the following different ways: pont neuf, duchess, anna, persillade, au gratin, scalloped. What is it?
8. What is the chief meat component of hasenpfeffer and Kilmenny Kail?
9. What are chitterlings?
10. From what fruit is kirsch made?
11. What cities are commonly associated with these dishes: bouillabaisse, paella, baked beans, onion soup, shrimp gumbo?
12. And what countries are commonly associated with these dishes: shchi, tournedos, molé, gnocchi, shish kebab?
13. What is yoghurt?
14. Which of the following are edible: rattlesnake, iguana, bullhead, manioc root, dandelion, grasshopper, shark fin, sheep's eye, periwinkle?

15. And what countries do you associate with these drinks: arak, marsala, tokay, saki, marc?

16. If you were trying to keep your weight down, would you order fried eggs or an omelet?

17. What is the main difference between Manhattan and New England clam chowders?

18. And what countries do you associate with these cheeses: Provolone, Brie, Handkase, Neuchatel, Gouda?

19. From what are the following drinks made: slivowitz, Calvados, mead?

20. Name at least three dishes that are so peculiarly American that you can almost never find them outside the United States.

Answers

The Country Quiz

1. Parsnip.
2. Bass.
3. Sassafras.
4. Locust—it will last longer.
5. Yes.
6. The Japanese beetle.
7. Trivet.
8. Tomato.
9. They are all horses.
10. One acre. It measures 208.8 x 208.8 feet.
11. The foal in the horse stable, the shoat in the pig-sty, the ewe in the sheep-pen, and the heifer in the cow-shed.
12. Concord.
13. Grouse, pheasant, woodcock, quail, dove, wild turkey, jacksnipe, partridge, etc.
14. Black, Canvas-Back, Golden-Eye, Mallard, Merganser, Pintail, Redhead, Ring-Necked, Teal, etc.
15. What isn't! Lilacs and dahlias don't bloom at the same time. The bonita is a fish.
16. Smell, sound, sight.

17. The domestic bull. More people are killed by bulls than by any other animal.
18. Shotgun.
19. None.
20. All except the hemlock.

The Ship and Sea Quiz

1. 600 feet.
2. Gunnel, bos'n, looward.
3. The Atlantic.
4. No breeze at all. When a ship was becalmed, it used to be towed by rowboats of which the oars were usually made from white ash.
5. Flotsam: goods found floating on the sea, usually after a wreck. Jetsam: goods thrown overboard from a sinking ship. Legan (or ligan): goods sunk and buoyed, to be retrieved later.
6. A knot is a measurement of speed—not distance. Distance, even on the sea, is reckoned in terms of nautical miles.
7. It was there, in the North Atlantic, that ships were becalmed, necessitating throwing overboard all perishable cargo, including live horses (for lack of fresh water).
8. All by eight bells.
9. The legal load line.
10. Port is the left-hand side of a vessel, starboard the right, *looking forward*.
11. The side away from the wind.
12. Africa: Cape of Good Hope. South America: Cape Horn.
13. Polar bears are found only in the Arctic, penguins only in the Antarctic.
14. The stormy petrel.
15. Wreckers who lured ships to the rocks with false lights—but who couldn't when the moon was out.
16. White, Black, Red, Yellow, Coral.
17. The third.
18. High tides.
19. They are not on the sea; they're on rivers.
20. Southeast.

The Food and Drink Quiz

1. Pancreas.
2. None. It is batter baked under meat, usually beef, absorbing the juices.
3. It is food creamed, or otherwise moistened, covered with bread crumbs and butter or cheese and baked until the top is brown. It need *not* be made with cheese.
4. It is black coffee with brandy (or rum) in it.
5. Fried beef and cabbage.
6. Rye, barley, corn, wheat, oats.
7. The potato.
8. Rabbit.
9. Stuffed pig intestines.
10. Cherry.
11. Bouillabaisse: Marseilles. Paella: Valencia. Baked beans: Boston. Onion soup: Paris. Shrimp gumbo: New Orleans.
12. Shchi: Russia. Tournedos: France. Molé: Mexico. Gnocchi: Italy. Shish kebab: Armenia.
13. Milk partly evaporated and then fermented, used as a food in the Levant, Bulgaria, etc.
14. All are, for all are eaten in various parts of the world.
15. Arak: Armenia. Marsala: Italy. Tokay: Hungary. Saki: Japan. Marc: France.
16. Fried eggs. It has fewer calories because it absorbs less butter fat.
17. The New England chowder contains milk.
18. Provolone: Italy. Brie: France. Handkase: Germany. Neuchatel: France. Gouda: Holland.
19. Slivowitz: prunes. Calvados: apples. Mead: honey.
20. Corn-on-the-cob, doughnuts, buckwheat cakes, cranberry sauce, pumpkin pie, clam chowder, tomato juice, etc.